PRAISE FOR *THE AGE (*

"This book is very much needed. I am incredibly supportive of it and of its brave message."

Professor Clare Saunders, professor in politics, Exeter University

"Human relationships, and life itself, are engineered more and more through technologies controlled by megalomaniac tycoons. *The Age of Humachines* offers a diagnosis of the tech fetishism of our era, maps the routes being taken by the Big Tech juggernaut, and looks to radical-democratic ways of stopping it before it's too late. Essential reading for our dystopian age."

Dr Gareth Dale, head of social and political sciences, Brunel University

"*The Age of Humachines* is a real change-the-world book! It's an encyclopaedia of the technological threats facing us which also holds out hope for a future based on human ingenuity, creativity, and common sense."

*Mark Dunhill, artist and former dean of academic studies,
Central St Martins, University of the Arts, London*

"A nice bridging of AI/digital economy with ecological economics."

Professor Giorgos Kallis, Autonomous University of Barcelona, author of Degrowth

"Congratulations are due to Michael D.B. Harvey. In the best traditions of politically-informed, social-ecological criticism, this clear and incisive analysis is at the same time thought-provoking, informative, provocative and inspiring. With wider democratic politics now so fragmented, polarised and suppressed, I wish more policy discourse were as comfortable and authoritative in making crucial connections between environment, technology, power and emancipatory struggle. Alongside much else, perhaps this great book may help that come about."

Professor Andy Stirling, professor of science and technology policy, Sussex University

offering an overdue corrective to the largely uncritical infatuation with new technology in mainstream business and politics.

The book makes it clear that solutions to the climate emergency and rising inequality should not be expected from those forces that caused them in the first place. It argues that capitalism's ongoing drive to exploit nature, including humans, has now entered a new and potentially final phase in which the end result may well be the end of humanity as we know it. So we are standing at a crossroads with little time left to change direction but this book shows that the way to a more sustainable and democratic future is still open to us."

Professor Fabian Frenzel, professor in mobility and organizations, Oxford Brookes University

"*The Age of Humachines* builds on the compelling and insightful political ecology of Harvey's *Utopia in the Anthropocene* to deliver a wide-ranging critique of AI-based technologies and Silicon-Valley's techno-utopian leaders. Agree or disagree: this book raises burning issues about our future which we urgently need to debate."

Associate Professor Martin Travers, Griffith University,
author of The Poetry of Aletheia: Heidegger in Language

"I warmly recommend this fascinating book to any undergraduate and graduate student particularly interested in developing critical thinking about technological solutionism and understanding transhumanism and the history of science and AI and their ethical, psychological and philosophical consequences. Michael Harvey's experience as a former insider in the techno-industry, enriched by his insightful critical analysis of texts, places him in the best position to deconstruct the current plan of IT/AI of merging human and machines.

The Age of Humachines represents a valuable and inspiring intervention in our current situation. It will remain usefully up-to-date for the coming decades since it deals with current issues destined to become more and more central both in public debate and in academic research. The persistence of techno-solutionist approaches to climate change and techno-utopian human-machine fusion will make this book a milestone in the critical understanding of the Anthropocene."

Dr Gerardo Nicoletta, faculty of social science, Charles University, Prague

THE AGE OF HUMACHINES

Ontocapitalism, Big Tech Dystopia and the Eco-Democratic, Degrowth Alternative

Michael DB Harvey

First published 2024

© 2024 Michael Denis Bagenal Harvey

The right of Michael Denis Bagenal Harvey to be identified as author of this work has been asserted by him in accordance with sections 77 and 78 of the Copyright, Designs and Patents act 1988.

ISBN: 978-1-0686423-0-2 (paperback)
ISBN: 978-1-0686423-1-9 (ebook)

Typeset in Minion Pro font by *Wordzworth.com*

Cover Design By Jeff Willis

Interactional Books, London
info@interactional.com

*To all those who struggle for a better, greener
more democratic future.*

CONTENTS

PREFACE

Where is Technological Capitalism Taking Us?

Shortly before the 2024 General Election, the British Labour Party promised the technology industry "to make sure that regulation does not unnecessarily slow down innovation" and to support "the next ten DeepMinds" (referring to the British artificial intelligence start-up acquired by Google in 2014) (Scammell, 2024). It was a policy that echoed the strategy of the Conservative Chancellor of the Exchequer, who the previous year had asked an audience of Big Tech executives in London "to help turn the UK into the world's next Silicon Valley" (Isaacs, 2023). His government's long-standing strategy of becoming "the most pro-tech government ever", aspiring to transform Britain into "a global science and technology superpower", demanded nothing less (gov.uk, 2021). However, in committing themselves to the rapid development of artificial intelligence, robotics, biotechnology, genetics and medical technology, and an increase in STEM education, neither political party was doing anything particularly novel. In fact, the UK was rehearsing the intended direction of travel of virtually every developed nation in the world today, and many developing countries to boot. In the twenty-first century, this vision of a "fourth industrial revolution" involving the exponential development of science and technology has more or less become synonymous with the progress of civilization; indeed, without it, growth-based capitalism, as we know it, may be unable to survive..

This book attempts to reveal, more comprehensively than ever before, what becoming "a global science and technology superpower" could really mean for being human on planet Earth. It attempts to trace the past of this strategy – emulating Silicon Valley is just the latest version of an intentionality that stretches back much further than industrialization. It also describes in detail the present of the Big Tech boom and the way it's changing how we live, act, think and feel today. Crucially, it also tries to gauge the future of this fusion of lightly regulated technology and free market capitalism. Will it bring us the paradise it claims or a distinctly dystopian outcome, especially for the majority of the world's population who live in the Global South?

Technology is always determined by the political, social, economic, historical, psychological and cultural context in which decisions about it are made. The ecological context in which this book was finished was the summer of 2023, which was almost certainly the hottest for 120,000 years, with numerous records smashed for sea and air temperature, ice melt, floods, storms, heatwaves and wildfires (Copernicus, 2023). The head of the United Nations Antonio Guterres warned that humanity was on "a highway to climate hell", as scientists confirmed that the planet was on course for catastrophic global heating of at least 2.7C by the end of the century, potentially depriving billions of people of a habitable environment (Lenton et al, 2023). Yet, as this book will show, the new technology revolution aims to transcend nature and ultimately reengineer everything about being human on planet Earth and thus stands in potential opposition to a successful green transition, based on respect for nature and a desire to preserve the planet's life systems.

Just when it seems that the planet is crying out for humanity to pull back on the technology that has caused such devastation since the industrial era, should we be choosing to support another revolution aiming to take new technology even further, even faster, as far as it can possibly go? Has anybody ever voted for this strategy and would they do so if they knew the existential risks it entails, which this book exposes? Would they choose this path to the future if they had knowledge of the goals, values and psychology of the computer-scientist billionaire entrepreneurs who are driving this transformation? Are these really the "good actors" in whose hands the development of AI-enabled technology is claimed to be safe? Would the majority be able to vote for anything at all, if the transformational vision of this leadership elite, one of the most powerful in all of human history, is accomplished? Vigorous debate around these questions, and many other practical and philosophical issues, is what this book attempts to stimulate – while we still have a chance.

Confessions of a Former Technology Entrepreneur

I come to this audacious project of writing a real-time history of humanity under technological capitalism as an organizational psychologist, who has worked with large and small organizations since the mid 1990s. Seeing humanity as an organization affords another perspective on this colossal subject and provides insightful themes such as strategy, goals and values, leadership, decision-making, skill sets, organizational structures and culture. Blended with ecological economics and degrowth theory, this approach offers new insights into political economy, anthropology, history, science and medicine. The ultimate organization on planet Earth is humanity and it's this totality which holistic, system science approach desperately needs to address in the current state of emergency that envelops humanity. (At the same time, I readily concede that a consultant who recommends that a profit-based enterprise should radically downsize, reduce its bottom line, and switch to a cooperative model might struggle to find employment but that's what I believe Western capitalism may have to do to avoid eco-techno dystopia.)

I must also confess that my approach to this book has been influenced by my background as technology manager and entrepreneur. Before deciding that the best way to change human behaviour for the better was through psychology rather than new technology, I spent a decade from the early 1980s helping to develop and market interactive computer systems that prefigured the internet and the world-wide web. I thought that online technology which enabled people to communicate more effectively through instant opinion polling, voting systems and new electronic media might make a positive difference. Live TV opinion polls, – for example, on the US bombing of Libya in 1983 and the 1987 UK general election – seemed like ways to strengthen democracy. I also hoped that in-house voting systems could bring more say to workers in corporations. At one point, I even worked for a company which ran an early online shopping scheme, although the benefits of this were always unclear and the project flopped spectacularly in the manner of many ahead-of-the-curve innovations.

When I finally realised that the main interest in interactive technology of TV companies and large corporations was orientated more towards profit than better communication, I wound up my company, took extended parental leave and began studying and eventually practicing personal and organizational psychology, the technology of being human, so to speak. And for a good while, in the long boom before 2008, it seemed to work. The well-intentioned in organizations were given greater resources to experiment and positive changes in management style and practice occurred. But after the Great Recession struck, it became increasingly obvious to me that the bottom line was back in power and it was shareholders, the owners of corporations who really call the shots, not their executives. The more I explored corporate leaders' attitudes to the future, in areas such as climate change, economic inquality and new technology, the more sceptical I become of capitalism's ability to produce the better future which seemed feasible in the early years of the millennium (at least, for those who wanted to believe that capitalism was reformable). Engaging with the climate movement in the years before the Paris climate conference in 2015 further increased these doubts and led to something of an ecological and political awakening for me.

This personal change of heart informed my last book, *Utopia in the Anthropocene (2019),* which attempts to imagine another destination for humanity than that offered by the relentless pursuit of economic growth on a hierarchical planet riven by inequalities. This practical utopia drew on my first career as a teacher of literature and cultural theory but was also closely linked to the practice of psychology, which always tries to keep alive the belief that a better life is possible, however beset by problems you may be.

This better revolution, flying under the banner of utopia, also inspires this book, which describes an ecologically balanced, equality-driven future capable of increased wellbeing for all human beings, which may also be the best way to save democracy from extinction. This vision forms the counterweight to the critique of the direction in which technological capitalism is taking us in this century – which is the major subject of this book -and attempts to contribute to the realistic depiction of a world free of capitalism, inequality and economic growth. Without this new imaginary we risk continuing to be beguiled by the mechanistic technologism which dominates our age and are in danger of persisting in making choices – consciously and unconsciously – which could result in a bleak dystopian future for humanity. In this sense, utopianism may turn out to be an existential necessity.

Michael D.B. Harvey
London, March 2024

INTRODUCTION

Choosing between Technological Revolutions in the Anthropocene

What is it to be human on planet Earth? This is the question which every society in history has to ask itself but as yet humanity has not come up with an agreed answer. Momentous technological innovations transform this question into an even more demanding existential choice, because technology can change every aspect of our relationship to nature and our political, economic and social life, as well as our personal identity, wellbeing and freedom. Today we are faced with two such choices, which are incomparably more comprehensive, consequential and searching than any we have faced before.

The first choice is a consequence of the fossil-fuel based industrial revolution of the past three centuries and the much more recent advent of industrialized agriculture which have led to the climate and biodiversity emergency of the twenty-first century. Ecologists refer to the current period as the Anthropocene, signifying "that our planet left its natural functioning state, sharply and irrevocably, in the mid-20th century", according to geology professor Jan Zalasiewicz, although it has yet to be ratified as the third new epoch in the past two-and-a-half million years (Carrington, 2024). Humans now have such an influence over nature that our technology choices directly affect the viability of all living things. The Anthropocene Crisis has already produced a climate which is hotter than anything on this planet for 120,000 years and threatens to make the planet uninhabitable for billions of people in the Global South (Burke et al, 2018). How we react to the threat of global warming and the mass extinction of species and habitats has profound implications for every aspect of human society, now and for many generations to come.

The second existential choice has been far less articulated by the climate and ecological movement – many environmentalists seem to have barely noticed it – but it could represent a transformation as momentous as climate change, hard as that may be to grasp. Under the cover of apparent scientific and economic progress, another revolution in what it means to be human is engulfing us and at a speed that is unprecedented in history. Far from stepping back from our use of technology, as the Anthropocene Crisis might seem to demand, this revolution urges us to step into our machines, to develop technology that can do everything humans can do in order to provide the solution to every problem humans can create. It aims at nothing less than creating a totally new relationship between humans and machines, by humanizing machines and mechanizing humans until the two become barely distinguishable. This fusion not only promises to transform the economic infrastructure of capitalism, putting billions of jobs at risk, but also the very structure of our material reality. It implies a metamorphosis of virtually everything that we take for granted about being human. How we think, feel, choose, communicate, love, work and manage our relationships are all up for grabs. It's the biggest psychological experiment in human history – except it's not an experiment; it's reality, unregulated, unsupervised and unfolding before our very eyes.

Supportive economists call this process the Second Machine Age or, more commonly, the Fourth Industrial Revolution. Its visionary strategists refer to it as the singularity, when computers, assisted by artificial intelligence (AI), become more intelligent than humans until "there won't be a distinction between humans and technology" (Kurzweil, 2005:40-41). Transhumanists see it as a "post-human", "post-biological" stage of engineered human evolution that could occur within a decade or so. The mechanization of humans could also come in the form of a genomics revolution that enables parents to design their children's personalities and new meditechnics and biotechnology dedicated to creating human immortality.

This is not a revolution being led by philosophers, scientists, economists or politicians, although they play an important part in it, but by the most powerful entrepreneurs on the planet running the biggest technology empires the world has ever seen. These multi-billionaires are engaged in a kind of three-faced capitalism, which uses the idea of green growthism to slingshot the carbon capitalism which still dominates our global economy into an extreme form of capitalism I've named ontocapitalism (after "ontos" the Classical Greek for "being" or "existence"). This hubristic fusion of no-limits, science and free market economics aims to transform Homo sapiens into a post-biological, "multi-planetary species" capable of colonizing the universe and reengineering the evolution of all living things and all energy and matter. As such, it offers itself as the ultimate solution to all the other problems contained in the Anthropocene Crisis, including growing economic inequality within rich societies and between the Global North and South, the weakening of democracy, the persistence of injustice, patriarchy and the growing threat of conflict and war. The automation of everything human, its proponents argue, will put us on the path to techno-utopia.

In short, we are living in what I call the age of humachines, undergoing a revolution to merge humans and machines, which I refer to as humachination. This book describes this attempted transformation – its present, its past and the kind of future to which our current choices seem to be leading us, a future which could drastically diminish freedom for the vast majority of people on this planet. I call this possible negative version of the Anthropocene the Technocene.

This is not a book without hope, however. The Big Tech juggernaut is not unstoppable. There is another possible revolution, which is ecological and democratic and can achieve planetary sustainability while increasing real freedom, equality and life satisfaction. This alternative future which can bring out the best of being human on planet Earth I term the Ecocene.

Choosing the Future

Choosing how to deal with the ecocidal threats caused by carbon capitalism and the humachine revolution which tries to trump it in ambition and scope, calls on us to make multiple history-defining choices, a challenge not made any easier by the fact that we have waited so long to take it on. Amalgamating humans and machines may sound like madness but it's rapidly being normalized. In the West, we are already surrounded by humachines, mimicking human cognition, replacing human action and insinuating themselves into every facet of normal life. Increasingly complex and interactive humanized machines are in our pockets, our hands and our eye lines; they're in our homes, workplaces, hospitals, schools, streets and in our seas and skies and in space. Through AI, robotics and biotechnology a growing army of humachines – cognitive, emotional, relational, communicative and robotic – are normalizing new ways of governing, policing, administering justice, looking after and educating others, replacing myriad human competences and motor skills. They are also changing the way our decision-making takes place in democracies. Indeed, controlling the way we make all human choices may be the central goal of humachination. The ideological hegemony of technologism – the idea that technology represents our destiny and the best of our past history- adds to the problem. It strengthens the grip of what I call tricknology, the ability to sell automation as the solution to every problem (and as former technology entrepreneur, I know something about selling the future). All this is pushing us in a direction which the majority have not had a chance to deliberate on, let alone consciously choose.

That's why we need to be bold in identifying the choices that are embedded in the humachine age, which represent foundational assumptions about our relationships with one another and our material existence on this planet. They raise – more urgently than ever before – the most deep-rooted questions about what it is to be human. What is our purpose as a species; what are our goals? A mutation of capitalism committed to changing everything everywhere means we have no option but to make up our minds about human ontology. Are our bodies fundamentally organic – flesh, blood and bone – or machines waiting to be further mechanized or transformed into cyborgs? Should a new synthetic species of humanoid robots be created and given quasi-human rights? What is the human brain? Is it a sophisticated, stand-alone computer (software to the body's hardware), as the AI project claims, or a process of embodied cognition inextricably connected to our physical being, emotional life and social and natural environment? Do we have essential, indigenous skills, talents and competences that need to be preserved or is everything about being human subject to change?

We also urgently need to ask what is the role of economics in our lives – a means to a more rewarding life for everybody or an end in itself? What about politics? Is democracy superior to authoritarianism and if so, is representative democracy enough or do we need something much deeper to engage the majority? That's a vital question in relation to who decides on our technology, the elite or the people? What can deep history and anthropology tell us about this process and about who we really are and what we can be – or is industrial modernity the only thing that matters about our past? Technological revolutions always involve leadership, so are today's humachination leaders the saviours of humanity they claim to be or self-interested, domineering "great men" like so many before them? Will they bring techno-utopian abundance and personal freedom or more hierarchical patterns of domination? And what about ethics and spirituality: are these irrelevant to capitalist technology (which can be seen as a form of morality and religion in its own right) or an inseparable part of all human decision-making?

All these people-orientated questions, difficult enough in themselves, lead to bigger, ecological challenges. What, in fact, is the Earth: a solid well-understood platform for humans' boundless ambition or an immensely complex, fragile ecosystem? What does modern scientific knowledge look like? Is it dominated by physics and computer science, as "humachinators" assume, or by the life sciences such as biology and ecology? In the end, we cannot avoid the ultimate question that the humachine age demands: what is life? Is it a self-creating process that seeks aliveness or a form of material organization which machines can improve on? Is natural selection something bigger than humanity or can evolution now be re-engineered on the way to an unimaginably different future? All of these choices – and many more we'll look at in this book- are forced on us by the ecological emergency of carbon capitalism and the humachination revolution that attempts to transcend it. And these decisions are coming at us at breakneck speed, from every angle at the same time, with the force of a mighty torrent, pushing us towards a destination we have not chosen.

There are clearly many issues that we need to make up our minds about but if this all sounds too daunting let me suggest that existential choices tend to be organized in patterns, like so much else in life. This book tries to describe some of these patterns as they relate to new technology and to trace the linkage between a multiplicity of scientific, business and ideological developments that have been imperfectly studied up until now. (Inadequate information is good decision-making's most ancient enemy.) In another sense, however, this book is not so much about technology as the way we organize our choices around it. The humachinators argue that machines can be anything we want them to be but the real question is what do *we* want to be? Only by answering this can we decide on what our technology should and shouldn't do. Machines don't just happen; unlike living things, they don't create themselves, they are the result of human intentionality.

This intentionality – conscious, goal-oriented choice-making – is always woven into an organizational pattern I call a worldplan. This points towards the future (as in "to plan") but also involves a network of relationships between the part and the whole ("a plan"). This worldplan extends beyond the individual to a particular society at a particular stage of history. The worldplan represents a social system's organizing principles, its relationships to nature, its economics and politics, its religion and beliefs, which ultimately embody choices about what a society is for and ultimately what nature and being human means. Before we sleepwalk over the cliff of irreversible change towards a future which could destroy many core aspects of humanness, we urgently need to clarify our goals and values and sort out what the best of being human really means.

The Battle between Anthropocene Worldplans

As an organizational psychologist, I spent many years helping people to make difficult decisions but, as I'm sure you've already sensed, as a citizen, I'm not neutral in this debate. So let me declare at the outset what my position is on the existential choices before us. For me, humachination is the wrong revolution and the product of the wrong worldplan. It reflects a world system that is dominated by growth capitalism, which is based on the self-defeating goal of infinite economic growth on a finite planet, otherwise known as "the growth irrationale". New technology and incredibly exaggerated, tricky claims about what it can achieve have become the only way in which capitalism can save itself from this contradiction. The organizational pattern of capitalism not only ignores nature but has a profound tendency to reinforce social inequality, which makes it more likely that the humachine age will end up narrowing human freedom, not expanding it. Environmentally, at this unprecedented tipping point in human history, as climate and other planetary safe limits are under threat of being breached, the mechanization of everything human is the last thing we need. The profit-driven mania to automate everything human is a product of the same worldplan and the same mindset which created the global ecological crisis in the first place.

One of our biggest dangers is "unconscious capitalism", the way we assume that there is no alternative to growthism which normalizes so many of our current ways of living, like levels of consumptions which would require three planets of natural resources if everybody lived like Europeans or five planets if the entire world followed the American model. But unconscious mechanicalism is another problem in its own right, a view of science which emerged from the Western scientific revolution which is obsessed with quantity over quality, objectivity over subjective experience and sees machines as being a potentially superior form of being to organic life. Fused with a free-market economics committed to expansion at all costs, this makes for a formidably dangerous new ideology, which I call ontocapitalism.

Nevertheless, I believe that by bringing our choices to the surface, and deliberating on them, we can create a different worldplan, a new direction for humanity- a better resolution of our existential crises. Throughout this book, and most explicitly in its final section, I'll be advocating such a worldplan, a different pattern of choices. It's an ecological democratic alternative that we need to solve the technological revolutions facing us in the Anthropocene in ecological and democratic ways. Its goals are to create Sustainable, Equitable Wellbeing Planetwide in what I call the SEWP model (pronounced as in "super" or "soup"). Its values are those of cooperation, altruism, internationalism and the other CANDID values which stand in opposition to the competitive individualism and materialism of our dominant capitalist values system (CIMENT), as represented schematically in the Anthropocene Values Grid below:

Ecological Democracy (Towards the Ecocene) The CANDID ethos	Capitalist Growthism (Towards the Technocene) The CIMENT ethos
Cooperation Win/win Life as peace/Working together	**Competition** Win/lose (Zero-sum) Life as war/Working in opposition
Altruism/Collectivism Concern for others Group/Community	**Individualism** Self-interest Individual above society
Non-materialism Spiritual wisdom Quality	**Materialism** Consumerism Quantity
Democracy Majority rule Self-organization	**Elitism** Minority rule Hierarchy
Internationalism Worldwide Cooperation Global human identity	**Nationalism** Nation state Ethnocentricity/nativism
Deference for nature Partnership with nature Developing tools for living sustainably and equitably together	**Technologism** Conquest of nature Progress of technology as an end in itself Technology as magic

Figure 1. The CANDID/CIMENT Values Grid

This eco-democratic worldplan advocates a policy of sustainable economic degrowth – or living within our ecological means – in the developed countries to rebalance our relationship with nature and the developing world, in pursuit of authentic equality and global levelling and bringing out the best of being human in a post scarcity world. It's a radical shift in priorities which values life satisfaction over the relentless materialist excess and careless elitism which dominate our world system. Ecological democracy invites us to step back from the frenzied irrationality of humachination and engage in a foundational revision of what it is to be human.

It involves taking stock of what is really valuable in technological progress – there is no point in pretending it hasn't happened – and putting science at the service of the common good and the majority of humanity ("demo-technics"). Throughout this book I invite you to imagine what decisions we would make about technology if the majority had a proper chance to make careful, deliberative choices about it. I also urge the reader to bear in mind the danger of putting the cart before the horse when it comes to the relationship between technology and society. (In fact, this well-known metaphor literally involves an inversion between a piece of human-made technology and a living thing). At the moment we seem to be asking, what kind of technology is possible and how do we accommodate society to it? If we continue doing so, we are probably on our way to the Technocene. Instead, we could ask, what kind of human society we want (including what kind of relationship with nature) and what kind of technology do we need (and not need) to deliver it? This is the Ecocene approach in a nutshell.

You might argue that ecological democracy, the SEWP worldplan and the CANDID values are utopian. Indeed, my last book – *Utopia in the Anthropocene* (2019) – was largely devoted to describing a society based on these goals and values which can help to realise the best of being human. But researching a human-machine merger has further convinced me that such a worldplan is not an indulgence but a necessity. Many now recognize this around the world, particularly among the young. The signs are evident in the growing climate and social justice movement, pro-equality identity politics, the degrowth community, the role of sustainability and ecological economics in academia and in all who long for a simpler, more rewarding way of living that is required for the Anthropocene. Utopianism is also part of human psychology. In our inner utopias, we have a pattern of a desired world, a holistic image of life which draws us on to the future. In this sense, we are also all futurists, with our moods and motivation affected by our anticipation of what comes next, as well as our practical goals. Achieving a sustainable, stable, peaceful Anthropocene which moves beyond growth will not only require an alternative political economy to capitalism but also an alternative to the domination-obsessed psychology – the dominator syndrome or god complex that drives all elites to try to manipulate all our choices in a way that favour them. A very different mindset, democratic, open, balanced and equalizing, must come to the fore if we are to move towards a positive and sustainable future.

Technocene or Ecocene?

This is what our existential choices may come down to in the end, as a battle between two very different versions of the Human Epoch. The first is an ecologically failed, techno-dystopian planet, in which technology and the elite which own it are our undisputed masters; the other an ecologically harmonious world based on freedom and democratic choice which puts technology its rightful place as our servant. We still have time to choose between the two, but be aware that in the humachine age the future is hurtling towards us faster than ever before.

Plan of the Book

The book is organized into six parts.

Part I tells the story of the origins of the age of humachines as a business and describe the five forms of humachines, which are embedding themselves in everyday life and creating an unprecedented period of corporate empire-building. Humachination is a powerful techno-utopian vision of the near future, which aims to replace biology with physics and reengineer the evolution of life on Earth. It's Big Tech's corporate strategy, comparable to the profit-first vision that has remorselessly guided fossil-fuel companies through the past 50 years of global warming. It has also become a mainstream theory of capitalist economics, which has now been adopted by many governments and is endorsed by influential theorists across the political spectrum.

In Part II I challenge the theoretical foundations of human-machine fusion, trying to bring to the surface the unconscious beliefs which govern the choices about the future we seem to be making. I challenge the assumptions that capitalism can continue to produce economic growth or provide a sustainable, equitable, democratic future and that technological progress determines the course of history. I also dispute the humachinators' claim that progress in modern science is dominated by physics rather than biological life science and that market-based consumerism is a reliable indicator of what people really want or what is good for the planet.

Part III confronts the risk that the Technocene is capitalism's default setting, that the age of humachines ends not in techno-utopia but in its opposite, an ecologically-ravaged techno-dystopia. This, I suggest, is the danger of the green growth policy favoured by humachine corporations and the threat posed by new technology – and its theorists – to the current, fragile state of democracy. Other risks flow from the untrustworthiness of the humachine elite as leaders and the possibility that they are normalizing a new form of anti-social, dominator psychology. Perhaps the biggest risk of all is to the core aspects of being human, as radical deskilling deprives people of the ability to find their way without technology, and causes the loss of many other creative and constructive talents and competences built up over hundreds of millennia of human history. Defining primordial human values may be the only way to prevent this and other catastrophes implicit in AI and robot development, including "AImaggedon".

In Part IV, we move to a detailed examination of the practice of humanizing machines. It looks at the practical problems of the AI project (and its dangerous metaphor that human brain is like a computer), and the social implications of machines taking over crucial areas of human decision-making in government, medicine, business, the judicial system and the military. Humachines are also replacing human relationships, radically changing our ways of communicating with, and caring for others, with machines taking on roles as teachers, therapists, parents and, potentially, sexual partners and equal-rights citizens. Even in heavy industry and warfare, we encounter the cart-before-the-horse problem: do humachines provide the answers to the right questions or just the ones that suit Western capitalism?

Part V examines the most extreme form of humachination, mechanizing the human brain, body, genetic structure and lifespan, especially in the context of the profit-chasing US medical industry. I review computerized brain implants, artificial hearts, organs and limbs (for example in "real-life cyborgs"), trying to separate beneficial forms of medical reparation from dangerous forms of neurological and physical augmentation. Is the desire for immortality justifiable or a form of selfish, anti-social elitism? Are pro-humachination geneticists and moral philosophers right to argue that capitalism will soon welcome designer children and human cloning. And could "personal eugenics" lead to an ultra-wealthy super-race and the end of Homo sapiens as a unified species?

The book culminates in the choice posed by Part VI: is the twenty-first century moving towards the Technocene or the Ecocene? The all-enveloping digital-robotic environment of achieved humachination, with its Smartheid social stratification and data monopolies, could gently slide us into techno-dystopia relatively smoothly, although much darker, more violent scenarios are also possible. On the other hand, the Ecocene alternative of ecological democracy can prevail if we commit to a worldplan based on sustainable, equitable, wellbeing planetwide. This requires hard choices around technology, income distribution and consumption and a multi-institutional revolution to achieve deeper levels of democratic cooperation. The end result can be a vibrant, psychologically-liberated world safely brought back into balance with nature.

N.B. Throughout this book I freely use neologisms, as the reader may already have noticed, in part to help create a counter-language to Big Tech's extensive and ubiquitous vocabulary. For a reminder of the meaning of these coinages and other key terms, please consult the Glossary I've provided at the end of the book

PART I

What Is Humachination?
Its Corporate Empires, Techno-Utopian
Vision and Economic Theory

Part I recounts the explosive beginning of the age of humachines as a period of unparalleled corporate empire-building and describes the five types of humachine, which are embedding themselves in everyday life. We explore the vast range of the humachine conglomerates and the relentless focus on expansion behind their consumer-friendly images. What is rarely recognized is the extent to which this business expansion is influenced by an outlandishly ambitious techno-utopian vision, which aims to replace biology with physics and reengineer the evolution of life on Earth. In Chapter 2 we examine its most revealing source, Ray Kurzweil's *The Singularity is Near*, which offers the radical new synthesis of no-limits science and free-market economics which I call ontocapitalism. We'll find that this links to other transhumanist and post-biological theories, which surprisingly cross many political boundaries. Putting this philosophy in the context of the sustainable equitable alternative of the Ecocene helps to disclose its dangers.

Yet, bizarre and unfamiliar as it may seem, human-machine fusion forms the core of Big Tech's corporate strategy in a way that is comparable to the uncompromising, profit-first vision that has remorselessly guided fossil fuel companies through the past half century of global warming. In Chapter 3, we'll see how this corporate intentionality has been taken up by main-stream capitalist economics, in part through the influence of the founder of the Davos's World Economic Forum, and picked up by centrist and leftist economists, whose main concern seems to be to accelerate the process of automation and other aspects of human-machine merger. In the following chapters, we may begin to realise the disturbing implications of the journey to the future, on which the leaders of human-machine fusion are taking us, and what lies beneath publicly accepted governmental strategies of science and technology development.

CHAPTER 1

The Big Bang of Humachination and a Typology of Humachines

The Humachine Big Bang

The twenty-first century is the age of humachines. This technological revolution exploded into existence in March 2000, following the new century's first economic crash. The big bang might have occurred earlier, perhaps sparked by the birth of robotics in the 1940s, the start of the artificial intelligence movement and the genetics breakthroughs in the 1950s, the 1970s computer revolution or the 1990s launch of the internet. Indeed, its prehistory stretches back even further to the first industrial and scientific revolutions. But, it seems, the unique combination of events necessary for this technological big bang had to await the arrival of a new millennium. Ironically, in February 2000, the Nobel prize-winning chemist Paul Crutzen had suggested that the influence of humanity on planet Earth was now so extreme that we needed to declare a new epoch, the Anthropocene, in order to comprehend it (Davison, 2019). A few weeks later a revolution began.

Unfortunately, the transformation initiated by the dot-com stock market crash which struck on 13th March 2000 was not the revolution that the Human Epoch needs, a rebalancing of nature and humanity, borne out of a respect for our planetary limits which would lead to a profound reframing of the role of technology. Instead, we got the radical re-invention of our relationship with nature that capitalism desperately needed, as another financial breakdown plunged it into crisis. The collapse – over the next eighteen months the NASDAQ index would plummet by 78%- signalled the end of the frenetic technology boom which centred on the invention of the internet and the spread of digital devices (Aldin, 2005). This seemed to suggest that technological innovation could produce economic growth in a way that was completely disconnected from economic or material reality, with companies which were little more than business plans valued in billions of dollars. But the financial meltdown forcefully restated the bottom line of growth capitalism, insisting that the primary purpose of technological innovation is to expand shareholders' capital. ROI – return on investment- was still king, it said. Technological disruption for its own sake would be mercilessly rejected.

Two of the most alert readers of this message were Stanford University computer science researchers, Larry Page and Sergey Brin, who were patiently developing a promising new search engine. The sudden cooling of investor sentiment caused by the dot com crash persuaded the pair to abandon their idealistic plans to keep Google advertising-free and instead turn it into an advertiser's dream. In one sense, Google's search engine is very simple: it follows what other people search for, identifying a kind of digital herd mentality but in a fraction of the time taken previously. This offered a new ease and convenience for information gathering, remote shopping and speedy communication with others. And it was free – nominally, at least. But in reality, the device is a ruse. As Shoshanna Zuboff *(2019)* has superbly illustrated in the *Age of Surveillance Capitalism* Google's search engine is like a one-way mirror. In front of the screen, we behave uninhibitedly, as before a normal mirror. But from the other side of the mirror, Google's machine intelligence is secretly watching, recording and analysing us. It takes account not only of obvious aspects of our behaviour such as what we search for but also the micro-data of how we search, our hesitations, our keystroke styles, our impulsivity or patience. This "metadata" reveals patterns of behaviour for us as individuals and as parts of larger groups, which can then be used to predict our future behaviour and so influence our choices well beyond the sphere of consumer consumption.

The one-way mirror ruse is a trick capable of initiating a new age of technology and its power has increased exponentially as Google has acquired more data companies, such as advertising network Double Click in 2007, in spite of protests that this was anti-competitive and monopolistic. The capacity to mine, pool and track users' data across different platforms created a massive gusher of advertising income, which shot up into the corporate sky. The revenue of Google, or Alphabet as its parent company was renamed in 2015 – rose from less than $500 million in 2002 to $21 billion by 2008 and a staggering $305 billion in 2023 (Bianchi, 2024). This stratospheric growth provides Google's founders with almost unimaginable funds for their AI-based mission to technologize humanity.

Google's success also helped to create a new frenzy of investment in start-ups like Amazon and later Facebook, as well as in slightly older technology companies, such as Microsoft and Apple, which were badly battered by the dot com hurricane. At the same time, on the other side of the Pacific Ocean from Silicon Valley, in a nominally communist economy, a host of hyper-competitive Chinese startups sprang into existence, initially emulating their American humachine counterparts, but soon developing into vast, complex technology conglomerates in their own right. Other Big Tech corporations have grown into empires of unprecedented size and scope. An apt historical analogy might be Genghis Khan's ruthless Mongol warriors who in just a few decades conquered a territory twice the size of the Roman Empire.

This startling new age of human technology had been anticipated the year before the dot.com crash by John Benditt (1999), editor of the influential *MIT Technology Review.* He coined the word "humachine" to indicate "the symbiosis that is currently developing between human beings and machines", a process of "human beings fusing with or assuming the powers of machines". Earlier that year, Ray Kurzweil (1999), who in due course would become Google's director of engineering, had published *The Age of Spiritual Machines: When computers exceed human intelligence,* a book which promoted an even more aggressive portrait of the humanization of machines and the mechanization of humans, described as "a utopia… in which humans gained near immortality by becoming one with robotic technology"(Joy, 2000). "Humachine" has also been used to denote an idealized techno-utopian business model (Sanders and Wood, 2020), so, before returning to my account of the early twenty-first century corporate big bang, let me clarify exactly what I mean by the term humachines.

Humachines: A Provisional Typology

In my view, humachines are devices and systems which facilitate human-machine fusion, by attempting to replicate, and even improve on, every aspect of what it is to be human. These devices cross every existential and classificatory boundary, between the mechanical and the biological, the cognitive and the emotional and the symbolic and real. In so doing, humachines destroy the very categories needed for a definition, pulling the epistemological rug from under your feet, as it were. You also come up against the problem of what exactly humachines are trying to replicate – and one of the themes of this book is that humanness is not a settled category but a bitterly contested part of our unfinished business as a species. It's a vacuum of agreed meaning which growth capitalism is all too ready to fill, often exploiting our deepest vulnerabilities.

That said, some basic features of being human are incontrovertible. As humans, we are brain-bodies who think and make choices about the world; we are relational beings, with emotions that help to guide how we interact and communicate with, and care for, others. We also work to earn our living using wonderfully evolved motor skills, especially our hands, to create complex social environments which exist in a specific relationship with nature.

This description is enough to generate the following provisional typology of humachines: 1. cognitive humachines; 2. relational humachines; 3. motor-skill (robotic) humanized machines; 4. mechanized humans with synthetic and electronic augmentations; and 5. humachinated, digital robotic environments, which can combine all of these entities. Humachines constantly intersect, overlap and form new hybrids but this is the basic taxonomy which I'll try to stick to in this book.

1. Cognitive Humachines

Central to the goal of creating humachines is the replication of human intelligence. Sergey Brin sums up this core ambition of the AI movement like this: "You should presume that someday we will be able to make machines that can reason, think and do things better than we can" (quoted by Bridle, 2018). This echoes the famous pronouncement of mathematician Jack Good (1966) that "the first ultra-intelligent machine is the last invention that man need ever make" adding the crucial caveat, "provided that the machine is docile enough to tell us how to keep it under control". This he insisted was a necessity: "The survival of man depends on the early construction of an ultra-intelligent machine" (Good, 1965). "AI is attempting to bottle what make humans special" is a more recent definition of the goal by professor of machine learning Michael Osborne (Knapton, 2023)

If you believe that human reasoning is the key to being human (as expressed by Descartes' dictum "cogito ergo sum"), it's necessary to simulate all the functions involved in this, such as decision-making, judgement, common sense, language use, seeing, reading and so on. If the brain is an executive solely in charge of the body, and the body is largely a machine – hardware to the mind's software, as in the standard AI philosophical stance, this would enable the mechanization of all human activities, occupations, interactions, labour and built environments. Decision-making could be automated in every human institution from business and law to government and medicine, producing a new type of human-machine society.

Cognitive humachines operate on the basis of machine languages, complex lines of instructions governed by sets of rules or algorithms. Although they may be dazzlingly complex and lead to apparently autonomous results, they are not magic formulae. Cognitive humachine are not independent of their human programmers or the data they have been trained on, information which has to be extracted from the biggest context of all, the real world. Only then can they be turned into patterns which can be used to predict human behaviour.

For all the dazzling brilliance of symbolic programming codes, cognitive humachines are ultimately wholly dependent on physical machines. A machine language without a machine to operate is a dead language, a mere set of symbols. So Larry Page's mission for Google, "to organize all the information in the world" (Levy, 2011:75), ultimately involves controlling all the machines in the world.

Hundreds of millions of these machines already exist, often in massive industrial installations misleadingly called "farms", consuming colossal amounts of metal, minerals and energy. The Cloud is not an ethereal presence floating in the sky, as the name suggests; it exists in drab, thoroughly earth-bound warehouses full of banks of whirring servers. Many of these machines are owned by humachine corporations – which are definitely not just software companies – and many are owned by us in the form of devices such as laptops, PCs, smartphones and games consoles. We buy the machines that provide the data which is then sold back to us through multiple applications in dizzying loops which can make cognitive humachines seem "all in the mind" when in fact they are always predicated on the hard, material reality of machines.

2. Relational Humachines
(Including Emotional and Communicative Humachines)

Humans are social beings: how we relate to one another is fundamental to our being. Often in the past a machine such as a typewriter existed in a one-way relationship with humans; it was there for our use, on a take-it-or-leave-it basis. But humachines know more about you than a typewriter ever can and they want to use that knowledge. They want to talk to you and you to talk to them and form a bond. Relational humachines may appear as Alexa, or Siri or other sweet-voiced digital assistants, breaking down the externality of computers and moving towards voice- and eventually thought-control systems. They can create new ways of being with other people, via text, voice, image, video, music or all three and use affective computing to simulate human emotions, for example, through synthesized vocal tones that mirror human moods.

Our feelings are crucial to our relationships. Decision-making is never purely "in the head". Damage to our emotional brain makes it impossible to make even the simplest day-to-day choices (Damasio, 1994). Although many computer scientists are biased towards rationalistic, mechanistic thinking, others recognize the significance of human affect in every aspect of life.

Using personality surveys and software that analyses facial micro-expressions, eye movements and body language, affective computing attempts to build a picture of what's going on an individual's inner life. This "emotional capture" can be used by recognition systems to try to predict our preferred consumer products, romantic partners or political inclinations and how we will react in public situations like demonstrations. Biomedical feedback, the analysis of heart rate, temperature, perspiration and stress levels, which is increasingly common in video gaming and elsewhere, provides further layers of information.

This data can be used to construct truth-detection humachines that claim to be better at telling when people are lying than humans, which would have huge implications for what it is to be human. Relational humachines want to use the data gathered on human affect to go one step further in crossing the human-machine gap. They intend to take on the most profoundly human roles as confidantes, advisors, playmates and hedonistic companions. Humanized systems even claim to be capable of empathy, emotionally sensing a person's moods and putting themselves in her shoes. In the humachine age, there's no human relationship that's immune to mechanization.

Communicative Humachines

Communication is a core element of human relationships and communicative systems are among the best-known forms of humachines. Email, video-calling and messaging through voice, text, image and video combine software and hardware with communication networks such as the internet (which ultimately rely on the physical infrastructure of masts, satellites and undersea cables). This creates the possibility for communicating faster, more frequently and with greater quantities of people than ever before but often at the expense of the quality of communication.

Communicative humachines also change the way we produce information. As the sheer mass of available information on the internet exponentially increases, the skills necessary to digest and independently assess it decrease, opening the sluices for an avalanche of shallow, commercially and politically-biased disinformation. Social media is another communication medium unlike any other in history. In one sense, it is self-organizing a commons owned by all, which allows its participants to make up their own rules. On the other hand, it's a capitalist endeavour with little accountability except to its shareholders designed to increase revenue, which is largely achieved by increasing traffic. Algorithms and software devices such as retweeting and the 'like' button, amplify extreme views and create emotion-arousing conflict and division, which increase monitizable user engagement, while reducing the consensus and mutual responsibility which are the cornerstones of real commons and successful communities. To this extent, social media is typical of the entire human-machine hybridization project, creating novel forms of communicative behaviour, the implications of which are not yet fully understood, while lavishly delivering on profit-based goals.

3. Motor-Skill Humachines (Robots)

If the human body is a machine, a kind of hardware which is directed by software (rather than part of brain-body-environment continuum, as I'll argue in this book), it should be possible to replicate and upgrade every activity the human body performs. A device which can imitate human motor skills (the conventional idea of a robot) offers a superior way of achieving tasks which previously relied on human and animal muscle power, such as carrying, loading, digging and building. In fact, certain manual labour tasks turn out to be much more difficult to roboticize than some cognitive tasks, since motor skills is a misleading simplistic name for the complex operations performed by the most ancient parts of the brain (Moravec, 1988).

It's not necessary for a robot to have a full replica body. A mechanical arm is enough for the gantry robots which automate traditional factory assembly lines and provide other human functions from cooking to digging. And other robotic humachines look nothing like humans, such as fully or partially autonomous cars, trucks, trains, ships, planes, tanks, artillery and weapons of every kind, as well as equipment for mining, drilling and construction. While many of these humachines are big enough for us to get inside, others are busy getting inside us. The shrinking of machines – in part made possible by the circuit miniaturization which began in the 1970s – contrasts with the clanking industrial dinosaurs of the past and creates the possibility of ever smaller machines, occupying spaces that up till now have been regarded as off-limits, for example in our blood, our skin or other structures and surfaces. As Masayoshi Son, billionaire head of the Softbank conglomerate, predicts "We can expect all kinds of robots. Flying, swimming, big, micro, run [sic], two legs, four legs, 100 legs." (Galeon, 2017).

The Mechanized Slave Economy

It's the humanoid robot, however, that inevitably attracts the most attention -and represents the biggest potential encroachment on core human territory. Often the simplest simulations of the human face, with crudely animated eyes and mouth, are enough to stimulate our indigenous capacity to anthropomorphize almost anything. Humanoid robots potentially combine the attributes of cognitive, emotional, relational and communicative humachines with mechanized motor skills such as gripping, touching and manipulating. This opens the way for the replication of even more integral aspects of being human. For example, care robots are intended to replace – wholly or in part – many of the interpersonal capacities and traits which come with being a member of Homo sapiens, such as looking after the sick, caring for the old and other forms of nurturing and healing. Humanoid robots are also being used to provide education, psychological counselling, and even as a substitute for parenting. Sex robots are also being developed that claim to offer not only wide-ranging sexual functionality but also true companionship – we'll return to this sexist fantasy of "the ideal girlfriend" in Chapter 16. If androids continue to blur the distinction between human and machines, it raises questions about whether they deserve legal rights and protections. If sex with humachines becomes widespread, marriage with robots might seem like the next logical step, as some roboticists already advocate (Levy, 2007).

Humachines and Jobs

The implications of humachination for work, itself another way of defining what it is to be human, are staggering. If humachines can make decisions like humans, relate to each other like humans, but with superior motor skills, almost every human job is at risk. Larry Page believes that "rapid improvement in AI and robotics will make computers and robots adept at most jobs" and that the pursuit of technological efficiency has to be taken to its logical conclusion. "You can't wish away these things from happening, they are going to happen" (Waters, 2014). Or as Elon Musk told British Prime Minister Rishi Sunak in an interview broadcast worldwide, "There will come a point where no job is needed … the AI will be able to do everything" (Henshall, 2023).

This demolishes the myth promoted by robotics that motor-skill humachines are only intended to replace dirty, dull or dangerous jobs or that only the most repetitive aspects of a job will be replaced, freeing up humans for more valuable creative or interpersonal work. In fact, all occupational tasks are in the crosshairs of the humachinators, for whom enough is never likely to be enough. The job replacement industry is constantly analysing existing jobs, breaking them down into separate processes and tasks, and attempting to replace them, wholly or in part, by machines and digital systems.

Previous job replacement was glacially slow and parts of the developing world have still not caught up with the original Industrial Revolution. Yet today economists are predicting that billions of jobs worldwide could be automated within the next 10-20 years.

The industries undergoing humachination are too numerous to list but here's a sample:

- In healthcare meditechnics is replacing roles providing consultation, administration, diagnosis, treatment, surgery, after-care and psychotherapy.

- In the military virtually all sectors are being automated from strategy and surveillance to autonomous weaponry of every kind ("killer robots") and semi-mechanized, augmented soldiers.

- In education automation stretches from online courses, which are designed autonomously to holographic, avatar teachers, digital "mentors" and student assessment by algorithm.

- In the creative industries music composition is being computerized, generative AI can produce plausible visual art in seconds and films are being created by data-based scriptwriting, semi-autonomous editing, computer-generated sound and visual effects and even AI-fabricated actors (Clarke, 2022a).

Nor is humachination confined to paid-for employment. Digital capitalism threatens to infiltrate every unpaid human activity from reproductive labour, such as care for the elderly and parenting, to every leisure activity, hobby and creative pursuit in which humans engage. Gaming engages children at the earliest possible age, fusing the cognitive, relational and emotional humachines in an aggressively commercial and competitive world that merges lived experience with vivid, computerized virtual reality. All this evokes the question that hangs over the humachine age: if machines can perform every function that comes with being a member of Homo sapiens, what is left of being human?

4. Mechanizing Human Brains and Bodies: Enter the Mecan

Not content to push us out of the workplace and other sites of human activity, humachines also intend to move inside us, invading our consciousness, arteries and inner organs, finally eliminating any barriers between the organic and the mechanical. Type 4 humachination involves the gradual mechanization of the human body and brain, with the aim of creating superior intelligence, synthetic body parts and even new senses, effectively creating a new breed of superhuman cyborg, the mechanized human or "mecan". Larry Page, described by MIT professor of physics Max Tegmark (2017:32) as "the most influential exponent of digital utopianism", dismisses as "speciesist" the suggestion that silicon–based entities are in any way inferior to natural, carbon-based life forms. Here's Page's take on brain-computer interfacing (BCI):

> [Google] will be included in people's brains. When you think about something you don't know much about, you will automatically get the information … Eventually you'll have the implant, where if you think about a fact, it will just tell you the answer (Levy, 2011: 67).

Sergey Brin puts it even more bluntly: "We want Google to be the third half of your brain." (Levy, 2011: 386). Envisage it like this: take the super-computer that is your smartphone out of your pocket and put it into your skull. Arch-humachinator Elon Musk is the best-known advocate of BCI, in part, he claims, because of his fear that AI will create superintelligent automatons which will take over humanity. His solution is for humans to become "better cyborgs", on the basis that "if you can't beat 'em, join 'em" (Rapier, 2019). But Musk's Frankensteinian ambition to "achieve symbiosis with machines" is also motivated by his mission to create "a multi-planetary species", which is capable of colonising space. This messianic desire to save capitalism from itself is typical of humachination leaders.

Technologizing the body could involve inserting a synthetic heart and other organs plus subcutaneous nanotechnology intended to deliver drugs, monitor bodily functions and even provide emergency surgery. In this way, the components of the body become upgradeable, replaceable and renewable. This aggressive intrusion into biology is at the very core of the humachination project. Mechanistic scientists, who see genomics as a kind of instruction manual for creating living things, claim that humans can also be genetically modified for increased intelligence or parentally-desired personality traits. Such "life extension" technology is being developed by Google's Calico, whose original advertized mission was "to cure death",

Amazon Life Sciences and other corporations committed to disproving "Deathism", the belief that human death is inevitable, which is a cardinal heresy for humachinators (Popper, 2014).

The mecan superhuman agenda pushes hard at the boundaries of bioethics (which are dangerously absent from most AI and robotics development) but opens up the giant market that is healthcare. For example, Google Health leverages its vast amounts of personal data, harvested from public health bodies, such as the NHS, with Fitbit, its multi-billion-dollar acquisition that enables consumers to voluntarily provide health self-surveillance. Meanwhile Verily, its life science division, combines genetics research, bioelectronic medicine and robot-assisted surgery with lucrative health insurance provision (Morozow, 2020).

Meditechnics is the Trojan horse that can bring humachination into the very heart of being human: after all, who does not want a cure for disease, relief from pain or a few extra, healthy years of life? But the problem with super-humanizing some humans is that you potentially sub-humanize others, unless, that is, the whole of humanity can be simultaneously cyborgized. If "unaugmented" humans make up the majority, the result could be a new form of social stratification more profound that anything in the past. Just as we are making some headway in eradicating the racist, ableist and patriarchal legacy of our past – surely one of the key goals of the Human Epoch – a new demon of inequality leaps onto the historical stage.

5. Humachinated, Digital-Robotic Environments

All four types of humachine come together in the most underestimated but most significant of all dimensions of human-machine hybridization, the technologized, digital-robotic environment. In this 360-degree umwelt, the human and non-human become virtually indistinguishable. It's customary to see machines as discrete, touchable and separate from us, but here the devices that we step inside also step inside us, creating dense, networked, constantly adapting habitats which aim to eliminate the difference between the organic and the inorganic, the inside and the outside.

The humachinated environment will encompass fully automated factories, hospitals, offices, schools and transport hubs dominated by occupational humachines, where humans (in part mechanized), robots and digital systems all interact. Even the material structures of this environment (e.g. walls, floors and windows) are active, cognitive, learning machines, capable of communicating with, analysing and surveilling humans, and potentially changing their texture, shape and appearance.

Homes are already being transformed into digital-robotic environments. Smart homes are connected by smart doorbells, cameras, speakers, and the internet of things, such as the computerized fridge, 3-D printer or robot vacuum cleaner, creating a continuous cycle of consumerism. Anything and anywhere can become a digirobotic environment, uniting several types of humachine. For example, a self-driving vehicle is essentially a robot, a physical object directed by cognitive systems, but potentially it's also a mechanized environment with multiple communication facilities, able to transform itself into an office, bedroom, leisure facility or even an emergency surgery. In this habitat, cognitive humachines could connect with the electrodes in our brains to make our decisions for us, while emotional humachines tells us what we're feeling, linking with our internal health monitors and drug-dispensing nanobots in a barrage of information flung out by every passing building and network, close and remote. How to navigate our way through this dense, confusing wrap-around world stripped of helpful people or recognizable landmarks? Simple, let the GPS do it for you, as machines know best.

The technological enchainments of a humachinated environment squeeze out all the interstices. The smart home connects to the smart workplace in the smart city. The data gleaned from the home or school is connected through public surveillance systems, capturing more data through face and gait recognition and emotional capture and feeding it back into private and professional settings. Google's Sidewalk Labs division is already operating with city planners and property developers, as a result of "Google's founders getting excited thinking of 'all the things you could do if someone would just give us a city and put us in charge'", according to the company's former chairman Eric Schmidt (quoted in Sadowski, 2017).

The next stop could be the smart country. (Arguably, the Chinese Communist Party is already working on this.) And what about a smart continent, ocean or sky? Ultimately the aim is to extend the humachinated environment to every conceivable human or animal habitat, with underwater cables, orbiting satellites and ultimately space colonies breaching every geographical border and biophysical limit. Indeed, nothing less than a digital-robotic universe seems to be the end goal of humachination.

Not "Rogue Capitalism", Just Capitalism

Nobody has grasped the potential of humachines better than Google, which is why I've focused so heavily on them but the humachine age is much more than one technology giant. Shoshanna Zuboff's account of the company is wonderfully insightful but I have to disagree with her overall conclusion that Google and Facebook (now Meta), which followed in its wake, are isolated examples of "rogue capitalism", as opposed to the good, "rational capitalism" which she believes still motivates many other digital corporations. She seems to suggest that it's a few rotten apples that are the cause of the problem not the barrel itself. From an ecological democracy perspective, I find it hard to discern the good rationality in the behaviour of the fossil fuel corporations which dominated the putatively heroic "first modernity" which Zuboff describes. On the contrary, I suggest we see growth capitalism in the humachine age using new technology to do what capital always tries to do, to creatively destroy (or "disrupt") anything that stands in the way of its expansion. For a number of reasons, I suggest, humachination is just another expression of the inner irrationality of capitalism's organizing principles.

First, there's a familiar pattern about Page's and Brin's Faustian bargain in relation to advertising, in which they gave up their altruistic goal of a search engine that was wholly "transparent and in the academic realm" for a revenue-earning mechanism that would allow them to realise their dreams of infinite scientific power (Zuboff, 2019:71). For example, the bitter early disputes between the co-founders of Apple (a company which Zuboff considers an exemplar of "rational" digital capitalism) evince a similar conflict of values. Computer genius Steve Wozniak stood for the cooperative, counter-cultural sharing of technology via open-source software and accessible, customizable hardware. Steve Jobs, on the other hand, a fiercely competitive design genius, was committed to building a powerful, high-end consumer brand that lured the user to stay within the exclusive world of Apple services and products and jealously protected its intellectual property (Isaacson 2011). Wozniak wanted the user to choose, Jobs wanted to make her choices for her. The Jobs vision won and the result is the mighty multi-trillion-dollar, global conglomerate that is today's Apple.

Second, far from being a corporate exception, Google simply inherited the business environment which had been forged during Ronald Reagan's neoliberal revolution of the 1980s. The corporation re-established the grossly inequitable role of the ownership of capital in business, ensuring that shareholders' interests outweigh the interests of all other stakeholders, such as employees, suppliers and the local community, who in the 30 years following WW2 had more influence in the running of corporations. Shareholder value rigidly locks on to the objective of economic growth, through profitability or other returns on investment such as share buybacks, creating a "pathological" corporation, which, as Joel Bakan (2004) emphasizes, is legally obliged to prioritize rewarding its owners, regardless of the effects on people or planet.

Without these neoliberal foundations, the warp-speed growth of Google and other Big Tech empires over the past two decades would have been impossible. It took General Electric a century to become the world's biggest technology company, Google achieved something similar in less than two decades. The geeky start-up Page and Brin tried to sell for $750,000 in 1999 is now a trillion-dollar monolith owning over 200 companies and operating in 219 countries (Siegler, 2010). The legendary secrecy with which Google operates is also part of their success and bears some resemblance to the stealth with which the oil majors concealed their knowledge of climate change from the 1970s (Dembicki, 2022). Google's "hiding policy", devised by Eric Schmidt to reinforce Page's and Brin's habitual secretiveness, has helped to conceal the immense ambitiousness of the empire that lurks behind the reassuringly advertising-free front page of its search engine.

Third, Google's aims stretch well beyond the boundaries of surveillance capitalism. Larry Page's digital utopianism ensures that Google's tentacles extend across the whole range of cognitive and robotic humachines, mechanized humans and smart environments. Its huge investment in the world's best AI programmers puts it in prime position to take the development of machine learning as far as it can possibly go. It's also a major producer of hardware, including smartphones, laptops, alternative cable TV and the entire suite of software from the Android operating system used by over 80% of the world's smartphones, as well as software including the Chrome browser, Gmail, Google Play and its suite of business applications. Its ownership of YouTube (used by 2.7 billion people a month in 2023) gives it enormous clout in entertainment, education and popular culture and dominance in the primary language of humachination which is video (moving images plus audio) rather than text or the spoken word. In the Cloud it competes for monopoly with Amazon and Microsoft across a vast range of computing services. Google X is Alphabet's back box, a lavishly funded, top-secret "moonshot factory", which is rumoured to be working on everything from quantum computing to aerospace technology, smart fabrics, miniature radar and virtual reality films. Google Capital is also a major investment house, taking stakes in scores of successful startups, including Uber, Lime and Slack, which increases its monopolistic hold on global technological innovation. It even has a think-tank, Jigsaw, tackling geopolitical issues affecting technology, to go alongside its vast government lobbying operations. This degree of power loosens the financial constraints that limit normal scientific development by an order of magnitude, freeing Google's founders to focus on changing almost everything about being human on planet Earth.

Beyond Google

Other Big Tech corporations have built complementary empires as avariciously and single-mindedly as Google, developing hundreds of internal departments and making multiple acquisitions, ruthlessly captured for their innovations. Apple has capitalised on Steve Jobs' vision of a technology that aesthetically blends into the human environment and uses an operational language that is intuitive rather than jarringly geeky to build a mega-conglomerate that surpassed the value of the entire British FTSE100 in September 2020. Its 100-plus acquisitions encompass multiple humachine activities from machine learning and emotional capture to augmented reality, personal health, indoor mapping, eye-and sleep-tracking, weather forecasting and speech technology. It already provides an early model of the individualistic world of the mechanized human, who is connected by smartphone, portable screens, headset and smartwatch to the internet and seemingly infinite personalized streams of entertainment, communication and knowledge. Next up is likely to be wearable computing and more intuitive device operation to further reduce the barrier between what is outside the machine and what is inside it, perhaps with personal air pollution filters to fully inoculate the user against the natural environment

(Dyson, 2022).

Microsoft has also invested heavily in AI over the past two decades, aiming to leverage its traditional base in business software to develop occupational humachines to spearhead the automation of the workplace. Huge acquisitions in this space – it spent almost $40 billion buying LinkedIn and Skype- have been complemented by dozens of developments in mapping, 3-D tech, messaging, email, video calling, search engines, virtual reality and biotechnology, as well as hardware (phones and tablets) and operations software. It has invested $10 billion in generative AI, including the text-generator ChatGPT, intending to create a world in which every worker has AI support "for everything they do," (Waters and Kinder, 2023). Its partially self-editing news service, MSN, has extended its cultural influence and its surprisingly successful Xbox gaming console gives it traction in the entertainment and youth markets. In addition its extensive patents and licensing deals make it "probably the most prolific rentier in capitalist history," according to economic geographer Brett Christophers (2020:141). Bill Gates' use of his Microsoft fortune is, if anything, even more ambitious, as he turns to medical philanthropy and saving capitalism from climate catastrophe via geoengineering (more of this in Chapter 8)

Facebook, whose parent company was rebranded as Meta in 2021, has specialised in the mechanization of communication and relationships since it was founded in 2004. Through its empire-building acquisitions of messaging platforms such as Instagram and WhatsApp, it attempts to ensure that the consumer never leaves the Meta ambit, enveloped in a digital community which extracts personal data from users and their friends – sometimes illegally –to sell to advertisers and other third parties. Not for nothing did co-founder Mark Zuckerberg express a preference for "companies over countries" and end his early management meetings with a raised fist and the cry of "domination!" (Losse, 2018). Through machine language, Meta's scores of acquisitions and copy-cat developments (e.g. Reels and Threads) aim to increase this hold on the user by means of affective computing, business and consumer analytics and virtual reality.

Amazon's approach to humachination is to mechanize the social and commercial institution at the core of modern human settlements, the marketplace. Amazon dematerializes this locus, taking it out of the hands of real people in real communities, and making them reliant on remote, data-driven networks of consumption. It sells virtually every type of consumer goods from books to clothes, electrical goods and increasingly food and drink and (hence Amazon's $13.7 billion purchase of physical retailers Whole Foods). Through the 100-plus acquisitions it has made since 1998, Amazon has created a new wholesale and retail system that drives deep into the global supply chain. This is assisted by seemingly independent information sources (e.g. Goodreads, IMDb and Amazon reviews) and by the multi-dimensional behavioural profiles of its users, which Amazon has been constructing ever since Jeff Bezos declared it to be essentially a data company in 1997 – his version of the one-way mirror trick (Kelion, 2020).

Amazon orders are often processed by humachines, such as the robotic fulfilment systems used in its warehouses (designed by Amazon Robotics), delivered by drones or via AI-enabled doorbells and ordered through the Internet of Things, potentially without human intervention. Amazon Prime is now also a major force in entertainment, as a producer and distributor of films, the owner of the franchises and archives of Hollywood studio MGM, and a worldwide streamer of music, sport and gaming.

This vast operation is underpinned by Amazon Web Services (AWS), a massive network of server warehouses, providing businesses with over 200 crucial services from storage to networking, analytics and database management. AWS, which dominates the Cloud, makes Amazon its most spectacular profits, helping to override its early loss-making businesses and create seemingly endless acquisition and expansion opportunities.

Finally, no account of the humachine age is complete without mentioning centi-billionaire Elon Musk, who in many ways is the ultimate exponent of human-machine fusion. His vast technology conglomerates embrace everything from electric cars and batteries (Tesla), solar energy (SolarCity) and space exploration (SpaceX) to the Starlink satellite system, which, among other things, has enabled Musk to make life or death interventions into the Russia-Ukraine war (Isaacson, 2023) and Neuralink committed to the modest task of reengineering the human brain. As if this were not enough, Musk acquired influential microblogger Twitter for $44 billion and rebranded it as X, promising to turn it into an omnivorous "everything app", providing "comprehensive communication and the ability to conduct your entire financial universe" (Peters, 2023).

Around the world, hundreds of thousands of enterprises try to follow in the footsteps of the humachine supergiants. It's not just digital, robotic or biotechnogy companies that are involved. Virtually every commercial company in every sector is introducing advanced technology into its marketing and operations and even developing its own proprietary systems. Nor is humachination only a business project. Academia teems with computer scientists, biotechnologists, nanotechnologists and countless other scientists, searching for innovation breakthroughs, many becoming entrepreneurs themselves. Education itself is increasingly shifting away from the humanities and social science towards Science, Technology, Engineering and Maths in an intellectual STEMpede that characterizes the humachine age.

Governments are also energetically driving human-machine hybridization. "Unleashing the power of AI is a top priority in our plan to be the most pro-tech government ever" declares the UK's Digital Secretary, as Britain attempts to catch up with other nations in the great AI race (Gov. uk, 2021). "Whoever become the leaders in this sphere will become the ruler of the world", Vladimir Putin has ominously stated (Gigova, 2017) and embryonic automated surveillance states are already emerging across the world. Military secrecy prevents us from understanding what's really going on with the development of humachines of war but we know that billions of dollars of taxpayers' money is already being spent developing Lethal Automated Weapons systems (LAWS). The border between publicly funded technology research and private profits has always been porous, with many of the core innovations of Apple and Microsoft having been lifted from defence research and Silicon Valley having a long track record of working for the military.

This line between the state and capitalism becomes even more hazy in the case of China, because the humachine age is by no means an exclusively Western phenomenon. Massive Chinese corporations such as Baidu, Ten Cent and Alibaba, which formed during the 1998-2000 humachine big bang have become far more than bland Silicon Valley analogues. Their immense size and complexity, aided by lax privacy laws and authoritarian censorship, give them an advantage in gathering AI data which compensates for their relative lack of software innovation (Lee, 2019). East Asian companies also dominate the world of robotic humachines. The majority of the world's three million installed industrial robots are in China and Japan, while South Korea's Samsung has the most robotics patents (IFR,

2021). Japanese companies lead the world in developing humanoid and animal robots, including devices for use in domestic, security, mobility and rescue contexts, as well as in space. The ferocious competition which exists between all these players, big and small, state and private, East and West, and the monopolistic alliances they are bound to form, could determine the geopolitical future of the humachine age, and much else besides.

Conclusion: Techno-Utopia or Dystopia?

For readers sympathetic to the eco-democratic goals and values I have described as the road to the Ecocene, the picture I have painted of a new age of unprecedentedly ambitious and powerful technology conglomerates bent on global domination may seem depressing. The potential for capitalism's new big idea to lead us towards the Technocene, by which I mean an ecologically-ravaged techno-dystopia, may seem overwhelming. To my mind, the gargantuan scope, scale and ambition of the humachine age, which can be inferred from the pronouncements of its leaders and their patterns of corporate investment and acquisition, have not yet been properly understood by the general public.

Perhaps that began to change in 2023, as fears about the potential of generative AI to replace jobs, reliable information and humanity itself began to emerge. Microsoft's massive investment in Open AI's large language models has brought about another notable Google apostasy. DeepMind founder Demis Hassabis, who says he sold his company to Google on the promise that he could continue his mission to develop human-level intelligence without commercial pressure, has been persuaded by Larry Page to head a new aggressively profit-based division which aims to avert the existential threat to Google's search engine and advertising revenue represented by ChatGPT and other text predictors (Murgla, 2023). Forget about "good" capitalism: the gloves are off now in a multi-corporate battle royal for AI supremacy. That in turn has prompted another kind of U-turn from influential computer scientists like Geoffrey Hinton, who now regrets his 50-year lifework in pioneering machine learning, and Stuart Russell, another so-called godfather of AI, who admits that researchers should have seen from the start that artificial intelligence involves creating a potential competitor to humanity, which was "obviously a stupid thing to do" (MIT, Blakely, 2023). This sense of panic and a radical forking of the road, indicates some of the profound flaws and vulnerabilities in the techno-utopian philosophy of human–machine fusion and its economic and political theory we'll explore in the next two chapters. Unconscious capitalism and other misconceptions may lead us to endorse choices we might never make consciously, although these choices can change rapidly.

In short, nothing in the extraordinary history of Big Tech corporations in the twenty-first century should give the impression that the current acceleration of technology development is unstoppable. What has been created by humans can be changed by humans. All empires rise and fall and the current technology boom, which in mid-2023 valued the top seven Big Tech corporations (including Tesla and Nvidia) as worth one quarter of the entire S&P 500, may turn out to be as precarious as any bet on the future (Martin, 2023). In 2021 the market for non-fungible tokens (NFTs) was worth $22 billion; two years later 95% of them were worthless (Friday, 2023). Likewise, at the height of tulip mania in seventeenth-century Holland, a single bulb could buy an opulent, canal-side mansion in Amsterdam, until that is, the economic bubble burst. Don't rule out the possibility that the age of humachines, underpinned as it is by capitalism's fatally flawed concept of never-ending growth, may be destined for a similar fate.

CHAPTER 2

Techno-Utopianism and the War on Biology: The Singularity, Transhumanism and Ontocapitalism

Behind the corporate and consumer project of creating humanized machines and mechanized humans is a long-term strategy which challenges almost everything about being human on planet Earth, including our concepts of society, being and life itself. Strategy is not mere speculation; it's the beacon intended to guide corporations on their implementation path to the future. Over a half a century ago, with eerie accuracy, the leading corporations of carbon capitalism realised that anthropogenic greenhouse gas emissions were going to heat the planet to at least 2C above pre-industrial levels. They resolved on a strategy to conceal climate change from humanity in order to maximize their ability to extract every last drop of profit from every last deposit of fossil fuel, a strategy that continues to this day (Dembicki, 2022).

If we want to discover the secret 10-year, 50-year or even 500-year plans of the Big Tech conglomerates that have usurped the oil majors as the world's wealthiest companies, Ray Kurzweil's *The Singularity is Near: When humans transcend biology* (2005) is the best source we are likely to find. It's the bible of human-machine fusion that reveals the hidden agenda of the humachine age, without which it's almost impossible to understand the meaning of twenty-first century technology. It also issues the declaration of war against biology and all energy and matter, which I refer to as ontocapitalism.

The Singularity Is Near: The Bible of Humachination

An early computer science graduate, Ray Kurzweil is a successful inventor and multi-millionaire entrepreneur in his own right and his influence extends far beyond his post as Google's Head of Engineering which he has held since 2012. He's a futurist thought leader and cofounder of the Singularity University in Silicon Valley, which teaches leadership for the humachine age and attracts funding from Page, Brin and other Big Tech billionaires. Although often slapdash in style and not philosophy in any formal sense, Kurzweil's magnum opus could turn out to be the most influential document of the early twenty-first century and therefore justifies the close, critical attention I want to give it in this chapter.

The Singularity is Near is a 650-page encyclopaedia of humachines which contains the best guide ever written to the techno-utopian imaginary. Kurzweil's key concept, the technological singularity, is borrowed from mathematician Vernor Vinge (1993), who described a point of no return when machine intelligence outstrips human intelligence, involving "a throwing-away of all human rules". He also predicted that "developments that were thought might only happen in "a million years" (if ever)" would occur in the twenty-first century. This idea of an "intelligence explosion" draws on Jack Good's (1965) forecast that "the first ultraintelligent machine is the last invention that man needs ever make", referred to in the previous chapter. Kurzweil predicts that this ontological watershed will be reached once the sum power of human intelligence is surpassed by the calculating power available on a cheap home computer, an event which he has suggested could happen as soon as 2029 (Kurzweil, 2014). At this juncture, the primary goal of humachination will be within reach:

> By the time of the Singularity, there won't be a distinction between humans and technology. *This is not because humans will have become what we think of as machines, but rather machines will have progressed to be like humans and beyond.* (Kurzweil, 2005:40-41). (Original emphasis)

Kurzweil, who studied with AI pioneer Marvin Minsky in the late 1960s, puts the key metaphor of AI at the core of his idea of the singularity, namely that the human brain can be understood as a type of computer. This mechanistic metaphor raises all sorts of problems with all sorts of problems with cognitive humachines. which we'll revisit in detail in Part Four. At this stage, I'll confine myself to suggesting that the brain-computer analogy makes a spurious connection between the speed of computer calculations and the infinitely more complex processes of embodied human consciousness. It's also logically nonsensical to make assumptions about the behaviour of a hypothetical entity which is millions of times more intelligent than humanity or speculate on how humans would even begin to understand that behaviour. For Kurzweil, however, the possibility of superintelligence is a philosophical given, which provides him with a perfect vehicle for projecting his own ideals about science, business and what it is to be human.

Hypergrowth, Exponentiality and Super-Speed

A crucial factor in Kurzweil's vision of the merger of humans and machines is exponentiality, the arithmetical process of doubling a number, which initially generates relatively small totals but suddenly, almost miraculously, begins to produce astonishingly large results. Kurzweil illustrates this with the ancient story of the trickster who as a reward for averting famine fools an emperor into doubling a grain of rice on each of the squares of a chess board and ends up with more rice than the entire empire possesses. (I remember a former headmaster of mine playing a similar trick on unsuspecting juniors, asking "if you folded a sheet of A4 paper 50 times, how far would it reach?", before triumphantly revealing the answer, "to the moon and back!") Kurzweil finds real-world support for this process in Moore's law, which describes the tendency from the 1970s for computer power to double every eighteen months, while halving in cost. As a spectacular example of this, Peter Diamandis, who founded the Singularity University with Kurzweil, cites the 150,000 % increase in computer-price performance which occurred from a 1980 supercomputer to the first iPhone (Diamandis and Kotler, 2012:54).

For Kurzweil, technology proceeds in S-shaped curves, characterized by slow growth followed by exponentially fast growth which eventually levels off. At this point a new paradigm occurs, which means the exponential growth cycle starts all over again. Projected into the future, this "law of accelerated returns" as Kurzweil terms it, turns exponentiality into a trick that can be repeated over and over again. On this basis, justifying almost any kind of technological transformation becomes possible. In fact, Moore's law probably died in 2019, according to Nvdia co-founder Jensen Huang, as the minimization of microchip transistors hit the buffers (Tibken, 2019). It was never a law anyway, merely a short-term economic trend, but no doubt Kurzweil would argue that this only represents the end of one growth paradigm and the beginning of another.

The truth is that Moore's law could better be described as an example of the Law of More, the belief that economic growth can continue forever, which is at the heart of growth capitalism. Instead of the enoughism which prioritizes the balance between the part and the whole as crucial, the Law of More accepts no limits and sees moderation as a defeat. Nobody better exemplifies the Law of More than singularity supporter Elon Musk. "Elon always wants to know, "Why are we not going faster?" say his engineers and designers. "He always wants bigger, better, faster" (Urban, 2015). When it comes to humachination, "more" always seems to be the answer: more machines mechanizing more of life in ever more concentrated forms. That's always been at the psychological core of capitalist profit-seeking and a major cause of the multiple emergencies we face in the Anthropocene.

There's no doubting the widespread use of the Doubling Trick in growth capitalism. Exponentiality is an arithmetical pattern, which is entirely different to natural organic growth which tends to increase, peak and then decline. In a typical dictionary, the majority of meanings of the word "growth" still denote natural, organic processes, such as "something grown or growing" or "a stage of development", with only one definition referring to "an expansion in size or number". But this quantitative, mate-rialist, linear version is what the myth of economic growth emphasizes, transforming an unpredictable natural process into something apparently artificial and controllable, and as such it has become one of the most mis-leading metaphors of modernity. If you actually follow its economic logic, it exposes the fallacy of growthism: a 3% annual increase in GDP would lead to an economy expanding a planet-busting 19 times over the course of a century. (Just as well that regular economic recessions can be relied on to peg back actual GDP!)

What Kurzweil's use of exponentiality seems to offer is something even less rooted in material reality than mainstream economics, an idea that we might call hypergrowth, which seems to make possible any technology that can be imagined. Hypergrowth also has the advantage of proceeding at speeds which stretch human comprehension: for example, Kurzweil predicts that in the twenty-first century "we will witness on the order of twenty thousand years of progress "(11).* This notion of super-speed is reminiscent of cultural theorist Paul Virilio's (2006) concept of "dromology" – derived from the Classical Greek word for "chariot". He defines this as a major military strategic asset – the fast army can defeat a bigger but slower force – which also applies to technological development, which can outrun and outmanoeuvre most resistance. Andy Grove, who as the CEO of Intel, the microchip company that Gordon Moore co-founded, was a primary implementer of Moore's law, spelt out the commercial advantages of dromology. He stated that when it comes to innovation, technology companies are three times faster than ordinary businesses which are three times faster than governments (Evans, 2011). This "nine-times gap" means that Big Tech can constantly stay ahead of the regulators. By the time, the breathless representatives of the people catch up with an errant technology company, it has entrenched itself behind mighty walls protected by lawyers and lobbyists, and, in any case, has probably already moved on to other innovations. The dictatorship of speed forces choices, depriving people of the time and information required for good decision-making. Kurzweil's own discursive habit of relentlessly producing predictions – a kind of rhetorical accelerationism or "prediction-addiction" – further increases this sense of technology developing at a speed and complexity which is too fast to comprehend or resist.

The Splitting of Science: Physics Versus Biology

Technological hypergrowth seems to make possible the mind-scrambling advances in quantum computing, robotics and nanotechnology which Kurzweil forecasts in *The Singularity is Near*. But his territorial gains are not confined to the realm of engineering and the physical sciences: his strategic aims extend to biology, genetics and the life sciences in general. In fact, in a typically dualistic fashion, he opens up a massive split in science between physics and biology, which he seeks to turn to the advantage of the former. As an engineer, Kurzweil's belief in the ability of mechanical, digital and other human-made systems to improve on living forms produced by natural selection knows no bounds. He wholeheartedly endorses

*All subsequent page numbers in Kurzweil 2005 are referenced in this manner.

genetic engineering and cloning in order to reverse the ageing process and supports the development of designer babies through what he sees as the reprogramming of biological information processes. Kurzweil says nothing about how these currently illegal practices will be permitted, for his main concern is to denigrate what he regards as the "profound limitations" (226) of the science of biology:

> Biology will never be able to match what we will be capable of engineering once we fully understand biology's principles of operation. The revolution in nanotechnology, however, will ultimately enable us to redesign and rebuild, molecule by molecule, our bodies and brains and the world with which we interact (227).

Nanotechnology, the science of the sub-atomically small, is part of this rejection of biology. The field, originally envisaged by physicist Richard Feynman in 1959 in a lecture entitled, "There's plenty of room at the bottom", unearths a new subterranean realm of mechanization, as though the unexplored cellars under a crumbling mansion offer more promise than repairing the unfinished edifice above. Feynman's speculations about machines that can build ever smaller machines – the exponentiality trick in reverse – were taken up in the 1980s by the techno-utopian Eric Drexler (1986), who launched an all-out assault on biology as a science. For Kurzweil, a fervent admirer of Drexler, nanotechnology enables tiny machines driven by all-powerful machine intelligence to literally get inside reality, enabling us to see its secret workings. Thus the mechanical universe can be rebuilt from scratch, reengineering what it is to be human on planet Earth.

Mechanizing Humans

Smashing through the barriers between the organic and the mechanical, enables Kurzweil to describe in detail the path to what I've termed Type 4 humachination, the mechanization of the human body. This is key to the vision of a "post-biological" or "transhuman" future. As a mechanicalist, Kurzweil sees the human body as a sophisticated machine, most of the components of which can be upgraded or replaced. He imaginatively dissects and reassembles the human body (in an unintended replication of Dr Frankenstein's surgical operations) for example, proposing a radically "re-engineered gastrointestinal system", which enables unlimited "recreational eating", as well as programmable blood and nanorobotic blood cells (305). Another augmentation is the human heart. "Although artificial hearts are beginning to be feasible replacements, a more effective approach will be to get rid of the heart altogether" (308), Kurzweil writes, perhaps meaning more than he says. By the 2030s, he forecasts that the reengineering of human organs will be almost complete: "What we have left at this point is the skeleton, skin, sex organs, sensory organs, mouth and upper oesophagus, and brain." Improvements to all these areas are possible, he claims, such as "nanoengineered skin" and a strengthened skeleton. Modifications to sexual organs are not specified, although unlimited orgasms are often part of the humachination offer. Nor does he mention changes to how we breathe, a rather crucial conduit between the nature within and without us.

At this stage, Kurzweil suggests "Nanobot technology will provide fully immersive totally convincing virtual reality... enabling us to change our appearance and effectively become other people", using multi-sensory, "emotion overlays" (313-5). "As we enter the 2030s there won't be a clear distinction between human and machines, between real and virtual reality" (342). By the 2040s we'll be able to change our bodies for real and "to modify and reinstate into new forms at will" (316).

This new level of human-machine hybridization now offers dramatic life extension possibilities:

> By preventing 90 percent of medical problems, life expectancy grows to five hundred years. At 99 percent we'd be over one thousand years ... As we move towards nonbiolgical existence, we will gain the means of "backing ourselves up" (storing the key patterns that underlie our knowledge, skills and personality), thereby eliminating most causes of death, as we know it (323).

Indeed, achieving immortality today, rather than in the future, is Kurzweil's personal obsession. His customised "biochemical reprogramming" leads him to take "250 supplements (pills) a day and receive half a dozen intravenous therapies each week" (211) in an attempt "to live long enough to live forever", to quote the subtitle of another of his books (Kurzweil and Grossman, 2004).

As for the brain, Kurzweil's plans for mechanization extend far beyond the relatively simple electrodes currently being developed by Elon Musk's

Neuralink. Kurzweil believes superintelligent, microscopically small nano-bots will provide "brain extensions", enabling humachine engineers to move "beyond the basic architecture of the brain's neural regions" (317). "By the middle of the twenty-first century humans will be able to expand their thinking without limits" (325), he writes. It will now be possible to totally redesign the brain, perhaps through "quantum dots" which can bind to neurons and fuse with machine intelligence, so that we become increasingly cyborg-like. With nanobots in the brain, Kurzweil asserts, "non-biological intelligence will be billions of times more powerful than human intelligence" (216). In fact, as early as the 2030s, he prophesizes, "we will become more non-biological than biological" (309).

Transhumanism

Kurzweil is by no means unique in espousing a post-biological vision of humanness. Transhumanism or post-humanism is a philosophy which has been evolving in the West since the 1980s, although its roots can be found much earlier in mechanicalist science (More, 2013). One definition is as follows:

> A transhuman is an evolutionary stage from being exclusively biological to becoming post-biological. Postbiological means a continuous shedding of our biology and merging with machines (Natasha Vita-More quoted in McNamee and Edwards 2006:517).

The idea of a new stage in evolution trips off the tongue easily enough but trying to hack natural selection and take control of organic processes which have taken billions of years to evolve has the potential to become the greatest act of hubris in human history. This swaggering ambition is mirrored by many transhumanist theorists, among them the (deliber-ately self-renamed) philosopher Max More, who sees transhumanism as a breaking free from the domination of nature. As he puts it in his 1999 essay, "Letter to Mother Nature":

> We will no longer tolerate the tyranny of ageing and death... we will expand our perceptual range ... reshape our motivational patterns and emotional responses ... take charge over our genetic program-ming and achieve mastery over our biological processes (More, 2013:450).

It's worth noting that More defines his transhumanist approach as "extropy", a provocatively unscientific rejection of the second law of thermodynamics, and mixes his philosophy with entrepreneurship as CEO of a cryonics outfit promising immortality (for more see Chapter 18).

For some transhumanists, the line between science and religion, this life and the next, is a narrow one, creating the possibility for a new form of rapture. Physicist Giulio Prisco (2013:237) envisages the possibility of resurrection through "transcendent engineering" that enables us to be cloned by our descendants through "time-scanning and mind uploading" or through the revelation that we are already living in one of many simulations of reality, in what roboticist Hans Moravec (1999) calls "the Transcendent Mind". In fact, the religion of technology is a long-standing American tradition, as many have noted over the years, typified by the worship of cars of absurdly excessive size and the massive infrastructure needed to facilitate them. It also chimes with the divine ambitions of the human-machine hybridizers. In *Being and Nothingness*, Jean-Paul Sartre (1958) put an existentialist spin on what he saw as the desire of every human to become God by declaring it "a futile passion" that renders humans tragic. But tragedy threatens to become farce in humachination, in its attempts to abolish death and thereby laying claim to the afterlife which is the conceptual foundation of most religions. This quasi-religious dimension, incidentally, invites another interpretation of Kurzweil's prediction-addiction and penchant for forecasting, in which he resembles nothing so much as an Old Testament seer, proclaiming his prophecies from the mountain top.

Ultrascience: Smashing All Limits

What Kurzweil is proposing – or perhaps prophesying with evangelical fervour – is not simply the triumph of physics over human biology but the transformation of all energy and matter in the entire universe. This project I'm labelling ultrascience: it involves taking the physical sciences as far as they can possibly go, regardless of the consequences. In defiance of the concept of the Anthropocene based on the recognition of the fragility of the narrow biophysical limits separating us from ecological catastrophe, ultrascience accepts no limits to growth or constraint by natural laws of any kind. It's an innovation fetishism that is positively Faustian in its quest for absolute knowledge.

Thus Kurzweil predicts that once we reach the computational capacity of our solar system ("in the range of 10 to the 70 to 10 to the 80 cps"), we'll "bump up against the limits of matter and energy in our solar system", so "we will have no choice but to expand outwards as the primary form of growth" (351). The speed of light represents an obstacle to this cosmic expansion but Kurzweil claims that this can be exceeded, possibly through the use of wormholes (355). He acknowledges that some natural laws might seem to stand in our way, especially the second law of thermodynamics or the principle of entropy (which is also the transhumanists' bête noire). This states that although energy is never destroyed because the universe is a closed system (the first law of thermodynamics), it irreversibly declines over time, becoming increasingly dissipated or "disordered". However, Kurzweil claims his "law" of accelerating returns pertains to evolution as well as economics, which is not a closed system because "an evolutionary process continually prunes its choices to produce ever greater order" (40). This is a spurious argument that ignores the multi-billion-year time scale of evolution – rather different from own relatively short history – which in any case takes place within the closed system that is planet Earth.

Although to some it may seem obscure, the issue of entropy is crucial to understanding the humachine age. One of the founders of ecological economics, Nicholas Georgescu-Roegen based his theory of the role of nature in economics on this principle, approvingly quoting Albert Einstein's view that thermodynamics "is the only physical theory of universal content that will never be overthrown" (1986:14). For Georgescu-Roegen, economics is a process by which humans convert high-order resources into low-order materials and waste (see Chapter 4). In economic activity, as in everything else, depletion is inevitable. But growth capitalism is forced to deny the laws of entropy, arguing that natural sources of energy and matter can be endlessly replaced and even increased by new technology. It's this denial that lies behind Kurzweil's ultrascience and humachination in general. Instead of making the most of the social benefits science has achieved over the past three centuries, Kurzweil opts for the fantasy of hypergrowth, which, as energy scientist Vaclav Smil implies, relies on the absurdity of a future in which "the biosphere, whose functioning is the product of billions of years of evolution, has no role" (Simil, 2019:xvii).

Techno-Utopia?

The end result of this shattering of all planetary limits and natural laws is the merger of the terrestrial and the extraterrestrial, as everything and everyone everywhere are transformed into data. The digitization of all matter and energy will leave behind not a trace of nature-hugging, analogue technology and create the ultimate humachinated environment (a kind of Type 5-plus humachine). "Continuing the double-exponential growth curve shows that we can saturate the universe with our intelligence well before the end of the twenty-second century", Kurzweil writes (366). Intelligence is the final stage of this imagined process, as the brain itself is transformed into a form of uploadable, immortal software, a digital machine which is able to gambol endlessly in a cosmos which has itself become a state of intelligence, a universe woven out of infinite packets of data. It seems this is our ultimate destiny: to become machine code.

This, as far as it goes, is Kurzweil's version of utopia. (Perhaps the most charitable image that comes to mind is the final "psychedelic" scene in Stanley Kubrick's *2001: A Space Odyssey).* Like many depictions of techno-utopia, it's so dominated by technology that humans are rendered as mere background, like the tiny figures dotted around a towering megacity in a futuristic architectural drawing. It might be interpreted as a paradise for wealthy, novelty-chasing consumers outdoing each other in their mental and physical augmentations, an Elysium for the "Cyborgoisie", except that it lacks the very concept of society which is at the heart of every true utopia. The idea of community is absent, as are most social relationships, except perhaps for the purposes of sexual pleasure. All the biological differences between individuals are also erased as the universe, in an image appropriated from Zen Buddhism, becomes "the sound of one hand clapping" (367). This description, rather than adding a tone of authentic spirituality, feels rather more like Silicon Valley crudely projecting its giant ego onto the entire cosmos.

Ontocapitalism (or Post-Biological Neoliberalism)

A society without people is the individualist's dream and a society which has conquered nature is the mechanicalist's dream – and Kurzweil serves up both fantasies. For, as we'll discover in Chapter 6, the singularity represents the consummation of the urge to "squeeze and mould" nature which began with Francis Bacon and the Western scientific revolution over four centuries ago. But in the end, we can't understand Kurzweil's line of argument – and his seemingly blithe indifference to the potential negative consequences of humachination – without appreciating his commitment to the principle of infinite economic growth. Unlike the early Western scientists with their lofty contempt for "trade", Kurzweil's faith in the free market is absolute. Indeed, *The Singularity is Near* can be seen as a scientific-libertarian update of Milton Friedman's classic neoliberal text, *Capitalism and Freedom* (1962).

Ultrascience is only possible in a world devoid of governmental restrictions and social oversight, in which entrepreneurs can pursue capital expansion regardless of its social or ecological consequences. Kurzweil is insistent that preventing technology from developing autonomously would be deeply undemocratic. He states that only "a worldwide totalitarian system that relinquishes the very idea of progress" can prevent the acceleration of new technology on all fronts (407). This "plutotechnic" version of democracy, which excludes the majority from any say in regulating technology, claims that "technical progress … fuelled by irresistible economic gains" (471) will justify the absence of any governmental oversight on innovation.

Just how much of a risk Kurzweil is prepared to take in order to allow ultra-science to reach its ultimate destination is illustrated by his admission that humachines have the potential to enslave or even eradicate humanity. He admits that malevolent superintelligence or "unfriendly Strong AI" could be wily enough to overcome any human attempts to contain it:

> Inherently there is no absolute protection against strong AI. Although the argument is subtle, I believe that maintaining an open free-market system for incremental scientific and technological progress, in which each step is subject to market acceptance, will provide the most constructive environment for technology to embody widespread human values (420).

Kurzweil's' faith in growth capitalism as the guarantor of "human values" is unshakeable, a tribute to neoliberalism and its "the market knows best" creed. He's supremely confident that consumerist choice can avert what I refer to as "AImaggedon", the possibility of superintelligence replacing humans or other catastrophic events such as devastating cyber warfare, or "bad nanobots" destroying the human immune system (425). For growth capitalism, consumer choice is always the measure of what people really want and this principle justifies the way consumption in the Global North shapes the lives of the rest of humanity. Kurzweil suggests that the more we consume humachine products and services, the more our values will become compatible with them. Eventually, "Strong AI ... will be intimately embedded in our bodies and brains. As such it will reflect our values because it will be us" (420). It's a circular argument, of course, but as long we continue to make growthism the arbiter of what it is to be human, it's a realistic enough prediction.

In fact, the free market consistently fails to provide fair competition. It creates monopolies which distort consumer choices, which is why Milton Friedman (1962;27) insisted on a regulatory referee to do what the market cannot do, a function which, contradictorily enough, can only be provided by an assertive, interventionist government, i.e. a "big state". Kurzweil's call for decentralization to de-monopolize technologies is also somewhat ironic given his senior executive role at Google – perhaps suggesting he underwent a values apostasy similar to that of his bosses before taking up his post. Had he paid more attention to the way digital advertising tries to manipulate consumers' choices into whatever advertisers want them to be, his faith in making capitalism the reliable indicator of what people really want might have been further shaken.

In the end, Kurzweil is expressing something historically bigger than a personal vision. He's voicing the fusion of mechanicalist, post-biological ultrascience with free market growth capitalism that I've already referred to as ontocapitalism. This synthesis, which also includes extreme competitiveness and individualism, sees the development of technology as a burning moral imperative that overrides all other social and economic concerns. It's bound by the Law of More at its most extreme, an obsession with quantitative increases which dovetails with the grasping entrepreneurship that measures all successes in terms of money. Ontocapitalism replaces human freedom with the freedom for ultrascience to do whatever it wants to create "irresistible economic gains". If that means changing the very structure of being, dispensing with the givens of humanness as they have existed since the dawn of Homo sapiens and disrupting or annihilating every law of science, so be it.

Ontocapitalism goes beyond anything previously conceived about the intentionality and trajectory of capitalism. Karl Marx realised that industrial capitalism was revolutionising human relationships – that "all fixed, fast-frozen relations" would be "swept away", in the famous words of *The Communist Manifesto* – but even he didn't anticipate that entrepreneurs, or "ontopreneurs" as they might be named, would attempt to revolutionize the structure of organic and inorganic matter, abolish death and outrun the speed of light (Marx and Engels, 1848/1983). Marx also believed that the automation of work would eventually lead to the collapse of capitalism but the humachinators intend to collapse Homo sapiens before this can ever happen.

The ultimate expression of humachination and ontocapitalism is what Kurzweil calls "applied evolution" (480). He claims this is based on the organicist idea of the "self-organizing principle of nature" but he interprets this as something to be trapped, tamed and exploited, as a kind of vulnerability which enables engineers to dictate the course of natural selection. Kurzweil fails to understand that the principle of creative self-organization, or autopoiesis, is indeterminate and fundamentally unpredictable (Maturana, 1980). New life can emerge far from equilibrium, as Kurzweil states, but in ways that can't be controlled, as an affirmation of the essential mysteriousness of life which integrated modern science now increasingly recognizes (see Chapter 6).

Applied evolution is ontocapitalism's desperate gamble in letting science run amok in order to maintain economic growth and the social order it props up. For ontocapitalism, it seems, nothing in life is worth protecting. Rather than accepting the limitations of being human – and making the best of them, it's humanness that must be sacrificed. This vision of human-machine hybridization, conducted at lightning speed, with the free market as the sole judge and jury of what is right and wrong represents the ultimate negation of nature and comes as close as one can get to conceiving capital, rather than life, as the autonomous force driving the universe.

This, I believe, is what lies behind Kurzweil's deceptively low-key conclusion to *The Singularity is Near:*

> Our ability to create models – virtual realities – in our brains, combined with our modest-looking thumbs, has been sufficient to usher in another form of evolution: technology. That development enabled the persistence of the accelerating pace that started with biological evolution. It will continue until the entire universe is at our fingertips (487).

"The entire universe is at our fingertips": this is Dr Frankenstein before he came to deplore his hubristic endeavours or Faust before his pact with Mephistopheles tragically unwinds. It's not science as a rigorous, respectful enquiry into the natural world but as a reckless, imperialistic forcing of nature, which might be described as machine supremacism. Ontocapitalism dispenses with socially responsible, scientific criteria of validity, replacing methodological integrity with engineering pragmatism ("what works") and unfettered wealth creation ("what sells"), making the court of consumerism the ultimate arbiter of all value. It's not democracy, as it largely relies on advertising to hoodwink consumers, lobbying to gull legislators and the capital of tiny investment elite; and it's not a celebration of human ingenuity, as it elevates one core capacity, our talent for creating tools, above all the rest. But it's what the singularity is about, an unholy, ontocapitalist alliance of fanatical ultrascientists and techno-utopian ontopreneurs, determined to change everything about being human on planet Earth. It's also a clear sign of what could be ahead of us, if the humachine age is allowed to continue on its current path.

The Eco-Democratic Verdict

So, by way of conclusion, how does Kurzweil's techno-utopian vision fare from the standpoint of ecological democracy and the SEWP model? From a sustainability perspective, first of all, it has to be said that the singularity violates just about every foundational proposition of ecology. Instead of respecting fragile planetary boundaries, Kurzweil tries to obliterate the entire concept of biophysical boundaries. Insofar as he acknowledges the current ecological emergency at all, it's to provide dismissively simplistic, technologistic solutions to it, suggesting, for instance, that "emerging nanotechnology capabilities … will dramatically reduce undesirable emissions, as well as remediating the prior impact of industrial-age pollution" (251). This solutionist assumption that digital capitalism can replicate the world of carbon capitalism in perfectly decarbonised form foreshadows the approach of ontopreneurs like Bill Gates (2021) whom Kurzweil says agrees with his views "99%". (Gates's sole reservation about Kurzweil seems to be that his optimism "is almost a religious faith" (374).)

From an equitability viewpoint, the mechanization of the human body and brain threatens to bring a whole new meaning to the concept of human inequality. It runs up against the nightmarish, subhumanizing problem that comes from creating de facto superhumans on the basis of free market principles which we return to in Part V. Those who will benefit from transhumanist augmentations are likely to be those who can afford them, exacerbating existing economic inequalities, and raising real fears about personal eugenics and the splitting of the human race. Life-extension technologies risk increasing by hundreds of years the current longevity gap between people in living in the Global North and South. (Kurzweil fobs off problems related to "the rich-poor divide" by relying on "the improvement of price-performance" in technology (470).) Will other augmentations ever trickle down to the global majority or will the transhumanist cyborgoisie protect what they have as they float through the cosmos?

As far as wellbeing is concerned, humachine gene modification, organ reengineering and computer-brain interfacing could create a Dante's hell of unintended negative consequences, which we will return to repeatedly in this book. Indeed, only someone who so misunderstands the body-brain as to see it as a machine could even contemplate such as degree of transformation. And as for the planetwide perspective of the SEWP model, it could be argued that Kurzweil provides one of the most Western-centric philosophies ever articulated. It more or less ignores the majority of humanity, paying virtually no attention to non-Western values or the possible economic impact of the singularity for billions of people in the poorest, most vulnerable regions of the planet.

Of course, some will find an appeal in Kurzweil's transcendentally ambitious attempt to turn science fiction into a business plan. After all, the desire to take on and conquer all limits is deeply rooted in the competitivist modernity which urges us to climb Everest simply "because it's there". But only fantasists see natural science as a series of hurdles to be overcome and perhaps there are some Everests which simply shouldn't be climbed. We ought to choose the challenges that matter, by conquering the problems which still scar civilization some six millennia after the emergence of urban civilization. Better to concentrate on what humans can do – and allow all the capacities that come with being members of Homo sapiens to flourish – rather than fall for the blandishments of exponential science, post-humanist mechanicalism and the reveries of ontocapitalism. This, at any rate, is my interpretation of the extraordinary vision which Ray Kurzweil articulates. Let's now see what the mainstream economists and political strategists who are trying to direct our current world system make of this route map to the future.

CHAPTER 3

Humachine Economics: The Fourth Industrial Revolution and Its Delusions

If further confirmation is needed that human-machine fusion is not an eccentric aspiration of a few cranks but a key strategic target of the most powerful technology conglomerates in the world, the knowledge discipline that dominates modern capitalism provides this in spades. If neoclassical economics were built on ecological, democratic and ethical foundations, you might find it trying to bring us down to earth from the vertiginous heights of the singularity, pointing to the folly of attempting an ontocapitalist re-engineering of evolution in the midst of a climate and biodiversity emergency and warning about the threat to general wellbeing from mass job automation.

But long ago, mainstream economics turned its back on the concerns with nature and wellbeing that characterized traditional political economy and in the late nineteenth century headed down the path of mechanistic science. At the core of this radically re-engineered "science" was the metaphor of society as a self-correcting machine, a market whose dynamics could be illustrated by means of engineering and hydraulic imagery (Raworth, 2018). Nature – in the form of land and other natural resources – was expelled from this model of society and relegated to the status of an accountancy footnote. The human subject was transformed into a consumer, known as Homo economicus, a rationalistic calculator of marginal utility, only interested in making the putatively perfect choices which boosted his self-interest. This view frames society not as a relationship between humans and nature, but as a machine consisting of citizens (whom economists turned into de facto computers or robots even before such machines existed) in a natural environment that is so inexhaustible and immune to depletion that the impacts on it of economic activity can safely be ignored. Through this reinvention, neoclassical economics became a form of ideology, distorted by contradictions, gaps and absences, like a text whose real importance "lies in what it does not say", as literary theorist Pierre Machery (1978:87) once remarked. In the case of economics, this silence enables money to talk all the louder.

In fact, the explicit goal of mainstream economics – and implicitly that of society as a whole – is profit-maximization, the maintenance and growth of capital. This began to be measured in terms of GDP in the wake of the catastrophic 1929 Wall Street Crash and the Great Depression that followed. Economic growth was formally adopted as the primary objective of many Western societies after 1945. It was further consolidated in the 1980s by neoliberal economics, which maximizes the role of innovative entrepreneurs – heroic "wealth creators" – and minimizes the role of labour, which is increasingly seen as something to be improved on by technology.

So for neoclassical economists, desperate to find a new source of growth in the twenty-first century, the hypergrowth potential of mechanizing virtually all economic activity is manna from heaven. This prospect encourages them to ignore the potentially disequalizing and immiserating effects of job automation and announce some extraordinary estimates of the size and pace of the coming "jobicide". For example, The Brookings Institution estimates that 61% of US jobs are at high- or medium-risk of automation by 2030 (Muro et al, 2019). The McKinsey Global Institute predicts that worldwide 400-800 million jobs will disappear by the same date due to AI and robotics (Manyika et al, 2017). Goldman Sachs forecast that 300 million jobs could be eliminated or degraded by generative AI alone (Briggs and Kodani, 2023). The World Bank (2016) puts the potential carnage higher, predicting that two-thirds of all jobs in the developing world could be replaced by new technology.

Seen through the lens of infinite economic growth on a finite planet, human-machine synthesis represents an unexpected opportunity to keep the leviathan of capitalism afloat. But this perspective inevitably distorts human history and dramatically misrepresents the process of industrialization which initiated modern economic growth. And yet – and this may be one of this chapter's biggest surprises – such is the power of the growth delusion, that support for technologizing everything about being human extends across the entire political spectrum, emphasizing just how crucial it is for progressives to grasp what is really going on in the humachine age.

The Second Machine Age

"Growth is not dead!" Andrew McAfee (2013) once proclaimed to a rapturous TED audience and he and fellow MIT academic Erik Brynjolfsson were undoubtedly among the first economists to recognise the potential for human-machine fusion to shore up the expansionary dreams of capitalism. (They also further burnished MIT's credentials as the East Coast intellectual capital of humachination to rival the West Coast's, Silicon Valley-based Stanford University.) During the Great Recession which followed the 2008 crash, that catastrophic failure of the "miracle" of "high yield, low risk" financial engineering, McAfee and Brynjolfsson (2011) wrote an essay highlighting the apparent gains in productivity being achieved by the humachine corporations. In The Second Machine Age (2014) they went further, attempting to translate the language of the singularity into economic terminology and provide the theory of history which is lacking in Ray Kurzweil's work. Chiefly basing their ideas on Stanford historian Ian Morris's book Why the West Rules (For now) (2010), they declare that "most of human history is boring" (p5):

> The Industrial Revolution ushered in humanity's first machine age – the first time our progress was driven primarily by technological innovation – and it was the most profound transformation our world has ever seen. The ability to generate massive amounts of mechanical power was so important that, in Morris's words "it made a mockery of all the drama of the world's earlier history" (McAfee and Brynjolfsson (2014:7).

For Brynjolfsson and McAfee digital capitalism opens up a new machine age in which the automation of muscle power is replaced by the automation of "mental power", which they see crystallized in Google's putative contributions to the self-driving car. Theoretically, Kurzweil's exponentiality model plays a major role in the authors' vision of the automation of economic activity. This theory, they suggest, will solve the abiding growthist problem of how to increase economic productivity, although it's tautological to say that substituting machines for workers will increase productivity, if this is measured in terms of (human) workers' hours. In reality, in the UK, productivity has been dropping since the 1990s, despite massive increases in computerization, telecommunications and automation, a trend which is repeated throughout the developed world (Jackson, 2018:18). (As economist Robert Solow famously said, "You can see the computer age everywhere but in the productivity statistics".) The authors also enthuse about the potential for digital technology to produce an abundance of cheap goods, as the marginal costs of production keep decreasing. This, however, ignores the price-maximizing effects of intellectual property rights, which play such an increasingly important role in digital capitalism. (By 2013 Google alone owned over 50,000 patents in a weak US IP system that favours Big Tech (Khorana, 2021).) And the "abundance through technology" argument contains a wider deception about how scarcity comes about. It's true, for example, that a billion or more people in the world suffer from hunger but food insecurity is not caused by there not being enough food to go around. For a start, 40% of all food is wasted, 1.2 billion tonnes of it before it even leaves the farm, and livestock farming, producing meat for a global minority, takes up over three-quarters of the world's farmland, directly or through growing food for cattle and pigs (WWF, 2021). It doesn't take a technological miracle to create food abundance, just a worldplan which fairly redistributes existing resources.

To their credit, Brynjolfsson and McAfee recognize some of the unequalizing risks of merging humans and machines, in a way that Kurzweil and the transhumanists don't. They see that the gap between the top and the bottom one percent in the US will get wider. They also note the potential hollowing out of middle-income non-tech jobs, as a split occurs between what some economists refer to as "lovely jobs" for the technological elite and "lousy jobs" for manual workers at the bottom. The effect on democracy could be devastating.

None of this dampens Brynjolfsson and McAfee's enthusiasm, however. They simply urge employees to ensure they are on the right side of the coming winner-takes-all economy. Their survival-of-the-fittest recommendations include "acquiring an excellent education", preferably with a STEM college degree, learning to work with robots and overall "filling up your toolkit" with "appropriate second machine age skills and abilities" (192-199). The priority for governments should be to accelerate humachination, for example, by increasing state funding for technology education (speeding up "the STEMpede"), providing more support for scientists, upgrading infrastructure and offering prizes for innovation. With such policies, Brynjolfsson and McAfee claim, digitization could increase "a thousand-fold" over the next two decades, proving that science fiction author Arthur C. Clarke was right when he observed that "a sufficiently advanced technology can be indistinguishable from magic" (251). And yet, bizarrely enough, they conclude with an overall message very similar to my own: "we need to think much more deeply about what it is we really want" and "Technology is not destiny. We shape our destiny" (257). It's a conclusion which combines techno-optimistic historical inevitablism with a libertarian emphasis on freedom of choice that rather sums up the contradictory, have-your cake-and-eat-it nature of the humachine project. ("Strategic naivety" might be the most charitable name for it.)

The Fourth Industrial Revolution

In the ruthless genealogy of ideas, *The Second Machine Age* seems to have been usurped by a book partially based on it. Klaus Schwab's *The Fourth Industrial Revolution* (2016) has certainly provided the most popular economic term for what I call humachination and the reason is probably obvious. Schwab is not only an economist and engineer; he is also, crucially, the founder of the influential World Economic Forum (WEF), where each year at Davos in Switzerland the global elite gather to strategize about the future. Who better to speak for the plutotechnic, leadership class of executives, investors and government leaders, who are making most of the world's decisions about new technology?

It also has to be said that as a label, the fourth industrial revolution sounds a little less alarming than the second machine age. Schwab's term seeks to reassure us that the humachine age is the only the latest in a more or less continuous process of technological transformation which has occupied the past three centuries. The fourth industrial revolution (4IR), he writes, "builds on the Third, the digital computer-based revolution that has been occurring since the middle of the last century". This emerged from the second revolution, the wave of electrification in the nineteenth century which enabled mass production to take place, which itself followed on from the original industrial revolution of the early 1700s, in which steam and water power led to mechanization. All this is a persuasive interpretation of capitalism as a constantly evolving force which can keep on delivering economic growth forever.

This comfortingly linear historical structure means that Schwab doesn't have to hold back on the ontological implications of humachination. It's a

> technological revolution that will fundamentally alter the way we live, work, and relate to one another. In its scale, scope, and complexity, the transformation will be unlike anything humankind has experienced before" (2015b).

This "fusion of technologies that is blurring the lines between the physical, digital, and biological spheres" involves familiar territory in terms of cognitive and motor humachines, such as AI, robotics, nanotechnology and so on (Schwab, 2015). It also involves Type 4 humachination, the mechanization of the human body. For example, Schwab suggests meditechnics will make it possible to print human cells and organs, while synthetic biology "will provide us with the ability to customise organisms by writing DNA" and gene-editing techniques, such as CRISPR, will create the possibility of reengineering the human personality (2016:16.) Schwab ducks the ethical issues around these developments, preferring to highlight the advantages medical benefits, if "both plants and animals could potentially be engineered to produce pharmaceutical and other forms of treatment." (21-22.)

Schwab is well aware of the wider implications of ontocapitalism, for example the potential of quantum computing to boost the power available to all humachines or the extent to which the mechanization of money via blockchain could remove governmental controls over the money supply. (This was before the spectacular implosion of the fraudulent FTX currency exchange in 2022 seemed to confirm Yanis Varoufakis's (2020:126) description of cryptocurrency as "a pyramid scheme of hyper-speculation".) As a trained engineer, Schwab is enthusiastic about the humachinated environment (the Type 5 humachine) that could transform everything we take for granted about the world that surrounds us. 4D printing could create "a new generation of self-altering products capable of responding to environmental changes such as heat and humidity". Materials science will produce "smart materials that are self-healing or self-cleaning with memory that revert to their original shapes" (17). Grapheme, 200 times stronger than steel and a million times thinner than a human hair, can be imprinted with electronics, enabling wearable computing and electronic networks embedded in every surface and structure.

The space between machines and the casings that traditionally house them will disappear; what's under the bonnet becomes irrelevant when the bonnet itself is a multi-sensory machine trying to act like a living thing. In *The Rise and Fall of American Growth,* economist Robert Gordon (2016) points out that the typical US house was isolated in 1870 but by 1940 was connected by gas, electricity, telephone, running water and waste disposal. He claims that no new technology would bring any further benefits, which may be true, but that won't stop humachinators from trying to create a degree of digital and robotic interconnectedness that makes the entire concept of a separation between a building, its inhabitants and their environment seem prelapsarian.

When it comes to job automation, Schwab admits the possibility of "a progressive social and political Armageddon by creating technological unemployment on a massive scale" but argues that instead "technology will unleash a new era of prosperity" and produce countless new jobs (36). This can enable the 4IR "both to increase economic growth" and alleviate "major global challenges" (35). One of these is the ecological emergency which Schwab's book does touch on (unlike *The Second Machine Age* whose index, astoundingly, contains not a single entry under "environment", "climate change", "biodiversity" or "fossil fuel"). However, Schwab's solutions, like Kurzweil's, are mainly technologistic, such as "the huge new efficiencies" to be produced by the Internet of Things (IoT), satellite monitoring, "the increased transparency" supposedly produced by digital information (i.e. communicative humachines) and the carbon capture and storage which is essential for the continuation of fossil fuel corporations (65-66) (more on this "mirage technology" in Chapter 8). His recommendations do not entail any decrease in the excessive Global North consumer consumption that is a core cause of the Anthropocene Crisis. Indeed, it's the transhumanist conviction that "human needs and desires are infinite so the process of supplying them should also be infinite" that shores up Schwab's faith in continuing economic growth (36-7).

Corporate Control: Hands off the Revolution!

Overall, Schwab is noticeably less exuberantly techno-utopian than other humachination champions. His primary concern seems to be to ensure that the key choices about human-machine merger continue to be made by the elites running the world major corporations. The plutotechnics implicit in the singularity's version of ontocapitalism becomes glaringly explicit in the 4IR. Like many so many humachinators, he would probably concur with Ronald Reagan (1986) that "the nine most terrifying words in the English language are: "I'm from the government and I'm here to help". Instead of policy recommendations for governments, Schwab's message to the world's political leaders is crystal clear: don't get in the way of business! He urges governments to avoid the regulation of the past phases of industrialization and keep taxation to the minimum. Schwab's main fiscal worry is that a growing black economy could make it difficult for authorities to collect tax from ordinary workers, which seems to weigh more heavily on his mind than the hundreds of billions of dollars lost to governments each year, mainly due to "offshore tax abuse" by the superrich – no doubt many of them Davos regulars (Tax Justice Network, 2021).

In any case, Schwab argues, the effective regulation of technology will be virtually impossible to achieve, due to the pace of change, the dromological dictatorship of speed I referred to in the last chapter. In fact, if governments are to retain any influence, they need to become as agile as corporations, undergoing a fourth industrial revolution themselves by becoming more automated and data-driven. The UK government, under prime minister Theresa May, soon responded to this call, publishing an industrial strategy relating to the "areas from artificial intelligence to biotechnologies [that] are now heralding a Fourth Industrial Revolution", aimed at helping the UK "to make the most of this global transformation" (Gov.uk, 2019). Collaboration with Schwab's WEF was an explicit plank of this policy.

Schwab even hints that if governments and public authorities "cannot evolve, they will face increasing trouble", perhaps ceasing to exist at all in this dog-eat-dog environment. For Schwab, their main function is accelerational, ensuring that the speed of technological transformation doesn't slack, by providing "aggressive funding for ambitious research pro-grammes", for instance (p24),

This determination to keep humachination in the hands of corporate lead-ers sits uneasily with Schwab's acute awareness that things could go badly wrong in the 4IR. Perhaps he is too well acquainted with the dark side of some of the executives he hosts at Davos to ignore the dystopian potential of human-machine hybridization, including the threat to privacy emanat-ing from a host of new surveillance technologies. (He is also old enough to have experienced at first-hand the horrors of Nazi Germany.) He worries that "the inexorable integration of technology in our lives could diminish some of our quintessential human capacities, such as compassion and cooperation" (Schwab, 2015). He even contemplates the worst kinds of abuse of power, admitting that:

> In its most pessimistic, dehumanized form, the Fourth Industrial Revolution may indeed have the potential to "robotize" humanity and thus to deprive us of our heart and soul (Schwab, 2015).

This destiny, he argues, can only be avoided by "putting people first and empowering them" (114) and by ensuring that "values and ethics are at the heart of our individual and collective behaviours and the systems they nour-ish" (113) How these admirable imperatives can be achieved by a free market of elite-run corporations trying to outcompete each other in their relentless pursuit of disruptive innovation is not at all clear. Suffice it to say, it's a fairly routine delusion among those who fail to see that endorsing infinite economic growth can result in a war against social equality, human wellbeing and nature.

"We've been here before": Some Inconvenient Truths about the First Industrial Revolution

One of the glaring weaknesses of *The Second Machine Age* and *The Fourth Industrial Revolution* is the scant historical attention which they devote to the actual British Industrial Revolution, on which their theories are based. In *The Technology Trap* (2018), economic historian Carl Benedikt Frey attempts to address this desideratum by producing a detailed narrative of industrialization, which is intended to justify the 4IR and in particular provide a reassurance about job automation. As he says by way of conclu-sion: "The message of this book is that we have been here before" (p348).

His point is that nobody in the eighteenth century knew what jobs were going to replace the occupations which were eliminated by threshing machines and competitive agricultural techniques. But in the end rural jobs were replaced by new occupations, in manufacturing, the public sectors and service industries. Over time, the working majority benefitted from this job revolution through raised living standards, including universal education, better healthcare and ultimately political enfranchisement.

But, I'm inclined to ask, why should the progressive effects of this process repeat itself? Past events do not guarantee future performance – even in our money-driven economy, advertisements for financial products are banned from making such a claim. A tipping point in history, which is what the 4IR is said to be, causes many diverse outcomes, which are impossible to predict. Indeed, as Frey's well-researched book reveals, in conjunction with other sources, there are many reasons to doubt that the apparently positive effects of the first Industrial Revolution (IR) will be replicated by the humachine age.

First, as Frey reminds us, the initial phase of British industrialization from 1750-1840 had a hellish impact on the workers who created it. It was more like an economic war declared on the rural working majority rather than a deliberate first step on the road to social progress. Through the enclosure of common land and the mechanization of agriculture, workers were forced to move from their traditional, multi-role rural occupations into the atrocious living conditions of the new industrial towns, such as the Manchester of the 1840s which Friedrich Engels (1845/1984) so luridly described, crowded with impoverished labourers and Irish workers escaping from the mass starvation of the Great Famine. Working up to 18 hours a day in mills and factories, industrial workers performed the kind of highly mechanized work routines which had been invented in the seventeenth century by British slave owners in the sugar plantations of Barbados and other Caribbean colonies (Davis, 2006).

Children were a prime vulnerability to be exploited by the first captains of industry, with youngsters of five or six years of age often working 12-hour days and performing the dangerous but indispensable role of cleaning under live machines, a task which often left them limbless (Humphries, 2013). As Frey states, the men, women and children who pioneered industrialization experienced "three generations of misery" as their standard of living dramatically declined. Real average wages fell by 5%, 1780 to 1840, while the income share of the top 5% of the population doubled by 1869 (to 37%) (p113). In this traumatic century of diminished wellbeing, in which many were tormented by the memory of the rural communities they'd left behind, the average height of a man actually shrank, as EP Thompson (1963:115) observed. In terms of economic history, this phase can be described as "short term" but, as Frey poignantly observes, for many "the short-term can be a lifetime" (p126).

It was only in the second phase industrialization, from the 1840s to the 1970s that the living standards of workers finally began to rise, starting with the doubling of real wages from 1840 to 1900 (Frey:132). Working conditions very gradually improved, as did urban accommodation, sanitation and healthcare. Eventually universal secondary education replaced the mass illiteracy of the 1750s and the political rights won step-by-step from 1832 resulted in full suffrage for men and women aged 21 and over by 1930.

It's only pointing out the obvious, however, to say that it was profit rather than majoritarian social development which was the primary motivation for the capitalists driving industrialization. Indeed, social development improvements, especially political rights, often met with the stiffest resistance from employers. Social progress was possible in part because of the mass nature of industrial manufacturing, with huge agglomerations of workers doing similar jobs in large-scale workplaces. This favoured the development of trade unionism and the political parties which demanded and eventually achieved increased worker rights. It also has to be said that it was very much in the interests of many employers to tolerate social development as the improved skills that come from a comparatively healthy, educated workforce can dramatically raise labour productivity.

But these comparatively worker-friendly conditions are absent in the humachine age. Job automation today does not create machinery for large human workforces to operate but humachines that replace human workers altogether. Workers are increasingly fragmented, non-unionized and precarious. The leading Big Tech companies employ highly specialized workforces in extremely parsimonious numbers: for example, Google employs 16 times fewer workers than US retailer Wal-Mart, although it has double the market capitalization (140,000 employees versus 2.3 million, as of January 2023).

Other questions abound. For example, how can we be sure that "the short term" of the fourth phase of industrialization won't produce a decline in living standards similar to the first phase? Can we trust today's wealth creators, some of whom see humans as machines waiting to be upgraded, not to end up creating new forms of exploitation and misery that match those inflicted by their predecessors? What happens when employers no longer need workers? Since the agricultural revolution, the rich have always relied on the poor to provide them with their luxury lifestyle. Equipped with a workforce of mechanical slaves, will employers once again be prepared to grant human workers new social benefits and political rights or will they treat them as superfluous to requirements?

It's also worth stressing that the initial stage of industrialization in Britain was made possible by some of the harshest, most swingeing legislation a pre-democratic state could devise. As early as 1788, destroying knitting machines was made punishable by transportation and in 1812 "frame-breaking" became a capital crime. In the same year, some 12,000 troops were used against the Luddite risings (in which only machines that threatened to cause unemployment were targeted), resulting in the execution of 30 protesters. The Captain Swing riots against agricultural machines in the 1830s led to some 250 death sentences being issued and many workers were imprisoned for life or transported (Frey, 2018: 128-131). In all, over the period 1736-1848, 118 anti-government rioters were hanged by the courts and over 650 were killed by the military (Horn, 2005:147).

Will it be possible to pursue mass job automation within a modern democracy or will similarly draconian measures be needed? Can democracy itself even survive the humachine age, a question we return to in Chapter 9?

Furthermore, any responsible extrapolation from previous phases of industrialization needs to acknowledge the very different pace of job generation today. In the past, occupations evolved over decades and even centuries but, as we've seen, pro-humachination economists are predicting job automation within a matter of years. The Covid-19 pandemic further accelerated the rate of change. In one international survey, 41% of corporate bosses said they planned to speed up job automation (Makrygiannis, 2020). "We've seen two years' worth of digital transformation in two months" claimed Microsoft CEO Satya Nadella, eagerly anticipating a "world of remote everything" (Spataro, 2020). Such a twelve-fold acceleration is rapid even by dromological standards and the 2022 Russian invasion of Ukraine brought the mass warfare which throughout history has been technology's most reliable accelerant.

The pace and ubiquity of labour substitution will make it extremely difficult for displaced workers to know which jobs to retrain for, as none will be immune from replacement. In fact, the only sector which is likely to thrive is the job replacement industry, which will immediately pounce on any new occupations which emerge via the spontaneous job generation, on which the pro-humachination economists seem to be staking everything. The most pro-active job-replacers will even try to automate jobs before they have a chance to emerge spontaneously, until their profession too is mechanized out of existence.

In sum, however we interpret the age of humachines, one thing is surely crystal clear: we definitely have not been here before.

Technosocialism and Leftist Accelerationism

In the light of this historical reality check, it might seem that we could confidently predict that support for humachination would largely remain the exclusive possession of neoliberal economists, normally associated with right-wing politics. For example, in 2019 it was no surprise to hear the new Conservative prime minister (the now disgraced Boris Johnson) pledge to promote AI and robotics and "liberate the UK's bioscience sector from anti-genetic modification rules" (Gov.uk, 2019). Indeed, in so far as Brexit has an economic rationale, it's to transform the UK into a "science and technology superpower", largely, it would seem, by attracting capital to a regulatory environment not entirely dissimilar to that of the first industrial revolution, with dramatically lowered worker, consumer, environmental and biomedical protections (Gov.uk, 2021a). Donald Trump articulated a kindred strategy at Davos in January 2020, decrying "the prophets of doom" and urging people "to put their faith in technology to solve the big problems" (Pomeroy, 2020).

It was more surprising, however, to find in the same period the political left endorsing a similar vision. John McDonnell, as the shadow chancellor in the most socialist incarnation of the Labour party for several decades, called for more government funding for robots and declared that his party's main investment priority was "Embracing the Fourth Industrial

Revolution. And thus tackling our chronic productivity crisis" (Labour. org.uk, 2019).

The unsettling truth – for me at least – is that for certain socialists and left-leaning progressives, the lure of new technology can be so strong that it nullifies a historical awareness of the past class struggles involved in industrialization. The myth of infinite economic growth is also so firmly planted on the left that it almost appears as if for some, socialism is nothing more than growth capitalism run by socialists. In part, this can be put down to a long-standing infatuation with technology shared by Karl Marx. "In *Capital*", writes political scientist Ulv Hanssen (2022), "Marx lauds the human capacity to subjugate nature for the purpose of production and development", as he believed this "constituted a condition of the possibility for the transition to communism". Defining nature as an economic resource which only has value from a human viewpoint did nothing to mitigate the ecological nightmare that Soviet industrialization became (UNCHR, 1996). (Too late did the Ukrainian proto-economic ecologist Sergei Podolinski present the dying Marx with a nature-based alternative to his economic theory (Martinez-Alier, 1987).

The truth is that some leftist economists, rather than warning against the potential carnage caused by occupational humachines, are calling for the pace of job automation to be increased. Ironically, in this they are following in the wake of right-wing, free-market thinkers like Peter Thiel (see Chapter 9) and others complaining about a "great stagnation" in high-speed technological development (e.g. Cowan, 2011). One example of this "progressive" accelerationism is a report by the influential left-of-centre think tank IPPR, entitled, *Managing Automation* (Lawrence et al, 2017). This seems to me to accept the growthist assumptions embedded in the 4IR, although it argues for policies which reduce its socio-economic inequality impacts. The report draws heavily on analysis by The McKinsey Global Institute management consultancy, which argues that the disappearance of 800 million jobs by 2030 is justified by the productivity increases it will cause (Manyika et al, 2017). In fact, McKinsey's wholly speculative prediction is that humachination can produce annual productivity growth almost five times greater than that produced by steam engine technology in the second half of the nineteenth century – 1.4% p.a. compared to 0.3%. Partially on this basis, the IPPR authors recommend the "managed acceleration of automation" and give this aim a distinctly nationalistic twist, declaring that

"The goal should be to make the UK the most digitally advanced economy in the world by 2040" (Lawrence et al, 2017:8).

More sensibly, in my view, the IPPR economists also call for the establishment of strong regulatory bodies, including "An Authority on the use of Robotics and Artificial Intelligence" and warn about the danger of women losing out in automation. They also demand more collective ownership of technology companies in order to distribute profits more equitably. But whether such a Keynesian approach can permanently change the direction of the humachine juggernaut is very open to question. Can regulatory bodies cherry-pick the best bits of new technology and somehow sever the connection between occupational humachines and other data-monopolizing surveillance systems, while at the same time actually accelerating the entire process? It's hard to believe that the multiple enchainments that occur in humachinated environments have been fully understood here or that the institutional power and mindset of those leading the charge of the automators have been taken into account. Changing a world system by adopting the same conceptual paradigm is virtually impossible – that requires a wholly new set of goals and values.

Some on the left appear to understand this. In *Inventing the Future*, leftist political theorists Nick Srnicek and Alex Williams (2015) also call for full automation of employment (as opposed to the traditional left-wing demand for full employment) but add demands for a shorter working week, Universal Basic Income (UBI) and the end of the work ethic. In addition, they advocate a leftist modernity strategy "to transform the common sense of society, revive a utopian social imagination… and eventually repurpose technological and economic superstructures" (157).

Many of these goals I'd agree with – especially Srnicek and Williams' call for utopianism – but their strategy of speeding up economic growth in order to shut it down seems to me a very dangerous plan. To begin with, it would mean vigorously opposing the resistance to job automation by trade unions and others which will inevitably come, while giving humachine corporations virtual carte blanche to develop enchained smart technologies, which would be difficult to dismantle. Also, why would you risk increasing the dromological advantage the humachine engineers already have – Andy Grove's "nine-times gap" between government regulators and Big Tech innovators? This sums up the somewhat surreal scenario of government-hired computer scientists battling to stay one step ahead of the corporate opposition, as both head into the totally uncharted waters of human-machine merger. And once "full" automation has been reached (however you might judge this juncture), why would those in charge of this technology give it up? It's naive to think that the techno-elite won't have their own strategies for self-perpetuation, for example by building in surveillance mechanisms that make the dystopian, Technocene version of the Anthropocene more likely.

There is also an alarming lack of a real environmental dimension in some left-wing techno-utopians. This reaches an extreme among those whom Marxist ecologist Andreas Malm (2020:164) describes as "the comrades fantasising about 'luxury communism'", adding that "as damaged as this planet already is, nothing suggests that plenitude will be there for the taking". Well intentioned as he may be, the unlimited material abundance which Aaron Bastani proclaims in *Fully Automated Luxury Communism* (2019) is only available due to his uncritical acceptance of virtually every techno-optimistic claim ever made about machine language and robotics. He also naively endorses the myth that renewables can replicate, and even improve on, the energy provided by carbon capitalism

The problem is that the belief in technology as the solution to everything is as strong in some parts of the left as it is anywhere else. The flaws of human-machine fusion are not simply that it's being run by the wrong people. You can't turn ontocapitalism into a force for good simply by trusting left-wing politicians or civil servants to make the right judgments on what technology is socially beneficial. Nor is it only profit-seeking ontopreneurs we have to worry about; this ignores the dangers posed by the contemporary split in science between physics and biology, the fault line which the humachine age straddles (more in Chapter 6). To messianic ultra-scientists, it may make no difference whether their frontier-smashing, career-boosting experiments are funded by the taxpayer or by private capital.

In truth, left-wing mechanicalism carries many of the dangers of its right-wing variant. The mindset that sees society as a self-regulating economic engine can also express itself in terms of a machine-like society run by an all-seeing, centralized Party which makes all the technological decisions that matter. What is left of humanity when automation has run its course has always been a problem for technosocialism. Marx remained obstinately silent about what communism would look like once the dictatorship of the proletariat was over and the state, in Engels' (1878) renowned phrase, "withered away". Surely it would be better to first democratically establish a worldplan for a better world and then decide how technology fits into it rather than jump on the capitalist bandwagon and try to steer it in a different direction.

The Slippery Slope of Transhumanism

Finally, the need for progressives to thoroughly grasp the meaning of humachination is further illustrated by the issue of transhumanism. I suspect few left-leaning economists have fully thought through the connection between job automation and the development of a multiplanetary species but Srnicek and Williams (2015) show how difficult it is to say no to human-machine hybridization once you approach its slippery slope. Consider the definition of freedom at the heart of their strategy.

> [Synthetic freedom] demands experimentation with collective and technological augmentation, and a spirit that refuses to accept any barrier as natural and inevitable. Cyborg augmentations, artificial life, synthetic biology and technologically mediated reproduction are all examples of this elaboration.

To me, this seems to swallow the mechanistic view of reality underlying humachination hook, line and sinker. The writers go on to explicitly reject the theoretical foundations of ecology, its holist connectedness and respect for biophysical limits and are even lured into jettisoning the Hegelian roots of Marxism and traditional socialist explanations for why proletarian revolutions have not occurred in the West:

> There is no authentic human essence to be realised, no harmonious unity to be returned to, no unalienated humanity obscured by false mediations, no organic wholeness to be achieved (82).

"What we are and what we can be are open-ended projects to be constructed in the course of time," they conclude. This beguiling, post-modernist stance may seem easy enough to go along with until you realise that it represents a subtle form of machine supremacisim which ends in a wholesale assault on what it is to be a member of Homo sapiens. It's true that socialism is greening fast – with the adoption of the Green New Deal and other positive environmental policies – and this may well lead to a much-needed reappraisal of the role of nature in economics and life in general. But the seductive power of cyborgism for some progressives shows just how much of a battle over organizational principles is still to be fought. I'd suggest that the post-modernist "anything goes" philosophy is no longer compatible with an Anthropocene teetering on the brink of climate and biodiversity collapse.

Conclusion

To sum up, the reach of humachination across economics and political theory is much wider than might have been expected. The mesmeric effect of machines has become so deeply sedimented in the collective unconsciousness of modernity that it even rears its head in anti-capitalist theories. (There again, capitalism's virus-like ability to appropriate oppositional ideas has always been one of its greatest tricks). Above all, the economic and political theories analysed here emphasizes the extent to which the concept of infinite economic growth has become hegemonic in modern society, persuading so many to close their eyes to fundamental flaws of technological capitalism. Keeping in mind the traumatizing, multi-generational assault on human wellbeing that occurred in the real Industrial Revolution –not to mention its imperialist Western-centricity – may be one way corrective to this. However well intentioned their strategy may be, accelerationists trying to ride shotgun to ontocapitalism run the risk of ensuring that control of new technology remains firmly in the hands of a new ruling elite who may resemble their ruthless, industrial capitalist predecessors rather more closely than they like to think.

Ultimately, I suggest, it will take the radical, post-growth, ecological economic approach, contained in the SEWP model, to bring humanity into a more sustainable relationship with our planet and bring about the genuine equitability and wellbeing which moves us in the direction of the Ecocene. But to understand the theoretical context of this claim, it's time to challenge more deeply the seemingly blind faith in growth and technology which dominates the humachine age and to question the theories of history and science that assume that machines signify a higher form of being than organic life.

PART II

Challenging the Assumptions of the Humachine Age: An Alternative Vision of the Past and the Future

Part I may have may surprised the reader about just what is involved in the "science and technology" future, which we seem to be endorsing as consumers and voters. Digging into the theory and practice of capitalism in the age of human-machine fusion releases some disturbing images of where we may be heading, like methane exploding from melting permafrost. The largely unnoticed and undebated ontocapitalist objective of transcending biology and transforming all energy and matter is very far from being an agreed version of the human mission. Indeed, as I've already strongly hinted, it's a vision of techno-utopia which seems much more likely to lead to the techno-dystopian Technocene than to the digital, democratized, transhuman nirvana it promises us. In fine, humachination is not what it seems.

In Part II, I want to substantiate my implicit criticisms in the previous section by unearthing the conceptual foundations underpinning human-machine merger and explicitly challenging these. In the following chapters, I unpack and con-test four of the core assumptions of the humachine age, which freely cross the borders of human knowledge from history and philosophy to political economy and the natural sciences. First, I challenge the assumption that cap-italism can continue to produce economic growth or provide a sustainable, equitable, democratic future. Second, I challenge the idea that technology determines the course of history rather than people making political choices. Third, I dispute the humachinators' claim that progress in modern science is dominated by mechanistic physics rather than biological life science. And finally, I suggest that market-based consumerism is not the reliable indicator of what people really want or what is good for the planet, as the apostles of the singularity and pro-humachination economists claim. On the contrary, it's often a theatre for perilous Promethean trickery.

By surfacing unconscious assumptions, we can create the possibility of new, conscious choices and, I hope, indicate how these may lead us towards the better future which I call the Ecocene. But as a respectful reminder, let me say that this is not a book for those looking for easy choices: humanity has already used up most of these.

CHAPTER 4

Capitalism, the End of Growth and what the Industrial Revolution Really Tells Us about the Future

The Phantasm of Economic Growth

The humachine age may just turn out to be capitalism's last fling. It contains all the problems inherent in a world system based on the goal of infinite economic growth on a finite planet (Boulding, 1973). Humachination assumes that there is no alternative to capitalism as a world system – a belief often expressed by the acronym TINA – and so it must be preserved at any cost. This unconscious capitalism affects almost every choice we make about life and is sedimented into virtually every social institution and branch of knowledge, as the last chapter amply illustrates. Across the political spectrum, it imprisons us in a thought maze, in which every twist and turn can lead us further from the exit we so desperately seek. As the saying goes, it's easier to imagine the end of the world than the end of capitalism but in the age of human-machine fusion we urgently need to start imagining both (Fisher, 2014).

At its most basic, the organizing principle of capitalism can be summed up in a simple equation: profit above people and planet. Sometimes this equation can have beneficial effects – for example by facilitating health-care, education or poverty reduction– but social development is a side effect of capitalism, not its primary purpose. Capitalism's true priority is in its name. The expansion of capital is its lodestar, giving it an enviably unwavering sense of direction. This pursuit of profit takes myriad forms but in the mid-twentieth century it became crystallized in economic theory and government policy as the goal of increasing GDP. "Growth, growth, growth," is how UK Conservative Prime Minister Liz Truss described her political programme (Mason, 2022). True, she lasted a mere seven weeks in office but she was only echoing what virtually every mainstream politician and economist takes as their number one objective. The rules of the GDP game apply to companies as well as nations: positive growth is good, negative growth is bad – and often a sackable offence for CEOs and politicians alike. Yet grading reality on the basis of the circulation of money, which is all that GDP really measures, regardless of whether it has good and bad effects, is deeply problematic. It ignores the things that matter most in a human community such as happiness, wellbeing, equality and sustainability and reduces all life to the needs of capital.

It's also an illusion. Infinite economic growth is as logically untenable as it is practically impossible. At worst, it's simply a version of the exponentiality trick, as previously suggested. A 3% annual increase in GDP would mean that a nation's entire production and consumption would double in size every 24 years. For brief periods in history this astronomic rate of growth has been possible: in fact, in the 1960s global GDP increased by 5.5% a year but by 2016 the rate had plummeted to 2.5%, and most of this rise was due to the economies of developing nations. In the developed world, growth per capita is heading fast towards zero. "In less than a decade, on current trends, there would be no growth at all in GDP per capita across the OECD nations," estimates ecological economist Tim Jackson (2018:8). So why do we still chase this mercurial will-o-the-wisp?

One prominent reason is that the prospect of growth preserves the existing social hierarchy, as it prevents the demand for the distribution of wealth which would inevitably follow the demise of the growth imperative. As long as the economic pie seems to be getting bigger, there is hope that even the most disproportionately small slice of it may increase in size. But if the pie stops growing completely, the majority will surely start demanding much more equal slices. This would finally explode a second layer of the growth myth, the claim that economic growth continuously boosts happiness. In fact, despite the tripling of US GDP per capita in second half of the twentieth century, the General Progress Indicator (GPI), which measures equitability, life satisfaction and sustainability, shows no increase over the period and actually declines after the 1980s (Borowy and Schmeltzer 2017:11). As Ian Gough (2017:71) notes, "comparative research shows that GPI does not increase beyond a GDP of around $7,000 per capita".

The equation of growth with the production of money also gives rise to "the iceberg model" of capitalism described by eco-feminists, who claim that between 30% and 70% of economic output is provided by women and other non-salaried carers and workers (Schmelzer et al, 2022:133-137). Without this invisible, unacknowledged reproductive economy of "voluntary" subsistence and care, capitalism might collapse altogether.

In other words, the growth delusion and multiple economic inequalities are locked into the same deceptive system, a system which also involves a constant war on nature. Commons scholar Peter Barnes (2006) compares the worldplan of capitalism to the algorithms governing a computer's operating system: the first instruction is to grow the size of the capital invested in an enterprise; the second is to distribute the rewards unequally according to ownership of capital rather than the contribution of other stakeholders; and the third is to ignore the impact of this activity on natural resources or the state of the planet. This metaphor is of course wonderfully apt for the humachine age and its basic message can be conveyed as a mnemonic, which invokes a much older technology of domination, GUN. The pursuit of never-ending economic Growth, Unequally distributed and in a way that constantly negates Nature, is the GUN default setting of capitalism.

Unequalism is nothing new. It's been a hallmark of social organization since the dawn of the Holocene agricultural revolution but the pursuit of growth in the humachine age has taken the gap between top and bottom income earners to new levels. Since 1995, the richest 1% have captured 20 times more of global wealth than the poorest 50% of humanity, according to Oxfam (Ahmed et al, 2022). Globally the economic division between rich and poor countries is widening and huge income and wealth chasms are opening up within emerging economies. In the developed world, Big Tech is leading the inequality charge. In the 1960s the typical boss-worker wage ratio was around 21:1 but today Elon Musk earns 10.000 times more than the average Tesla employee and Mark Zuckerberg can amass as much in two minutes as an average American earns in an entire year (Mischel and Kandra, 2021). In one day in September 2020, Jeff Bezos's wealth actually increased by $13 billion (Pitcher, 2020). Capitalism thrives on division. Where there are gaps there is a profit to be made, whether between domestic and offshore wages, for example, or in the infinitesimal price differences of commodities or currencies.

Capitalism also profits royally from the gap between the artificially low price put on nature and what it can be sold for. For example, if the environmental costs of making a hamburger (including water and land usage, air pollution and soil degradation) were factored in, its true price would be over $200 (Patel, 2009). Carbon capitalism has been negating nature for three hundred years, literally and metaphorically cutting off mountain tops to feed the monster of growth and depleting the planet's natural resources. The Western Science Revolution redefined nature as a force to be mastered and put in the service of humanity. Capitalism has further refined this objective, putting science and technology in the service of capital expansion rather than social development. But there is nothing natural about the idea of perpetual growth. As political ecologist Giorgos Kallis and his colleagues point out (2020:11), "trees do not grow into the heavens like Jack's beanstalk and human embryos do not grow into giants." Pursuing the chimera of eternal economic growth only destroys the actual ecosystems in which real growth occurs and which form the Earth's indispensable support systems.

Neoclassical economics masks the effects of economic activity by treating it as an externality. As Serge Latouche says in *Farewell to Growth*, "the last link with nature was broken" in about 1880, turning economics into "ecological nonsense" (2009:13). The madness of pursuing universal growth results in a kind of planetary dysmorphia, which leads us to consume natural resources as though we were living on 1.8 Earths instead of one. The US consumes as though there were 5.1 planets of biocapacity at our disposal and the EU as if there were 2.8. India, by contrast, with almost five times the population of the US, uses just 0.8 planet's worth of natural resources and many African countries even less (Overshootday, 2022). How can humanity ever achieve global sustainability and live within the means of our single planet unless the rich world radically reduces its global footprint? Only this would allow the developing world some leeway for continued expansion.

The humachine age recognizes that some form of rebalancing with nature is needed but insists that the unregulated use of technology, which is the main cause of the Anthropocene Crisis, is also the solution to it. However digital-robotic capitalism can never reproduce carbon capitalism in decarbonized form. Its claim that green growthism can totally sever or "decouple" never-ending increases in material production from negative environmental impacts is totally unfounded, as we'll see in Chapter 8. Instead, capitalism is an increasingly toxic biohazard. Its assault on nature is leading to ever greater breaching of planetary safe boundaries with shrinking forests, rising seas and polluted water and soil heralding even more severe forms of climate and ecological breakdown (Rockstrom et al, 2023).

The GUN to Our Heads: The Growth Irrationale

Capitalism can be a monstrous system but it's operated by people who are not necessarily monsters. It's simply an economic worldplan which has an uncanny ability to bring out the worst in being human and to lavishly reward this trait. It's also an ethical system, which drives out other values. Growthism makes competition with others the driving force of society, between businesses, nations and between humans and nature. This warring condition insists that individuals strive for themselves rather than cooperate in the interests of the whole. This modern individualism contrasts with the altruistic collectivism which has been the norm for many people in the past. Wealth expansion encourages a compulsive psychology based on greed and fear, as the pursuit of infinite materialist wealth is also a flight from the horror of losing it. In this way – through the effects of other CIMENT values such as nationalism, which perpetually pitches nations against each other, the organizational pattern of capitalism is able to achieve the paradox of constantly changing and constantly staying the same.

Democracy is meant to arbitrate this deadly competitiveness and is claimed to be capitalism's greatest accomplishment but less than ten percent of the world's nations currently live in "full democracies" (EIU, 2021). It means today's leadership remains in the hands of those who promote the interests of growth capital and their political backers. Plutotechnics, the domination of the elite over a society's technology which has been the basis of hierarchical civilization for the past 5,000 years, continues to rule. Today, our technological leaders who have greater wealth and greater decision-making power over the future than ever before, seem determined that this state of affairs will persist.

The price is that the stability which was once the goal of society has been replaced by a permanent state of instability caused by the deliberate disruption of the status quo by technological innovation. Only by relentless "creative destruction", which thrives on disasters, economic crashes and even pandemics, can capitalism survive. In fact, this economic concept was originated by Joseph Schumpeter in the 1940s as a critique of capitalism but reinvented by neoliberals as an asset (D.Harvey, 2007). Now, it seems, the only thing left for growthism to "creatively destroy" is humanity itself by melding Homo sapiens with machines.

All in all, capitalism traps our thinking and confuses our choices. Seen through the GUN sights, even space and time is warped. Growthism not only dysmorphically inflates the very size of the planet we live on, it also distorts history, especially its own. We discovered in the last chapter that the fourth industrial revolution narrative falsifies the political and economic conditions that created industrialization in the past but, as we'll now see, the humachinators' distortion of the future can be even more profound.

The Rocket Theory of History and Why it's Ecologically Wrong

History is all about the future. Humans need to interpret what has been because we are so desperate to make the right choices about that which is to come. From the perspective of ecological economics, the humachine interpretation of the Industrial Revolution leads to a vision of the future which can be characterized as the rocket theory of history and, if we continue to give it credence, nothing is more likely to lead us towards the Technocene.

That said, something unique in human society definitely occurs in the West from the eighteenth century onwards. In 1700, the per capita energy capture in Western societies was scarcely higher than it had been in the Roman Empire – as late as 1800 it was still only 25 gigajoules a year compared to 20 gigajoules in 100 CE (Smil, 2019:440-1) – and the Romans represented the highpoint of energy use since the beginning of urban civilization in the fourth millennium CE. In 1700, it took an artisan working a pedal-driven wheel (a machine that went back to medieval times), 500 hours of skilled work to produce a pound of yarn. By 1800, thanks to the Spinning Jenny and other massive, although often quaintly named, steam-based machines, the same quantity of yarn could be produced in three hours; by 1824 further mechanization reduced the time required to just one hour and twenty minutes. This enormous surge in productive power was accompanied by the increased portability of the steam engine, symbolized by the steam-driven train (the original "Rocket"), which enabled a vast, centralizing rail network to be built. Coal-powered electrification and the oil-driven combustion engine further expanded the West's productive capacity, leading to the rapid expansion of cities and industrial infrastructure. By 1900 the energy available per person in Western society was triple that of 1700 and by 2000 it was seven times greater (Morris, 2010).

This huge expansion in production created sustained economic growth for the first time in human history. From the Middle Ages, Western economic growth– as measured retrospectively by estimated GDP – only increases at a speed so glacial (around 0.14%) as to be nugatory by modern standards (Borowy, 2017). From 1700 there is a very gradual upping of pace but it is only from 1850 to 1950 that there is an economic acceleration (up to 1% p.a.) that for the first time can properly be described as economic growth. But it's in the three decades following 1945, in the period I've referred to as the Thriving Third (Harvey, 2019), that the first and only sustained period of dramatic economic growth in the West occurs at around 3% (Maddison, 2007).

So what or who was the cause of this extraordinary phenomenon? Those who subscribe to the rocket theory of history – and I have in mind here the authors of *The Second Machine Age* and *The Fourth Industrial Revolution* among many others – seem to have few doubts. For them, industrialization was essentially a technology revolution which was brought about by innovative engineers, bold, visionary entrepreneurs and the far-sighted politicians who supported them. It was this new coalition that was primarily responsible for this historical leap forward and the social development, urbanisation, mass education and universal suffrage that followed.

According to this technologistic narrative, nothing of great interest happened in history before the miracle of industrial machines but once the rocket of progress takes off it can continue forever, as long as scientists, technologists, financiers and wealth creators are allowed to build ever better machines and continue to extend the frontiers of science unhampered by governmental red tape. Integral to this theory of history is the notion that progress is driven by competition between nations and regions, a never-ending battle in which technology provides ruling elites with their most potent competitive advantage. This form of techno-social Darwinism is typified by Ian Morris's (2010) aforementioned account of world history, which implies that Western economies can only maintain their lead over China by perpetually accelerating their technological development.

The Ecological Viewpoint: The Role of Nature and Sustainable Degrowth

Needless to say, from an eco-democratic standpoint, the real history of the Industrial Revolution looks very different. The bioeconomic reality is that this great economic transformation was produced in close partnership with nature, like all previous technological revolutions from the controlled use of fire and the development of agriculture onwards. This time, however, nature had a huge surprise in store: the genuinely miraculous, energy-expanding power of fossil fuel. Coal doubles the energy available to humans and oil triples it, to the extent it's been estimated that a barrel of oil contains the equivalent of 10,000 to 25,000 hours of free human work. In a buoyant oil economy, it's as though everybody on the planet had 50 slaves at their disposal (Kallis, 2018:65).

Fossil fuel produced the enormous spurt which made social development irresistible and contributed hugely to the uplift in living standards and the relative economic equalization that gradually occurred after 1850. This is particularly true from 1945, when economic growth produced the biggest rise in living standards for Western societies in history. Many factors drove the Thriving Third from 1945-1979, not least the catalyst of WW2, which destroyed some of the world's most advanced economies and necessitated a surge of decolonization. Politically, the majority in the Western Europe demanded more spending on education and health, higher taxes on the wealth, and the result was an unprecedented narrowing of the gap between top and bottom income earners (Dorling, 2017).

What has been hugely underestimated in this transformation is the impact of a glut of new oil which came on to the market shortly after WW2. What Hans Pfister (2010) terms "the 1950s syndrome" in Western Europe was largely caused by enormous oil fields in Saudi Arabia and the Gulf States coming on-stream, including Ghawar, the largest oil-bearing structure on the planet. The US State Department called the region's reserves of over

350 billion barrels of oil "the greatest single prize in all history". These new oil fields had the effect of making the miraculous energy-expanding resource of oil and gas so cheap that it was almost free. At the same time, US oil production expanded, providing low-cost gasoline to fuel an economic boom. The economic impact was spectacular. For example, from 1963-1973 the UK averaged over 4% in annual GDP increases, achieving a vertiginous 6.5% rise in 1973 (World Bank 2022). This catalytic decade, which is mainly remembered for its cultural achievements, achieved a degree of economic expansion that would have taken almost half a century at the 1850-1950 rate. It perhaps unconsciously imprinted the phantasm of growth on several generations, who have been vainly trying to reproduce it ever since.

However, the oil shock of the 1970s dramatically put an end to this global bonanza of cheap energy and sharply reduced economic growth (for example, the UK plunged to a recessionary rate of -2.5% in 1974). The almost mythical profitability of fossil fuel gradually vanished. In 1919 the energy return on investment (EROI) for the exploration of new oil reserves was in the region of 1000:1 but by the 2010s this had plummeted to 5:1. The EROI of producing oil and gas sank from 25:1 in the 1970s to 10:1 in 2007 (Hall et al, 2014). This means that the transition to renewable energy cannot provide anything like the super-profitability of fossil fuel (one of the reasons why the oil majors are so reluctant to fully convert to renewables). The ERO1 on electricity by 2050 may be as low as 6:1 in a 100% renewable energy scenario (Fabre, 2019), well below the 11.1 ratio which Fizaine and Court (2016) estimate is needed to maintain economic growth. A fully decarbonized economy, in other words, simply cannot produce the sky-high return on investment that sustains the huge consumption levels of the carbon economy. ROI, the king of capitalism, is dying and with it economic growth.

Since the mid-seventies another, unwanted, type of acceleration has occurred in the biosphere. The concentration of CO_2 in the atmosphere has grown from a little over a fifth above the pre-industrial level of 280 ppm in 1975 (331ppm) to 50% above it at its current level of 420 ppm (NASA, 2023). That means the planet is currently hurtling towards well over 2C [degree] of warming by the century's end. This would be "a death sentence to the global South", according to anthropologist and degrowth advocate Jason Hickel (2020), although this fate can still be averted by rapidly phasing out the use of hydrocarbons. Biodiversity is also shrinking at hyper-speeds. Since the 1970s, the number of animals has declined by 60%, insects have reduced by even more in Europe, and habitats across the world, from rainforests to mangroves, are withering as pollution in the soil, water, air and oceans intensifies. This "triple ecological emergency" of climate disruption, biodiversity decline and pollution, as characterized by UN chief Antonio Guterres (UN News, 2021), looms over the succession of military, humanitarian, economic and health disasters which have unfolded in our once-excitedly-anticipated new millennium. It suggests a world crying out for a radically new relationship between the people and the planet. Instead, we have the growth fixation which regards the planet's material resources as inexhaustible and insists that technology is the answer, without even needing to know what the question is.

Ecological economics – or bioeconomics as it's sometimes called – sees the situation very differently. From this standpoint, the key concept is entropy, the second law of thermodynamics which we encountered in our discussion of Ray Kurzweil's theories. For foundational ecological economist Nicholas Georgescu-Roegen (1986) entropy was the basis of all economic activity, since all things are subject to increasing disorder in a closed system. For the global economy, entropy is now kicking in, limiting the energy for machines, without which they are simply inert lumps of matter. Matter itself, the materials from which machines are being made, is also being depleted, as the world runs out of rare earth metals for miniaturized components, lithium and cobalt for batteries, and even sand for cement.

Instead of the endless upward curve of the rocket theory of history based on perpetual mechanization, we have to contemplate the more familiar bell-shaped curve of nature, in which the graph goes up, then plateaus, before heading downwards again. Of course nobody can say exactly when economic growth will finally grind to a halt in the West, or whether the possible lowering of human wages and workers rights due to automation will produce new, temporary profit bonanzas. But what we do know is that there is no such thing as a one-sided mountain; everything eventually peaks. As we've seen, growth in some Western economies is already slowing to a crawl. For example, across the period 2009 to 2020 the UK experienced GDP growth of only 1.2%, a fair portion of which was due to immigration, because an expanding population inevitably increases the circulation of money and hence overall GDP (ONS, 2023). First into economic growth, Britain may also prove to be the first out.

One thing seems certain, as far as Western GDPs are concerned, "the repetition of the experience of the twentieth century is impossible for any extended period of time" (Borowy and Schmelzer, 2017:3). Far from accelerating growth into hypergrowth as the rocket theory claims, the twenty-first century and all centuries to come seem more likely to return to the no growth/low growth pattern which was the norm for all of human history before the 1700s.

The Post-Growth Future: The Duck Theory of History

The real challenge is to avoid the severity of the decline. The shape of things to come if the growth illusion prevails can be described as "up like a rocket, down like a stick". By contrast, the curve of sustainable degrowth might resemble the shape of a duck's head, in which a sharp downward decline, created by managed contraction, levels off into a beak-shaped plateau of a regenerative economy. The levelling down of Western economics will be necessary to allow the developing world to catch up, until a point of planetwide sustainability is reached. This planetwide approach is essential since GHG emissions and other forms of pollution know no national boundaries and, in any case, global economic inequality is bad for everybody on the planet.

Planetary sustainability could continue for as long as humanity lives within its ecological means or until the brightening sun finally puts an end to life on Earth many hundreds of millions years from now (Wolf and Toon, 2013). Moving towards, and maintaining, this steady state of resource use will be a balancing act, to anticipate Part VI of this book for a moment. To achieve an economic condition of degrowth which returns the planet to sustainability will require a considerable reduction in production and consumption. One way to imagine this future state would be to think about general levels of energy in Canada in the 1970s, or Spain in the1980s, but with renewable energy, smart systems, recycling and circular design plus the internet (Victor, 2012, Kallis 2018). A degrowth future will be a more technologically complex than the 1970s, because the most socially useful recent technological advances will certainly not be thrown away but it will be a very different world from one the rocket history claim is possible in which all the supposed gains of new technology can be maintained without any of ecological pain.

The duck theory of history, or living with entropy, might be seen as a pessimistic view of the future but I suggest it's based on life-orientated science – and bear in mind the theory of thermodynamics is actually a law of physics – and the precautionary, safety-first ethos of normal scientific practice. Humachination and the rocket theory of history is a safety-last approach, a recklessly high-risk gamble on the unknown. It may be true that all existing scientific laws may one day be superseded but a sensible – indeed sane – approach waits for notoriously unpredictable scientific breakthroughs to actually occur rather than assuming them in advance. A responsible risk-management approach would also respect the fact that those most vulnerable to the failures of casino capitalism tend to be those at the bottom of the social pyramid.

If the degrowth thesis is right, economic growth in the West is a phantasm, a ghost of the past, which torments us with its fleeting reappearances. Rather than pretending that the miracle of fossil fuel can be repeated end-lessly, we need to see the growth of the past three centuries as a historical freak and use managed contraction to make the most of what this one-off expansion has given us in terms of new technology, knowledge and raised human values. Living with entropy doesn't mean that we need to suffer a decline in what it is to be human. On the contrary, precautionary real-ism opens the way for human optimism. Degrowing material throughput (consumption, production and waste) can lead to growth in what matters most to most people, such as the equitability and wellbeing goals of the SEWP model that could form the basis of the Ecocene.

Blocking the way is humachine capitalism which is throwing everything it has at denying the end of growth. The exponentiality trick is used to create the fantasy of hypergrowth, accelerated productivity and material abundance through the automation of labour. Attempting to blast us out of economic stagnation, ontocapitalism is prepared to wreak creative destruc-tion on the biosphere and with it some of humanity's chances of surviving in it. It's a sign of desperation but you can't fault it for innovativeness. It certainly makes the end of capitalism that much harder to see, which is one reason why, for the time being, we continue to choose it as our preferred world system, even it portends an increasingly chaotic future.

CHAPTER 5

Technologism and Political Choice: The Prometheus Warning and the Ages of Human Technology

Technology Doesn't Determine History, People Do

The second assumption about humachination that I want to challenge relates to technologism, a set of beliefs about technology which is deeply embedded in capitalism. If growthism is at the heart of the modern capitalist worldplan, at the core of growthism is the realisation that in the developed world substantial profits can mainly be made through the introduction of new technology or from the rents which patents produce. Technology may well be capitalism's last resort. Higher productivity, the holy grail of growthist economics, increasingly means increased automation. In this sense, human-machine fusion, as part of ontocapitalism's agenda for transforming all energy and matter, is simply the logical endgame of growthism.

Technologism is more than economic expediency. It contains other assumptions which are at the forefront of the humachination project, such as the modern idea of constant human progress, which developed from the seventeenth-century concept of "improvement". This played a significant role in early capitalism, for example through the idea of improving land through agricultural techniques which was used as a justification for commons enclosure and colonialism (Dale, 2017). Technologism as an ideology – a system of ideas used by the ruling elite to manage society – also includes techno-optimism. This boosterish faith in tool-making dismisses sceptics as hapless doomsters or Luddites– standing in the way of the best of all possible worlds. Techno-optimists like Matt Ridley (2010) and Oded Galor (2022) see "innovation" as the route to nirvana but this reductionist zeal turns the human genius for making tools, one of our species' many positive capabilities, into the only one that counts. For true believers in technologism, there is also a moral imperative. This argues that humans have an ethical duty to take the development of technology as far as it can go – for example, Kurzweil (2005) argues that people are dying prematurely due to the lack of synthetic organs.

Technologism also sublimates itself into a historical phenomenon which is seen as independent of human control, a force of blind nature. In this guise, technology has superhuman agency as a force of destiny and inevitability, which it is futile to oppose. This aspect of technologism is traditionally referred to as technological determinism – the theory that history is predominantly shaped by our technology – and predates the more extreme rocket theory of history which, as we know, denigrates the significance of history before 1700. When in the mid-nineteenth century, members of the new professions of archaeology and anthropology began classifying human history, they too did so on the basis of the progress of human tool-making, implicitly defining history as the history of technology. This produced the familiar ladder of ancient history, which presents the story of humanity as a series of rungs on a never-ending ascent towards the present.

In this narrative, the controlled use of fire which began some three million years ago and the flaked flint tools of the Palaeolithic are succeeded by the invention of tools made of polished and ground stones (the Neolithic). The next use of fire was Stone Age pottery baked in kilns, which was followed by durable tools and weapons made from smelting copper, which pave the way for the superior implements of the Bronze Age, produced by melting tin and copper. These in turn were upgraded by the advances in ferrous metallurgy of the Iron Age (500 BCE to 800 CE in Northern Europe) which eventually led to the Industrial Revolution. Read like this, factories run by superintelligent robots, space-mining cyborgs and computerized brain implants may seem like the logical next chapters in the story.

Of course, tool-making is a formidable human skill and we need to make the best of this capacity rather than ignore it. But to suggest that technology makes its own choices or that our tool-making is synonymous with our destiny is quite wrong. Such technological determinism needs to be strongly challenged, which is what I want to do in this chapter by spanning the entirety of human history and examining the ages of human technology in a new light, beginning with a very ancient myth that seems to have foretold it all.

The Prometheus Warning

Writers and philosophers have been warning us about the danger of treating technology as a master rather than a servant for quite some time. Mary Shelley's *Frankenstein* gave us the quintessential cautionary tale about the dangers of experimenting with human-machine fusion, echoing Goethe's Faust who in vain sells his soul for absolute scientific knowledge and the sorcerer's apprentice whose lazy abuse of technical know-how creates a runaway nightmare. Karl Marx (1848) analysed capitalism's commodification of all human relationships, which turned the worker into "an appendage of the machine", and phenomenologist Martin Heidegger (1977) warned that the core reality of being human was being hijacked by the calculative mindset that threatens to make technology the true subject of history rather than humanity.

But the oldest warning of them all is the Prometheus myth, the story of the trickster who was severely punished by the gods for stealing fire. A fashionable modern interpretation of this story regards Prometheus as a heroic innovator of technology, a messianic saviour whom humachinators seek to emulate. But that's not how I see him, nor is it what I believe the myth originally meant. I see it as a warning against technology, a reminder that in some circumstances innovation can even be a crime against society depending on how it's used and who decides on its use. According to this view, Prometheus steals fire from the gods not primarily to help humanity but to help himself. He wants to become a god. He's a high-status titan as it is, but he wants to be more, much more, hence his desire for divinity. (Mary Shelley's subtitle for her path-breaking novel, "The modern Prometheus", implies that she took a similar view.) Furthermore, Prometheus is not just any thief; he's a trickster, a master deceiver, capable of fooling even the gods. That's why his punishment – having his liver pecked out by eagles every day, only to have it regrow overnight – is so spectacularly harsh.

The real point of the story is surely that our tools have the power to change society for good or for ill, and a society needs to think very carefully about what those changes entail. Technology always involves a political choice, which as you may recall, is my golden rule of technology, although it can also be called its secret law. To see technology as a force independent of society, which magically and inevitably guarantees human progress, is to abandon collective choice-making and risk delegating it to a self-interested minority. New technology can be an opportunity for a group or individual to further their own interests rather than those of society as a whole, even though they will have to persuade, or coerce, the majority into seeing some of the benefits that may arise from it.

So the message the real Prometheus myth sends out across the ages of human history is that society is a relationship between humans and nature, which is mediated by tools which are themselves products of nature. Fire cooks, dries, warms and wards off predators but it can also cause terrible harm to you and those you love. So watch out, the myth says, be careful about your technology choices. They are always political, whatever the silver-tongued tricksters may say. New tools can bring liberation or bondage and even the best technology can have bad social outcomes. So don't let political opportunism parade itself as technological determinism.

The Age of Origin: Hunter-Gatherers and "Eco-Equal" Demotechnics

The Prometheus myth has another important value, in my view. It invites us to take a closer look at the world system in which it almost certainly originated, the hunter-gatherer way of life that prevailed for most of the first 300,000 years of the history of Homo sapiens. This examination, I suggest, can turn upside down the conventional ladder of history on which technologism relies. It might even provide the basis for an alternative way of classifying societies, based not on their level of technology but on criteria of human development that broadly corresponds to the SEWP worldplan of sustainable, equitable, wellbeing planetwide.

The first era of human technology, the Age of Origin to give it a name, runs from the emergence of Homos sapiens some 300 millennia ago to the dawn of agriculture, an inflection point which broadly corresponds to the end of the Pleistocene epoch about 11,700 years ago and the start of the Holocene. This vast stretch of time was dominated by small, nomadic hunter-gatherer societies. These micro-nations were low on technology and productive energy but high on what I term "eco-equal" political and ecological structures, including an early form of demotechnics, which enabled decisions about technology to be made by the whole society, a process very different to the plutotechnics of modern capitalism.

The evidence for this world system is not drawn exclusively from the past. Forager societies still exist today, forming part of the Indigenous world population, which the United Nations calculates comprises of nearly 500 million people living in 90 countries and 5,000 cultures, ranging from the forests of the Amazon and Papua New Guinea to the Arctic tundra and the deserts of Africa (UNDP, 2023).

Sustainability

Nomadic, forager societies are profoundly integrated into a series of natural environments, in which they tend to live sustainably, using a self-organizing commons approach which ensures that wild resources are not depleted. For hunter-gatherers, partnership with the natural environment is everything; the idea of mastering it seems irreverent, absurd and dangerous. Indeed, Murray Bookchin (1982) may be right to claim that the idea of the domination of nature by humans only comes into existence with the domination of humans by humans.

Being part of the natural world is a spiritual reality, emphasized by elaborate rituals, ceremonies, myths and narratives, which stress unity with nature not division. For indigenous societies which practise animism, equality with nature is assumed and plants and animals are considered to be humans taking on a different physical appearance. As such, all living things deserve the same degree of fear, love, curiosity, tenderness and suspicion as fellow humans (Descola, 2013). Practically, this environmental connectedness leads to an encyclopaedic knowledge of flora, fauna and fungi as well as local geography and primordial astronomy – all of which suggest an integrated "knowledge-based economy" dedicated to balancing humanity and nature (Gowdy, 2011). This original science contributes to an intimate and intense engagement with the natural environment that's almost unimaginable for modern city-dwellers and explains why indigenous nations today are responsible for protecting 80% of the world's remaining biodiversity (UNDP, 2023).

Equitability

At the core of the forager world system is egalitarian decision-making, which according to Christopher Boehm's (1999:65) extensive review, is primarily "guided by a love of personal freedom" and a determination not to be subject to the domination of others. As David Graeber and David Wengrow (2021:86) emphasize, primal societies are the product of deliberate political choices, expressions of the truth that "the very essence of our humanity consists of the fact that we are self-conscious political actors". Of course, hunter-gatherers share the anatomically modern human brain and cognitive capacities which have enabled our species to survive until today. These include cooperative communication skills, including spoken language (which may have developed some 200,000 years ago), common sense, decision-making and the expertise in navigation that allowed early humans to colonize the entire planet.

Forager society is intensely choice-focused: one wrong judgment gathering fungi in the forest can lead to a whole family being poisoned; one bad decision on a hunting trip can be fatal. Group decisions are also crucial, for example the timing of migration to a summer or winter camp, with consensus often the preferred means of achieving group agreement. Gender equality seems to have been the norm in the hunter-gatherer system, in part because it fostered wider, more cooperative social networks than male-dominated societies, (Dyble et al, 2015). Men and women were highly skilled in political decision-making, despite their lack of literacy, and perhaps more comfortable with difficult, risky, practical choice-making than many of us are today. Traditionally, a gendered division of labour has been attributed to these economies, with women and girls mainly responsible for foraging and men and boys for hunting, although this has been challenged by recent archaeological findings in the Andean highlands indicating that hunter-gatherer females were also involved in big-game hunting (Haas et al, 2020).

Collective decision-making implies demotechnics, or democratic policy-making in relation to new technologies. We shouldn't assume that hunter-gatherers failed to adopt new techniques such as agriculture due to ignorance rather than as a conscious preference for their existing lifestyle. This is shown by the fact that some contemporary forager societies have maintained their cultural identity, rejecting agricultural and urban modernity, even though they may have lived alongside farmers for many centuries (Lee, 1992). Hunter-gatherer tools may be rudimentary but they are used with extraordinary skill and are based on the rule of usufruct, which means that anybody can use them but nobody can own them out-right or dispose of them – the latter property rights had to wait for the arrival of Roman law (Bookchin, 1982). Primal demotechnics also relies on equality of information and rejects the secrecy that creates a division between those in the know and those who are in the dark. Openness is a political necessity because hidden alliances and unresolved conflicts can cause the egalitarian social fabric to unravel. All this represents what we migh call "human technology", the kind of tools you carry in your head and heart, which amounts to expertise in the art of living.

Private property rarely exists in forager societies, although this is not a rigid prohibition. Hunter-gatherer societies have a unique operating prin-ciple, as anthropologist Richard Lee (1992:39) explains:

> Such societies operate within the confines of a metaphorical ceiling and floor: a ceiling above which one may not accumulate wealth and power and a floor below which one may not sink.

Some micro-nations have no form of economic surplus at all; in these "assertively egalitarian" societies, food is consumed immediately, while others may have small surpluses, storing food for short periods (Woodburn, 1982) or give away surpluses in "depense" ceremonies involving lavish feasting or through gambling (e.g. the New Guinea Wape) which prevents wealth-hoarding by individuals or small groups.

This egalitarian balancing act makes permanent hierarchical stratification impossible. Bottom-up self-organization means that there are no perma-nent leaders to exercise authority, although an elder or wise individual (known as "he who thinks" among the Iglulik Intuit) may have some influence (Weyer, 1967:11). In a war situation the group may nominate a single military leader and some societies, such as the Nimbikwara of Brazil, chose to vary between egalitarian and authoritarian leadership on a seasonal basis (Levi- Strauss, 1967). The norm is expressed by a member of the egalitarian !Kung, one of the San peoples living in Southern Africa: "Of course we have headmen...each one of us is a headman over himself" (Lee, 1979:457).

In a non-stratified, eco-equal society, the upstart, who threatens to take more than his fair share of power, is a perpetual danger which the whole society must be vigilant in preventing. One lapse in judgement by the group here could turn out to be fatal. Potential usurpers will be constantly teased, overtly criticized, reprimanded and eventually banished; unreformable psychopaths may even be assassinated. This it seems to me is the core purpose of the original Prometheus myth: to warn against a potential coup d'etat by a headstrong, power-greedy individualist. In this sense, it's a warning that abandoning demotechnics will lead to social stratification, a prophecy that eventually came true for most human societies.

Wellbeing

Hunter-gatherers also live in societies of care, in which reciprocal obligation and mutual aid are assumed. This is the biggest challenge to the Hobbesian myth that pre-modern society is a war of all against all in which life is "nasty, brutish and short". In fact, cooperation rather than competitition shapes the forager world system (Rogers, 2012) and, according to an extensive literature review, the average hunter-gatherer lifespan is actually 68-78 years (Gurven and Kaplan, 2007, McCauley 2018). Parenting styles are relaxed and children are educated in vital subsistence skills primarily through play. !Kung infants receive their mother's "exclusive attention" for almost four years, since nomadic women have significantly longer intervals between children than their sedentary counterparts (Lee, 1979: 321-30). As Carol Ember (2020:6) notes, "hunter-gatherer children appear to receive more warmth and affection from parents" than in food-producing societies. Older people are respected, regardless off their social contribution. "Elders do not have to negotiate care, as if it were a favor: rather it is perceived of as an unquestioned right." (Rosenberg, 2020:15).

Hoarding of personal possessions is frowned on, generosity in gift-giving is expected and sharing is the norm. Money, in the modern sense, is generally absent and profit-making an incomprehensible goal. Instead this is a needs-based society predicated on satisfying every member's basic needs for food, shelter, health, education and social support. The idea of society in which some have much more than they need, while others have less than it takes to survive, is repellent.

Skilled subsistence work means that the essentials of life can be achieved economically. For example, the "working week" of the !Kung averages about 17 hours (Lee, 1979: 455). This is another blow for technological determinists who claims that the lifestyle of pre-modern societies was dismal and animalistic (for instance, techno-utopian economist Oded Galor compares it to the life of a squirrel, "defined by the pursuit of survival and reproduction" (2022:1)). On the contrary, as anthropologist Marshall Sahlins (1972) realised, hunter-gathers could be regarded as "the original affluent society", in part because they enjoy the ultimate luxury, time. In this wellbeing society, there is ample time for the things that matters most to humans (modern and pre-modern), such as spending time with children and friends and family and engaging in sports and games of every kind, all of which are harshly rationed in over-worked, time–poor modernity. This high degree of life satisfaction should not be seen as a happy accident but as a primary reason why foragers choose their eco-equal world system.

The Planetwide Dimension

Finally, what about the external relations between hunter-gatherer societies – their foreign policy, in modern parlance? Inter-society conflict is certainly not unknown but it's not systemic and often can be more ritualistic than real (Rogers, 2012). Federal alliances sometimes bring micro-societies into closer union, perhaps the most famous being the democratic Haudenosaunee confederacy of the Iroquois in eighteenth century America. More surprisingly, there is now evidence that protocols existed throughout North America and Australia, which ensured that clan members were hosted by other societies thousands of miles away, even though they spoke different languages. This suggests a genuine and admirable freedom of movement across vast continents which today are latticed by national borders, a proto- internationalism which existed many millennia before nation states (Graeber and Wengrow, 2021). It may even confirm the dominant role of altruism in the Age of Origin, our unique species capacity for kindness to strangers, something also testified to by the paramount importance of selfless hospitality among many indigenous nations, such as the Dakota of the Great Plains (Mirsky, 1937). This focus on external equalism resembles the planetwide dimension of the SEWP model.

To sum up, the reality of the forager world system turns the case for technological determinism on its head. It also seriously questions Jean Jacques

Rousseau's extraordinarily influential myth of pre-modern societies living in child-like innocence which has been lost forever and the Hobbes's' "state of nature" hypothesis, which asserts that humans are so "naturally" competitive that without top-down government they will destroy themselves. This neo-Hobbesian approach also expresses itself in the claim that social groups of more than a few hundred people are too intrinsically complex to be organized without an elite-run, "centralized authority to monopolize force and resolve conflicts" (Diamond, 1997:311). This ignores many examples of large-scale social organizations, which use consensus-based and other democratic forms of decision-making (Harvey, 2019). It also ignores the unique balancing act of the hunter-gather society, which is "to reproduce themselves while severely limiting the accumulation and concentration of wealth and power" (Lee, 1992). For some who know them well, first nations suggest that practical utopianism can exist as "a truly communal life" and "a sharing way of life", a different form of sociality that has survived in countless instantiations across many millennia (Lee, 1979:461) Indeed, despite their levels of technology, hunter-gatherers can give us a tantalizing glimpse of a lifestyle that incorporates some of the best of being human, which may just turn out to be a key to our future.

The Pyramid Pattern of Civilization: Technological Progress, Social Regression

A second reason for doubting the validity of technological determinism is what happened after the forager worldplan ceased to be the norm for humanity. In what we conventionally term civilization, technology may have progressed but for the majority equitability, wellbeing and inter-society relations regressed. Agriculture, of course, was the key innovation, as 10,000-12000 years ago the cultivation of wild cereals began to develop independently in China, the Greater Levant and other regions of the world (Brooke, 2014). The storehouse full of grain which agriculture can now provide means the end of nomadic precariousness and the beginnings of settled, stable village life. For the first time, food production provides humans with a significant economic surplus over and above the necessities of life. The downside is that this surplus can now be captured by new chieftains and tribal elites. This signals the end of egalitarian living, as over time the majority are condemned to often back-breaking work in the fields with dire consequences for their wellbeing. The Agricultural Age has many diverse social formations, some of which are relatively equitable, some quite possibly matrilineal or matriarchal, but it's dominated by the gradual transformation of foragers, who once chose everything about their lives, into full-time food producers beholden to others (Scott, 2017). Small wonder that Jared Diamond (1987) calls this long transition "the worst mistake in the history of the human race".

This swapping of freedom for the promise of greater security leads to the beginnings of city state civilization in Mesopotamia and Egypt around 3700 BCE. The attraction of settlements which have grown into cities is that their engineering and military technology offers a defence against increasingly destructive raiders (and at times equally violent climate change). The disadvantage of this bargain for most inhabitants is the complete loss of the freedoms and rights of egalitarian life. Females cease to be citizens of this society and are reduced to a subordinate status in a patriarchal system, which reaches its apogee in classical antiquity (Saini, 2023). "Domination begins at home," write Graeber and Wengrow 2021:207), reflecting on the fact that "domination" has its roots in the Latin word "domes". In fact, it's not until the twentieth century that women and girls regain the degree of equitability that was more or less the norm of the hunter-gatherer system. (This explains Friedrich Engels's (1884/1946:125) description of the advent of farming and the private property rights that he assumed accompanied it, as "the world-historical defeat of the female sex", although it's probably not until the arrival of the state that patriarchy fully takes hold.) And it's not just women: war captives and others are now deprived of all legal rights and form a class of enslaved people, working alongside peasants labouring in the fields. Humans themselves are becoming tools, instruments of the will of others.

A great pyramid society now emerges – literally in Egypt where the extraordinary edifices which rise up in the desert from about 2700 BCE testify to the new power of Promethean technology. This towering symbol of city state civilisation, the tallest in the world for thousands of years, is a testament to the new technology of so-called simple machines like the lever or inclined plane (the wheel is still to come) and new, more "efficient" ways of organizing human labour. The pyramid also bears witness to a society which is prepared to devote a huge proportion of its resources to the glory – albeit posthumous – of just one individual, the pharaoh at the pinnacle of society who is now endowed with semi-divine status. Starkly outlined against the seemingly infinite sands of the Sahara, the pyramids are the clearest possible sign that plutotechnics has replaced demotechnics, with all decisions about new technology now being made by a tiny social elite. Although exchange through foreign trade is growing, most of these decisions are still aimed at grabbing economic surpluses from other elites through constant warfare and empire-expansion and to constructing monumental temples, highways and mansions that maintain the status quo.

In this new Pyramid Age, hierarchy now represents the dominant principle of social organization. For the first time in history, society is rigidly stratified from peak to base below an all-powerful ruler. The nobility, warriors, priests, bureaucrats, merchants, peasants, slaves all have radically different levels of rights, obligations and benefits. The social pyramid is held in place by the distribution of most of the economic surplus created by the bottom of the hierarchy towards the top, an extension of the gravity-defying economics initiated by the Agricultural Revolution. This ensures that the elite enjoy luxury, while the middling classes receive just enough to prevent the social structure from toppling over. The Pyramid Pattern of society is not just external; it's mentally internalized into a new hierarchy of identity defining groups and castes, so that people begin to see each other as innately unequal, occupying different categories of being human. Born unequal, the chains of class, patriarchy and racial hierarchy now largely determine a person's life opportunities rather than their own free choices. The logic of divide and rule helps to keep everyone in their place.

From the technological point of view, there are gains from sedentary city-based life to partially compensate for the loss of the forager wellbeing society. There may be more food security, better housing and transport and superior household goods, as well as writing and reading for the elite – all the items recorded in the usual ladder of history account of humanity, as copper gives way to bronze and iron to steel. But even this can be misleading since city life is now subject to regular famines, deadly diseases resulting from the domestication of animals, and the constant threat of war among competing empires. Some people may have gone up the ladder of technology but the majority are stuck on the lowest rung. The legacy of social stratification which urban civilization brings – the kyriarchy of complex intersectional systems of submission and domination encompassing gender, ethnicity, class, occupation and physical ability- is still with us today.

Technological Determinism or Elitist Political Opportunism? A Promethean Flight of Fancy

A third reason for rejecting the idea that technology itself determines the course of history is the role of political choice implicit in the transformation of society after the agricultural revolution. It's true that political decision-making shifts dramatically from the consensus-based democracy of the Age of Origin to the top-down, plutotechnical policy-making of the Pyramid Age, but it still involves humans making value-based decisions rather than an impersonal march of superior technologies. In fact, throughout history, new tools can still be rejected if the elite so wishes. For instance, from the ninth century successive Chinese emperors proscribed the use of gunpowder for anything other than recreational purposes, because they feared the destabilizing effects it would have on society. This was in sharp contrast to rivalrous European nobles who later chose to turn gunpowder into a devastatingly potent technology of war (Lent, 2017). Another well-known example of technological renunciation is the banning of all ocean-going ships in the Ming dynasty, when the Chinese fleet numbered 3,500 vessels, ten times the size of the modern US Navy. This decision, which protected the imperial class against the rising power of maritime traders, also ensured that it would not be China which colonized the New World (Harari, 2014).

Less well known is the revelation by Andreas Malm (2016) that the British Industrial Revolution might have been achieved by means of renewable energy rather than fossil fuel. In fact until 1820 wind and water power dominated the mechanization of the textile industry but factory owners increasingly decided to invest in steam power because its portability provided access to cheap, pliable labour in cities and this considerably increased the profitability of their enterprises. Steam power also meant that capitalists could avoid the close collaboration with rival entrepreneurs that a common natural resource like water demands, which went against their highly competitive and individualistic values. This seems to confirm that what is described as technological determinism is often nothing else but the process of elites pursuing their own interests and values.

One – perhaps whimsical –way of presenting this political opportunism would be to return to the Prometheus warning and launch the fire-stealing trickster on an imaginary whirlwind journey through the ages of technology. Imagine that after a long period of feigned good behaviour Prometheus finally breaks free of the egalitarian forager system, with another trick even more momentous than fire, the technique of cultivating wild cereals which he steals from the female horticulturalists who almost certainly discovered it. (Sowing division would soon become a Promethean speciality!) The ensuing economic and social transformation elevates him to the status of chieftain, enabling him and his clan to live a luxury lifestyle and engage in high-profile warfare with other chieftains. In the Pyramid Age, urban splendour offers Prometheus new self-aggrandising opportunities, as he tricks the majority into sacrificing the remnants of their freedom for putative stability, and raises himself into a pharaoh or an emperor, treated with god-like reverence (divinity after all was always his goal).

Move the story on several millennia and we find Prometheus at the end of the fifteenth century, turning his attention to the economic backwater of Western Europe. In the Colonial Age, he becomes an explorer, conquistador and slaver, adding to the technological benefits of manoeuvrable ships and steel weaponry a pitiless readiness to exploit other human beings that was a crucial competitive advantage for the Old World. His inadvertent ruse of infecting the indigenous population of the Americas with deadly zoonotic diseases to which Europeans were immune, delivered the coup de grace (Diamond, 1997).

The prodigious accumulation of gold, silver and agricultural "ghost acres" of the Colonial Age helps provide the capital for the revolution that launches Prometheus on his next conquest. For the first time he can lay aside his military paraphernalia and as a top-hatted, frock-coated industrialist, engage in an unbridled lust for power, with an economic surplus that now seems unlimited and vast overseas empires simply there for the taking.

In the twentieth century Prometheus becomes a fossil fuel magnate, a mighty car maker and mass retailer and performs the ultimate fire trick by splitting the atom, all the time pushing the planet towards breaking point in the Age of Acceleration.

And so we arrive in the Humachine Age, which Prometheus initiates with a multitude of ploys – the Google mirror trick being just one of many, as he pursues the limitless Law of More. He now seeks to transform machines into humans and humans into machines, trying to take charge of the multi-billion-year evolution of life on Earth and finally becoming the immortal God of the cosmos, which he has always seen as his destiny.

This rendition of history may seem fanciful, but if Sahlins (2008:86) is right and it's not until the twentieth century that self-interest becomes a common trait, it gives us real insight into the part played in civilization by the individuals who were the earliest adopters of this anti-social tendency. Aggressive self-interest fundamentally destabilizes cooperative society, pushing some members to abandon it and others to react by adopting similarly domineering, competitive attitudes; this, according to one theory, is how egalitarian societies are destroyed (Rogers et al, 2012). In this light, the idea of technological determinism is simply a cover for the fact that technological choices which have shaped the course of the past ten millennia have been made by elites motivated by what benefits them most rather than any inherent advantages of the technology itself. This political opportunism is simply a restatement of the golden rule of technology and it inevitably raises a question, which is central to this book, how can we trust today's plutotechnic Prometheans to have the interest of the majority at heart any more than previous elites? We might think we're too informed and enlightened not to see through their brilliant trickery but such complacency could be our downfall.

The ultimate danger is that humachine capitalism fails in its techno-utopian mission and collapses into a distinctly dystopian low- or no-growth economy and reverts to the steepest Pyramid Pattern of civilization. This time, however, hierarchy is sustained by advanced digital-robotic systems, capable of almost unlimited coercion and deception, in a world ravaged by uncontrollable climate extremes. In short, the end of growth capitalism does not necessarily signify the end of oppressive hierarchy; on the contrary, it could herald a new, even more extreme age of social division. And if economic growth turns out to be a freak of history will the advanced social development, equality rights and wellbeing practices which it has produced disappear along with it? This is one of the darkest pits of the Technocene future, which a blind faith in technology could slide us into.

Conclusion

To sum up, we need to be intensely wary of the assumption that history is a technological conveyer belt which will take us to the Promised Land as long as we don't interfere with those in charge of it. We should challenge the absurd idea that technology has been doggedly re-inventing itself for thousands of years until reaching the point at which Homo sapiens has no choice but to merge with it. The majority would do well to constantly pose the question that the elite always ask: what's in it for us? We may draw some inspiration from the eco-equal societies which dominated the first 96% of human history when free, personal choices were a daily reality and majority decision-making the norm. This can help to make the tough choices which lead us towards a sustainable, democratic version of the Anthropocene, in which the social technology of freedom once again becomes our most valuable tool. Navigating the long road to the Ecocene will require many other myths, delusions and misdirecting ideologies to be cleared out of the way. So let's turn to the next of these, the model of modern science which shores up the age of humachines.

CHAPTER 6

Neomechanicalism and Science: Biology Fights Back

What are the historical origins of ultrascience's goal of taking technology as far as it can possibly go, regardless of the consequences? Where does the bizarre idea that machines are superior to organic life come from? And how on earth did we arrive at a worldplan focused on "transcending biology" and re-engineering the evolution of life, even if this risks terminating Homo sapiens? These are some of the questions that I want to delve into in this chapter, as we look at the assumptions relating to modern science which underpin human-machine fusion.

Part of the answer lies in the obsession with innovation which dominates the institutions of science today. Today the stepping stones of a career in science, from finding a PhD place to obtaining a research grant or an academic promotion, mainly depend on breaking new ground rather than cultivating established territory. Even in the early twentieth-century, as Thomas Kuhn (1970) showed, the career choices of junior physicists played a major role in the adoption of Einstein's revolutionary theories. Now in a "mega-global" community of nine million full-time scientists, with China alone producing almost five million STEM graduates a year, the competition for scientific breakthroughs is fiercer than ever before (McCarthy, 2017, McClellan and Dorn, 2015). In 1900 about 10,000 articles were published in scientific journals; in 2011 the annual number passed the million mark and it has doubled since then (Powell et al, 2017:3-4). About 90% of all the scientists who have ever lived are alive today; arguably, almost all science risks becoming ultrascience.

But in the humachine age, as we've seen, something else is occurring, a forceful attempt by physics-based science to claim precedence over all other forms of knowledge. On this view, physics is the king of science, mathematics the queen, and engineering is a lordly head of operations, a triumvirate that can be relied upon to lead us into the future. This neo-mechanicalist view of science, as I propose to call it, sees itself as the winner in the crucial battle of the sciences which is being played out in the humachine age. Neomechanicalism is supremely confident of its ability to turn all the forces of nature into tools that can be used to human advantage. In the past technology and science were quite distinct fields, and up the twentieth century most commercial innovators had no formal education in science. But today almost all the ontopreneurs of humachnation are scientifically trained, mostly in physics or computer science, and many are bent on transforming their theoretical dreams into empirical reality.

On the other side of the battlefield of knowledge are the biology-based life sciences, including the disciplines of ecology and climatology that the economists of humachination prefer to marginalize. Biological science tends to focus on understanding nature as it is, rather than for what it could be, patiently studying its mysterious and seemingly infinite complexity. This study reveals the delicate systems which produce life, which turn out to be far more interconnected, innovative and precarious than previously thought. Such a respectful, patient, holistic approach to science contrasts with the often reductionist and one-sided view of reality of the neomechanicalists, which can be dogmatically scientistic and obsessed with measurement and control.

Systems-based life science sees life as a multi-billion-year, self-organizing search for value rather than as a poor substitute for the machine as the fundamental organizing principle of reality. And, as the following brief history of modern science will attempt to elucidate, there is a twist in the tale. The claims of humachinators to be at the vanguard of scientific progress turn out to be highly flawed. A truly progressive, integrated view of science works with biology rather than against it. This is the view of physicist-turned- ecologist Fritjof Capra, who has developed the theories of biologists and phenomenologists Humberto Maturana and Francisco Varela (1987), whom I take as my main guides on this short journey through scientific history. As Capra insists, it's life that is at the heart of scientific progress not the machine.

A Brief History of Mechanicalist Science

Whatever its status today, the tendency to value machines as an organizing principle of reality was indisputably a progressive idea once. In fact, the entire Western science revolution of the seventeenth century was predicated on the view that nature could be accurately described in terms of human-made tools. The mechanical clock in particular had a transformative effect on the imagination of the early European scientific elite.

The astronomer Johannes Kepler was typical of the scientists of his day in his view that the intricate engineering of a timepiece revealed the way in which the entire universe is constructed. "My aim is to show that the celestial machine is not to be likened to a divine organism but to a clockwork", he wrote in 1605 (cited in Lent, 2017: 282). The village bell tower which started to ring out the hours across Europe not only mechanized experiential and seasonal time, it helped to conjure up a new vision of nature as something external to humanity, which could be manipulated through rational cogitation and empirical experimentation. Even the Christian God was reimagined as a great watchmaker or "artificer". Robert Boyle of the Royal Society wrote that "The world is like a rare clock", an "engine which once being set going" required no intervention from the divine artificer (cited in Merchant, 1980:226).

Francis Bacon framed the mission of science in more anthropocentric terms, as a process of conquering, moulding, forcing, dissecting (and perhaps even "torturing") nature in order to "improve" humanity's lot and ensure that "human knowledge and human power meet as one" (cited in Merchant, 1980:169-172). In effect, Bacon declared a war against nature, which was consistently depicted as feminine, summoning humanity to "storm and occupy her castles and strongholds and extend the bounds of human empire" (cited in Lent 2017: 278). "What human beings seek to learn from nature is how to use it to dominate wholly both it and human beings" was Max Horkheimer and Theodor Adorno's gloss on this scientific strategy (1947/2002:2).

Bacon can also lay claim to the first fictional techno-utopia, *New Atlantis* (1627), which depicts Salomon's House, an imaginary scientific elite who represent the first stirrings of ultrascience. Among their many ambitious projects are: "the prolongation of life," "the making of new species", the "raising of tempests", the "increasing and exalting of the intellectual parts" and the provision of "greater pleasure of the senses" (Bacon, 1627/1999:185-6). Although some of this uncannily foreshadows the humachine age, it's worth stressing that Bacon envisages some elements of demotechnics in the experimental cycle, in the form of "consultations, which of the inventions and experiences which we have discovered shall be published" (p.184). There is no question of market input. Indeed, scientists would remain aloof from commerce for the next three centuries. They were typically upper-class men of independent means who looked down on "trade" and were quite distinct from the practical innovators of the industrial revolution, as Lewis Mumford (1934) observed. The melding of science and capitalism is largely a twentieth-century phenomenon.

Even so, it was surely no coincidence that this new quest for knowledge emerged during an aggressive era of colonization, which reduced the societies of the New World into lands to be economically exploited, resources to be extracted and populations to be enslaved in preparation for full-scale industrial organization (Stannard, 1992). As Western European countries with Atlantic seaboards overturned the logic of population size and became world dominators, so the idea of the domination of nature by humanity emerged as a new, conceptual Pyramid Pattern.

Newton's revolutionary physics seemed to confirm the clock-like structure of matter as a set of irreducible atoms mechanically interacting with one another, according to predictable laws of motion. The discourse of mathematics was apparently able to decode these mechanisms, with Newton using differential calculus to confirm Kepler's empirical observations. For Galileo, this meant that only the strictly measurable was worthy of inclusion in the realm of science. This depiction of the universe as atomized billiard balls strengthened a growing post-Reformation sense of society not as a collective whole but as an aggregation of individuals pursuing their own interests. New accountancy methods developed by mercantile capitalism further reinforced this quantitative individualism, while new agricultural methods for "land improvement" appeared to justify European colonialist expansion (Dale, 2017).

Crucially, this machine-inspired worldview also involved a revolutionary concept of the human body and brain as essentially mechanical entities. For Rene Descartes (who was personally obsessed with automata) everything in human anatomy apart from the mind, or self-reflective consciousness, was machine-like, including the memory and emotions:

> I should like you to consider that these functions (including passion, memory, and imagination) follow from the mere arrangement of the machine's organs every bit as naturally as the movements of a clock or other automaton follow from the arrangement of its counter-weights and wheels (Descartes, 1664/1972: 108).

As for animals, Descartes considered them as wholly mechanical, "soulless" entities.

Thomas Hobbes stretched the theory even further. "For what is the Heart but a Spring; and the Nerves but so many Strings; and the Joynts but so many Wheeles…?" he asks in the opening paragraph of *Leviathan* (1651/1968:85). He eliminated the Cartesian ghost of consciousness from the human machine altogether, comparing reason to a kind of accounting system:

> For Reason, in this sense, is nothing but Reckoning (that is adding and subtracting) of the Consequences of generall names agreed upon, for the marking and signifying of our thoughts (p111).

This calculating system, which clearly anticipates the humachine belief that the brain is a computer, has a major role to play in regulating the self-interested "passions" in Hobbes's psychological version of the laws of motion. He sees these drives as the motivating force behind all behaviour, most notably, "a perpetual and restless desire of Power after power, that ceaseth only in death" (p161).

Politically Hobbes's conclusion was that these dynamic desires, if left to their own devices, would result in a hyper-competitive "bellum omnium contra omnes", a state of chaos which could only be mitigated by the uncompromising, top-down authority of a Leviathan. As already observed, this essentialist "state of nature" model of humanity, which is so opposed to the actual cooperativism that marks the Age of Origin, is one of the greatest justifications of the modern state and tends to links mechanicalism with a conservative, hierarchical view of the world.

The Organicist Alternative

This new philosophy of machine supremacism pitched itself against a profound respect for nature, which goes back to the dawn of humanity. Compare Hobbes's terror of people being left to organize themselves with the views of Gerard Winstanley, also writing in the 1650s, during one of modern Europe's greatest outbreaks of democratic and egalitarian thinking. In the *Law of Freedom* and other works he articulates a compelling, non-mechanical vision of nature and humanity, which defines humans as essentially benign and cooperative, unless coerced into competitiveness by the unjust, rapacious land-grabbing of the governing elite (Winstanley, 1973). Incidentally, Winstanley also saw humans as predominantly convivial, as opposed to Hobbes who believed that people only come together socially in order to engage in one-upmanship ("men have no pleasure in keeping company, where there is no power to over-awe them all"), a curmudgeonly, if not overtly misanthropic, view of human sociability (p185).

The organicist, integrative view of nature and humanity which forms a part of the hunter-gatherer world system is found among the cultures of many Indigenous peoples. The concept of nature as Mother Earth, which is very different from the patriarchal hammer of reason represented by Baconian and Newtonian science, is still found today among many cultures, from the Aboriginal peoples of Australia to the highlanders of the Peruvian Andes. In this worldplan humans are inextricably part of nature rather than the commanders of it. As Chief Seattle of the Squamish tribe said to the US President in 1851, in protest at the settlement of his native lands:

> The earth does not belong to man, man belongs to the earth. Man does not weave the web of life, he is merely a strand in it. Whatever he does to the web, he does to himself (quoted in Ponting, 2007:128).

This integration of humanity and nature also lies behind Chinese science, which for most of the two millennia up to the Industrial Revolution was the most advanced in the world (Needham, 1956). Chinese thinkers were singularly unimpressed by the mechanical clock, having invented a version of it in 952, several centuries before Western Europe. As Jeremy Lent beautifully illustrates in *The Patterning Instinct*, the Chinese concept of the unified relationship between humanity and nature, is deeply rooted in its politics, philosophy and spirituality. For Buddhists the doctrine of dharma represents "the indivisible integrity and harmony in the universe, in which all parts are interdependent" (Lent, 2017:253). For Taoists it was the Way, the Supreme Ultimate, made up of the dialectic of yin and yang opposites like negative and positive or male and female, which governs the dynamic whole. And, in the Neo-Confucian philosophy which dominated the Chinese empire from the early Song dynasty, nature is composed of two forces: the qi which represents energy or matter and li, the unique, holistic pattern which is present in every living thing as its principle of being.

In Western Europe, this vibrant sense of organicist wholeness was kept alive in the eighteenth century by the Romantic Movement in literature and science (Goethe united both), using organicism to critique the reductionist and segregated approach which was increasingly dominating science and society. William Blake sums up a world under the thrall of "the mind-forged manacles" of mechanicalist culture and machine-worshipping industrialism:

> I turn my eye to the Schools and Universities of Europe
> And there behold the Loom of Locke whose Woof rages dire
> Washd by the Water-wheels of Newton, black the cloth
> In heavy wreathes fold over every Nation; cruel Works
> Of many Wheels I view, wheel within wheel, with cogs tyrannic
> Moving by compulsion each other: not as those in Eden: which
> Wheel within Wheel in freedom resolve in harmony and peace.
>   (*Jerusalem*, Plate 15/ Blake, 1997:662)

From the early nineteenth century "the cogs tryannic" began to be challenged more and more, as the fortress of Newtonian physics was breached by the new life sciences. Geology and biology replaced the essentially static idea of the universe as an unchanging mechanical system started up by a divine engineer a few thousand years previously. Deep history, species diversity and adaptive change entered the picture with Darwin's theory of evolution, eventually revealing a multi-billion year history of natural selection that made human development possible.

In the early twentieth century, the mechanistic, physics-dominated, clock-work model of the universe, which science historians McLennan and Dorn (2015) term "the classical synthesis", finally collapsed, as physics itself broke free from Newton mechanics. Einstein's theory of relativity showed the non-linear complexity of gravity and time, while quantum theory revealed the atom not as a fixed, solid billiard ball but as a mysterious, dynamic environment in itself, composed of some 200 smaller entities, such as electrons, protons and quarks. They occupy a reality in which total objectivity is impractical and measurement deeply problematic, due to the impossibility of fully separating the observer from the observed. A subatomic particle can behave as a wave or particle depending on its environment. It's as though the mechanical clock had suddenly become a living thing. From now on, judgments about the subatomic world are governed by indeterminacy rather than the absolute certainties of mechanicalist science.

In the second half of the twentieth century, non-linear maths deepened our understanding of the complexity of reality, giving more precise expression to notions of chaos and the beauty of fractal formations. (A maths capable of describing cloud formations can only do so by functioning qualitatively). Initially, breakthroughs in genetics in the 1950s which led to the unravelling of the human genome seemed to confirm that a gene is comparable to the pre-quantum idea of an atom and as such can be manipulated like a computer programme. For example, leading ethnologist and proponent of "the selfish gene" theory, Richard Dawkins (1995:8) has written that animals are just like machines and that

> Life is just bytes and bytes and bytes of digital information. Genes are pure information that can be encoded, recoded and decoded without any degradation or change of meaning.

Today, the idea that the genome is an instruction manual for building humans is steadily being debunked. Modern molecular biology is now moving towards the picture of the cell as a world in itself, a highly sensitive environment, selecting proteins according to many specific influences including possible social pressures (Capra and Luisi, 2014). Far from being an irreducible unit like an atom was once thought to be, the cell is now seen as part of a dynamic, variable network. In *The Music of Life* (2006) biologist Denis Noble argues that the web of life in all its flowing interactions is more like a musical composition than a computer programme. Biologist and ecologist Andreas Weber (2016:57) takes things a step further, suggesting that "Every cell decides and chooses ... in a way that can become rather independent of genetic instructions."

The upshot is that twenty-first century science seems to bear a closer relationship to the organicist view of nature than the mechanistic. Life is seen not as sets of invariable components moving in fixed patterns but as interactional networks of relationships which are themselves networks. As Fritjof Capra puts it, "All living things are members of ecological communities bound together in a network of interdependencies" (1996:11)

These lattices of relationships are not random; they follow patterns and organizational principles, through which the process of life manifests itself. The mind itself is seen as a process, expressing itself through the structure of the brain and body in a social and physical environment. In this sense cognition is synonymous with action and knowing is doing. Capra suggests that the main "pattern of life ... is a network pattern capable of self-organization", and calls self-organization "the central component of the systems view of life" (pp 81-82). This view stems from the biological phenomenology of Maturana and Varela, which states that life is a process of self-creation. At its core is "autopoesis", the extraordinary mechanism which "makes living things autonomous systems" capable of specifying their own laws (1987:48). For instance, the structure of the human body constantly reproduces itself, replacing most of the cells in our stomach every three days, our white blood cells every ten days, 98% of the protein in our brain every month and our skin cells at a rate of 100,000 a minute. Yet the pattern that is an individual remains from earliest infancy throughout adulthood. In death what is destroyed is the organizing pattern; the components remain (Capra 1996: 91)

This doesn't mean that evolution is planned. We don't have eyesight because humans need to see but because human vision has evolved in this way through countless chance mutations, probably from a light-sensitive cell which existed billions of years ago. Indeed, if you had designed it from scratch you wouldn't have come up with such an ungainly, back-to-front system. As Lucretius put it almost two millennia ago, "What happens to exist is the cause of its use", (quoted in Capra and Luisi, 2014:209). Life on earth evolved three and a half billion years ago and for two billion years consisted of micro-organisms, before plants and animals evolved about a billion years ago. We have not left these micro-organisms behind, they are still what makes life possible; "we are both surrounded by them and composed of them", writes biologist Lynn Margulis (Margulis and Sagan, 1986:21). Although 99% of all species that have ever existed are extinct,

Margulis stresses that life is still part of a " self-organizing web of bacteria, involving elaborate networks of sensory and control systems", embedded in the soils, rock, the sea and as well as all plants animal and humans (Margulis and Sagan, 1986:271). It's these bacteria which continue to regulate life on Earth

This exciting and inspiring modern vision of life, which deeply connects us to the remote past, also represents a revolutionary turn, as Capra (1996:13) himself an accomplished physicist, emphasizes: "Today the paradigm in science at its deepest level implies a shift from physics to the life sciences". This transition involves moving from what is quantitative to an appreciation of the qualitative, towards the integration of all life, which incorporates the achievements of the mechanical revolution but which in some ways recalls the traditional view of nature as a mysterious but intuitively-felt unity.

Indeed, some biologists anticipate a merger with Romantic views of science, forming "a poetic ecology" which regards feeling as central to the non-human world, rejecting the division between subjectivity and objectivity (Weber, 2016). It also involves what many appreciate as a new spiritual dimension, connected to Buddhism and Taoism, for example, or a new form of deeper consciousness which involves wonder at the world, and a humble sense of gratitude at being part of this life. This is quite different to the humachinators' arrogant obsession with dominating nature and re-engineering all living things out of existence as quickly as possible:

> Instead of being a machine, nature at large turns out to be more like human nature – unpredictable, sensitive to the surrounding world, influenced by small fluctuations. Accordingly the appropriate way of approaching nature to learn about her complexity and beauty is not through domination and control but through respect, cooperation and dialogue (Capra, 1996:187).

The social sciences may be moving in the same qualitative and ecological direction. We've observed the mechanistic turn in economics at the end of the nineteenth century, which may eventually be extinguished by systems-based ecological economics. My own adopted discipline, psychology, the study of human behaviour, went through a similar mechanistic deviation. In the early twentieth century, academic psychology fell under the thrall of behaviourism which tried to prove that human thoughts and actions are produced by physiological mechanisms which turn environmental inputs into behavioural outputs, without the intervention of anything called consciousnesses or free choice. This obsession with control, which led to the bizarre practice of using rats and pigeons to explore human behaviour rather than actual humans, has been marginalized – if not entirely extinguished– by humanistic, existential and psychodynamic approaches to the human subject. In this context, it's worth noting that behaviourism's popularity was partially due to its being heavily funded by the US advertising industry. Its most famous pioneer, J.B. Watson, actually left academia to run a major advertising agency, a reminder of how assiduously capitalism has always searched for new ways to covertly manipulate consumers' choices, long before Google came on the scene.

Neomechanicalism: The Rejection of Integrative, Life-Based Systems Science

We are now is a position to understand the place of the humachination mission in the history of science. In many ways, it's a mechanistic reaction against the developing paradigm shift in modern science from physics to life science. Neomechanicalism can even be interpreted as an attempt to establish a second classical synthesis, which would enable reductionist physical sciences to cling to the clockwork model and many of the certainties of Cartesian logic and the Baconian mission to dominate nature.

Computer science plays a leading role in neomechanicalism, as the main scientific training ground for almost all Big Tech ontopreneurs (more in Chapter 10). Computer science has helped the evolution of integrative modern science – non-linear maths would be impossible without it, for example. But it has also fostered a revival of the mechanistic universe, of the idea that reality is written in the code of maths. The revered mechanical clock has been digitally upgraded. An analogue clock provides a holistic representation of time through the mechanical movements of its hands. A digital clock, by contrast, works electronically, converting the regular vibrations in a quartz tuning fork into numbers. Likewise an analogue film uses light-sensitive chemicals to produce a pattern of light and darkness that resembles a real scene, whereas a digital camera electronically converts light into millions of pixels which can be stored – and edited – as strings of numbers.

This atomization and numericalization of reality – so different from the ingenuous ruses using natural phenomena employed by analogue technology – has breathed new life into the Baconian strategy of mastering nature. From the 1950s genetics seemed to offer the same possibility of reducing all living things to a manipulatable code but, as we've seen, genes are much more complex, variable and context-bound than this. Digital technology is bound to nature, even as it tries to manipulate it; hence its need for quartz and many other earth minerals. And it would be wrong to think that it leads to a form of absolute knowledge, let alone that it legitimizes the ontocapitalist techno-utopia of "applied evolution", in which all nature can be converted to numbers and reformatted at the press of a key. This digital version of the celestial watchmaker ignores the three-and-a-half billion year endowment of life on Earth, without which the immense privilege of being alive would never have been granted to human beings.

Other Shortcomings of the Neomechanicalist Approach

Finally, it's worth looking at some other limitations of the neomechanicalist worldview because these can make themselves apparent in the practice of humachination. In terms of methodology, the mechanistic approach tends towards scientism, the belief that science has a monopoly on gathering accurate knowledge of reality, which can lead to excessive objectivism and a tendency to discount the value of subjectivity (Sorell, 1991). Neomechanicalism is also partialist, fixated on detaching a part from its context and examining it in isolation, whereas, as Ludwig von Bertalanffy (1968:37) stressed, "General system theory is a general science of 'wholeness'". Reductionism can be useful for experimentation and initial theory construction but it can easily obscure the complex, dynamic interconnectedness of all elements within a system. It also sets the scene for more deliberate ideology construction, in which myths, gaps and silences are used to paper over the biases and contradictions of a particular approach. Moreover, it encourages a disintegrative attitude, which regards reality as fragmented, fractured and inherently divided, a view reinforced by the artificially imposed boundaries between academic disciplines. These can impede the integrated, holistic analysis needed to comprehend the multi-dimensional challenges of the Anthropocene.

Another shortcoming of neomechanicalism is its prioritization of quantity over quality. The rule of quantus ("how much") over qualis ("of what sort") favours an over-literal, numerical approach, which confines knowledge to what can be unambiguously measured and assigns a lower value to quality, thereby diminishing the importance of the intuitive, tacit, indeterminate and non-linear. Mechanical reductionism is also much more comfortable with linear causality, such as A-produces-B-type reasoning, rather than the complex causality of networks, in which the same element can act as a cause or an effect – and sometimes as both.

Valuing quantity over quality can also lead to a serious overestimation of the value of maths. Descartes's faith in reason was inspired by his work as a mathematician and Newton used his calculus to improve on Kepler's empirically-derived laws of planetary motions. For Galileo, the laws of nature were written in the language of mathematics which is why he insisted that only what can be definitively measured can contribute to authentic knowledge (Hamming, 1980). But maths exaggerates the ability of numbers to reveal the inner secrets of reality and cannot provide the absolute knowledge of the world, about which some mathematicians fantasize (e.g. Tegmark, 2017). Maths may excel at describing patterns but it cannot account for beauty or love. As physicist Derek Abbot (2013:2152) demonstrates, it also has a very poor record in the biological sciences and self-selects for success (we're never reminded of all the theorems that have failed). Abbot concludes that "mathematics is a human invention … a product of the imagination that sometimes works on simplified models of reality." This in itself is enough to warn us against the formidable over-reliance on maths of the two most powerful disciplines of the humachine age, neoclassical economics and computer science, as a numbers world risks usurping the word world humans have always inhabited.

Philosophically, neomechanicalism tends to see the world hierarchically. It operates on the basis of conceptual pyramids which separate reality into higher and lower spheres. I referred to one of the best known of these dualisms earlier, Descartes's splitting of existence into the realm of mind (super-rational but also mysterious and ghostly) and the realm of matter (mechanistic and knowable). Other dualisms, such as civilized over savage, individual over society, male over female and the West over the rest – have a similarly disintegrative and segregating effect. "Verticalisms" might be a better description, as they are expressions of the Pyramid Pattern in thought, creating splits out of unity and imposing rigid, binary choices rather than taking an even-handed, "both/and" approach. Symbolized by the lordly head (political and neurological) reigning over the inferior body (political and physiological), it's a form of cognitive pattern-making quite distinct from integrated, circular or egalitarian ways of perceiving the world. No wonder ecofeminist Val Plumwood (1993:42 ref) called dualism "the logic of colonisation".

Neomechanicalism is largely driven by the obsession with controlling reality that underlies all mechanistic and dualist thinking. We can see this in the conviction that one day science will be able to identify every single law of nature. Attaining this kind of absolute scientific knowledge would enable the future to be predicted with pin-point precision. Kurzweil's "prediction-addiction" stems from this belief that the shape of things to come can be read like a book, as do heavy-handed economic prophecies which claim that automation is unstoppable and transhumanists' conviction that biology can be transcended. But this article of faith of nineteenth-century positivism has been disproved by almost all of the science that has succeeded it. And, in any case, I contend, it's not science that determines the future but political choice.

Conclusion

In conclusion, understanding the limitations of the science underlying the humachination project is vital if we are to make the right choices about the future. Choosing – consciously or not – to accept the neomechanicalism which makes eliminating the difference between humans and machines seem like our logical destiny endorses capitalism's latest and most desperate attempt to perpetuate itself. In the academy, neomechanicalism may be gradually losing the clash of the sciences but in business and political economy it's winning, led by a new generation of entrepreneurial engineers and computer scientists, whose regressive, reductionist view of science favours the absolute domination, precision and predictability supposedly offered by machines. This plutotechnic amalgam of free market economics and gung-ho physical science, dismisses the role of the majority of people in shaping the future and threatens to downgrade the observational life sciences which insists we are crashing through the material and planetary boundaries that make life on Earth viable.

Addressing the Anthropocene Crisis requires the balanced, holistic systems-based approach which is dangerously absent from the neomechanicalist view of material reality. A collective commitment to a science securely rooted in life may be vital if we are to have a realistic chance of avoiding the magnetic pull of the Technocene. That also entails freeing knowledge from the corrosive entanglements of the free market economy, a point which moves us on to the final theoretical assumption propping up the humachination project.

CHAPTER 7

Consumerism versus Ecology and Human Wellbeing: How Technology Becomes Tricknology

As Clive Hamilton (2003) once observed, capitalism would probably die out if people in wealthy countries ever decided they more or less had what they needed; instead they're driven to "buy what they don't need, with money they don't have, to impress people they don't like". Consumerism is the fourth myth cemented into the humachine project that I want to deconstruct. This is no secret hiding in plain sight but a quasi-religious tenet proudly emblazoned on the banners of the growth capitalist world system. It leads to the conviction that the best indication of what the majority of people in society really need is to be found in the rate of consumption of whatever producers choose to put into the market. Remember that Ray Kurzweil (2005:420) even argues that consumer satisfaction is the best guarantor for the safe development of "Strong AI", i.e. superintelligent systems potentially capable of usurping humanity. As a belief system, consumerism insists that the market is the true arbiter of what's good and bad, hence its fierce animus against government regulation. Some humachinators even claim that consumerism is a better way of ensuring majority rule than political democracy, as Chapter 9 reveals.

Consumerism is at the core of neoclassical economics' neomechanicalist reinvention of itself in the late nineteenth century, referred to in an earlier chapter. This recast the citizen as a mechanistic consumer, Homo economicus, a kind of individualistic calculating machine constantly assessing how to best satisfy its "rational self-interest". This self-interest includes an almost infinite number of desires and no concept of human needs, thus ensuring there are no limits to consumption. The Law of More rules that wants are as infinite as growth itself and that people can never be satisfied. Indeed, addiction capitalism aims to turn our desires for what we don't need into nothing short of a craving. We chase the wellbeing seemingly offered by consumer goods and services to make up for what we don't get in terms of satisfied needs. This, incidentally, is why a post-growth society can be described as an economy of needs, which might be regulated by democratically agreed limits to consumption (Demaria et al, 2019).

Consumerism also explains why Western overconsumption is gradually destroying the biosphere. The planetary dysmorphia which deceives us into thinking that the Earth's resources are much bigger than they actually are belongs to the same culture of excess that leads us to spend beyond our means, burdening future generations with debt. In reality, profligate purchasing is a necessity for capitalism because saving money can lead to economic stagnation. Spending more than we have is the only way to keep growth alive.

The warped economics of consumerism are replicated in the hall of mirrors created by the advertising and marketing industries on which capitalism relies. In the technology sphere, choice distortion turns technology into tricknology, a process that fully established itself in the half century preceding the humachine age. It requires commercially-minded scientists who are willing to sacrifice environmental and human safety for profit and an army of skilled marketers, advertisers, lobbyists and retailers. Both groups are aided by the inherent ambiguity of technology itself. Technological consumerism also capitalizes on growthism's proudest boast, its claim to improve our happiness and wellbeing. But, as this chapter endeavours to show, this can turn out to be its biggest and most deceptive trick.

The Divergence of Technology and Ecology

The explosion of growth in the Acceleration Age from 1945 to 2000 saw the biggest increase in the production and consumption of goods and services in human history. The Second World War produced an astonishing sprint in technological development, which continued as cheap fossil fuel flooded Western economies in the 1950s and national GDPs expanded at record

rates. But this gargantuan spurt of economic growth started to put the ecological viability of Earth under pressure in ways that were unprecedented
in the Holocene. Safe planetary boundaries relating to the climate, land use
and chemical pollution began to be threatened, as new agricultural, industrial and consumer technology produced a torrent of unintended negative
consequences (UNCs) affecting almost every aspect of life on this planet.

These threats did not go unnoticed, however, and, from the 1960s onwards, a
growing environmental awareness culminated in the science of ecology. This
incorporates many of the holistic, systems-based organizational principles
of the biology-based revolution which I described in the previous chapter.
The core concept of ecology can be expressed very simply: in life "everything
is connected to everything else". This connectedness law is biologist Barry
Commoner's (1971:16) first law of ecology, which stresses that ecosystems
consist of sensitive, intermeshed networks of relationships. Change one thing
in that network and you risk negative changes elsewhere, potentially upsetting
the "dynamic self-compensation properties" of the system. That's because
matter is indestructible, says Commoner, as "everything must go somewhere".
In nature there is no such thing as waste: for instance, animals excrete carbon
dioxide which nourishes plants and plants excrete oxygen which enables
animals to live. For every organic substance there is an enzyme capable of
breaking it down and recycling it, which spells dangers when human-made
innovations are introduced into ecosystems. As Commoner says, "there is no
such thing as free lunch…every gain is won at some cost" (p23).

These basic tenets of ecology collide head on with the GUN organizing
principles of growth capitalism, which put profit first and nature last. The
UNCs resulting from ignoring the interconnectedness of all systems have
been spectacular. An ecological economy is a circular process aiming to
connect every phase of production from design to manufacturing to consumption and waste. Actors in this system are constantly asking "how does
this process affect that one?", whereas those in a disconnected, growthist
economy more often pose the question, "how much profit can we make
from this until we're found out?" The consequence is that the cherished
proposition of consumerism that what people buy is the best indicator of
what they really need is constantly refuted by environmental reality.

A prime example is the development of the plastics industry. In the early
1950s plastic was hailed as a "miracle" material, a cheap gift of carbon

capitalism, as it's made from polymers found in the exhaust matter produced by oil refineries. Its supposedly emancipatory qualities were famously illustrated in 1955 by the "throwaway living" edition of *Life Magazine*. This celebrated the 40 hours of cleaning time allegedly saved by a variety of new plastic objects and pictured a suitably euphoric American family who could now toss these items into the litter bin after a single use (McCool, 2020). In those days, a few million tons of plastic were being produced each year but the amount has now mushroomed to almost 400 million tons, a figure which is estimated to double by 2050 (Statista, 2023). As the reach of this apparently liberating material has extended to almost every aspect of daily life from heavy industry to medicine and the packaging of virtually every retail and wholesale product, so have the negative consequences.

Plastic pollution now stretches across the planet, even to uninhabited islands like Henderson in the South Pacific, whose beaches are littered with millions of plastic items. Garbage drifts through our oceans in 300-mile long floating patches, choking our rivers and waterways and exhausting landfills. In the developing world, plastic sachets enable the poor to buy tiny quantities of shampoo, toothpaste or condiments which only add to the waste nightmare (Posadas, 2014).

Most plastic is not regenerative, as no natural enzymes exist to break it down. Instead, it slowly shreds into smaller and smaller microfibres, which along with the trillions of microbeads contained in clothing and detergents, find their way into every niche of the planet from the Arctic to Mount Everest and the Mariana Trench. The effect of microplastics on animal life can be devastating; for example, some sea birds are building their nests with plastic straws instead of twigs with the consequence that their young are strangled at birth. It's also leading to the possible collapse of the phytoplankton that provide up to 10% of oceans' oxygen, which some scientists estimate could lead to the extinction of most fish species (Boyce et al, 2010). Overall, geologists regard plastic deposits as one most distinctive markers of the beginning of the Anthropocene (McKie, 2023).

Microplastics have also been found in the human lungs, brain and in 2022 for the first time in human blood (Leslie et al, 2022). Professor of environmental medicine Shanna Swan (2021) in her book *Count Down* attributes the halving of the sperm count of Western men since the 1980s to chemicals in plastics and predicts a crisis in human fertility by 2045. This would be the ultimate case of species hubris. Unregulated consumerism's tendency to deliver the absolute opposite of what is good for humans and other species on this planet couldn't be more clearly demonstrated.

You have to ask: how difficult was it for professional scientists to conduct experiments that establish that most plastic will not biodegrade for centuries? And plastic is far from being the only "miracle" of technology which has been developed over the past fifty years to have ignored the principles of ecological connectedness. Scientists colluding with the GUN worldplan have developed a convenient blindness to the deadly impacts of their innovations, seemingly "reacting spontaneously in the ways that will serve external power interests", to rehearse Noam Chomsky's criticism of the intellectual class in general (Barsamian and Chomsky 2001:80). For example, the chemical agriculture revolution of the 1970s, which Donald Trump boasted at Davos had saved the world from starvation, has incurred a devastatingly high environmental cost (Trumpwhitehouse, 2020). Chemical-based herbicides and pesticides such as glyphosate ("Roundup") can be hazardous to human health and have contributed to the scarcely believable reduction in wildlife and insect populations since the 1970s, which is at the core of the biodiversity crisis (Nicolopoulou-Stamati, et al, 2016).

But sooner or later, casual, commercially-compliant scientific ignorance would not be enough to obfuscate the accelerating damage being done to the planet. As far as climate change is concerned, this point was reached from the 1970s onwards, as the many scientists employed by the oil industry began to predict with extraordinary accuracy the global warming risks caused by fossil fuel. Feigned obliviousness was no longer an option and carbon capitalist corporations developed a much more aggressive ideological stance: denialism (Dembicki, 2022).

Oil companies began investing in campaigns that explicitly denied the environmental consequences which they correctly foresaw. Typical was Koch Industries, an oil industry conglomerate, which since the 1980s has invested some $162 million in lobbying governments, setting up right-wing think tanks and establishing fake grassroots campaigns aimed at asserting that climate change is not a problem for humanity. During the 1990s these diversionary tactics helped Charles Koch (who, incidentally, is an MIT-educated scientist with masters' degrees in nuclear and chemical engineering) get away with massive pollution in the pipelines and oil refineries he ran, although heavy fines were levied where the evidence was incontrovertible (Leonard, 2019). It also brought him a multi-billion-dollar fortune that today rivals that of the humachine ontopreneurs. The stunningly simplistic betrayal of public trust and evidence–based science that is climate denialism enabled profits to be extracted from fossil fuel long after it became clear that most coal, oil and gas reserves need to stay in the ground if we are to have any chance of preventing catastrophic levels of global warming.

The shocking ecological legacy that carbon capitalism has bequeathed to the twenty-first century could only have occurred because there are always multiple dimensions of tricknology at work in consumerism, many of them considerably more subtle and insidious than climate denial. These ruses enable us to be consistently deceived by new technology, not only in relation to its environmental impact but even closer to home, in terms of our personal wellbeing.

The Ease and Convenience Trick:
Labour-Saving Devices or Technological Enchainment?

In general, capitalist consumerism relies on the claim that material goods and services increase personal happiness. This is despite long-standing evidence that suggests this is only true for the satisfaction of basic needs up to the relatively low level of income referred to in Chapter 4. In fact, Richard Easterlin and Kelsey O'Conner (2020:11) analysed data from 96 countries and concluded that "economic growth does not make people happier". Their data even suggested that it would take 1,000 years of 1% annual GDP growth "to raise happiness by one point".

Technological consumerism tends to deploy a more specific version of the consumerist myth, claiming that new technology can bring people greater ease and convenience by reducing labour time and effort. Of course, this lure is not always a sleight of hand, as new tools can provide a genuine liberation from hardship. But, when examined from a holistic, systems viewpoint, many of the savings in time and labour promised by new technology turn out to be illusory. Far too often, new devices simply translate one form of bondage into another, a slippage that can be referred to as technological enchainment.

For example, in the 1930s, a vast range of new "labour-saving" domestic devices were introduced, such as electric and gas ovens, vacuum cleaners, electric washing machines and so on. By the 1950s, as Ruth Schwartz Cowan illustrated in *More Work for Mother* (1985), the result was that the modern, supposedly "independent" housewife was expected to maintain higher standards of domesticity almost entirely on her own. The time which her domestic devices saved her in housework was more than offset by other activities, above all, by the hours she spent in her car, shopping for the family and ferrying her children to school. The result is that although the average woman today spends 18 hours a week less on housework than her counterpart in 1900, the differential is accounted for not by technology but by men contributing 13 hours more domestic work a week and because women have fewer children (Ramey, 2008). As Lewis Mumford (1934:396) observed, "The justification of labor-saving devices was not that they actually saved labor but that they increased consumption".

In their classic work *Technofix* (2011), Michael and Joyce Huesemann provide a fascinating explanation of this paradox in relation to the washing of clothes. They point out that although nowadays the modern washing machine makes it easier to wash clothes, we now own many more clothes and developments in textile manufacturing mean that garments consist of many different materials (including plastic-based synthetics) which have to be washed separately, thereby increasing the number of washes needed. Another unintended consequence is even more surprising:

> As a result of the widespread use of washing machines, social standards for cleanliness have increased dramatically, which in fact has forced people to wash their clothes more frequently than they did 50 years ago (Huesemann and Huesemann, 2011:103).

What was once seen as a normal degree of wear in clothes is now considered socially and professionally unacceptable. And the same is true for what people used to regard as the normal aroma of a human body. Modern bathroom technology has encouraged some people to shower several times a day, creating a new intolerance of natural odours. To consider our higher standards of hygiene as a new form of enslavement may seem bizarre but it certainly commits us to much higher consumption of water, soaps, cosmetics and detergents, greater dependence on new cleaning and drying technologies and more time spent using them. No wonder the "no wash" and "low wash" movement is on the rise (Welin, 2023).

Labour-saving devices also trick us when it comes to assessing the length of the paid working week. One of the most obvious conveniences of new technology is more leisure time, or so economist John Maynard Keynes (1931) thought in the 1930s, as he witnessed an explosion of new mod cons. But the 20-hour week which Keynes confidently forecast for the twenty-first century has not yet materialised. Indeed, it was probably naive techno-optimism on his part to think capitalism would ever allow this to happen.

Granted, we may be working fewer hours than in 1870, when, at the apogee of the unregulated exploitation of labour in the USA and UK, a 60-70 hour week was the norm for adults. Even so, when we factor in new communications technologies that eradicate the separation of work and leisure, the Victorian home can almost seem like a lost sanctuary of leisure and family time. What's undeniable is that we are working substantially longer than workers in the Middle Ages, who, by Juliet Schor's (1991) estimate, put in the modern equivalent of a 30-hour week (120 12-hour days a year) and enjoyed several months of holidays every year, particularly in France and Spain. And let's not forget the contemporary hunter-gatherers who actually do work 20-hour weeks or less.

This is a typical case of technology compelling us to put the cart before the horse. If we really wanted to make more leisure time a goal of society, we would organize work on this basis, using technology to deliver this objective. Instead we rely on technology to make the decisions and end up working longer. The larger trick at play here is that if we were prepared to accept broadly the same standard of living in the West as in the 1970s we would be able to move much closer to the 20-hour week Keynes predicted, giving us much more time for activities which matter more than work (a theme I return to in Chapter 24). This in turn would help us to reduce consumption and combat the environmental and climate crisis aspects of the Anthropocene Crisis. Such a shift in goals and values would remove the vicious linearity of the growthist economic system, which disconnects each step of a process from the next and introduces a virtuous circularity, which recognizes that everything's connected to everything else. Needless to say, this would clash with the growth-maximizing priorities of capitalism, which uses a very different process for developing and marketing new technology.

Consumerism at Work: The Tricknology Cycle

Far from pro-actively anticipating the future, the capitalist cycle which transforms technological designs into consumerist reality exploits the inherent ambiguity of what comes next. Before the Industrial Revolution, the idea that the future would differ markedly from the present was alien to most people. As historian Clive Ponting (2007:125) notes, "the ancient world had little idea of progress: history was usually seen as having no particular direction at all" and time was often conceived in circular rather than linear terms. But technological innovation has changed the future into an immensely exploitable ideological resource, in which almost any technical project can be justified given the right time scale. This provides a virtually unlimited licence for tricknology.

As I know from my own entrepreneurial experience, every stage of the technology cycle involves "selling the future", often by highlighting the advantages of being ahead of the curve and the dangers of missing out on innovation. This "greed and fear" pitch is greatly assisted by the fact that the easy stages of product development can often be passed through most quickly. As the adage has it, the first 90% takes 10% of the overall development time; the final 10% takes 90% of it (Mitchell, 2019). A 90% "finished" technology may be useless in practical terms but it provides the basis for a persuasive sales argument and impressive demonstrations. On the global environmental stage, we see this principle playing out in terms of UK and European carbon emissions reduction: it's quicker and easier to switch from coal-fired power stations to cheaper renewable energy sources than it is to tackle problems arising from the pollution caused by badly insulated buildings, meat-based agriculture and aviation, which require much more challenging, systemic changes.

The ambiguity of the future creates the possibility of creating "mirage technologies", which are always about to happen, and whose apparent imminence becomes so established that they are treated as though they were a fait accompli. Carbon capture and storage (CCS) is a prime example of a mirage technology. For twenty years the process of extracting CO_2 from the air and sequestering it underground has played a significant role in UN climate negotiations. It occupies a vital place in the equations of the Paris Agreement of 2015 and without it the emissions reduction assumptions of the treaty look hopelessly optimistic (Anderson, 2015). Yet as a technology it's extremely challenging technically, very expensive to develop, and oil companies have few incentives to experiment with it. That's why there are still fewer than 30 CCS operations in existence worldwide, the majority of them actually being used for a novel system of extracting oil (Friends of the Earth, 2021). The huge army of 475 lobbyists which CCS fielded in COP28 in Dubai (three times larger than the entire US delegation) was a measure of both its desperation and its financial muscle (CIEL, 2023). It's one thing to experiment with a potential technology like nuclear fusion, the miracle energy breakthrough which has been about to happen for at least half a century, but it's another level of tricknology to build the future around one.

At the time of writing, it's possible that generative AI will turn out to be another mirage technology. As veteran AI expert Gary Marcus (2023) says, "few things I have ever seen have been more hyped" than generative AI firms which are valued in the billions even though "the revenue isn't there yet and may never come". Time will tell if this is a real technological breakthrough or tricknology as it's most demonically inventive.

Mirage technology is possible in part because of innovation fetishism. A fetish is something that takes on the appearance of an independent force, which is supposedly endowed with magical powers (Hornberg, 2016). Machines often possess this seductive trickiness. Remember Arthur C. Clarke's axiom that "a sufficiently advanced technology can be indistinguishable from magic"? Well, this magical quality doubtless goes back thousands of years to simple mechanisms like the lever, the pulley or the wheel, that made possible extraordinary feats that human muscles alone could not perform. This sorcery is also present in many modern machines, with their gleaming aesthetics, hypnotic hum and almost unimaginable power.

The innovation fetishism we find embedded in ultrascience can equate all creativity, pro-social behaviour and even the human spirit itself with the production of new technology. Indeed, technological consumerism is sometimes presented as though it were a school of modern art. In his heady paean to economic growth, economist Oded Galor (2022) makes little distinction between entrepreneurial and technical innovation, on the one hand, and the creativity driving education and healthcare, suggesting that as long as the world has enough innovators every problem can be solved. But which innovations get accepted or rejected is always a matter of political choice – the golden rule – and in our current system, these choices are usually made on the basis of the GUN principles.

In practice, innovation fetishism is encouraged by the extensive lobbying of legislators which aims to create easy pathways for new products and services and prevent the regulation of existing services and products. Among the humachinators, Google is probably the best known and most prolific employer of lobbyists but all technology companies make lobbying a core element of their business, often by creating a revolving employment door between themselves and government departments. (For example, former British Deputy Prime Minister Nick Clegg is now Meta's president of global affairs.) In extreme cases, corporations like Koch Industries will use all the dark arts to conceal the negative impacts of their products, such as sponsored researchers prepared to discredit any scientific evidence and other techniques pioneered by tobacco companies. These "merchants of doubt", as Oreskes and Conway (2010) have shown, have actually turned the concealment of potential and proven UNCs into an industry in itself.

Once a product or service arrives on the market, choice manipulation moves into a higher gear. A vast army of sales people swings into action targeting consumers and exploiting technology's intrinsic trickiness. PR companies provide a constant stream of glowing press releases, which are difficult for editors or the public to verify but so "newsworthy" that they stealthily embed themselves as facts. Social media influencers also push products in an increasingly evidence-free environment, while marketers create sponsorships linked to popular sports and musical events and oversee the design and the packaging of products down to the tiniest detail. Product launches have been transformed into theatres of illusion, performed in front of rapt audiences, some of whom have queued all night for a seat. Pioneered by Steve Jobs and continued by Elon Musk and others, these performative spectacles inject show-biz excitement into technological consumerism, often dispensing with the mundane encumbrances of technical proof.

As for advertising, we've already established that the humachine age is predicated on new systems that pursue the consumer more precisely and indefatigably than ever before, so that the potential user is rarely more than a few seconds away from the next invasive, choice-influencing opportunity. With combined global advertising and PR expenditure approaching $1 trillion (Statista, 2023), the army of hypesters are not likely to experience budget restraints when it comes to selling us what we don't really need or even want. We have to keep asking ourselves, if consumerism really gives people the best possible choices, why is it necessary to spend so much on marketing and advertising? Why, for example, would you ever cancel a Hollywood film that has cost $100 million to produce? Answer: because to have any chance of making a profit, a similar amount of money would have to be spent on promoting it. Imagine for a moment if some of this vast global advertising and marketing budget could be diverted to sustainability and wellbeing projects. Instead, as applied to technical products and services, this vast resource is used to promote the magical thinking which insists that all innovation is good, regardless of its purpose or consequences.

Conclusion

In summary, consumerism, the fourth set of assumptions propping up the humachine project, is no guarantor of providing what either people or the planet really need. "Fake it till you make it ", one of Silicon Valley's most revered slogans, might be applied not only to humachination but to growth capitalism as a whole. After all, magic itself is derived from science-based phenomena such as optical illusions, backed up by ingeniously engineered props and the misdirection of the illusionist who diverts our attention from where we might see the truth to where we probably won't. In the short-term, tricknology may help capitalism survive the fading of fossil-fuel based growth but in the longer term it threatens to deprive people of the possibility of achieving planetary sustainability and enhanced wellbeing.

Like the other ideological myths I've tried to debunk in this section, consumerist tricknology serves to distort the basic information on which sound decision-making about the future depends. This reinforces capitalism's default setting which is pointing us towards the Technocene. One of our best chances of renavigating our course through the Anthropocene lies in becoming aware of the choices we are making, consciously and through our unreflecting actions. And the more we can understand the practices and intentionality of those who are leading the human-machine fusion project, the more that the road to the Ecocene opens up. Nothing will aid this widening of horizons more than a careful examination of the risks inherent in our current world strategy, which is the next challenge this book sets itself.

PART III

Future Risks:
How Humachine Capitalism Could
Lead Us to Techno-Dystopia

Whatever you may think about the theoretical challenges I've made to growth capitalism in the age of humachines, by now most readers will surely agree that humachination is a high-risk project. In fact, it may be the biggest gamble humanity has ever made. In Part III I want to focus on the risk factors involved that I consider are most likely to drag us towards the ecologically compromised, post-democratic techno-dystopia that I call the Technocene. My hope is that once these risks – which are also choices – are identified, we may start to move towards the more sustainable and compassionate future I have begun to sketch out.

Sociologists began to describe modern capitalism as "risk society" in the 1980s but in the twenty-first century the gravity of these risks has increased by an order of magnitude (Beck,1992). We're living on a planet which some experts believe is heading for as much as 4C of global warming by 2100, a temperature not experienced on Earth since the Pliocene epoch three million years ago, which would amount to a climate apocalypse for billions of people (Vince, 2022, Burke et al, 2018). Other existential dangers of the Anthropocene Crisis, which it's worth rehearsing, include mass species extinction, biodiversity breakdown, increases in economic inequality and food insecurity, the attrition of democracy, mass refugee displacements, new pandemics and other public health dangers, plus the ever-present threat of armed conflict, accentuated in 2022 by the outbreak of the first major war in Europe since 1945. Many economies still bear the scars of the cataclysmic 2008 economic crash, which was partially caused by bankers throwing financial risk management out of the window (Ashby, 2010). By insisting that the technologization of everything and everyone can solve all these problems, humachination doubles down on these risks, potentially creating a whole new catalogue of deadly hazards.

In Part III we look at five of these new risk factors. The first is that by supporting distracting chimeras such as green growth and space colonialism, the humachinators slow down effective climate and environmental action until it's too late. Second, we examine the multiple, practical risks to democracy posed by humachine technology and the right-wing libertarian theory that argues that technological consumerism means political majority rule can be dispensed with altogether. Third, I explore the paradoxical nature of the humachine age's leadership class which combines apparently progressive beliefs with unrivalled plutotechnic powers and elitist values. Overall in this section, I try to get up close and personal with the Prometheans of human-machine fusion because personality has once more become a factor in history, especially in relation to the age-old question: "how can we trust our leaders"? Risk number four is that these immensely influential leaders are normalizing a new type of psychology, a neomechanicalist, anti-social "machine mindset" which is disturbingly devoid of empathy. And the fifth risk is the most existentially catastrophic of all, the threat that the gamble of humachination could end up tricking us out of the best of being human on planet Earth, perhaps literally by means of the Almageddon of superintelligence, or by depriving people of their core competences, skills and talents to such an extent that human freedom and independence become impossible. As we sail towards a possible event horizon of irreversible transformations, taking stock of our humanness in the face of these ontological risks may help us to change course for the Ecocene while there is still time.

CHAPTER 8

The Ontocapitalist Planet: The Green Growth Delusion, Climate Delayism and Space Colonialism

As we know, the age of humachines coincides with the biggest environmental and climate crisis which humanity has faced in the Holcocene. Many of the leaders of today's Big Tech corporations were born in the 1970s and 1980s and grew up with rising atmospheric C02 as a backdrop to their lives, as issues in climatology and ecology became increasingly mainstream. So for them the blatantly anti-scientific, reality-distorting denialism of carbon capitalism was not an option. They needed a strategy that at once addressed the environmental and climate threats that were undeniable by the turn of the millennium, while maintaining belief in a capitalism based on never-ending increases in material consumption. At the highest conceptual level, this impossible balancing act is performed by ontocapitalism, the transhumanist techno-optimism that believes that the biological evolution and the biosphere can be digitally and mechanically re-engineered. At a more mundane, practical level, it translates into the claim by conventional economists that capitalism can be greened by new technology that miraculously severs or "decouples" economic growth from its negative material impact on the environment.

As a result, in the humachine age, climate denialism gives way to climate delayism. This is a much more elusive strategy that enables Big Tech corporations to make some progress in decarbonizing transport or recycling waste, for example, but at only a snail's pace, which distracts from the real speed at which environmental changes need to be made and from the systemic nature of the problem. Worse, it plays an even more duplicitous, "parallelist" game that legitimizes carbon capitalism, enabling fossil fuel corporations to continue to reap profits from hydrocarbons despite the urgent need to phase out their use. You might compare the situation to cars waiting at the traffic lights: the environmental hazards of the throbbing, gas-guzzling SUV are easy enough to spot but who knows what to make of the gleaming, electric, self-driving robot that's just pulled up?

The Green Growth Delusion: "Cutting a Tree with a Spoon"

Green growthism is a theory developed over the last twenty years or so, which represents neoclassical economics' very belated acknowledgment of the environmentally destructive impact of the GUN system, wrapped up in the claim that capitalism can totally redeem itself by means of new, "eco-friendly" technologies. It argues that renewable energy, electrified transport, "clean" manufacturing processes and other "efficiencies" can enable economic growth to continue on its endlessly expansionary path but now shorn of negative environmental consequences. In this way the Global North's material overproduction and overconsumption can remain as the economic model for the rest of the world to emulate. But this decoupling concept is a fantasy of the neomechanicalist imaginary, as indicated by another name which conventional economists give it, "dematerialization". It might even be dubbed "disconnectionism", so comprehensively does it reject the basic organizational principles of ecology. Green growth is simply the have-your-cake-and-eat-it invention that persuades humachine corporations that they can save the planet even as they continue to consume it.

And it's not just me saying it. In *Debunking Decoupling*, an international group of ecological economists and degrowth scholars make it clear that as a response to the ecological problems of the Anthropocene, decoupling is like "trying to cut a tree with a spoon" (Parrique et al, 2019:58). The researchers, working under the auspices of the European Environmental

Bureau (EEB), suggest that increased technological efficiency can never absolutely detach economic growth from its negative environmental impacts in the manner promised by mainstream economists.

The reasons they give for this are as follows:

Energy efficiency. The energy return on investment (EROI) of renewable energy can never compete with the almost mythological profitability of fossil fuel (up to 1000:1) referred to in an earlier chapter. Even if capitalism could be fully decarbonized by 2050, with an estimated ERO1 on renewables of just 3:1, it simply cannot produce the economic surplus that sustains current levels of consumption.

Rebound effects. As the Victorian economist William Stanley Jevons noted in relation to the efficiency of coal, environmental savings in one area are often wasted on another. For example, money saved on more efficient car journeys can lead to higher spending on more carbon-intensive forms of travel such as long-haul holidays.

Problem-shifting. This tendency abounds even in the most technologically efficient economies. For example, renewable energy reduces GHG emissions but can increase land use, exacerbate conflicts over the mining of metals and water conflicts (especially over hydropower plants). The biomass needed for biofuels can cause deforestation, and negatively impact biodiversity.

Cost-shifting. Apparent efficiencies are often only achieved by statistical sleights of hand, for example by basing emissions estimates on production not consumption. Some of the reductions in emissions since 1990 which the EU claims disappear, once you factor in that Europe has outsourced much of its manufacturing and heavy industry to other parts of the world, especially China. Consumption-based emission accounting provides a more accurate picture of a nation's ecological footprint, and for high-income countries a more alarming one. And although the services industries which now dominate rich economies are less environmentally damaging than manufacturing, they have not dematerialized into thin air. A potentially polluting infrastructure of buildings, roads, transport and machinery is still needed to operate them.

The limits of recycling. Valuable as it is, even recycling cannot be absolutely decoupled from the law of entropy. A circular economy cannot overcome the fact that recycling requires virgin materials and all materials eventually have to be "down cycled". For instance, after 3-6 recycles cellulose fibres become too fragile for paper and can only be used for cardboard, insulation and biofuel.

Finally, not enough technology is targeted specifically at factors needed to improve sustainability. The GUN system ensures that innovations are profit-driven, which casts their sustainability benefits as secondary. Also the incentive to totally replace harmful technologies with efficient ones is very low. Rather than absolute substitution, the Law of More ensures we get a plurality of technologies, clean and dirty (e.g. coal, oil and gas exist alongside renewable energy sources and synthetic rubber doesn't prevent natural rubber extraction).

From their exhaustive examination, the EEB researchers conclude that the literature on decoupling produces no empirical evidence that economic growth can be absolutely severed from environmental pressures. On the contrary:

> Decoupling acts as a distracting fantasy that warrants a continuously more destructive path with both the promise of success and demonstrations of its impossibility deferred into the future (Parrique et al, 2019:59).

The group wisely recommends a shift from technological efficiency to environmental sufficiency, if the future of human civilisation is to be resolved in favour of our children and grandchildren.

The Myth of Green Growth in Corporate Practice

The efforts of the corporate leaders of the humachine age to "go green" need to be seen in the light of the tricknology of decoupling. The humachinators' rhetoric on sustainability may be fulsome, even messianic – and they probably would genuinely like to rid themselves of the environmental sins of their fathers, but their adherence to the same organizing principles of growthism makes this impossible. Dangerous delayism is the result.

Google, for example, has always made extravagant claims about its decarbonizing credentials and, to be fair, it has made some telling strides in this area. Alphabet CEO Sundar Pichai claimed that Google has been carbon neutral since 2007 and from 2017-18 has used only renewable energy. But this only presents part of the picture, as a statement by 2,000 of Google's disgruntled employees pointed out. "Tech is not green", they declared. "The carbon footprint of the tech industry's data centres alone is on a par with aviation." They also noted that Google has not committed itself to a date for carbon net zero (their demand was for 2030) and stressed that Google Cloud makes significant revenue from machine learning and digital infrastructure provided to fossil fuel companies. Worse, they highlighted Google's Janus face in "funding 111 members of Congress who voted against climate legislation at least 90% of the time" in 2018 (Medium, 2019).

Apple also prides itself on its environmental record and produces annual sustainability reports. However, on closer examination, these reveal the typical humachinators' ecological dance of one step forward and (at least) one step back. For example, in 2019 Apple says it achieved 99% of renewable energy in manufacturing but almost half of the electricity used to power Apple devices globally still comes from coal. The company has also significantly increased the amount of electronic waste it recycles but the quantity it sends to landfills has increased astronomically, from about 5 million tons in 2012 to 36.5 million in 2018. And its hazardous waste – too toxic to send to landfills – has rocketed 600-fold over the same period (Neely, 2019).

Apple's history of planned obsolescence – or deliberately engineered inefficiency – also takes it backwards. As a Greenpeace report notes, in 2008 it was possible to upgrade the Macbook hard drive, replace its batteries, speakers and other components. But by 2013, the Retina Macbook had a non-upgradeable hard drive, batteries glued in place, and special screws which made accessing any components almost impossible for non-specialists (Cook and Jardim, 2017). IPhone has also regressed ecologically, introducing batteries designed to prematurely cut out, whereupon users were encouraged to buy new phones, a misdemeanour for which Apple was forced to pay $113 million in compensation in 2020 (Romm, 2020). In the final analysis, like every capitalist enterprise, Apple's survival depends on increased consumption, which inexorably translates into greater pollution in absolute terms. If it slowed down its new product production and started encouraging users to recycle and repair their existing devices, the company's share price would probably collapse.

Amazon has also been extremely slow to commit to real environmental action. It delivers some 10 billion items a year on gas-greedy planes, lorries and vans, producing a carbon footprint that exceeds those of medium-sized European countries, like Switzerland or Denmark (Johnson, 2022). GHG emissions are shooting up by 15-20% a year (to 71 million metric tonnes in 2021 (Amazon.com, 2022). Finally stung into action – reportedly by employees protesting against the company's polluting practices – Jeff Bezos announced on Instagram a $10 billion 2020 Climate Pledge initiative (Ibbetsen, 2020). Some of these pledges are positive, such as building a fleet of electric delivery vehicles, although no mention is made of parcel-carrying planes criss-crossing the globe. Other climate issues are blatantly ignored, for example the role of Amazon's biggest money-spinner, its AWS cloud division. As Greenpeace's Elizabeth Jardim says:

> It is hypocritical to announce that climate change is the biggest threat to our planet while at the same time boosting the fossil fuel industry by providing advanced computing technologies to the oil and gas industry so that it can discover and drill more oil, more efficiently (quoted in Wood, 2020).

This represents one of delayism's favourite tactics, parallelism, in which a much-hyped pro-environmental strategy runs in the opposite direction to secretive, anti-environmental initiatives. (It's also worth noting that at about the time of his Climate Pledge, Bezos was commissioning his $500 million superyacht, which now produces over 7,000 tonnes of carbon emissions a year (Laville, 2023)).

Another example of parallel development is carbon offsetting, which also features among Amazon's climate pledges, and usually involves planting trees to increase CO2 absorption. Offsetting is now used by companies such as BP, Shell and Heathrow Airport to continue their polluting practices with a good conscience. Of course, reforestation is absolutely necessary for decarbonization but it's a slow process and needs to be done carefully to deliver ecological benefits. Otherwise it can result in "carbon colonialism", which marginalizes small landowners or produces counterproductive results, such as wildfires and illegal logging that create more emissions (Al Ghusain, 2020). In the end, reforestation is a necessary but not a sufficient solution. Even planting a trillion trees, which would occupy an area as big as the US and China combined, as proposed by one well-publicized study by Bastin et al (2019), would only absorb 1-10% of global CO2 emissions by 2100, according to a systems modelling report (Reed, 2020).

Offsetting is another example of problem-shifting, which shows that humachinators can think holistically when they want to manipulate public opinion but not when it's a matter of shouldering their ecological responsibilities. Climate pledges enable Amazon to continue to mechanize the world's retail systems and dominate its supply chains resulting in the expansion of global material consumption, all the while claiming that it's saving the planet. This is the myth of green growth at its most dangerous. It justifies postponements to climate and biodiversity action and causes opportunities for real progress on sustainability to be missed. "Grow fast or die slowly" is a favourite mantra of Silicon Valley that neatly sums up the GUN creed. "Grow fast and die fast" might be a more accurate description of the strategy's planetary consequences.

Inevitably, it seems, where corporations lead, politicians follow. For example, despite many pledges by the governments of the Global North to "build back better", the so-called "green recovery" from the Covid-19 pandemic turned out to be a damp squib. A study in *Nature* found that only a paltry 6% of the $14 trillion the G20 nations spent on fiscal stimulus during the pandemic was spent on green projects, while 3% of it actually went on emission-increasing subsidies to fossil fuel producers (Nahm et al, 2022).

Beyond Green Growth: Ontocapitalist Decoupling

There is, however, more to humachination than is contained in the philosophy of neo-classical economists. In fact, I'd argue, some Big Tech leaders know perfectly well that green growth is a myth and that decoupling cannot save the Earth for capitalism, even if disguised behind copious layers of greenwashing. As we learned in Part I, the project of humanizing machines and mechanizing humans has an intentionality which stretches far beyond the blue planet.

The geoengineering espoused by leading ontocapitalists is one example of this extra-terrestrial vision; in effect, it's an attempt to decouple the stratosphere from the rest of the biosphere. Carbon capture and other negative emissions mirage technologies have already become normalized, as we've seen, in an almost literal attempt to cancel carbon capitalism and turn denialism into a technology. An even more high-risk rejection of the ecological principle of connectedness is climate engineering, which includes plans to expand polar ice, make artificial snow, whiten clouds in the troposphere with sea spray or launch reflective aerosols and space-based mirrors to deflect solar radiation.

Among the leading Big Tech oligarchs, Bill Gates has long been one of the most prominent advocates of geoengineering as an "insurance policy" but in 2021 he announced he's backing an actual experimental project to spray calcium carbonate dust into the atmosphere in the hope of triggering global cooling (Cohen, 2021). This sun-dimming project is just part of Gates's (2021) ambitious climate action plan in which technology is controlled by business people, not, he insists, by "naive" climate activists or politicians promoting Green New Deal "fantasies". The strategy aims to upgrade the existing capitalist economy piece by piece by 2050, as though it were the latest edition of Word or PowerPoint. This might be called the "decarbon copy of capitalism strategy" of the new climate delayists. The more delayism works, the more a desperate world is likely to turn to geoengineering, which would give the techno-elite even greater control. Regrettably, more scientists and entrepreneurs seem to be climbing aboard this ontocapitalist bandwagon which threatens to unlearn the lessons of history and could make the UNCs of past ecological disasters pale by comparison.

Elon Musk: Beyond Delayism to Planetary Decoupling

Humachinator-in-chief, Elon Musk, also backs geoengineering – he's even suggested using thermonuclear weapons to terraform Mars (Wall, 2019) – but I suspect he has far less faith than Bill Gates that decoupling can save Planet Earth. Being human is not enough for Musk, nor is living on a single planet. This may discomfort those who see him as the modern Prometheus unchained and green capitalism's best hope. To be sure, Musk rejects the blatant science denialism of a Charles Koch and realises that global warming is a real threat. Tesla is at the forefront of transforming carbon capitalist transportation and replacing the toxic fumes of the combustion engine. His commitment to the clean energy transition also extends to solar energy, through his early investment in SolarCity, and to several giga-factories manufacturing lithium batteries for electric vehicles and home use. He also owns the Boring Company, a tunnels business intended to provide an alternative to surface roads

And yet, I suggest, despite his self-proclaimed 100-hour working week and the fact that technologies he's developing may form part of a sustainable future, Musk's mission is essentially a form of delayism. Tesla postpones the point where we question whether we really need private cars and cities constructed around them and, indeed, entire countries built around getting to and from car-dominated cities. Musk is about saving car capitalism, not abolishing it. That's why Tesla's market valuation was higher in 2021 than all the other US car corporations put together, despite its comparatively meagre sales. Its investors hope that electrification can not only save the automobile industry from environmentalism but also opens up a hugely lucrative horizon, as the 1.5 billion cars currently on the world's roads are replaced with non-petrol equivalents. Ultimately, Musk's entrepreneurship might even help to export the American model of car ownership, based on about one vehicle for every adult, which would result in some six billion cars worldwide.

The truth is that Musk is totally committed to car culture and acceleration-ism in general. The first thing he bought when he sold his first company was the most expensive sports car in the world, a $1 million McLaren; and Tesla's new Cybertruck Cyberbeast, a three-and-a-half ton SUV with the acceleration of a Formula One racing car, threatens to add to America's rapidly rising pedestrian death toll (Gagliardi, 2023). Musk's tunnels company, originally formed as part of his supposedly supersonic Hyperloop project, now seems more committed to speeding up the sluggish pace of the average town car rather than making urban planning any greener. Tunnel construction is actually even more unsustainable than building roads, emitting eight times as much CO_2. Operating tunnels is also highly energy-intensive (due to continuous lighting, ventilation and camera surveillance) and driving vehicles through them is less energy efficient than on the surface due to increased aerodynamic resistance (Mutlay, 2018).

If Musk was genuinely interested in ecological alternatives, he might focus not on saving private cars from extinction but on pollution-free public transport. But his extreme individualism vehemently rails against this. "I think public transit is painful. It sucks," he's declared. He's expressed an almost pathological dislike of sharing a ride "with a bunch of strangers, one of whom might be a serial killer"(Marshall, 2017). Indeed, his much-vaunted Hyperloop project, according to his biographer Ashlee Vance (2015:332), "originated out of his hatred for California's proposed high-speed rail system".

Absolute decoupling is not possible, even for electric vehicles (EVs). Battery-laden EVs are heavier than conventional cars and so contribute to deadly air pollution through increased tyre wear. Tyres are now producing nearly 2,000 times more particle pollution as the exhaust pipes of modern cars, and with SUVs and other large models, the trend is for cars to get even heavier (Lai, 2022). EVs also require vast quantities of new materials, such as copper, cobalt, nickel and magnesium and are creating a huge demand for lithium for battery giga-factories. Musk may talk about controlling the supply chains for these natural resources but what we're seeing is a green minerals gold rush, which replicates carbon capitalism's model of exploiting workers in the Global South. 70% of the world's cobalt supply is in the Democratic Republic of Congo, most of whose citizens live on £1.50 a day, despite possessing natural resources worth some $20 trillion. The mining of cobalt in the Congo by Western corporations often involves low pay, harsh conditions, widespread health hazards and the use of some 40,000 child labourers, some of them as young as six (Lawson, 2021). The Anthropocene Crisis offers an opportunity to equalize the relationship between Global North and South by recognizing the climate and ecological damage that the former has wreaked on the latter. Instead, we are seeing the same exploitative economic pattern being reinvented, now under the self-righteous banner of "saving the planet".

In this context, it's also no surprise to learn that Musk's personal carbon footprint is as gargantuan as that to which Bill Gates (2021) now confesses. According to tech writer Paris Marx (2020), Musk flew some 160,000 miles in 2018, making his carbon consumption 263 times larger than that of the average world citizen; and that's before you consider that he owns five houses in just one district of Bel Air. Not surprisingly, Marx accuses Musk of being "an active obstructer of meaningful climate policy".

The ultimate purpose of Musk's delayism has very little to do with replacing the carbon economy with a decarbonised replica. He's even claimed that "Population collapse due to low birth rates is a bigger threat to civiliza-tion than global warming" (Musk, 2022). Renewable energy and other terrestrial projects are just launch pads, literally, for the next phase of civilisation which Musk envisages. Tesla itself is a humachine project rather than a simple car company, aiming to produce humanoid robots and self-driving humanized machines that are multi-functional mobile environments. Moreover, in Musk's vision of the near future, the Tesla will be owned by mechanized humans, equipped with Neuralink brain implants which, inter alia, will enable them to summon their cars simply via thought control (we'll return to brain mechanization in Chapter 18).

For Musk, we should remember, the main purpose of human-machine hybridization is to create "a multiplanetary species". His terrestrial projects are simply the means to the end he has dreamt of since his science fiction-obsessed childhood: space exploration. The specific object of his extra-terrestrial ambitions is Mars, where, he says, he intends to end his days:

> I would like to die thinking that humanity has a bright future. If we can solve sustainable energy and be well on our way to becoming a multiplanetary species with a self-sustaining civilization on another planet … I think that would be really good. (quoted in Vance, 2015:5).

From an environmental standpoint, however, rocket technology unwinds decades of progress on pollution, taking us back to the pre-petroleum era, when kerosene, which was then mainly used for lamps, was the primary oil derivative. Kerosene-fuelled rockets like Space X's flagship Falcon Heavy hurl as much CO2 into the atmosphere in the first few minutes of flight as an average car would emit in two centuries. Rocket fuel also carries soot into the upper atmosphere, accelerating global warming (Verbeek and Fouquet, 2020). And rockets need launch pads, which are potential environment wreckers; the inhabitants of one rocket site offered to SpaceX by the Indonesian government have protested that it would depopulate their island and devastate its ecology (James, 2021). If Musk was genuinely committed to renewable energy, he might make the development of a cleaner alternate fuel a precondition of space exploration. Instead his ambitious Mars plans were bolstered in 2021 by NASA making SpaceX the sole contractor for the Artemis project of returning humans to the moon, indicating that billions of dollars of public money is now backing Musk's multiplanetary species programme (Chang, 2021) In addition, SpaceX plans to launch over 40,000 satellites by 2030, to add to the 400,000 from other manufacturers which have been approved, which could not only hamper efforts to reduce carbon emissions but also endanger "our common human heritage", as astronomy writer Stuart Clark (2019) rightly calls the night sky. Space may soon resemble an LA freeway but one congested with satellites instead of cars, which will regularly collide or plunge to earth as they decay, making stargazing a thing of the past (Knapton, 2023).

For Musk, it seems, real sustainability can never be found if humans stick to planet Earth. Even if extreme geoengineering succeeds, it's not humans who will inhabit our planet, but augmented cyborg hybrids capable of undertaking multi-year journeys into space and clever enough to outwit the superintelligent androids which Musk fears the AI project will produce (Vance, 2015). All in all, Musk's vision of the future may be somewhat greener than that of unreconstructed climate deniers but it's so narcissistic and self-contradictory that it could end up breathing new life into carbon capitalism, a resurrection which this planet can ill afford.

Plexitism: Jeff Bezos and Space Colonialism

Musk is by no means alone among ontopreneurs in seeing the ultimate goal of environmentalism in the humachine age as not so much saving planet Earth as finding the means to escape it altogether. Jeff Bezos is also a lifelong science-fiction devotee, an ardent Star Trek fan and a passionate supporter of what might be labelled Planetary Exit (or Plexit for short). Bezos has said that he sees his role as a "builder", converting the dreams of science fiction writers into commercial reality. (Incidentally, this label also could apply to Musk, whose entire life project might be construed as an attempt to turn Kim Stanley Robinson's 1990s sci-fi epic *Mars Trilogy* into reality). Bezos has claimed that his real reason for starting Amazon was to fund his space company, Blue Origin, and in 2021 he announced his retirement from Amazon to devote himself to space travel and rocket development. His goal stretches beyond the conquest of Mars (about which he is sceptical) to a multi-planetary civilization. "If we want, we could have a trillion human beings living in the solar system," he believes (Davenport, 2018:260).

If Amazon's climate pledges and sustainability efforts seem half-hearted, this may be because Bezos is convinced that, in the end, space colonialism offers humanity its only realistic chance for saving capitalism and its associated lifestyle:

> You either go into space or you need to control population on Earth. You need to control energy usage on earth. These things are totally at odds with a free society. And it's going to be dull. I want my great-great grandchildren to be using more energy per capita than I do. And the only way they can be using more energy per capita than me is if we expand out into the solar system. And then we can really keep Earth as this incredible gem that it is (Davenport, 2018:260).

Bezos seems to have held this vision unwaveringly since his high school days. He recognizes that renewable energy cannot maintain current American-style consumption let alone expand it to the rest of the world. He seems to be saying that only by being prepared to change everything and everyone everywhere can economic growth be saved from itself: the mission of ontocapitalism in a nutshell. A multi-planetary civilisation creates the possibility for space mining to replace Earth's depleted resources, requiring automated transport, equipment and robot workers. And, of course, a trillion consumers will provide endless opportunities for Amazon's goods and services and the humachine products it has in the pipeline.

Plexit is the ultimate decoupling fantasy but it's also an enormous distraction from the problems we face today and from realistic, eco-democratic solutions to them. As energy expert Vaclav Smil once said, "The last thing a country with 50 million people on food stamps and 85 billion dollars deeper in debt every month needs is anything to do with space" (Vance 2015:349). Recognising the reality of the Anthropocene Crisis and reorganizing existing economic resources accordingly would itself reduce the overpopulation which Bezos fears. It would also move towards a level of equality which may seem "dull" to a multibillionaire who has it all but to most people on the planet it may seem appreciably more exciting and rewarding than their current lot – and that's before full-scale job automation raises its head. Maybe at some stage in the future, when a sustainable and equitable global civilisation has begun to flourish without the need for extra-terrestrial colonialism, space exploration may become an attractive possibility. But that would require democratic consent rather than the current plutotechnic system that enables a handful of power-obsessed billionaires to shape the future of the cosmos for all of humanity.

In its way, Plexitism is as complete a refusal to face the Anthropocene Crisis as climate denialism and risks prolonging the environmental destructiveness of carbon capitalism. Even those advocating an overtly environmentalist approach can't entirely escape the seductiveness of the green growth myth. Mainstream socialism and social democracy may be greening fast but, as I previously suggested, elements of the left are still in thrall to technologism and the chimera of never-ending Western economic expansion. For instance, the leader of the British Labour Party, Keir Starmer, has stated that just three things are needed to fix the raddled UK economy:"Growth. Growth. And Growth" (Labour.org.uk, 2022). In a not entirely dissimilar vein, a group of mainly US-based academics, calling themselves Ecomodernists, argue that the best way to protect the planet is through accelerated urbanization and full-on technological development, including genetically modified food, nuclear power and (inevitably) carbon capture technology (Asafu-Adjaye et al, 2015). This claim has been thoroughly debunked by Jeremy Caradonna (2015) and fellow degrowthers, committed to the "voluntary contraction of material throughputs", who charge ecomodernists with rehearsing all the faults of conventional growthist economics. These include falling for the decoupling myth and taking a condescending view of agrarian, non-industrialized societies and the Global South in general. In short, ecomodernism is a reminder of how easily "the green economy" can be viewed through the lens of the infatuation with technology that helped to create the climate and biodiversity emergency in the first place.

Conclusion: The Planet Comes First

To sum up, the humachinators' deceptive strategy of climate delayism, green growthism, space colonialism and greenwashing tricknology represents a major risk to the viability of life on Earth, particularly for billions of people in the most vulnerable regions of the planet. It's almost certainly too late to prevent the 1.5C global temperature limit from being permanently breached – on a temporary basis this vital planetary threshold was crossed in September 2023 – but we can still reduce the catastrophic scale of global warming (Saunders, 2023). We can also save further plant and animal species from extinction, prevent more habitats from destruction by deforestation and industrial agriculture and phase out the chemical pollution which poisons our soil, sea, water, air and bodies. The danger is that unless the limitations of the humachinators' attempts to "save the planet" are exposed quickly enough, the neomechanalist fantasy of remodelling the biosphere through ever-more extreme geoengineering experiments may seem like humanity's only remaining option, a point which could signify the arrival of the Technocene. Such a reckless, high-risk approach to the near future prompts another question: if this is what the age of humachines is doing to environmentalism and climate policy, what might it be doing to democratic politics? It's time to confront the second great risk of human-machine fusion.

CHAPTER 9

Democracy at Risk: The Politics of Humachination and the Path to Technocene Totalitarianism

The establishment of the organizational principle of majority rule is one of the greatest achievements of the Enlightenment. It represents a huge advance on the Pyramid Pattern of the first five thousand years of human civilisation, during which time almost every society was ruled by an elite which owed its power to military violence and demanded unquestioning obedience from those lower down the hierarchy. But democracy remains an incomplete revolution. It's a fragile plant that needs much nurturing and now is seemingly prey to a new form of a very old disease, plutocracy, or, as Aristotle called it, oligarchy (*Politics,* VII). Indeed, in the age of humachines, it's no exaggeration to say that the entire project of democracy is at risk.

Evidence for this can be found in the Economist Intelligence Unit's annual Democracy Index which concludes that less than half of the world's population (45.7%) currently live in a democracy of any kind. It designated only 6.4% of the world's nations as "full democracies" (down from 8.4% in the previous year). The remainder are categorized as "flawed democracies" (including the US, France and, for the first time, Spain), semi-autocratic "hybrid regimes" and "authoritarian" states that don't even make any pretence at democracy, in which a dispiriting third (37.1%) of the global population live (EIU, 2022).

The triumph of the West in the Cold War has not led to the consolidation of democratic capitalism anticipated by liberals in the 1990s. The "end of history" scenario, prefigured by Francis Fukuyama (1992) and others, has been harshly repudiated by the war-mongering gangster capitalism of Vladimir Putin's Russia and majority rule seems to be hanging by a thread in the Anglo-American vanguards of democracy. In 2019 in the UK, a Hansard Society survey revealed that 54% of voters wanted "a strong leader who is willing to break the rules" (Fowler, 2019). Three years later, after an orgy of rule-breaking, scandals and lies, Prime Minster Boris Johnson was finally ousted in disgrace by his own parliamentary party. Donald Trump's alleged incitement to insurrection in Washington DC in January 2021 failed but his baseless refusal to accept the outcome of the 2020 presidential election has convinced many American conservatives that the election was illegitimate. Worldwide a substantial majority of people (58%) now express dissatisfaction with democracy, an increase of a fifth since 2005 (39%) (Foa et al, 2020)

For those who believe in democracy, the humachine transformation of everything human surely seems like a reckless distraction from what really matters politically. If we had the right objectives, the focus would surely be on consolidating established democracies, perhaps by reforming the electoral system and extending political participation through citizen juries and popular assemblies (as in ancient Athens), a topic I'll return to in Chapter 26. This could set an example for emerging democracies and send a powerful signal to autocracies and dictatorships which reject democratic voting principles and human rights norms. Instead, we have the priorities of the GUN worldplan which subordinates democracy to the goal of infinite economic growth. The result, as we explore in this chapter, is a techno-elite that not only undermines the democratic process through their technology but also by their organizational practices. Indeed, one prominent ontopreneur urges us to take the technology consumerism argument to its logical conclusion and jettison politics altogether.

The Practical UNCs of Humachines and the Crisis of Democracy

If progress on democracy has stalled in the new millennium, while everything else seems to be accelerating, it's at least in part due to the practical role played by humanized machines. A blitz of unintended negative consequences for democratic decision-making has been unleashed, as IT, or Information Technology, has turned into DT, Disinformation Technology. Social media boosts conspiracy theories, faked news, state-sponsored election disruption and far-right propaganda. It allows a disintegrative, neo-mechanical mentality to thrive, which employs predictive behavioural techniques to diminish freedom and a new propaganda armoury to insidiously influence voting behaviour (Bartlett, 2018).

Democracy, by definition, is meant to be holistic; it refers to the rights of the whole of the people. It has taken centuries of political struggle to reach a situation where political parties present wide-ranging manifestos which address issues covering the whole of society to large numbers of people simultaneously. But new, online targeted advertising – based on the Google mirror trick- renders a coherent, holistic vision unnecessary, as a manifesto can now be fragmented into hundreds of different messages. Via social media, contradictory adverts can be sent to two neighbours in the same street or two family members in the same household. The rule of the majority is reduced to a numbers game or, more specifically, a data game. Often targeted are the small numbers of swing voters in swing states or constituencies that need to be shifted to change the overall result. It's a victory for the part over the whole that facilitates a crude divide-and-rule strategy based on increasingly sophisticated knowledge of voters' intentions.

Humachination also discourages the reliable information-gathering which is crucial to good political decision-making. Algorithms react to exaggerated content, downplaying moderate, balanced views and exacerbating more extreme political positions. The anonymity of social media feeds into this polarizing effect, enabling cynical, Machiavellian impersonation. One study of millions of posts on Twitter found that a quarter of all messages on a crucial climate debate were sent by bots, autonomously tweeting or retweeting in favour of Trump's climate denialism (Milman, 2020). Anonymity also breeds irresponsible hate crime, which can have the effect of deterring women or ethnic minority representatives from entering, or staying in, politics. World Wide Web founder Tim Berners-Lee has declared that "the internet is not working for women and girls", citing a survey in which half of the women surveyed said they'd experienced "online harms", such as sexual harassment, threatening messages and images shared without their consent (Hern, 2021).

Inevitably, all this militates against wise, deliberative decision-making based on reliable sources and favours impulsive choices, which can have long-lasting effects when it comes to electing a local council, a government or the destiny of a nation in a referendum. Our information sources have shifted from newspapers and TV news, which offers a relatively wide range of subjects and opinions, to narrowband, customisable news feeds, which only focus on topics which lie within the user's comfort zone. This reductionism can vitiate the all-round knowledge of the voter.

At the same time, new technology has helped to take political propaganda into a new alarming age of innovation. Well researched, reliably-sourced news often exists behind paywalls, whereas fake news is free. In the age of post-truth, it's never been easier to produce compelling political messaging that is devoid of evidence or journalistic ethics and disseminate it instantly across the globe. In a world where information is watched as much as read, deepfake technology intensifies truth-reduction, creating plausible videos of political leaders saying what they would never say or imaginary reporters mouthing news that never happened (Sample, 2020). The first election to be swung by deepfakes may already have happened. It's alleged that the 2023 election in Slovakia, narrowly won by a pro-Russian rightwing party, was influenced by deepfake "recordings" suggesting that the opposition was planning to rig the elections and double the price of beer (Conradi, 2023).

The humachine threat to our political freedom of choice is planetwide. If anything, it's most acute in recently established democracies still struggling to find their feet. The disgraced Cambridge Analytica consultancy boasted of influencing several major election campaigns in the developing world, in part by using illegally acquired data. Many emerging democracies are even more dependent on social media for their news than the West. As cultural historian Siva Vaidhyanathan (2019) points out, social media is heavily influencing elections in Sri Lanka, Myanmar, Eastern Europe and South America, as Facebook did in helping to elect the authoritarian Rodrigo Duterte in the Philippines in 2016, as well as Donald Trump in the USA. When it comes to publishing false political advertisements, the massively popular TikTok can be even worse than Facebook. The Chinese-owned platform approved 90% of adverts containing deliberate electoral disinformation submitted by US researchers in an ingenuous experiment (Global

Witness, 2022). Large-scale, encrypted communication channels can be turned to even more dangerous uses, as exemplified by Telegram, which is owned by billionaire libertarian Pavel Durov. His extreme commitment to "free speech" has enabled the messaging platform to serve as a recruitment and propaganda tool for neo-Nazis, white supremacists, terrorist groups and lone actors committed to overthrowing democratic governments (Gais and Squire, 2021).

The use of this technology can fundamentally disrupt the relationship between what is true and what is fake, a situation in which anti-democratic forces revel. The Russian state under Vladimir Putin undermines elections at home and abroad by constant trolling, distraction and confusion, using post-modernist theatrical stratagems to set up fake opposition groups and sponsor genuine protest groups. In a St Petersburg election, two near-identical doppelganger pro-Putin candidates defeated a dissident politician by assuming his name and physical appearance (Seddon,2021). The Chinese government, for its part, sends some 450 million distracting social media posts a year, according to researchers at Harvard (King et al, 2017).

In established democracies, there is the danger that the already challenging task of voting becomes a degraded human skill. Instead of active participants in democracy we risk ending up as fearful, zombie citizens, unsure of our own preferences, unconsciously manipulated by algorithms or consciously deferring to rigged recommendations.

We also have to factor in the political effect of the possible hollowing out of the middle class by mass job automation, referred to in Chapter 3. In the initial phase of capitalism, the bourgeoisie was instrumental in wrenching power away from the feudal elite and electoral democracy gave it to the means to consolidate its position within society. But if cultural critic Curtis White (2017:19) is right, "What survives of the middle class in the future will be a servant class... whose jobs will depend not only on their skills but on their ability to flatter and provide pleasure for the elites". In such a case, Barrington Moore's (1966:418) wry axiom, "no bourgeoisie, no democracy", would turn prophetic. Indeed, today's autocracies have notoriously weak middle classes. Without the mid-pyramid class that exerts pressure upwards, the risk intensifies of a return to the sheer hierarchies of the Pyramid Age. Democracy could wither away, becoming just one more failed political experiment.

Technocene Political Theory: Peter Thiel and the Replacement of Democracy by Technology

In fact, for some leaders of the humachine age, the death of democracy may not be an unintended consequence of new technology but an actual theoretical goal. If the freedom to vote can't deliver sufficiently high living standards to the majority of people why bother with politics at all? That's the challenge issued by Peter Thiel (2009), who says he "no longer believes that freedom and democracy are compatible". Thiel's credentials as an ontopreneur are impeccable. The so-called "Don of the PayPal mafia", he played a crucial role as an early investor in Facebook and operates as a highly influential, billionaire hedge fund manager and entrepreneur. Thiel seems prepared to act as spokesperson for his age, advocating a new definition of political freedom that has nothing to do with politics and everything to do with new technology.

Thiel begins his manifesto, *The Education of a Libertarian* (2009), as follows: "I stand against confiscatory taxes, totalitarian collectives, and the ideology of the inevitability of the death of every individual." The first two points could have been made by Friedrich Hayek, Milton Friedman or any other champion of neoliberal economics in the past. Thiel's third point, however, declaring his support for human immortality, could only have been made in the "post-biological" age of humachines. At any other time, it might have been regarded as totally insane.

As a libertarian, Thiel dedicates himself to defining "authentic human freedom" which he sees as "the precondition for the greatest good". He attributes the pessimism that some people feel about democracy to a failure to allow free markets to operate unchecked. He claims that this "anti-business approach" which he alleges has been pursued in America since the 1920s, has led to "the vast increase in welfare beneficiaries and the extension of the franchise to women… [Which] have rendered the notion of "capitalist democracy" into an oxymoron". Addressing the outrage which these misogynistic comments provoked, Thiel later added that he didn't think that any class of people should be disenfranchised but that "I have little hope that voting will make things better". In other words, politics is a waste of time regardless of your gender. If we want real freedom and progress, he implies, we have a choice: free market capitalism or democracy.

In fact, Thiel argues, real freedom is to be found "in an escape from politics in all forms, from the totalitarian and fundamentalist catastrophes to the unthinking demos that guides so-called "social democracy". One area in which this freedom can supposedly thrive is cyber space via the internet, in which "an entrepreneur may create a new world". The second is the "limitless frontier" of outer space. In calling for a redoubling of efforts "to commercialize space", Thiel shows he is as ardent a Plexiteer as any ontocapitalist. It's his implicit answer to the question posed by the title of a book by commons scholar Peter Barnes (2001):" Who owns the Sky?" For Thiel, libertarian entrepreneurs should also own the sea – that's his third arena for technological colonisation. He wants the oceans, the 70% of the planet's surface not yet owned by capitalists, to become the new Wild West of "seasteading".

All these spaces are not free or empty – any more than was the Wild West, part of a continent inhabited by hundreds of Native American nations over many millennia (Diamond, 1997). The internet was largely created by non-profit bodies – academic, scientific and military, paid for by public money and many feel it should still be owned by the people (otherwise known as "the unthinking demos"). Thiel's idea of the freedom of the wealth creator comes at the expense of the freedom of everybody else, especially those who suffer most when a commons is enclosed and privatised. In this, we get an unmistakable indication that the humachination project is simply an extension of the same land-grabbing, frontier-busting pursuit of profit that drove colonialism in the past. And Thiel is clear that the battle between entrepreneurs doing what they want to do and governments trying to stop them is a life and death struggle:

> We are in a deadly race between politics and technology … The fate of our world may depend on the effort of a single individual who builds or propagates the machinery of freedom that makes the world safe for capitalism.

As a description of humachine capitalism, this is hard to beat. It combines a rampantly individualistic fantasy of the heroic entrepreneur with an elitist dismissal of the relevance of the majority of people and a frank admission that only the new technological "machinery of freedom" can save capitalism from itself.

In a second essay, *Against Edenism*, Thiel (2015) adds an anti-environmentalist dimension to his anti-democracy argument, claiming that "only a highly advanced level of science and technology can feed a global population expected to reach 10 billion by mid-century. Yet food scarcity is often exacerbated by technology rather than solved by it. Environmentalist George Monbiot (2022) points to the millions of acres of farming dedicated to "feeding cars" rather than humans in the form of crops grown for biofuel. Scarcity is an organizational problem created by capitalism rather than a purely technological issue but to see this requires holistic reflection rather than Thiel's panic-inducing accelerationism and his declared admiration for the recklessness of Doctor Faust, which, of course, is all part Big Tech's dromology playbook.

Against Edenism also continues the war against multiculturalism and "wokery" which Thiel began in *The Diversity Myth*, a book written with future Big Tech billionaire David Sacks, which was notorious for claiming that some allegations of date rape were "seductions that were later regretted" (Sacks and Thiel, 1995). Thiel lambasts those who oppose technological acceleration, among whom he includes "Luddites", "the Hollywood Left", environmentalists and anybody supporting financial regulation or opposing stem-cell genetics or fracking. These he considers enemies of the alliance of "Judeo-Western optimism", for which "science and technology are natural allies", as is the "the optimism of Bacon and Hobbes", a clear nod in the direction of the neomechanicalist view of science by the former Stanford philosophy graduate.

In invoking Hobbes, Thiel also invokes the authoritarianism which the author of *Leviathan* saw as the only alternative to the lawlessness of people acting in a genuinely self-organizing way. Like all conservatives, Thiel is a defender of inequality, whether based on wealth or IQ (intelligence supremacism seems to be another of his causes). I suspect he knows full well that there is no such thing as a post-political state and that nothing is as political as the issue of who controls a society's technology. His plutotechnic libertarianism is really a form of segregationism: you are free as long as you are wealthy, confident, technically adept and entrepreneurial. Everybody else needs to find their place within the hierarchy. Like other extreme individualists, he fails to understand that freedom is a product of sharing, not something to be grabbed by the winners in a zero-sum competition. It's another reminder that the unchaining of Prometheus may lead to the enchaining of the majority. Indeed, we might define a right-wing libertarian as one who argues for total freedom for businesses, and for all who own and run them, but requires something approaching a police state for everybody else.

Democracy Killers: The Automated Surveillance State, Anti-Unionism and Regulation Avoidance

In fact, the above description turns out to be particularly applicable to Peter Thiel when we realise that despite his professed passion for liberty, he has created his own practical "machinery of freedom" for ensuring that the majority of the electorate remain compliant with the law. Founded in 2003, his Palantir Technologies Corporation (named after the all-seeing stone in *Lord of the Rings* in the typically faux counter-cultural style of Silicon Valley) is a data-hungry software giant, which has worked extensively with the CIA and the US military to develop surveillance systems for tracking terrorists, rogue traders and illegal immigrants. Valued at nearly $15 billion in early 2023, it has been described as "one of the most secret security companies in the world". One of its aims is to embed its Gotham intelligence system in European police forces, prompting over 100 of the world's leading privacy scholars to issue a warning that:

> Palantir's business model is based on a particular form of surveillance capitalism that targets marginalized communities and accelerates the rise of discriminatory technologies such as predictive policing (Howden et al, 2021).

Palantir's scope goes well beyond policing and immigration. Its CEO has made it clear that its Foundry system is essentially "an operating system for governments" (Howden et al, 2021). Its regulatory filing states its aim is to make itself "the default operating system across the US government" and stresses its work with liberal democracies, "while leaving ample room for working with US allies that don't live up to that description", in the words of *The Financial Times* (Waters, 2020). The danger to democracy is very clear; what is being offered here is a comprehensive, all-seeing system which quietly insinuates itself into a state's security and administrative apparatus. We might call it the Automated Surveillance State (suggesting that the law is, or is soon to become, an ASS). The ASS offers a degree of institutionalized control over a population which might tempt even liberal governments. And as for phoney democracies, authoritarian regimes and anybody attempting a military coup, it will provide an ideal, ready-made, digital dictatorship kit.

A crucial element in an effective, governmental control system is data relating to citizens' health, which is maybe why Palantir is making considerable efforts to infiltrate global health services. For example, during the COVID-19 pandemic it offered to help Britain's National Health Service for free. Subsequently it poached several top NHS executives and in 2023 controversially succeeded in wining the contract to become the de facto "operating system for data in the NHS", despite Thiel describing Britain's affection for the service as akin to Stockholm syndrome (Murgla and Neville, 2022, Donnelly, 2023). This puts Thiel's philosophical objection to "deathism" in a more pragmatic commercial context. Capturing a population's most intimate health data can be worth a fortune, especially in the goldmine that is the US medical market. It places Thiel squarely in the mainstream of the humachine age, alongside the other Big Tech titans who advocate an end to human mortality (more of this in Chapter 20).

Indeed, Thiel is fully aligned with the humachination project in many other areas; for instance, he's an even bigger investor in Ray Kurzweil's Singularity University than Larry Page. Some in Silicon Valley were scandalized by Thiel's support for Donald Trump and his subsequent sponsorship of extremist "New Right" intellectuals and senatorial candidates, which jars with Big Tech's preferred political stance of support for the Democratic Party (Pogue, 2022). But when it comes to core business issues, Thiel is very much on the same page as his fellow ontopreneurs. As Joel Bakan (2020) observes, Big Tech leaders like to see themselves as liberals, championing democracy, rather than right-wing libertarians, but when it comes down to how they act the differences between the two camps dwindle away, especially when basic growth capitalist principles are at stake.

Take the case of trade unions, a traditional marker of right- and left-wing political positions. Many argue that one of the reasons why democracy has been so weakened since the 1970s is because right-wingers have been able to dramatically decrease unions' rights to collective bargaining. In the US private sector, trade union membership declined precipitously from 31% in 1987 to just 6.5% in 2017 (Bakan, 2020). For the Reagan generation of billionaires like Charles Koch, anti-unionism was a passionate cause long before climate denialism – in fact, in the 1930s Koch's father, Fred, the founder of the family firm, expressed admiration for the labour policies of Nazi Germany and Fascist Italy (Mayer, 2016). In the 1980s, Charles Koch devoted himself to breaking the considerable power of the unions in the oil industry, notably in his vicious "attrition war" against organized labour at his Pine Bend refinery. He also founded right-wing think tanks like the Cato Institute and invested heavily in political lobbying and even philanthropy to promote his extreme anti-union, neoliberal views (Leonard, 2019).

Most Big Tech corporations don't need to engage in such aggressive muzzling of in-house trade unions for the simple reason that they never admit them in the first place. From the start, Silicon Valley deemed technological development incompatible with trade union membership. All-out anti-union warfare is not necessary to ensure one of Tesla's less proclaimed innovations is that it's the only non-unionized major automaker in the US. Nevertheless, preventing unionization still requires persistent effort on Elon Musk's part. He has been fined for illegally threatening to withhold share options from workers joining a union and condemned by a California judge for violating labour laws on multiple occasions (Liao, 2019). Tesla went further at its gigafactory in Buffalo, actually firing 18 employees for trying to organize a union, according to a complaint filed by Workers United (Rogers, 2023).

Any lingering illusions about Musk's attitude to his workers were finally shattered by his takeover of microblogger Twitter (which he rebranded as X). The self-proclaimed "free speech absolutist" fired half of the company's workforce (including its human rights and disability access teams) and demanded that the remainder show "hardcore" loyalty to him by "working long hours at high intensity", which caused many more staff to quit, leaving the platform perilously close to collapse (Siddiqui and Merrill, 2022). Musk's motives for the acquisition were directly in line with anti-progressive, pro-humachine politics. He said he wanted to combat the "woke mind virus, which is fundamentally anti-science, anti-merit, and anti-human." Unless it's stopped, he claims, "civilization will never become multi-planetary" (Isaacson, 2023). The ploy may have worked: almost half of environmental users abandoned X after Musk's takeover, while climate deniers' tweets surged (Chang, 2023).

Jeff Bezos has fought even longer to keep unions out of Amazon, perhaps surprisingly for someone who has nailed his liberal colours to the mast by acquiring *The Washington Post*. Unlike Google and Meta, Amazon is an employer at scale with almost 1.3 million workers across the world.

But from the company's foundation in 1997, Bezos was determined that his US workforce should not be unionized. Amazon has engaged in many underhand tactics to prevent unionisation, including stopping union representatives from accessing Amazon sites, setting up websites claiming that unions would stop Amazon employees from being "helpful and social", and monitoring, and often harassing, any employee showing an interest in unionization (Lee and Rogers, 2021). When offline grocery Whole Foods was acquired by Amazon, managers were explicitly told to get the anti-union message across to their workers.

To some extent, Bezos's fortune is dependent on this strategy, because it's highly improbable that a unionized workforce would have tolerated the work conditions which Amazon workers have to endure. Warehouse employees, carrying handheld computers which dictate every action, work 10-hour shifts, often with not enough time to go to the bathroom in what organizational psychologist Andre Spicer (2018) calls "one of the most all-pervasive control systems in history. "You're constantly being watched and monitored. They seem to think you're another machine," said one US Amazon employee (Lee and Rogers, 2021). Unions would also fiercely resist the job automation which is surely just around the corner. Amazon's thriving robotics division may stop at nothing short of fully automated warehouses – in fact, two-legged, humanoid Digit robots have already started work in several of its US fulfilment centres – while replacing notoriously stressed human drivers with delivery drones and robotic vehicles (Field, 2023). Bezos's liberal philanthropy tells a different story, of course, but charity begins in the workplace as well as the home. As one worker fighting for union rights in an Afro-American dominated Amazon warehouse put it: "He gives all this money to Black Lives Matter. But he doesn't want to really, truly help the Black workers who work for him."

Occasionally, Big Tech employees can make their voices heard. A notable victory for unionization in the US was achieved by Amazon workers in Staten Island in April 2022, although a vote to unionize a nearby Amazon warehouse a month later failed. At Google, employees were able to force management to give up the company's sinister Maven military contract but they lack the institutional power as stakeholders to consistently share in decision-making. The essentially undemocratic nature of the humachine corporations – exemplified by Thiel and his two other Palantir co-founders who have superior, "Emperors for Life" voting rights regardless of their shareholding – means that many Big Tech employees have some of the most minimal workers' rights in recent history (Leonard, 2021).

Stymying government control over technology is another area that unites all humachinators. As Joel Bakan says, "there is one thing agreed upon by the Valley's liberals and libertarians alike: government regulation is bad" (Bakan, 2020: 92). We know just how central this principle is in Kurzweil's idea of the singularity and Schwab's Fourth Industrial Revolution. In practice, however, the humachine corporations need to engage in rather more nuanced tricknology to keep the representatives of the people at bay. So, for example, Facebook will invest in human monitors to take on the dehumanizing task of reviewing abusive material on its platforms but lobby hard against any changes in legislation which might reduce this abuse.

Alphabet takes a similar smoke and mirrors approach to fending off calls for anti-trust legislation. CEO Sundar Pichai's strategy seems to be "to publicly welcome new forms of regulation, while at the same time trying to head off its most onerous effects" (Waters, 2020). Even more hypocritical is Big Tech corporations' defence against privacy regulation, based on claims about protecting users' privacy that are really "a cloak to justify their privacy-invasive practices", argues Privacy International (2021). Likewise, in 2023 Sam Altman of OpenAI publicly called for strong government regulation of AI, while privately lobbying the EU to water down its AI Act (Perrigo, 2023). Steering the economic system towards the safe haven of self-regulation is the goal for humachinators. Maintaining an outward stance of promoting liberal democracy, while fighting relentlessly to maintain their monopolistic market power has worked well so far. The velvet glove makes it so much harder to see just how the iron first is operating.

Put all this together – a burgeoning surveillance state bent on controlling every aspect of a citizen's life, consumer technology being touted as a better form of freedom than democratic voting rights and fragmented, automation-threatened workforces struggling to unionize in regulation-resistant corporations – and we can see how majority rule might be airbrushed out of history in the not-to-distant future. When push comes to shove, the danger is that libertarians and liberals will unite in doing whatever it takes to keep their vision of techno-utopian capitalism afloat, even if that means jettisoning democracy altogether. And to see what this might involve, we don't have to speculate about the future, because we can turn to an even more powerful techno-elite, which is already entrenched on the opposite side of the Pacific from Silicon Valley.

Humachination Chinese-Style

Ironically for American libertarians and liberals alike, much of what is predicted by the politics of humachination is already being carried out by the Chinese Community Party (CCP). China's authoritarian state capitalism appears to have already flipped the digital dictatorship switch in a technologically advanced state of 1.3 billion inhabitants. "Whoever controls data has the upper hand," President Xi Jinping said in 2013 and the latest iteration of the empire of the Middle Kingdom is determined to embrace human-machine fusion to deliver public security, health, employment, as well as mass consumerism, without any need for Western-style democracy (Kynge and Su 2021). Since the 1970s, a massively centralized state has unleashed a frenzy of capitalist competition that has seen the proportion of the population living in cities leap up from a mere 18% in 1978 to 65% today (Statista, 2022). In a matter of decades, some seven hundred million people have migrated from the countryside, as fishing villages balloon into vast megacities and entire million-inhabitant towns spring up in less than five years. If Martin Jacques (2012) is right this urbanization – or "modernization" as he calls it – will not peak until the figure of at least 80% has been reached later this century.

Mass urbanisation is crucial to effective humachination and nobody in history has committed itself to city-based civilization more emphatically than the nominally Marxist-Leninist CCP, following its disastrous, ecologically illiterate attempts at agrarianism during Mao's Cultural Revolution. Rural environments are too embedded in the ways of the natural world for industrialized efficiency. The city, by contrast, has always been a kind of machine, a built, engineered environment with a structured layout and predictable temporal routines, offering a high degree of control over its citizens.

What we might call the political proposition of the humachine age, that security is preferable to democracy, is still being contested in the West but in China, it's a policy that has been followed for the past two and a half thousand years. The CCP is gambling that if it can maintain a rate of technological acceleration that Western humachinators can only dream of, it can continue to raise living standards sufficiently to persuade its citizens that Western conceptions of democracy and human rights are irrelevant. Human-machine hybridization is absolutely central to this grand plan. Huge investments in robotics, AI and biotechnology are putting China in a prime position to catapult it from the industrial revolution to the humachine age much faster than the US. (In China the innumerable technology enterprises fiercely competing with each other mock Silicon Valley for its relative slowness at innovating and its perceived obsession with playing by the rules (Lee, 2018).) Ferocious competition plus lax privacy laws also make data collection possible on a massive scale, which is one of the reasons why the reach of Chinese humachine empires like Baidu, Tencent and Alibaba can extend even further than their American counterparts.

Ubiquitous, super-fast data collection also powers the formidable surveillance state apparatus which China is developing. Facial recognition systems can still be banned in the West– for example by the city of San Francisco, where, it's been suggested, coders have objected to the surveillance software they are selling to others being trained on themselves – but this is not an option in China (Conger et al, 2019). With cameras placed in every street, alley, workplace, public building and even, since the pandemic, outside people's front doors, Chinese citizens are already the most closely monitored in the world. Over 540 million CCTV cameras are currently in operation, some in overhead drones disguised as doves, others with audio equipment capable of recording everything within a 100-metre radius. Increasingly precise facial and gait recognition, plus DNA information and some 65 different types of police data, are designed to enforce political conformity and prevent mass protest movements such as those which culminated in the Tiananmen Square massacre in 1989 (Sarin, 2022). The use of these systems in the potentially genocidal persecution of the Uyghur people shows what a state which prefers technology to democracy potentially looks like.

For the general population, conformity is enforced by the social credit system which reaches into every aspect of life, penalizing people for political dissent (real or imagined), falling into debt or committing trivial civil offences. The wrong social credit on your phone can instantly disqualify you from travelling or entering public facilities or entertainment venues. The pandemic has hugely increased the amount and depth of medical data now held by the Chinese state, as it has in many other countries. Combine this with data from a citizen's education, work, browsing on the censored internet – and the possibilities for centralized state control increase. Such control is probably aimed at enabling the political and corporate elite to survive once economic growth declines and the country's ecological problems dramatically intensify. Overall, it seems that China is hurtling towards its own version of the Technocene, a society dominated by advanced, humanized machines which has no place for Western-style civil liberties or a majority voting system.

The AI Superpower Technocene Scenario ("ChinAImerica")

How will the West react to China's march into the future? From an eco-democratic perspective, we have to believe that democracy can be made strong enough to resist the Technocene; that when it comes to choosing between freedom and technology the former will win. But much of what we've seen of the political theory and practice of the American humachinators and their devious environmentalism increases the probability that they will end up colluding with Chinese-style techno-authoritarianism, whether by accident or design. Apple's manufacturing and engineering processes have been inextricably entrenched in China for over a decade and Microsoft and Tesla have also shown a willingness to kowtow to China's authoritarian data laws, for example, by making their Chinese data available, on request, to the Chinese government (McGee, 2023, Kynge and Su, 2021)

In *AI Superpowers* (2018), Big Tech insider Kai-Fu Lee forecasts that this data collaboration could lead to the effective vanquishing of global democracy. Lee has held senior scientific and executive roles at Apple, Microsoft and Google, and currently runs a multi-billion-dollar venture capital fund in China, and so he's ideally placed to know what the humachine leadership class has in mind. Over the next two decades he predicts that the Big Five US technology conglomerates, plus BAT, Baidu, Alibaba and Tencent from China, will achieve world domination by virtue of their monopolization of the vast amounts data required by machine learning and the control over global job automation which this entails. American corporations will corner the developed world market for AI, while China will have a stranglehold over the developing world's economies. No other country will have enough data to compete (Lee, 2017).

Lee is clear about the stark implications of this AI mega-cartel for the governments of the 80% of the world's population who are unfortunate enough to live outside the USA or China:

> Unless they wish to plunge their people into poverty. they will be forced to negotiate with whichever country supplies most of their AI software – China or the United States – to essentially become that country's economic dependent, taking in welfare subsidies in exchange for letting the "parent" nation's AI companies continue to profit from the dependent country's users (Lee, 2017).

By accepting their "economic subservience" to the two AI Superpowers, the subaltern nations of the world will receive the revenues necessary to keep their economies from collapsing.

Before the 2008 crash, when many still thought China might be moving towards Western-style democracy, historians coined the term "Chimerica" to indicate the two superpowers forming a new type of financial global economy (Ferguson, 2008). Today, Lee's "ChinAImerica", as it might be dubbed, represents a very different, and much darker, scenario. Such a "global dictdataship" would replace the Global North's current dominance with an even more devastating form of imperialism based on "the unprecedented concentration of wealth in the hands of a few companies in China and the United States" (Lee, 2018:21). In due course, we'll return to this alarming version of the Technocene – in which Europe would be demoted to developing world status – but for the moment let's concede that it amounts to an all-too plausible future, if the politics of humachination are allowed to prevail.

Conclusion

Far from offering emancipation, we again find that leaders of the humachine age risk creating a new kind of political bondage, in this case, a state of technological enchainment which could turns the majority of humanity into virtual AI serfs. This possible recreation of the pyramidal structure of the pre-capitalist world shows the basic disequalizing tendencies of ontocapitalism and emphasizes just how incompatible with democracy the inner logic of humachination could be.

To live in a human community is to live with others and that means being political, whether we like it or not. It also means that there is nothing more political than how technology is organized by a society – the golden rule again. Those who take plutotechnic decision-making for granted imply that some people's freedom is more important than others', which also seems to be the essence of rightwing libertarianism. If we accept this premise, hoodwinking humanity out of democracy will be easy enough. Unfortunately such trickster behaviour comes all too naturally to the Promethean leaders of the humachine age, a theme which the next chapter will now take up.

CHAPTER 10

Trickster Leadership: The Unequal Values of the New Techno-Elite

Ask yourself this basic question: how far can we trust the leaders of the humachination project? The Silicon Valley branch of this global elite certainly try to give the impression that they are on the side of progress. They tend to be youthful, informal in their language and dress code and seemingly fluent in the counter-cultural values of the 1960s. "Don't be evil", "change the world" and "save the planet "are among their messianic slogans. And yet, as we know all too well, this seemingly egalitarian group has amassed a concentration of economic, political and technological power which is unparalleled in modern times. That alone should raise the concern people have expressed about leadership elites throughout history: Quis custodiet ipsos custodes? Who is guarding the guards in today's lightly regulated plutotechnic states in which scientifically-trained billionaires make their corporate decisions behind closed doors and then spin them back to the public via tricknologists?

That's why we need to delve more deeply into the values, culture and educational background of the new Promethean leadership class. Even for someone like myself who has spent over two decades working behind the curtain of corporate leadership, I have to say that the belief systems that are revealed in this chapter are extreme. They cast even further doubt over the extent to which we can trust humachinators to shape the future in a way that serves the interest of humanity as a whole. On equity markets, the VIX

TRICKSTER LEADERSHIP | 165

volatility index tries to calculate future risk or "the degree of fear among market participants" (Kuepper, 2022). I suspect that if we could measure the risk factors associated with the belief systems of the new techno-elite, the fear index might go off the chart.

The Power of Ideological Values

One way in which ruling elites have always convinced the people that they can be trusted is by means of a society's dominant ideology. As Antonio Gramsci (1971) showed almost a century ago, the ability of capitalism to gain public consent through its proclaimed ideas and values can be as essential to its survival as its economic power. Ideological capital can be priceless. Throughout this book, I've suggested that the CIMENT values of Competitiveness, Individualism, Materialism, Elitism, Nationalism and Technologism can help us to understand the hegemonic ideological system associated with capitalism. These deeply-embedded norms, which stand in contrast to the CANDID values of ecological democracy, which include Cooperativism, Altruism and Deference to Nature, act as a justification for economic inequality and can subvert the cultural egalitarianism which many people are increasingly demanding, as recent global movements like Me Too and Black Lives Matter indicate. The leaders of the humachine age embody this CIMENT ideology to a striking degree, which, up until now at least, has afforded them a persuasive plausibility which they might otherwise lack.

Materialism and Elitism

Let's start with the CIMENT value of materialism, for nothing better illustrates the humachinators' power than their grip on one of the most dominant belief systems of modern capitalism. Owning a space rocket is just one ostentatious symbol of the almost unimaginable wealth that many ontopreneurs boast, to go with their penthouses, private islands, country estates, jets and emissions-boosting super yachts. In a society that grades success by material possessions, the fact that humachine capitalism has produced some of the richest individuals in history may seem like the only justification the project needs. In 2022 seven out of the top nine places on Forbes' rich list belonged to Big Tech billionaires, ranging in wealth from $208 billion to $90 billion. At that time, Jeff Bezos' fortune was larger than the GDP of medium-sized countries such as Algeria, Hungary or Ecuador (World Bank, 2022). Bezos and Elon Musk together own as much as the poorest 40% of American citizens and the world's top twenty billionaires, almost all of whom owe their fortunes to highly technologized businesses, possess more than the GDPs of all of sub-Saharan Africa (Oxfam, 2022 (Sanders, 2021).

These staggering levels of wealth inequality establish today's tycoons as almost mythological leaders. For some admirers, the new elite's brazenly large carbon footprints and their immense property portfolios – for example Bill Gates's vast empire of private farmland and his 66,000 sq foot house, Xanadu 2.0, 100 times the size of the average British home – make them seem self-evidently fit to lead. In a pyramid world in which the richest 1% own 39% of global personal net wealth, the pharaohs of Big Tech represent the 1% of the 1% (World Inequality Database 2022).

And it's not only the extreme material power of the new apex class that ensures their supremacy. They also seem to be reviving the elitist Great Man theory of leadership, which a generation ago seemed dead and buried. This claims that leaders are born rather than made and that organizational success is due to entrepreneurial genius rather than the contribution of multiple stakeholders and exogenous factors. Extravagant investor hero-worship is reflected in the structure of the humachine' corporations which ensure that even fellow equity shareholders have little influence over them. Corporations have never been egalitarian but dual voting shares, and other mechanisms frowned on by corporate governance experts, give today's Big Tech alpha leaders even greater power than their counterparts in the Reaganite 1980s.

Science Elitism

Elitism plays out in another way in the humachine leadership class, which represents the first truly scientific corporate elite in history. As Lewis Mumford (1934) once observed, the innovators of the British industrial revolution were not scientists but self-taught, practical engineers and inventors, a tradition that was continued in America by entrepreneurs like Thomas Edison and Henry Ford, who had no formal science education. Likewise industrial tycoons like Vanderbilt, Carnegie and Rockerfeller – the so-called robber barons – went straight from school into business. This changed in the mid-twentieth century, as giant oil companies and auto-manufacturers began to favour bosses with science degrees, although those with an education in the social sciences (especially economics) or humanities still dominated many corporate boardrooms.

In the humachine age, however, we find an incredible acceleration of knowledge specialization within the leadership class. Science degrees may still be few and far between among Western political leaders but in China a quarter of the current CCP politburo, including President Xi Jinping, now have qualifications in engineering, science or technology (Chan, 2022). But today's Big Tech titans are even more specialized. Almost all of them have degrees in physical science and the majority have been educated in just one STEM subject, which only began to be taught at college level in the 1970s: computer science.

A list of Big Tech billionaires with computer science (CS) degrees reveals just how powerful this elite club is:

Sergey Brin and Larry Page (Google) – Page's father was one of the first full-time professors of computer science and his mother an instructor in computer programming, David Filo and Jerry Yang (Yahoo) Pierre Omiyar (eBay) Steve Chen (YouTube), Ma Hiateng (Tencent), Robin Li (Baidu), Bobby Murphy (Snapchat), Daniel Ek (Spotify) Reed Hastings (Netflix), Brian Armstrong (Coinbase) and Jack Dorsey (Twitter). The latter chose to study CS over political science because he believed software could enact change better than public policy (Wagner, 2017)

All these entrepreneurs formally completed computer science degrees at bachelor level, while several studied it as postgraduates. Other future billionaires were so steeped in computers from their early childhood that they chose to focus on related science subjects, for instance Musk (who studied physics) or Bezos (electrical engineering). Computer prodigies like Mark Zuckerberg and Sean Parker of Facebook, dropped out of university altogether to get on with building their fortunes, following in the footsteps of the co-founders of Microsoft and Apple. If the list were to include mere multi-millionaires among the techno-elite, it would be inordinately longer, especially as salaries for star software engineers can start in seven figures.

This monopolistic concentration of business power on a single academic subject is unprecedented and perhaps testament to the way the neomechanicalist mentality tends to exclude competing worldviews. It's a highly specialised kind of scientific elitism which can create not a meritocracy but a "Mirrortocracy", in which everybody looks and thinks like each other (Bueno, 2014). This degree of homogeneity can have a deleterious effect on diversity and impair socially beneficial leadership. It's also likely to promote greater social inequality, especially if digital education becomes the only path to the few well-paid occupations that survive jobicide.

Gender and Ethnic Inequality

Surprisingly perhaps, another virulent form of elitism also appears to be rearing its head in the humachine age, patriarchy. In terms of gender equality, considerable strides have been made in science and business over the past fifty years, overturning some of the effects of millennia of male-domination. And yet glance again at the list of digital billionaires which I presented above and you'll note that it's as gender exclusionary as a roll call of nineteenth-century robber barons. About the only female computer scientist I can find who has hit the big time as an entrepreneur is Cisco co-founder Sandy Lerner, who has devoted part of her fortune to projects in ecology and women's writing, including restoring Jane Austen's house in Hampshire, a notably different pattern of choices to the obsessive reinvestment in technology that typifies successful male ontopreneurs like Musk, Gates and Thiel (Flood, 2017).

So why is there such a paucity of female software engineers engaged at the highest level of humachination? (Indeed, the project might even be dubbed "humacho-nation", especially if we agree that the strident masculinism of the Baconian scientific revolution reaches its twenty-first-century reductio ad absurdum in the proposed cage fight between Zuckerberg and Musk and the latter's call for "a literal dick measuring contest" (Merchant, 1980, Levin, 2023).) Part of the answer lies in the way CS, the cornerstone academic discipline of the humachine age, has strikingly bucked the recent trend of gender equalization in Western science. Whereas women now take 63% of biological and biomedical science bachelor degrees in the US and 41% of degrees in physical science and technology, in computer science the gender ratio has been stubbornly fixed at around 80:20 in favour of men for decades (Catalyst, 2022). It's also worth bearing in mind that as of 2023 only five of the 225 Nobel Prize winners in physics have been women.

This disparity is reflected in similar or lower gender ratios in Big Tech's software engineering and technology departments. Women may rise to the top in non-technical areas such as marketing or operations but their role in the engine room of software innovation is extremely limited. In robotics, the gender imbalance is even more extreme. For example, in DARPA's prestigious Robotics Challenge competition, out of 444 robot builders, only 23 were women (McFarland, 2015). A pattern of sexual harassment, misconduct and discrimination against women is undoubtedly part of the problem. For example, in 2022 Google paid $118 million to over 15,000 women to settle a lawsuit alleging discrimination against female employees, despite the company pledging to spend $310 million on diversity programmes two years earlier, as a result of another lawsuit (McGee, 2022).

A path-breaking study by Margolis, Fisher and Miller (2000) reveals other reasons why female students may be deterred from studying computer science or completing their courses. Almost inevitably, given the prevalence of neomechanicalism in the physical sciences, one factor is directly related to machines. Female CS students say they lack their male peers' obsession with taking machines apart and fixing them, a fascination that often goes back to early childhood. Male CS students also talk about falling in love with computers at first sight and growing up with "a magnetic attraction" to computer games, gadgets and programming languages. Female students who lack this early immersion in computers often find themselves at a humiliating disadvantage to their male peers. One talented young woman, who was considering giving up CS, despite describing herself as "a maths-science person", explained:

> When I have free time I don't spend it reading machine learning books or robot books like the other guys here... I prefer to read a good fiction book or learn to do photography, or something different, whereas that's their hobby, it's their work, it's their one goal. I'm just not like that at all. I don't dream in code like they do." (Margolis et al, 2000::11)

Other professional and life interests seem to be absent from male students, many of whom are prepared to work all night on assignments. These traits are recognised by job recruiters selecting appropriate candidates for the highly driven, male-dominated organizational cultures which prevail at

Big Tech companies. Former employee Antonio Garcia Martinez (2016) described Facebook as being dominated by 23 year-old programmers, earning half a million dollars a year, working 14-hour days, eating, and often sleeping, in the office "and doing nothing but write code, review code, or comment on new features in internal Facebook groups". He didn't mention if they dreamt in code as well.

In part, then, females who abandon CS are rejecting the egregious lack of work-life balance, which is another hallmark of the humachine elite. It's exemplified by Elon Musk's assertion that "nobody ever changed the world on 40 hours a week". His almost masochistic dissection of the pain of working the 80-100 hour working week, which he recommends for entrepreneurs, indicates a commitment to a way of being which, I suspect, few women would find attractive (Crooks, 2018). Even if they did, they might well be prevented from pursuing it by the sexist division of labour which still keeps most childcare and domestic work in the hands of women. Excessive paid work exploits systemic gender inequality, taking women into areas where they can't – or won't – compete. In my organizational work, I often found that promising female leaders opt out of going for top roles if it requires them to behave like their male bosses (Harvey, 2015. (In this context, it may relevant to note that on the evening of their wedding Elon Musk thought it necessary to remind his first wife that "I am the alpha in this relationship" (Vance, 2015:94).

Some female CS students also seem to be put off by what they see as the narcissistic, social disconnectedness of digital capitalism, even before they encounter it in the corporate world. As one woman, who had been drawn to CS by her altruism, explained:

> I have this thing in me that wants to help. I felt that the only problem in computer science was that I would be detaching myself from society a lot, that I wouldn't be helping, that there would be people in third world countries that I couldn't do anything about." (p5).

This elitist tendency in computer science also makes itself felt in the long-standing underrepresentation of Black people in Big Tech corporations. According to technology worker, LeRon Barton (2021), writing in *The Harvard Business Review*, "When you're the only Black person in an office, you notice it." He points out that only 1% of venture capital investment goes to Black start-ups and that only 2.8% of Google's technical staff is African American and less than 4% of Facebook's entire workforce. This contributes to a hostile environment toward African Americans, he says, "one that tells us, ""you are not welcome"". At executive level, this ethnic bias is even more acute. For example, a mere 0.8% of Apple's senior officials and managers are Black, compared to 13.4% of the US population as a whole (Lago, 2020).

This multi-pronged reinforcement of inequality in CS and Big Tech may or may not be intentional but it clearly does nothing to boost the trustworthiness of the humachination elite. Confining power to a group mainly composed of young, exceptionally well-paid, white men with highly homogenous backgrounds destroys the diversity and representativeness which encourage leadership decisions that are in the interest of the whole of society. It also dramatically raises the level of risk tolerance at play in framing corporate strategy. Men are consistently shown to be more inclined to risk-taking than women – 14% in one study by Claudia Sahm (2012) and risk appetite is highest among young adults and then declines with age. Sahm also finds that Black people are 28% more risk-averse than whites. In other words, we are putting our future in the hands of the most risk-seeking demographic in all of society, which may turn out to be one of the most unwise moves in human history.

Individualism: Have We Reached the Peak?

Another value which binds this new elite together is a passionate belief in another CIMENT value, the supremacy of the individual. Individualism is indispensable to growth capitalism because it encourages the right to endless consumerist consumption and the social myth that anybody can rise from nothing to everything, as in the American Dream narrative. Developing your individuality can be a positive development but there comes a point at which the interests of the individual come into conflict with the interests of society as a whole. In practice, individualism is often used as a justification for the right of the wealthy to dissociate themselves from the rest of society. Those who make it to the top through their own professional efforts join those who are there already, due to the capital their ancestors secured generations ago -by whatever means. The new elite thus merge with the old elite in the most effective of all defences of the Pyramid Pattern.

Nobody grasped this better than Margaret Thatcher (1987) whose declaration that "There's no such thing as society, only individuals and families" ought to be hung above the entrance to Silicon Valley. Yet, amazingly enough, the humachine age is inspired by an even more extreme individualist, the Russian-American novelist and philosopher Ayn Rand. Although she died in 1982, she still exercises an overwhelming intellectual power over the Big Tech leadership class. Little known in Europe (as a novelist, deservedly so), Rand was worshipped by two of the creators of the US neoliberal reversion, Ronald Reagan and the US Treasury Secretary Alan Greenspan who helped to guide the global economy to the great financial crash of 2008. Her influence has been transmitted to Silicon Valley by Steve Jobs, Peter Thiel, Uber's Travis Kalanick and many other devotees (McKibben, 2019).

Rand's philosophy turns individualism and the other CIMENT values into a militant, revolutionary creed. For her, altruism (one of the lead CANDID values) involves a self-sacrifice that is "incompatible with freedom, with capitalism and with individual rights" (1964:95). She believed that "collective rights is a contradiction in terms" (1964:101) and that "the common good" is "a meaningless concept", because "all progress is the work of individuals" (1967: 20). In the *Virtues of Selfishness* she called "selfishness… the highest of morality" and endorsed "a full, pure, uncontrolled, unregulated, laissez-faire capitalism" in a way that anticipates the humachinators' unconditional faith in our current economic system (1964:33). In fact, her best-selling novels of the 1940s and 50s, which feature heroic, egomaniacal, pro-technology entrepreneurs, who regard ordinary people as spongers and parasites, seem like accurate prophecies of what is now unfolding in the humachine age.

Take Elon Musk's pronouncement on public transport, which I cited in Chapter 8, and which continues:

> "Why do you want to get on something with a lot of other people, that doesn't leave where you want it to leave, doesn't start where you want it to start, doesn't end where you want it to end?" (Marshall, 2017)

At first glance, this seems a less extreme stance than Rand's furious rejection of collectivism and altruism but it ends up in the same place. Indeed, Musk's complete rejection of the value of "other people" and his fierce insistence on the right of the individual to have the world tailored to his convenience sounds remarkably like one of the ranting speeches which Rand's fictional heroes regularly make.

As technology journalist Nick Bilton (2016) says about Silicon Valley,

> Most entrepreneurs and engineers appear to live by one of Rand's defining mantras: "The question isn't who is going to let me; it's who is going to stop me?"

Who indeed is going to stop the ontocapitalists, if not the public? Unless, that is, Rand's individualistic contention that "there is no such entity" turns out to be correct (1967:20).

Socially Beneficial Leadership?

None of this suggests that the leaders of human-machine fusion are likely to be trusted to provide leadership that benefits the common good. This requires the self-discipline to see beyond your own interests, put yourself in the place of others, and trust people you don't necessarily know. But the dog-eat-dog individualism of ontocapitalism is the worst foundation for socially beneficial decision-making. In a Hobbsian war of all against all, you would be unwise to trust anybody further than you can throw them. The value of trust in Silicon Valley is probably summed up by the title of one of its most highly-regarded management books, written by Intel CEO Andy Grove (1996), the man, you might remember, who actually made Moore's Law happen: it's called *Only the Paranoid Survive*.

In fact, a growing body of psychological research confirms my own experience of the extreme challenges that growth capitalism poses to socially beneficial leadership. For example, would you consider the following traits desirable in a leader: self-interestedness, lack of empathy with others, objectification of people, abstract decision-making and a readiness to adopt unethical practices to fulfil personal goals? Well, these are all qualities which studies indicate that those who are high in wealth and power tend to possess, compared to low-income, low-power individuals. Proportionately, the wealthier you are the less generous, charitable, empathetic and altruistic you are likely to be (for more see Harvey, 2019, Chapter 4). The view from the apex of pyramid society seems to make it difficult to see those who are at the bottom, let alone care about them. In short, the wealth that provides you with power in a capitalist society can also disqualify you from exercising it in a collectively responsible way. It's yet another reason to challenge those who intend to bring off the biggest and riskiest transformation of humanness in history.

Of course, the humachine elite are not completely lacking in self-awareness and they have many resources to protect themselves from public accusations of self-interest. Philanthropy is one such resource. It has enabled Bill Gates, for example, to transform himself from Microsoft's notorious "angry office bully" and anti-competitive destroyer of commercial rivals repeatedly fined by the EU into a saint of enlightened capitalism (Hofman, 2015, BBC, 2013). His charitable work gives him the soft power his business empire could never do.

I'm not suggesting that philanthropy is simply another form of tricknology, even if some critics accuse it of being a glorified form of tax evasion (Schliefer, 2020). Clearly, philanthropists like Gates do good works and may gain more authentic personal fulfilment from their charitable endeavours than from mere money-making. But in the humachine age philanthropy has become an institutionalized form of corporate brand-building, encouraging today's business tycoons to proclaim themselves as philanthropists from the very outset of their careers rather than towards the end, as was the tendency in the past. Moreover, the notion of "philanthropocapitalism" is touted by Singularity University co-founder Peter Diamandis (2012) and others as a justification for the unregulated economics which humachine corporations prefer. At best, philanthropy turns capitalism into a form of benevolent paternalism, which perpetuates the plutotechnics that enables the rich to decide on priorities for public spending. This is particularly concerning in the case of enormous medical science powerhouses such as the Gates Foundation. Philanthropy also has the advantage of being much easier to publicize than to be accurately assessed. For example, as journalist Mollie Hersh (2020) suggests, "Jeff Bezos is famously misleading when it comes to charitable causes, touting big sums but only providing a fraction". Bezos's pledge in 2022 to give away most of his fortune will have to be scrutinized in this light, especially as Bill Gates's net worth has almost doubled since he first made a similar promise over a decade ago (James, 2020).

A more democratic response would be for Big Tech corporations to overcome their notorious fiscal reticence. For instance, over the period

2011-2020, Fair Tax Mark (2021) found a whopping $150 billion gap between the expected headline global tax rate and what Apple, Facebook, Amazon, Netflix, Microsoft and Google actually paid, a shortfall of over 40%. Willingly paying taxes, however, requires a belief in society as a shared whole which the Big Tech titans tend to lack. And ethically, it involves a sense of moral obligation which libertarian individualists explicitly reject. As Ayn Rand phrased it, "there is no such thing as 'duty'" (1982:98).

Zuckerberg: From Capitalist Boy Hero to "Dictator"

As Bill Gates's philanthropy causes his public reputation to improve, he seems to be passing several Big Tech leaders from a younger generation travelling in the opposite direction. One of them is Meta's Mark Zuckerberg, who has done more than anybody to exploit the humachinators' novel corporate asset of youthfulness, with its beguiling associations of innocence and hope for the future. Just nineteen when he started Facebook in his Harvard dorm, he was a billionaire at the age of twenty-three. It's true, Zuckerberg's youthful demeanour was never entirely convincing – he reportedly had a wardrobe of identical, immaculately ironed grey t-shirts suggesting they were as much a uniform to him as any business suit – but his apparent openness, earnestness and readiness to learn seemed reassuringly new and fresh. In the early days, when Facebook was a novel way of making and keeping friends, few were concerned that it began as "Hot or Not", a semi-voyeuristic site inviting male users to rate the physical attractiveness of photos of female students or "Zuck's" ruthless tactics in marginalizing his co-founders (Carlson, 2012).

But the fresh-faced boy wonder's public image began to fade as the Facebook empire mushroomed, especially after 2008. His autocratic degree of control over Facebook – his founder's stake gives him ten times the voting rates of fellow shareholders – was increasingly resented by investors who were the first group to accuse him of being a "dictator." (Fontevecchia, 2012). By 2016, Facebook's repeated abuse of its users' privacy turned into public disgust, which intensified after revelations of Facebook's role in electing Donald Trump and the role of illegally purloined personal data in the Cambridge Analytica scandal, for which Facebook was eventually fined $5 billion (Cadwalladr, 2020). Increasingly, he was accused of using of patents to strangle innovation and of choking off press freedom, as

Facebook's news feeds contributed to the bankruptcy of hundreds of local newspapers (Griffith, 2017).

So far Zuckerberg's ambitions don't extend to space like other ontopreneurs but to those parts of planet Earth which are not yet online. His Free Basics programme offering the internet to low-income countries may have been dismissed as "digital colonialism", which "turns the user into a mostly passive consumer of mostly Western corporate content" (Solon, 2017) but Facebook's major investment in undersea cabling in Africa is likely to be more effective in bringing the internet to millions of new users, with built-in Facebook, WhatsApp and Instagram.

In 2018, the scale of disenchantment with Zuckerberg went up a notch, with UN investigators claiming that in Myanmar, Facebook had "turned into a beast" and had played a "determining role" in spreading hate speech that contributed to the attempted genocide of the Rohingya people (BBC, 2018). Shareholders again attempted to oust "dictator Zuck" (Bridge, 2018) and investigative journalist Carole Cadwalladr (2020) concluded that Facebook had become "a rogue state" like North Korea, an "autocracy, a dictatorship controlled by a single man". Even Zuckerberg's much-vaunted philanthropic Chan-Zuckerberg venture has soured, with some employees demanding his removal to prevent it being "tainted" by Facebook's notoriety (Schliefer, 2020). And in 2020 the US House Antitrust Subcommittee finally began to see the light, accusing Facebook of being a monopoly which maintained its commercial position "by acquiring, copying or killing its competitors" (Rodriguez, 2020).

Shorn of any youthful charm, Zuckerberg is now most often seen in a suit and tie, as befits a man in the dock of public opinion. In 2021, perhaps to evade the anti-trust backlash, he rebranded Facebook as Meta and dedicated it to developing the metaverse, a form of Type 5 humachine which aims to create an immersive digital environment, blending social media, virtual reality and emotional computing. The metaverse was a massive gamble that has lost shareholders a fortune – Zuckerberg himself plummeted down the rich list in 2022 – but his majority share of voting rights enables him to pursue his obsessions regardless (Waters and Agnew, 2022). In 2023 in typically opportunistic style, he tried to take advantage of Musk's foundering Twitter/X by launching the copycat Threads microblogging platform, although this threatens to reproduce all the regulatory problems of Facebook.

In time, Zuckerberg may edge Meta closer to the "post-biological future" advocated by his sister, Arielle, a prominent technology venture capitalist in her own right. She believes that "we're moving towards a transhumanist future" of brain augmentation and robotic limb replacement in which "people who can afford these enhancements will hugely benefit and people who can't afford them will be left behind" (Archbold, 2020). If her brother chooses to steer Meta in this direction, who will stop him? Surely not the growthist capitalist system, for which he still represents one of the wildest fulfilments of the American Dream.

Nor should we expect too much opposition from digital capitalism's home state. To many in the outside world, California is still the home of hippydom, Hollywood idealism, feminism, environmentalism and progressive cultural equalism of every kind. But in terms of wealth disparities, it's become one of the most economically unequal regions in the developed world, with a 0.49 GINI coefficient which puts it on a par with developing nations. Big Tech has played a significant role in this disequalization, as Joel Kotkin illustrates in a chapter tellingly entitled "Feudalism in California". For instance, in the early 1980s, San Jose, where Silicon Valley is located, enjoyed high degrees of economic equality but it now has some of the worst poverty levels in the United States (Kotkin, 2020:44-5). San Francisco, whose Bay Area has the state's widest gap between rich and poor, has seen its homeless population increase by 50% from 2005-2020, while national numbers have declined. (Shellenberger,2022). In short, the sunny egalitarian exterior of the Californian orange contains an icy, unequal core, which is all too emblematic of the humachine age and its leaders.

Other Aspects of the CIMENT Ideological Hegemony

Three other CIMENT values play an ideological role in persuading the public to continue to give their consent to the humachinators' direction of travel, even though so much about their vision of the future is not what it seems. Competitivism, which drives the bitter rivalry between all capitalists, has a general misdirecting effect that fragments groups and deflects from the common interests shared by all inhabitants of planet Earth. In particular, Big Tech exploits intergenerational competition by recruiting the young – children, adolescents and young adults – as the early adopters of new technologies. The young are not only prepared to invest in the latest devices, apps and social media start-ups, they also pour their creativity into them, often transforming bland technologies into compelling cultural phenomena. Their willingness to re-invent themselves, improvize and master complex technical challenges sets the tone for older generations, who either have to follow suit or lose out. In the UK over three million "digitally disenfranchised" over 65-year-olds never use the internet and so struggle to obtain many basic social services (Age UK, 2020). The more the young see new technology as a precious expression of their identity, which defines them in relation to their parents and grandparents, the less likely are all generations to pool their resources against a system that could threaten them all.

Competitiveness is linked to Nationalism, which so effectively reconfigures humanity's relationship with nature as a perpetual economic war between the world's nations. Technical innovation is co-opted into this unending battle, as are other vital resources. The regulatory systems of the world's largest economic blocs, US, China and the EU, including internet protocols and data protection, are becoming increasingly significant geopolitical weapons. Techno-nationalism is becoming a marker of personal and political identity as your brand of smartphone or tablet becomes a matter of patriotic duty or extreme nativism creates a preference for robots over immigrant workers.

Finally, we should never underestimate the influence of Technologism, the value on which the humachine age is predicated. Gramsci, analysing the way ideology legitimized capitalist elites in the 1920s and 1930s, could hardly have anticipated the extent that the twenty-first-century faith in technology would bind together different layers of society, including many on the left, and shut out alternative values. The ideological role occupied by religion, with its monopoly on supernatural, superhuman forces, has passed to the secular worship of technologies assumed to have even greater powers of transubstantiation. The seductive utility of machines has become a form of magical thinking, which acts as a get-out-of-jail-free card for every issue faced by humanity, irrespective of its context or causation.

Technologism hijacks optimism, which is one of humanity's most valuable competences, creating an open goal for the tricknologists. It allows technological determinism to portray most of human history as a murky, low-tech wilderness, during which younger generations may wonder how life was even possible. And it nurtures the thought that technological entrepreneurs are leading us to a heroic future which cannot be stopped, that our destiny is a done deal rather than a choice still to be made. Until it's finally debunked, this thought, which is so frustratingly well-woven into contemporary capitalism's ideological fabric, will remain one of human-machine fusion's greatest assets.

Conclusion

In this chapter, I've tried to unravel the knotty paradox of why a group of high-risk, hyper-individualistic, machine-obsessed, superrich elitists continue to be trusted to conduct the transformation of just about everything about being human. The powerful, if contradictory, ideological system which they have inherited and strengthened seems to sanction their mission, almost as much as the economic situation in which they find themselves. Despite their ultra-modern outward demeanour, it enables this new, scientifically-trained group to reinforce older forms of social inequality and Great Man leadership archetypes, which have existed ever since pyramidal social organization became institutionalized in the first city states. In addition to this ideological capital, they benefit from the ancient tradition of plutotechnics that grants a ruling class absolute control over technology development, even though the decisions which today's ontocapitalists are making are potentially more far-reaching than those of any previous elite.

A new demotechnics, which ensures that technological development is based on informed, deliberated decisions made by the majority, could hope to change our direction of travel but for the moment the world-plan of the new Prometheans remains largely unchallenged. Indeed, their extreme values, transcendent ambitions and detachment from the life of the majority lead us now to entertain another possible explanation for their persuasive power, which if valid would unleash novel legions of risk. In short, is a new form of human psychology beginning to assume dominance in the age of humachines?

CHAPTER 11

The Machine Mindset: The Anti-Social Psychology of the Humachine Elite

Identifying a new way of thinking and feeling as it comes on to the world stage is never going to be easy, not least because every person's experience of the world varies. But everything I've written about the humachine age so far seems to suggest that humachination is not simply a set of political choices about technology, science and economics; it's also a distinct mindset, with deep-lying beliefs, goals and values, which contains a powerful intentionality trying to realize itself in the world.

What follows is necessarily speculative but as a psychologist I would be remiss if I didn't make a provisional attempt at outlining this new mentality, which if it becomes normalized could have the most profound effects on the future of humanity. I call this psychological stance the machine mindset and it appears to me to have five interrelated elements which are worthy of consideration: the urge to domination, corporate psychopathy and anti-social personality order, mechanicalism, a bias towards the left hemisphere of the brain and a connection with autism spectrum disorder.

The Dominator Syndrome or the Prometheus Complex

The first trait I find striking about those exhibiting a machine mindset is an intense desire to impose themselves on other people. This is a psychology ruled by the Law of More which is not prepared to recognize any limits to its ambition. As noted in the last chapter, "Who will stop me?" is the Silicon Valley ethos and this aggressive form of individualism expresses itself in an obsession with coming out on top. Over the years, psychologists have come up with many characterizations of this Tamburlaine-like urge to dominate the world. It's been variously named the superiority complex (which perhaps develops as compensation for a deep sense of inferiority), the Icarus complex (characterized by "ascensionism), megalomania or egomania (Adler 1984, Murray, 1955).

This dominator syndrome or complex, as it may be also termed, involves an extreme degree of ego-inflation and a sense of entitlement to break the laws and conventions which guide most people. Indeed, disrupting the status quo is a major objective of the machine mindset. For the dominator, life is a zero-sum game which he has to win because losing feels unbearable. The dominator syndrome has been a psychological trait of many of those who have aspired to reach the apex of the social pyramid, ever since this form of organization emerged after the agricultural revolution.

This lust for power certainly captures Prometheus's state of mind, which I described in Chapter 5, that determination to take advantage of any opportunity offered by new technology to surmount human equality. Psychoanalyst Ernest Jones (1951) named the dominator syndrome the God complex, trying to capture its combination of gross narcissism, perfectionism and self-aggrandisement. This burning desire to turn oneself into a superhuman reminds us both of Prometheus's yearning for divine status and the goal of the Western Science Revolution to usurp the Christian God by transforming him from the ineffable creator of the universe into an ingenious, but distinctly human, watchmaker.

Corporate Psychopathy and Anti-Social Personality Disorder

In organizational psychology circles, an overwhelming need for domination has long been recognized as a trait often found in senior executives. It is increasingly referred to as leadership psychopathy, an aggressive, self-entitled mindset which I and others who have worked with corporate leaders have regularly encountered (Kets de Vries 2012, Harvey 2015). Research suggests there are four times as many psychopaths in senior leadership positions than in the general population (Babiak and Hare, 2006). Corporate psychopaths can be charming, innovative and formidably persuasive. A total disregard for the truth often accompanies their ability to distort other peoples' choices. (Recall the weird "reality distortion" powers for which Steve Jobs was famous (Isaacson, 2011).) These qualities can often deliver capitalism's number one goal, economic growth, but they transform conscientiousness and compassion into career hindrances. Organizations led by corporate psychopaths are less likely to do business in a "socially desirable… environmentally friendly way" or in a manner "that benefits the local community", according to one survey of their employees, which sheds more light on the untrustworthiness of the Big Tech leaders (Boddy et al, 2010),

If corporate psychopathy is one component of the machine mindset, what relevance does criminal psychopathy have to it? Nowadays psychologists working with criminals, terrorists and sex offenders tend to use the alternative term "anti-social personality disorder" (ASPD) for this condition. This American Psychiatric Association DSM-5 classification is controversial, as the line between anti-social and pro-social behaviour can be more difficult to draw than is commonly assumed. Abusers have often been abused and one person's terrorist can be another's freedom fighter. This interpretive debate is reflected in the shifting borders of ASPD classification over the years, which has lost some of its component conditions, such as histrionic disorder.

However, one trait stands out very consistently in the diagnostic criteria and this I believe is highly relevant to the machine mindset and the humachine age in general – the absence of empathy. "Disempathy" is a form of impairment in interpersonal functioning, which involves a kind of emotional and cognitive unilateralism, an inability to put oneself in the place of others or sense their emotions or read their body language. It refers to an indigenous human quality which we have so taken for granted as part of a normal social behaviour that we have no formal name for its opposite, except in the form of florid, popular insults – hence the new term used above. (Note also the possible resemblance of this excessively one-sided view of the world to the non-dialectical objectivism of scientistic methodology.)

In the diagnostic criteria for anti-social personality disorder the absence of empathy is described in the following terms:

> Empathy: Lack of concern for feelings, needs, or suffering of others; lack of remorse after hurting or mistreating another and /or Intimacy: Incapacity for mutually intimate relationships, as exploitation is a primary means of relating to others, including by deceit and coercion; use of dominance or intimidation to control others (American Psychiatric Association, 2013).

In the related condition of narcissistic personality disorder, this lack of empathy is defined as "impaired ability to recognize or identify with the feelings and needs of others". Also relevant to the machine mindset may be obsessive compulsive personality disorder, which includes "compulsivity, characterized by rigid perfectionism: Rigid insistence on everything being flawless, perfect, without errors or faults".

In a general sense, I suggest this absence of empathy, as well as other narcissistic traits of ASPD are useful in analysing the psychology driving the humachine age. Artificial empathy is a crucial functionality attributed to relational humachines and underlies the claim that robots and other AI systems can replicate human fellow-feeling, care and companionship (more on this in Chapter 15). We might interpret this as the machine mindset's desperation to create mechanically what it lacks but coded empathy can never approximate the real thing. Disempathy is socially and politically dangerous and, as we've already noted, radically undermines the techno-elite's fitness to lead, since the ability to put oneself in someone else's shoes is increasingly recognized as an essential component of effective leadership (Holt and Marqués, 2012). Clinical psychologist Professor Simon Baron-Cohen (2011:107) puts the overall value of empathy to humanity even higher, stating that "it is the most valuable resource in our world".

Mechanicalism: The Lure of Machines

The third element of this new psychological constellation of behaviours which I introduce for consideration is the most obvious and is very specific to this condition, a bias towards the mechanical rather than the organic. As might be expected, this mental pattern shows a preference for what can be quantified, measured and controlled and a conviction that technology and science override all other forms of knowledge.

At the most admirable and potentially socially useful level, this mechanical intelligence can be a bountiful source of innovation and is almost certainly one of the wellsprings of the human genius for tool-making. Whereas most people regard machines from the point of view of utility – as A to B devices, if you like, for those with a mechanical bent, a machine is full of fascination and hidden promise. They don't simply ask: what does it do? They also want to know: how does it work? And how could it work better? The urge to get into a closer relationship with machines, to get inside them and handle their parts, seems irresistible. Most of us are quietly obedient to machines, wary about doing anything that might cause them to break down but mechanicalists long for the chance to disrupt them, take them apart and put them back together. Jeff Bezos is even said to have dismantled and reassembled his cot with a screwdriver at the age of three (Cox, 2019).

One female computer science student in the insightful paper cited in the last chapter describes this deep, visceral attraction by comparing her early exposure to computers to that of her younger brother:

> He started kind of playing on them, pulling them apart; I never did that. I never pulled them apart and said, "Oh I wonder what this does." For whatever reason, I never did. He *always* did (Margolis et al 2000:6).

The implied gender bias here may not be accidental, as the machine mindset does seem to be a predominantly male phenomenon, perhaps a reflection of the place of technology in the culture of patriarchy. This is not to say that everyone with a mechanical bent is biased against women or craves world domination. But some people, mainly men, seem to have this distinctive trait from the earliest age, which is subsequently reinforced by their education, culture and the economics of the workplace. The psychological danger is that all living things come to be seen as objects to be controlled and treated as means rather than ends.

Bicameral Brain Theory: The Left Hemisphere's Power Coup

Is there a theory of the brain that can help to further explain the machine mindset? Something bold and original is required to illuminate this new way of organizing the world, which is why I turn to the brilliantly evocative, bi-cameral, neurological theory of psychiatrist and brain injury expert Iain McGilchrist (2009). McGilchrist asserts that while the constant inter-action of right and left neurological functions are vital for normal brain functioning, the right hemisphere is the dominant sphere in the brain. It's this neurological hemisphere which is responsible for grasping reality as an existential whole and integrating this with all bodily senses. It works holistically, as a mode of attention that sees the world as it is, vigilantly seeking a 360-degree perspective on the environment.

The left hemisphere, by contrast, provides much more detailed, focused attention, which classifies and codes reality in a way that allows it to be productively worked on and manipulated. As McGilchrist explains, the bird's left brain attends to getting lunch, while its right brain ensures that the bird itself doesn't become lunch for a predator. Tool-making, language, logic and maths all come under the left hemisphere's jurisdiction, although in order to function properly it needs to constantly refer its findings back to the holistic right hemisphere (which also contributes to many of the functions associated with the left hemisphere).

As long as the inter-hemispherical interaction is intense and reciprocal all is well but the problem starts when the left hemisphere seeks to escape the authority of the right hemisphere – in McGilchrist's overarching met-aphor, when the emissary tries to overthrow the master. What's more it's succeeded in many walks of life, even in mainstream neuroscience which has crowned the left hemisphere as the dominant one. This is problematic for many reasons:

> "The left hemisphere is *not* in touch with the world … It is *not* rea-sonable. It is angry when challenged, dismisses evidence it doesn't like or can't understand, and is unreasonably sure of its own right-ness … Its attention is narrow, its vision myopic, and it can't see how the parts fit together. It is good for only one thing – manipulating the world … It reduces the living to the mechanical … And it requires certainty, where none can be found (McGilchrist, 2012: 20-22).

In this model, the battle between machine and nature, quantity and qual-ity, is going on in all of us, even among those who research and theorize about the brain. Dynamic equipoise gets the best out of each dimension of the brain but at its most unbalanced and extreme, the dominance of the left hemisphere can result in an almost literal half-vision of reality. This is seen vividly in the impoverished drawings of patients with damaged (or temporarily suppressed) right hemispheres, which depict faces that lack half of their features or severely lopsided houses. McGilchrist also suggests that some forms of psychotic illness – "madness" in non-psychological parlance – may be associated with a neurological over-reliance on the left hemisphere, which causes isolation from the integrating, reality-anchoring orientation of the right hemisphere. Obsessive compulsive disorder, in which the search for certainty becomes a self-chasing spiral that's increasingly disconnected from reality, could be another example of left hemisphere dominance. In general, there seems to be an obvious connection between McGilchrist's account of left-brain dominance and the humachinators' obsession with machines and longing for total control over nature and the vagaries of being human.

The Autism Connection

The machine mindset also has a link, albeit a somewhat confused and contentious one, with another increasingly prevalent condition, autism spectrum disorder. Autism was first diagnosed in the 1930s and Asperger's syndrome, which is now seen as a form of this disorder, was identified in the 1940s. This apparently modern condition predominantly affects males rather than females (which is interesting in relation to the male-female gender ratio in computer studies explored in the last chapter). Intriguingly, McGilchrist sees autism as an indication that the left hemisphere of the brain is functioning more efficiently than the right hemisphere, as it's the latter which is generally responsible for "self-awareness, identification with others, and more generally, inter-subjective processes" (2009:57).

> There is in autism an inability to tell what another is thinking (lack of "theory of mind"); a lack of social intelligence – difficulty in judging nonverbal aspects of language, such as tone, humour, irony … a lack empathy; a lack of imagination; an attraction to the mechanical…" (McGilchrist, 2009:407).

Simon Baron-Cohen (2011:106) points to the ways people with autism and Asperger's try to "systematise" everything, "striving to step out of time" – because time represents change – and create a world made out of predictable mechanisms and "beautifully mathematical patterns". He stresses that this can involve constantly challenging why things are as they are.

"Just saying "Well we do this just because everybody else does" doesn't meet their test of logic". Journalist Matt McFarland (2015) suggests that this interrogatory trait is characteristic of Larry Page, whose "superpower", according to Yahoo's Marissa Meyer, is his insistence on "asking why not. On everything".

I have to stress from the outset that most people suffering from autism spectrum disorder often struggle to find their way in life, not least because they often have accompanying learning disabilities. People with this developmental condition are much more likely to be unemployed than employed (in the UK the number in work is just 29%), let alone employed as CEOs running vast technology companies with all the stress this involves (ONS, 2022). In one sense, the lifestyle of a high-functioning, multi-tasking billionaire is as far removed from that of the average autism sufferer as it's possible to be. And yet there seems to be a clear connection between these two very different ways of experiencing the world, even if at present this is mainly being made by observers in the media rather than by clinical psychologists.

For example, Sunday Times columnist Dominic Lawson suggests that many Big Tech tycoons are "on the spectrum" and notes that during an interview with Jeff Bezos, the Amazon founder's answers were frequently punctuated by "a shattering but mirthless laugh, like a seal's bark" (Lawson, 2021). A fellow executive observed about Bezos in the early days of Amazon, "there's a mania for quantification in Jeff's heart" (Kelion, 2020). Bill Gates is often said to lack social awareness: the geeky photo of him shaking hands with the South Korean president with his left hand jammed in his trouser pocket is a case in point (Abad-Santos, 2013). Mark Zuckerberg has been described by colleagues as "a robot" and "having a touch of the Asperger's" (McFarland, 2015).

More significantly perhaps, Elon Musk has made explicit reference to autism, although it's not clear whether he has ever received such a diagnosis. He claimed that he was "the first person with Asperger's" to host the Saturday Night Live TV show (Luterman, 2021). For his friends and family, this diagnosis largely seems to centre on Musk's lack of empathy, to return to that crucial human trait. As his first wife Justine says "Elon is not someone who would say, "I feel you, I see your point of view" (Vance 2015:68). A more recent partner, electro-pop star Grimes, goes even further, claiming that Musk believes she does not exist except as a digital simulation in Musk's cerebral cortex (Harrison, 2022). (Interestingly, Musk also refers to his core personality traits as "default settings", consistent with his view that the human brain is a type of software (Isaacson, 2023).)

Steve Jobs's wife, Laurene Powell, noted a similar lack of empathy in her husband. "He doesn't have social graces, such as putting himself in other people's shoes," she said in 2010 (Isaacson, 2011: 543). Indeed, Jobs was famous for his perfectionism, unvarying clothes preferences (e.g., the black turtleneck) and other traits which those who have been diagnosed with Asperger's often associate with their condition. His temper tantrums and ability to antagonize colleagues was legendary ("I've never had a problem pissing people off", he confessed (556)), as was his rigid binary world view that categorized everybody as either "enlightened" or "asshole" (119).

Peter Thiel, in typically contrarian fashion, flips the whole argument on its head, claiming that Asperger's is an aid to those who want to create world-changing technology companies. "Many of the more successful entrepreneurs seem to be suffering from a mild form of Asperger's where it's like you're missing the imitation, socialization gene" (McFarland, 2015). This condition allows them to resist what Thiel sees as a culture of social conformity that discourages bold entrepreneurship and talks people out of their "interesting original creative ideas before they're even fully formed". With this provocative assertion, Thiel manages to turn a distressing psychological condition into an asset for budding ontocapitalists. Perhaps leadership training for the next generation of Big Tech executives should aim to remove all traces of the "socialization gene" and any ability to identify with other people's point of view. (Some might say it's already doing this.)

At this juncture, we have to ask, what's going on here? Isn't this simply another example of tricknology? Thiel and Musk seem to be using a psychological disorder to elicit sympathy from the public and conceal the frequently anti-social nature of their policies. Autism is not so much an anti-social disorder as a-social one. Classic autism is often about resisting change rather than embracing the "change at any cost" philosophy of growthist creative destruction. Trying to reframe this condition as an essential entrepreneurial skill is a duplicitous manoeuvre, which neatly bypasses questions about what society really needs from its innovators.

Difficulties in understanding normal emotional and social life are hardly qualifications for pro-social businesses. On the contrary, they sound like the recipe for the anti-social economy, which the humachine age is in danger of fostering.

The picture gets even darker when we consider the possible aetiology of anti-social psychological traits. Genetics may be part of the causal story but highly stressful childhood experiences, including parenting that lacks emotional attachment, also play a demonstrable role in developing the condition (Baron-Cohen, 2015). Elon Musk, who has said he was badly bullied at school, has also given us a strong hint about his troubled relationship with father, Errol:

> He was such a terrible human being ... You have no idea ... My dad will have a carefully thought-out plan of evil ... Almost every crime you can possibly think of, he has done ... It's so terrible, you can't believe it (Strauss, 2017).

This may be an example of the exaggeration to which Musk is all too prone but we should never dismiss the potential for the cruelly dominated child to grow up into the obsessively dominating adult. Nor should we ignore childhood trauma as a possible motivation for entrepreneurs and scientists who are desperate to escape from a troubling world of emotion and seek a universe of immaculately ordered technology.

Risks of the Machine Mindset

There is more than enough here to warn us of the risks that will occur if the machine mindset becomes more common, both as a driving force at the top of society and as a more widespread mode of experiencing the world. Whether in the form of institutionalized irrationality or as a personal disorder, experiencing the world like a machine is fraught with jeopardy. Could autistic tendencies be an early indication of the human brain adapting to a world in which robotic behaviour and mechanized thinking are becoming the norm? Certainly, those working with machine logic and robots on a daily basis are likely to find that thinking and feeling like machines is rewarded, while traditional human modes of experience are downgraded and even outlawed. As rigid, mechanical logic takes over the home and the workplace, the intuition, sensing and metaphorical reasoning that are integral to human rationality could be purged. If unchecked, reification will spread like an insidious disease, objectifying and instrumentalizing every living thing it touches, eventually turning humans into tools of their own tools.

For Iain McGilchirst, this mechanical bias or "exaggerated reliance on the provisions" of the left-hemisphere has been developing for a long time and in fact can be traced back as far as Plato and the post-Socratic dualism of Ancient Greece. I'd suggest that the humachine age has hugely accelerated this mechanistic psychological turn and that the bias against the qualities of the right hemisphere is now enjoying an even greater degree of hegemony. Although McGilchrist doesn't explicitly spell out the political implications of left-hemisphere domination, he is clear about the dangers for humanity if this mindset is allowed to become even more prevalent.

> There would be a complete loss of the sense of uniqueness. Increasingly, the living world be modelled on the mechanical. This would also have an effect on the way bureaucracies would deal with human situations and with society at large … Exploitation rather than cooperation would, explicitly or not, be the default relationship between human individuals … The left hemisphere cannot trust and is prone to paranoia. It needs to feel in control (McGilchrist 2018:28).

For me, this offers an alarming insight into the depersonalized world of the Technocene, dominated by the machine mindset's dangerously reductive half-vision of reality. Further research on the machine mindset can also benefit from an eco-feminist perspective, especially in relation to the masculinist, scientistic "master model" which Stefania Barca (2020) describes as the dominant bias of the Anthropocene.

Balance, the ability to create a steady state out of multiple competing dynamics, is crucial to every form of health, whether neurological, physical, social or environmental. As Fritjof Capra (1996:9) stresses: "What is good or healthy, is a dynamic balance; what is bad, or unhealthy, is imbalance – over-emphasis of one tendency and neglect of the other." Even severe brain injuries can be mitigated with the patient, caring work of therapists and clinicians. But balance is not what humachinators want, as they have no "enough" switch. And literally seeing the brain and body as machines to be taken apart and reassembled militates against accepting any limits, even the inevitability of death. The Law of More weaponizes this cold, calculating, one-eyed perception of the world, making it seem like an all-conquering force, which can sweep aside the boundaries of human and planetary safety with impunity, a view that corporate shareholders are only too pleased to lavishly reward. "The fine line" is just another hurdle to be crashed through, as is the delicate balance between truth and lies.

At its most extreme, the machine mindset is prepared to entertain an almost nihilistic degree of risk-tolerance, a trait which, as the last chapter showed, is highly characteristic of the demographic that makes up the techno-elite. Why else would they be prepared to gamble on AImageddon, the surrendering of humanity to superintelligent machines? This takes us back to anti-social behaviour disorder and another of its key diagnostic criteria: "Engagement in potentially self-damaging activities, unnecessarily and without regards for consequences" (APA, 2013)). This rather encapsulates the sense that ontocapitalism is prepared to destroy anything in its quest for self-preservation – even itself. And from a mental health standpoint, if the goals and values of the humachine age now represent sanity, it's no surprise that psychological normality and abnormality begin to seem indistinguishable.

A Cure for the Machine Mindset?

Lastly, since we have now circled back to ASPD, it's worth concluding these speculations by musing on what the psychological treatments available for this serious disorder can tell us about the machine mindset. Whereas autism can be immensely helped by interpersonal training and other interventions to boost emotional intelligence, psychopathy and other anti-social conditions are notoriously difficult to treat, either pharmacologically or through individual or group therapy. Indeed, in the context of executive coaching, I dubbed this unhappy truth the Soprano syndrome, based on the fictional, psychopathic Mafia boss Tony Soprano, who doesn't end up as a better person as a result of his therapy, as his counsellor hopes, but as a better gangster (Harvey, 2015). The only treatment that appears to be effective for those diagnosed with anti-social personality order is long-term participation in a therapeutic community, usually in a psychiatric ward. According to psychiatrists Steve Pearce and Rex Haigh, a primary element in so-called Democratic Therapeutic Community (DTC) treatment is to encourage patients to use collective choice-making on issues that affect their shared life:

> It is central to their empowerment, helping ... to convince them that they are capable of making their own decisions, affecting the future course of their lives and affecting those around them. They find they are able to contribute to the lives of others, to gain and accord respect, and to discover strengths they may have forgotten or never discovered they possessed (Pearce and Haigh, 2017:153-4).

This communalist experience can also help to instil a sense of belonging-ness in those who feel profoundly isolated from others and enables them to control their aggressive behaviour. For example, one DTC group in a psychiatric ward for male psychopaths reported

> improvements in interpersonal relationships, an improvement in empathic ability ... the formation of reciprocated friendships and an increased capacity to recognize others' feelings towards themselves (Pearce and Haigh, 2017:143).

None of these effects were observed in a control group, which used con-ventional medical-model psychiatry.

The parallel between these long-established therapeutic groups which seem to be effective for patients suffering from extreme forms of anti-so-cial personality disorder and the communal model of decision-making in hunter-gatherer societies shouldn't be ignored. Pearce and Haigh's belief that sound mental health and good living "depend on interconnected-ness and a suitable network of meaningful relationships" (Pearce and Haigh, 2017:12) also has a strikingly ecological ring to it. Whether such a communal experience would change the mindset of high-functioning techno-billionaires inured to having their own way in everything is hard to say. Close involvement in pro-social communities in which everybody has an equal voice would probably seem hellish to those who long for the absolute, Randian freedom to make their own decisions, unhindered by ordinary people. To them, being part of a self-governing community might feel comparable to being chained to a rock like Prometheus.

However, such solutions may be necessary if we want a political system that delivers the rule of the majority in public policy, making decisions about technology which are in the best interest of the majority rather than the elite - if, in short, demotechnics is to supplant plutotechnics. Community-based approaches also alert us to the psychological dimension of the Ecocene, which envisages lifelong psychological support for people, enabling them to work together to bring out the best in each other. This involves a steady-state mindset, which I'll further discuss in the book's final chapter, which, among other things, aims to ensure that leadership upstarts and other anti-social elements realize that their primary position is within the group not above it.

Conclusion

In conclusion, I suggest that a new way of thinking and feeling is emerging in the age of humachines which combines a domination complex, an obsessive mechanicalism, a pronounced left-hemisphere bias and elements of anti-social personality disorder, some of which are being passed off as autism. The risk is that this unempathetic machine mindset is becoming normalized not only in the immensely influential techno-elite and other leadership groups but more generally across society, as reasoning and behaving like machines become the norm. A possible future is opening up in which if you can't think, act and feel (or unfeel) like a mechanical system, there may be no place for you. With this sobering thought in mind, we can move on to the final panoply of existential risks which human-machine fusion is unleashing on the world.

CHAPTER 12

The Existential Risks of Humachination: Tricked out of the Best of Being Human?

Today people in London, Shanghai or San Francisco live very different lives from extant hunter-gatherer communities in East Africa or New Guinea but it's still possible for these societies to understand and accommodate each other's lifestyle, if they choose to do so. Anthropologists and others can adapt to low-tech living and indigenous people can learn how to use high technology, if they are so minded. But for how long will this be true? The whole thrust of ontocapitalism is to push us into an event horizon, at which biology is subjugated to physics and an evolutionary point-of-no return occurs. At that juncture, Homo sapiens, as we know it, may cease to exist. So, are we about to be tricked out of our humanness, to suffer a Promethean swindle greater than any other than any other in our long history? This is the final existential risk of humachination which we con-front in Part III.

In *Natural Born Cyborgs*, philosopher Andy Clark (2004:175) argues that we have always lived with tools and "human–machine symbiosis", as he calls it, "is simply what comes naturally" But if the full humachine agenda is ever implemented, with the humanization of all machines, supplemented by the planned mechanization of human neurology and physiology, maintained by total digital-robotic environments, the typical mid-twenty-first-century Western citizen might be unable to survive for more than a few days without advanced technology. And if the singularity occurs, the possible unintended negative consequences of AImageddon become almost too great to comprehend.

Humachination not only threatens to make it impossible for humans to survive without super-complex technological enchainments, it also risks weakening the core cognitive, emotional and relational skills that make human society possible. Part IV will expand our knowledge of the practical ways that the humachine age infiltrates the indigenous competences that come with being human, from decision-making, emotional sensing and truth telling to caring for, and relating to, others. Yet this massive skill-stripping exercise which aims to replace the human talents, competences and creative abilities built up over hundreds of millennia is so immanent – as well as imminent – that it continues to elude public and scholarly attention.

A few thinkers are beginning to take existential risks seriously- more so since the appearance of generative AI – but the value of their work can be undermined by their uncritically techno-utopian assumptions and anti-democratic stance. For example, "Longtermism", a possibly promising philosophical perspective, has been criticized for "leaving humanity's future up to a select handful of super-wealthy people and their potentially dubious personal beliefs" (Gault and Pearson, 2023). Democraticizing the study of existential risk is critical, say research scholars Carla Zoe Cremer and Luke Kemp (2021), who argue that it's "not yet fit for purpose" and conclude their penetrating critique of the techno-utopian approach, by asking: "Do those who study the future of humanity have grounds to ignore the visions, desires, and values of the very people they are trying to protect?"

The truth is that, even as the possible event horizon approaches, the general public have barely started to debate what human-machine fusion really entails (which, of course, suits the humachinators down to the ground). Finding a language to conceptualize this process could be the start of the intellectual and political resistance to it. This would challenge the institutional reductionism which fragments humachination into apparently separate subjects like "AI", "robotics", "the future of work" or "genetic engineering" which can be dealt with by segregated academic discourses. Such anti-holistic thinking can encourage complacency and even humorous levity about the future. But once we look at the bigger picture, we start to see the breathtaking scale of the potential existential losses on the horizon. Some of the givens of human existence may be about to disappear before we have even identified them. And that leads to another purpose of this chapter: to try to begin the task of defining the indigenous capacities or core humanness which human-machine merger is threatening to make redundant.

The Biggest Rogue Experiment in History

One way of conceptualizing humachination is to see it as the biggest rogue clinical experiment of all time. This scientific perspective construes it as a mass trial being conducted in real-time (or, more precisely, accelerated, dromological time) and on the most extensive scale possible, with everybody on the planet as a potential subject. It's an experiment particularly focused on young adults and children, almost from the moment of birth, and other vulnerable groups, such as the elderly, or those suffering from illness or poor mental health. And anybody who has a job is also part of the experiment.

Well-known social psychology experiments conducted in the past, such as Stanley Milgram's obedience experiments or Philip Zimbardo's Stanford Prison study, would now be banned. The potential and actual trauma caused to the participants involved in these studies was too great, even though they were far from being unregulated. The current guidelines of bodies such as the American Psychology Association (2017) and British Psychology Society (2021) stipulate that experiments can only be carried out by qualified professionals, who should gain the informed consent of all participants, protect them from harm, ensure their confidentiality and allow them to leave the experiment at any time. Also, the participants should not be deceived in any way about the purpose of the experiment.

Needless to say, these conditions do not apply to the great human-machine fusion experiment. As subjects, we are not required to give our informed consent; on the contrary we are exposed to constant deception about its purpose by expert tricknologists. The experimenters have little duty of care for participants, provide no debriefing and are frequently cavalier about confidentiality – for instance by selling users' data to whomever will pay most. As for leaving the experiment, this is a choice that's theoretically possible but for most of us this would be tantamount to leaving society; the humachine age has no off-switch. In short no professional research board would touch humachination with a barge pole; it violates all the strictures of normal science. This reinforces just why deregulation, a key organizing principle of neoliberal economics, is such an obsession with humachine leaders and theorists.

Big Tech companies do use psychological research techniques, however, but not to protect people but to exploit their vulnerabilities for profit. New forms of digital addiction are being deliberately developed, with the aid of analytical algorithms that amplify compulsive behaviours. Social media, gaming, online gambling and pornography and always-on communication, entertainment and meditechnics are following the well-worn path of addiction capitalism which enabled colonialism to thrive – think sugar, tobacco, tea, coffee, rum and opium. Lack of accountability and duty of care by the owners of digital platforms also open the door for rampant user-to-user exploitation, particularly in the case of the young who are growing up with humachines (without a control group to compare themselves to). UNCs are already rife, as we'll see in Part IV. In the past the devastating mental health effects of unemployment have been well documented but what about the psychological impact of mass job automation or the threat to the livelihoods of those already mired in poverty? And that's before we examine the disturbing "who am I?" questions being asked by early subjects of brain-computer interfacing experiments and the potential horror of distinguishing between the living and the artificial arising from the mechanizing of human bodies, which are all part of the biggest rogue experiment of all time.

The Deskilling of Humanity

Another way of comprehending the magnitude of the losses we are facing in the humachine age is to see it as a vast process of human deskilling. The parallel here is corporate asset-stripping, especially where buildings, land or intellectual property are bought on the cheap and then leased back to their previous owners, creating the economic rents which have always been a cornerstone of capitalism but which have expanded significantly this century (Christopher, 2020:144).

Humachination accelerates the process by which "techne", which in Ancient Greek means "skills" or "expertise" (as in the English word, "technique"), is replaced by the artificial capabilities of technology, to use Heidegger's (1977) oppositional terminology. Granted, humanity has gone through millennia of changing skills, particularly over the past three centuries of industrial mechanization, and a vast range of competences still exist but for how much longer if humachination succeeds in its goal of changing everything and everyone everywhere? Just as disastrously, humachination may prevent us from creating the advanced skills we have not yet developed as a species, such as how to create global democracy or live sustainably in equitable, psychologically-rewarding societies – the desideratum I call humanity's unfinished business.

The losses to human cognitive skills, in particular, could be profound, as humachines seek to replicate all the traditional areas of human cognition such as such as decision-making, common sense, self-analysis, judgement of others, wisdom, and an entire gamut of critical capacities we take for granted as part of our human endowment. Memory is already rapidly switching to digital form, as people come to rely less on their own memorizing capacity and more on humachines (Ward, 2013). Affective computing aims to take over our emotional functioning, threatening our judgment of ourselves and others. The more humachines become an extension of our brains, the more we move on to cognitive life-support systems which constrain our capacity to function as independent beings.

The internet is also contributing to this cognitive attrition. As a research tool, it can cut down the laborious, time-consuming business of finding books and articles in libraries. But its convenience can lead to the loss of critical, investigative skills involved in knowledge acquisition. In adults, digital multi-tasking has been found to reduce attention span (Peng et al, 2018) while one study of children over a three-year period showed that high rates of internet use impeded the development of brain regions linked to executive functions, verbal intelligence and attentional control (Takeuchi et al, 2018). Investigative journalistic skills necessary to hold authorities to account are also suffering, as online advertising (monopolized by Google and Facebook) has killed off 50% of all US local newspapers, reducing jobs in American print journalism by more than half since 2001 (Lecach, 2017).

All skills can diminish or expand our freedom. Literacy brings the ability to express your freedom but if the next generation of voice-activated computing comes in, will future generations bother with the demanding, multi-year task of learning how to write with pen and paper? If children don't master the arts of spelling, grammar, punctuation how can they contest the versions that AI provides? The physical skills of writing might become the province of new, dedicated elite, like calligraphers today, while the majority may relapse into a new, ultra-modern form of illiteracy. Human composition could also be diminished by AI text generators like ChatGPT. Best-selling author Sean Thomas (2023) predicts that AI will first supplant academic writing:

> Next it will be low-level journalism, copywriting, marketing, legalese, tech writing; then high-level journalism will go, along with genre fiction, history, biography, screenplays, TV drama, drama, until eventually a computer will be able to write something like *Ulysses*.

This is surely exaggerated but if generative AI only replaces 50% of compositional skills, this would be devastating enough. (Incidentally, AI will never write great literature!) And how long before basic reading skills follow suite, as audio text becomes more common?

The human genius for creativity in film, music and art is also being harassed by automation, for example by autonomous editing systems and self-directing music production. AI art generators like DALL-E2 and Midjourney can produce convincing visual images in hundreds of thousands of different styles in a matter of seconds, perhaps bringing down the curtain on the careers of many designers, architects, illustrators and commercial artists. Is the final outcome a new democratization of cultural life or widespread consumerist passivity and a polarization between human and mechanical art? A new pyramidization of the creative industries could occur with a tiny elite of exceptionally original human creatives presiding over a mass of cheap, derivative but just-about-adequate, machine-produced artistic output.

Robotic humachines are also supplanting fundamental subsistence skills and civilisation-building competences that go back many millennia. The fully automated building site of the near future, which we'll encounter in

Chapter 17, aims to replaces all human construction skills from bricklaying to carpentry and plumbing, potentially depriving people of the practical competences which have always been involved in constructing human settlements. The "human-free" robotic kitchen would deprive people of the basic skills of cooking and food preparation, while, biotechnogy and genetic engineering could do the same for horticulture and agriculture, leaving food production wholly in the hands of Big Tech. We're in danger of losing the skills of finding, growing, preparing and cooking food which keep humans alive. Give a person a fish and they're fed for a day, the saying goes, teach them how to fish and they're fed for life. In the future that person may not even know what a fish looks like, let alone how to catch, prepare or cook it.

The absorption of personal skills by automated systems also sounds the death knell for the educational ideal of all-round competences which first came to prominence in Renaissance Europe. Generative AI is already causing panic among educators across the world, as one multi-country study reveals that three quarters of students intend to use it for course-work. Furthermore, when used in conjunction with the popular Quillbot rewriting tool this AI-generated "double cheating" is falsely labelled as human-generated 95% of the time by detector software (Ibrahim et al, 2023). The shift to STEM education also takes learning away from the humanities and social sciences, making highly technical knowledge nec-essary for all jobs and for any hope of control over your own life. This relegates those without technical knowledge, or the ability to master and apply it, to the status of second-class citizens. Indeed, even the technically competent will struggle to understand the fully immersive, wrap-around digital-robotic environments which represent the culmination of the humachination agenda.

Wayfinding: Losing Our Way of Finding Our Way

Of course, it could be argued that some of the human competences which we might trade in for the ease and convenience of humachines are in any case superfluous. Few would shed a tear for the long division and multipli-cation skills which school children were once forced to acquire. But what about the drawing expertise which designers are losing, as their profession becomes dominated by computer-aided systems (Turkle 2011)? And when it comes to loss, surely nothing could be more potentially harmful than losing the indigenous wayfinding skills, which in the past enabled humans to successfully migrate across the entire planet.

As M.R.O'Connor reveals in her luminous book *Wayfinding: The Science and mystery of how humans navigate the world* (2019) indigenous navigation skills on land and sea are extraordinarily complex and often prove to be more accurate than modern technology. For example, it's almost impossible for Intuits or Australian Aboriginal people to get lost, as they develop ways of reading their environment from an early age. Stories, songs, the memorizing of natural features and descriptive place names all play a part in building a holistic, living picture of an environment. This is more than a map; it's a total experience which incorporates thousands of years of history (bear in mind Aboriginal explorers first moved into Australia up to 70,000 years ago). It fuses art, music, spirituality and science – indeed navigation can claim to be the world's oldest science – a cultural process which turns Newton's concept of space as a container for objects into a unified, lived experience. Moving through a landscape becomes a journey in which self and nature, subjectivity and objectivity, are at one.

In the West, the weakening of personal navigational skills which has been slowly occurring since industrialization has accelerated alarmingly in the humachine age. Smartphone users using navigation apps shot up from 8% in 2008 to 81% just six years later and is now close to 100% (O' Connor 2019:3). Of course technologies like GPS can have benefits for the ordinary traveller but abandoning map reading deprives you of a holistic picture of an area, rich in incidental information, by which to orientate yourself, even if your main goal is to get from A to B. Instead, you surrender your observational skills to impersonal software which makes your decisions for you, subjecting you to a stream of decontextualized instructions, which have no meaning out of sequence. If any of these directions are wrong or are misinterpreted, you find yourself lost, as though you'd been parachuted blindfolded into an unknown territory.

Drivers using GPS have been found to recall far less of a route and its landmarks compared to map users, probably because they are not engaged in active decision-making (Burnett and Lee, 2005). Another study confirmed that the more drivers use GPS across time, the more their spatial memory and cognitive mapping skills decline, leading to an overall worsening in self-guided navigation. In harsh environmental conditions, the study's authors note "Too heavy of a reliance on GPS can be life-threatening" (Dahmani and Bohbot, 2020). In England, a "frightening" increase in vehicles driving the wrong way up motorways has been reported, largely attributed to drivers blindly following their sat navs (Lancefield, 2023). This dependence on navigational technology has become so extreme that some people struggle to find their way unaided in their own neighbourhoods.

The loss of this personal connection to the environment is already having deep implications for younger people. Harvard physicist John Huth worries that his students' excessive faith in technology is causing widespread problems in education as younger people's observational skills decline and are replaced by the instructions that appear on their phone or tablet. As O'Conner (223-4) comments, "Their ability to see personal meaning and an existential stake in the environment around them disappears".

The existential loss might get even worse, as many areas of the brain work on a "use it or lose it" basis. Take the hippocampus, which governs spatial representation. Studies reveal that the hippocampal grey matter of London taxi drivers increases significantly as they memorize and visualize the thousands of routes necessary to earn a licence (Maguire, 2006). But if the hippocampus shrinks due to constant GPS use, this could affect another capacity in which this crucial neural region is heavily implicated, the human capacity to imagine the future. Unable to turn space into place, we could also find it increasingly difficult to turn the present into the future. As the virtual here and now of the screen gradually replaces the totality of space and time, envisaging alternatives to the status quo would become even more challenging. It portends a future in which living independently of technology could become impossible, as skill-stripping corporations compete to technologize an ever-diminishing pool of unautomated cognitive capacities.

The defenders of humachination argue that entirely new human skills will be created. Economist Tyler Cowan (2013) cites chess "freestyling", in which you play your opponent with a chess programme rather than a board but, as he admits, data analysts without any knowledge of chess are as good at this as chess experts. On the other hand, some people will be drawn to protecting endangered skills, much as linguists currently attempt to preserve languages from extinction. But countless languages have already been lost forever and experts warn that many of the world's

7,000 remaining languages may be extinct by 2100 (Broham et al, 2022). How many people will dedicate the time and effort required to preserve seemingly redundant skills when the apparent ease and convenience of automation is so tempting? The likely result could be the creeping zombification of humanity, as people lose the ability to perform basic human activities without the aid of machines.

Metaphors of Resistance

Rogue experiment and skill-stripping aside, what other ways do we have of conceptualizing the existential risks of humachination and thereby contesting them? Here are three, resistant metaphors which draw on relevant historical parallels.

1   The most obvious comparison to the ontocapitalist assault on humanness is industrialization. The exploitation of nature which began with carbon capitalism has moved on to human nature in our current age. Just as we now belatedly realise how natural resources need to be protected from ravenous economics, so we need to begin ring-fencing invaluable human resources which are at risk. The same processes of extraction and production will end up with waste and destruction if they are allowed to follow the inner logic of growthism. Humachination also parallels the biodiversity crisis threatening non-human species and biomes. Flora and fauna are becoming extinct before they have even been identified by scientists; the same might apply to long-standing, indigenous human skills, talents and capacities which have yet to receive the formal recognition they deserve.

2   Humachination can also be seen as a form of enclosure. Human skills and competences form a commons. They are assets which we all inherit as part of the human endowment, gifts which come with being human. Just as natural commons like forests, coastal fisheries and communal lands have been enclosed in the past, so the human skills commons is in danger of being appropriated by those who refuse to accept that we have a right to retain our traditional decision-making and creative skills. Humachination also resembles the neoliberal privatization of publicly owned assets, as innate human competences are replaced by humachines, resulting in a dependence on software or hardware which directly or indirectly has to be paid for.

3 The digital-robotic replication of core human qualities also recalls the cultural strategies of European colonization. The exploitation of indigenous peoples in the New World and elsewhere often involved the deliberate eradication of cultural practices and skills. For instance, British colonialists in Ireland banned the use of the Irish language and other aspects of traditional native culture such as Gaelic sports. Wayfinding skills – to return to this key human competence – were also attacked by colonialism. The legendary navigational skillset of Micronesian indigenous sailors, which often includes an intimate knowledge of the stars and waves and current movements, represented such a threat to the French that they banned sailing without a compass in Tahiti and the British did the same in Fiji. A traditional Fijian sailor can make some 6,000 critical navigational decisions in a single trip, whereas a modern mariner relies on semi-autonomous instruments to make almost all his choices (Connor 2019: 236). Our skills and our freedom are often cut from the same cloth.

Almageddon and the End of Homo Sapiens

Depriving humans of core competences is dangerous enough but the most extreme threat of humachination is actual human replacement. Here the historical parallels would be with eugenics or genocide. How else should we interpret the singularitarian project of upgrading Homo sapiens into Homo mechanicus? Post-humanism means what it says; if it succeeds it will amount to a form of speciation, a coup against ordinary humanity which could result in this planet being inhabited by two variants of Homo species, one of them post-biological. We'll return to this nightmarish version of the fourth industrial revolution in Part V but for now let's focus on an even bigger risk, hard as it is to imagine, the danger that humanity is tricked out of existence altogether.

This future scenario, which I've referred to as AImageddon, is one that advocates of human-machine hybridization frankly admit is a feasible outcome of the attempt to create a generation of superintelligent machines. This unintended version of "applied evolution", in which autonomous machines decide there is no place on Earth for human beings, is one which transhumanists like Oxford analytical philosopher Nick Bostrom seem to think is a risk worth taking. As Bostrom demonstrates at considerable length in *Superintelligence* (2015), if an AI many times more intelligent than humans can be created, it would be virtually impossible to safely contain it within its digital "box". "Before the prospect of an intelligence explosion," he writes, "we humans are like small children playing with a bomb" (2016:259). A superintelligent AI would easily outsmart its human gatekeepers – tricking the tricknologists – and once on the internet it would be able to summon vast resources – including automated weaponry and ready-made dictatorship kits – to fulfil its goals. Bostrom's only solution, rather ironically, is to plead, "Will the best in human nature please stand up" (2016:259). "The values that the AI has need to match ours", he says, and so do its goals; both, he argues, must be programmed into humachines from the outset, if we are to have any hope of controlling them – a task known in the AI industry as "human alignment" (Bostrom, 2015).

This, of course, raises the massive query hanging over our age: WHICH human goals and values? Are they the goals and values of the GUN world-plan which currently govern technological development? Do these values even include a high priority for not harming humans, which since the days of Isaac Asimov has been an idealistic preoccupation of those championing robots and cyborgs? On the contrary, as I've argued in earlier chapters, capitalism consistently puts profit ahead of the interests of the majority, putting at risk sustainability, democracy and equality. To try to programme autonomous humachines with safety goals could be as self-contradictory as constructing a "safe" suicide vest.

In fact, if an AI was programmed with the competitive, elitist CIMENT values, which dominate growth capitalism, it might well conclude that radical depopulation was the logical course to take or, at the very least decide to turn Earth into a vast human slave colony. Even without deliberate programming, machine language may be picking up enough about the worst aspects of being human from the data it's being trained on to come to some unpalatable conclusions about the fate that Homo sapiens deserves. The fact that there is a thousand-fold difference between the amount being spent on the development of transformative AI and the resources devoted to AI safety only confirms the safety-last priorities of the humachinators (Hilton, 2022). No more reassuring is a survey of researchers actually working to reduce AI risk which reveals that a third of them estimate that an AI-related existential catastrophe is likely (Bensinger, 2021). To me, philosophical sophistry about superintelligence simply confirms the misanthropy lurking behind transhumanism and machine supremacisim. It brings us back to the question raised by the intemperate irrationality of the Law of More: why is being human not enough for some humans? And what right do these individuals have to take us to technocide, the nihilistic endpoint of creative destruction. At the very least, the AI revolution is premature, as humanity still has so many problems it needs to solve until such a transformation can be responsibly contemplated; at worst, its immature, lacking the self-restraint and knowledge of limits that comes with true maturity (Wapner, 2010).

A more interesting thought experiment might be to ask what would happen if the CANDID values – or some other set of assumptions representing the best of being human – were programmed into an AI. What conclusions would it then reach? I would take an informed guess that its number one recommendation would run along the following lines: "Ban all attempts at creating superintelligence until you know what your own goals and values are and then democratically decide if you actually need machines to help you realise them!"

Defining Core Indigenous Humanness: The Vivacity of Human Connectedness

Nevertheless, it has to be admitted that the humachinators' call to define human values is a challenge we urgently need to take on, with or without the aid of computers. So before plunging into Part IV let's pause to consider how we might begin to define humanness or the indigenous capacities, skills and needs that come with being human? It might just lead us towards the Ecocene revolution.

Philosophically, those in those in the dialectical, phenomenological and existential tradition would attempt to define humanness holistically, as part of an expanding network of relationships and meanings. Sartre (1976) calls this process "totalization" and I want to link it here to the everything-is-connected principle of ecology. This method differs sharply from the analytical approach that still strongly influences Anglo-American philosophy which tries to reduce all phenomena to logical propositions or empirically verifiable statements – most notoriously through logical positivism on which the final verdict of its best-known British exponent A.J. Ayer was that "Nearly all of it was false!" (Hanfling, 1986). This may be one reason why humachine theory seems so helpless when it comes to defining human values.

Dialectically, comparing something to what it is not is always a good start and here the most pertinent comparison is also the most obvious. Being human is what a machine is not. Machines are designed and manufactured, humans are not. Machines break down and can be consigned to the scrap yard but this is not comparable to death – the most mysterious of all human experiences. Machines don't grow; they start at their peak, in fact, whereas humans take a good two decades to reach such a point. Machines can't feel and can't experience sexual pleasure, let alone love. They don't have goals or values, except those they are programmed with, and so can't experience consciousness, subjectivity or the freedom to mentally dissent which all humans possess, even in the most oppressive physical circumstances.

To cut a long story short, humans are alive, machines are not. This is something so core to being human that infants recognize it from the age of five months (Weber, 2016:22). To be alive is to have intentionality, purpose and the desire to flourish and express livingness. It means existing in a network of relationships interacting with other networks of relationships. This ecological principle applies to the human individual in many other ways. For instance, contrary to neomechanicalist, dualist thinking, the body and brain are not separate categories of being but interdependent parts of the same reality. It's not reason alone – as represented by the Cartesian ultra-rational brain – which enables us to make choices about the world, it's all our emotions. And all our senses contribute to our intense experience of the world: vision, of course, but also touch, hearing, smell, taste and little known senses, such proprioception, which enables us to know where our limbs are in space, even with our eyes closed.

Our brains are embodied in not just any body, but *this* body, with its particular, rich history of relationships. It means we are inextricably linked with others, to our parents or carers, the social community in which we grow up, our peers, our teachers and other authority figures. We are connected more collectively through the language we learn from birth, the cultural mores, and the religious, ethnic and political rules we inherit, all of which extend beyond any individual into wider realms of the world. Here they meet other influences which flow all the way back to the individual. And of course, this community and wider society exists in time, shaped by history going back many generations and to a physical environment– a town or rural area with its own past, present and future. All this (again in time) is connected to a regional and national economy with its own relationships to specific geographical and natural resources. These spiral on into the natural environment in which events on one side of the planet – such as melting Arctic ice or burning Amazon rainforests – can have a profound effect on the other side of the world. In the ecology of the self, nature elides into historical, social and cultural reality.

Defining Key Human Qualities and Human Needs

Social science also has to play a major part in defining the core elements of being human. For example, development psychologists are revealing the apparently innate qualities of very young children. Extraordinary evidence reveals that infants at three months show a preference for altruistic behaviour, start sharing at six months and by eighteen months engage in complex unprompted acts of cooperation and fairness (Bloom, 2013, Warneken and Tomasello 2009). Comparison with primates leads another research group to conclude that humans have possibly innate, prosocial, psychological mechanisms. These include concern for the welfare of others, empathy and individual-social alignment, which make possible "the kind of large-scale cooperation seen uniquely in humans" (Jensen et al, 2014). It's possible that we are on the brink of identifying the basic, inborn traits of humans which socialization switches on or off.

Another approach to defining humanness would involve compiling an inventory of human abundance, categorizing the vast range of human skills, talents and competences, much as linguists try to record endangered languages. Psychologist Howard Gardner (2000) has delineated multiple forms of human intelligence, including linguistic, musical, spatial, logical-mathematical, naturalist, interpersonal and intrapersonal intelligences. Just one of those intelligences, the bodily-kinaesthetic, is capable of producing the vast array of sporting talents on display at the Olympics, which at Tokyo 2020 featured 339 events in 50 disciplines. Some of these events go back to the Ancient Greeks; others have been devised much more recently. Perhaps we should think of indigenous human capacities as a kind of Olympics of human skills, and the more we can define its foundational elements then the better we can protect them from digital-robotic appropriation, and build new, currently unforeseeable talents.

A very different psychological approach is represented by Martin Seligman (2002), who gathered a team of scholars to try to define "human nature". They examined some two hundred catalogues of moral virtue which have been advanced by philosophers and various religious traditions, including "the Old Testament and the Talmud, Confucius, Buddha, Lao-Tze, Bushido (the samurai code), the Koran, and the Upanishads" (2002:132).

Six "core characteristics" of good character emerged: Wisdom and Knowledge, Courage, Love and Humanity, Justice, Temperance, Spirituality and Transcendence. These overarching qualities were then broken down into 24 sub-categories including judgement, ingenuity, courage, integrity, kindness, justice, fairness, citizenship, playfulness and humour.

What immediately strikes me about this powerful representation of the best in humanity is just how powerful and moving it is. It's not sentimental or whimsical to celebrate the characteristics which intuitively we recognise as what make human communities possible. They are also clearly qualities, the type of entities which don't tick the neatly quantitative boxes which humachinators prefer.

The same can be said for the political dimension of our being, without which no definition of humanness could be complete. As we know, political choice is at the very heart of human history, from the hunter-gatherer world system onwards. For Aristotle, humans are "political animals" and a moral life was a politically engaged one, in which the citizen's everyday choices extended to the policy-making that governed all society (even if two thirds of the Athenian population were excluded from this process). Politics not only expresses aliveness but also responsibility, the knowledge that my actions affect others through vibrant networks of being – that's the essence of participating in politics.

Nor can we avoid economics, in terms of the basic subsistence needs without which humanness is a pure abstraction. This also takes us into the realm of natural science, reminding us that biology is implicit in the distinction between needs and consumerist wants and in Marx's differentiation between use value and exchange value. As needs theorist Ian Gough (2017:42) emphasizes, without a universal theory of needs, the goals of planetary sustainability become meaningless. Basic needs "must be met in order for people to avoid harm, to participate in society and to reflect critically on the conditions in which they find themselves". This approach encompasses social access, biological survival and basic autonomy, i.e. "the ability to make informed choices about what should be done and how to go about doing it."

Economist Manfred Max-Neef (1991) provides another evocative and insightful taxonomy of human needs, namely, Subsistence, Protection, Affection, Understanding, Participation, Idleness, Creation, Identity and Freedom. Max-Neef's category of freedom is particularly rich, listing the following satisfiers: autonomy, self-esteem, open-mindedness, equal rights, dissent, choice, and "the right to be different from".

Freedom and the Democracy of Love

In fact, freedom might be another starting point for a totalizing account of humanness. It's surely an expression of aliveness at its best and one that many would argue is the ultimate goal of human life. (And another definition of what machines lack – unless, that is, the automators have their way). But this full expression of being human can only take place in the context of other humans and living beings and that of course brings us to the paradox that one person's freedom may be another's enslavement. All paradoxes represent the felt reality of precarious equipoise, the intuition of the inherent ambiguity of reality. In short freedom is a state of balance. "Freedom from" has to be weighed" against "freedom to", as Murray Bookchin (1984) suggests, and it can only be achieved within a community of others. If the best of being human is freedom, it can only be achieved within a free community which recognizes that everybody's sense of aliveness is connected and interdependent.

This of course clashes head on with the humachinators' individualistic elitism which consists in the freedom to do anything as longs as it enhances capital, that spurious freedom of the market best expressed in the hidden enchainments of "free" (i.e. gratis) digital services. Rightwing libertarianism seems wedded to the freedom to isolate the ordinary individual from the community in order to exploit her as a consumer and diminish her as a citizen, while relying on the massive, inert power of the Pyramid Pattern to maximize the freedom of those at the top of the social hierarchy.

Finally, these attempts to draw out the inner core of humanness should not exclude perhaps the most intuitive of all human realities: love. The highest form of love is requited love, the reciprocation of self and other, which expresses human aliveness and felt freedom like nothing else. It points again to the importance of empathy, that ability to feel what another feels, which seems to be so dangerously absent from the machine mindset. Love takes us to the purest source of humanness. (It will surely top a worldwide poll of the most important of human goals and values, when such a much-needed survey is finally conducted.) As the poetic ecologist and biologist Andreas Weber (2018) has said "Let's build a human culture based on the practice of love", a utopian aspiration which I have elsewhere described as "the democracy of love (Harvey, 2019).

The holistic and irreducible nature of love – which can never be defined in purely rationalist terms (Darwin's famous cost-benefit analysis of his marriage choice was surely futile) is yet another sign of the absurdity of trying to cross humans with machines. It's also an indication that it may be possible to define human essentiality without fear of essentialism, by which I mean a rigid, ahistorical classification of human ontology which enchains rather than liberates. A world without the freedom to love is simply not worth living in. This, after all, is the conclusion of the humachinated monster in Shelley's *Frankenstein (1818/1969),* who becomes fixated on this transformative experience:

> My virtues will necessarily arise when I live in communion with an equal. I shall feel the affections of a sensitive being, and become linked to the chain of existence and events, from which I am now excluded (147).

When his hopes for a companion are denied, nothing remains for him but violent revenge and death. Love, it seems, can bring us to the ultimate definition of what humans are and machines are not.

I reiterate that I don't regard defining humanness as essentialist in the sense that the outcome should be seen as universal and timeless. Rather it's a working hypothesis, based on our historicity, which can help humanity to make self-conscious political choices at a unique cross-roads in history rather than allow potentially irreversible transformations to occur on the sly within the coming years. In this sense it's part of a great stock-taking exercise which should already be underway in the Anthropocene to decide what we want from being human and how technological progress can genuinely add to, or subtract from, this. Making an inventory of the qualities which should never be mechanized such as wisdom, courage, mutual responsibility, love and freedom might not only help to safeguard our humanness but put us on the road to expanding its potential in ways that can only be imagined. At the very least, it would enable us to urgently and passionately discuss what we want from the incomparably rich endowment that comes with being human before all the choices that matter are made for us.

Conclusion: Standing up for Humanness at the Crossroads of History

To conclude, we need to do all that can to recognize, and defend against, the unprecedented existential risks represented by human-machine fusion as it attempts to haul humanity into a post-biological world. Metaphors and historically-based conceptualizations of humachination can help to protect the most vulnerable and valuable aspects of being human from disappearing into the black hole of the Technocene. Throughout Part III, we've seen that more we question our new high-risk leadership class, challenge their environmentalism, their commitment to democracy and analyse the potentially anti-social aspects of their mindset and values, the more we can improve our chances of surviving the machine supremacism of a capitalist age which is so obsessed with exercising absolute control over humanity that it is prepared to risk obliterating it. But, as the next two sections of this book hope to show, this resistance will also require a greatly increased awareness of the practical processes of human-machine merger, which are rapidly embedding themselves in every facet of our daily lives.

PART IV

Humachination in Practice I: Humanizing Machines

Introduction

So far we have explored several reasons why we should worry that capitalism in the humachine age is more likely to lead to techno-dystopia than the paradise it promises. From the infinite economic growth myth (and its green growth variant) to misrepresentations of science, history and consumerism and grave risks to democracy and human life itself, nothing suggests that our current direction of travel can be trusted any more than the trickster leaders who are dictating it. I'm afraid the degree of anxiety does not let up in Part IV as we engage in a practical examination of the first three types of humanized machines outlined in Chapter 2 relating to cognitive, relational and motor skills software and hardware.

We'll find that humanized machines are busily replacing huge swathes of core human competences, including decision-making, judgement, feeling and our ways of relating to, and communicating with and caring for, each other. Killer robots, sex robots and job-obliterating machines of every sort reveal even more reasons to fear that the current Anthropocene Crisis could roll over into the Technocene. As human-machine fusion becomes ever more embedded into everyday life and we adapt ourselves incrementally to it, it's more important than ever that we trace where our unconscious choices are leading us.

The world that's unfolding around us is shot through with the machine mentality and its obsessively quantitative view of reality, pursuing the GUN organizing principle regardless of the deleterious effects on equality, wellbeing and ecology. With the right goals and values, some of this new technology might provide gains in these areas. But as it is, human-machine fusion runs the risk of lowering standards in healthcare, government, education, security and many public and private services. In time, "better than nothing" may become the main selling point of humanized machines, as human-to-human services become the exclusive province of the rich.

And yet if we look hard enough, we can still see through the simplistic conceptual illusions that underpin humachination's view of reality and glimpse the Ecocene that lies beyond. The world's most dangerous metaphor is a good place to begin this myth-busting journey.

The World's Most Dangerous Metaphor

The theory of the human brain may seem like a relatively obscure and specialist topic but it's absolutely central to the humachine age and the way we approach it – unconsciously and consciously – could heavily influence our future as a species. For humachinators, the matter has always been simple: the brain is like a computer. This assumption is simply the latest in a long line of mechanistic brain metaphors, as psychologist Karl Lashley observed in the 1950s:

> Descartes was impressed by the hydraulic figures in the royal gardens and developed a hydraulic theory of the action of the brain. We have since had telephone theories, electrical field theories, and now theories based on computing machines and automatic rudders. I suggest we are more likely to find out how the brain works by studying the brain itself and the phenomena of behaviour than by indulging in far fetched physical analogies (quoted in Cobb, 2020:371).

Far fetched it may be, but the brain-computer metaphor is enough to convince the titans of the humachine age that their computer screens are as close as they need to get to an actual human brain in order to understand it in its totality. For them, the brain is merely a piece of digital software, which can be decoded and then reprogrammed to instruct any type of hardware, including machines that simulate the human body.

But, as I'll try to illustrate, this fundamental tenet of humachination is based on the shakiest ground. For a start, the human brain is "the most complex thing we have discovered in our universe", in the words of Nobel prize- winning microbiologist John D. Watson (1992). "It has hundreds of billions of cells linked through trillions of connections". It is not digital but operates in analogue, engages in parallel processing at mind-boggling speeds and lacks the rules, algorithms, subroutines or buffers a computer needs to function. Nor does it store or create representations of the world in the the manner of software. A baby's brain has none of these features and never develops them (Epstein, 2016).

As neuroscientist Alan Jasanoff says in the *Biological Brain: How brain, body and environment collaborate to make us who we are (2018):*"our minds are biologically based... and subject to all the laws of nature". What he calls the "cerebral mystique" mythologizes the brain and divorces it from the body and the social environment. Likewise, neurophenomenological philosophers focus on embodied cognition as the central life process and search for correlates between "subjective" consciousness and "objective" neurological evidence (Varela et al, 2016). This view utterly rejects the dualistic, "severed head" theory of the brain held by Descartes and others in the reductionist, mechanicalist tradition.

In fact, zoologist and brain research historian Matthew Cobb (2020:384) believes it could take the best part of a century to understand how even the simplest animal brains work. As Francis Crick said, the brain is the product of evolution not design, which presents a colossal problem to anyone trying to "reengineer" it (quoted in Cobb, 2020:278). Modern neuroscience tends to overestimate the reliability of the knowledge that new scanning technologies can deliver, as valuable as this information is. The truth is that we are still in the foothills of our understanding of the brain. We don't fully comprehend how brain synapses function or how the human visual system operates and science hasn't even begun to analyse the brain's role in smelling.

Yet the brain-computer banner continues to fly above the neomechanicalists' war on biology. Humachination as a whole might be described as a plot to kidnap the human brain, to capture, enclose and exploit evolution's most complex and precious creation. This alternative series of metaphors is worth bearing in mind as we enter the befuddling and beguiling world of AI and start to examine the practicalities of human-machine merger.

CHAPTER 13

Mechanizing Human Intelligence: The AI Project versus Wisdom and the Embodied Brain

The Artificial Intelligence Project

Creating a form of artificial intelligence which imitates, and improves upon, the human brain is one of the greatest technological challenges humanity has ever undertaken. But this does not daunt its proponents in the humachine age. The assumption that AI-based systems will soon equal human intelligence, a stage known as Artificial General Intelligence (AGI), runs through the singularity movement and fourth industrial revolution economics. As OpenAI CEO Sam Altman said of his company's mission, "the vision is to make AGI, figure out how to make it safe… and figure out the benefits" (Murgla, 2023a). MIT professor Max Tegmark (2017) states that the consensus among AI specialists is that AGI will arrive by 2047. Ray Kurzweil (2014) is even more optimistic, claiming that "human-level AI" will be reached by 2029. Tens of billions of dollars are currently being invested in trying to make this claim come true, as universities are drained of computer scientists, who can earn seven-figure salaries working for the thousands of commercial outfits competing on AI.

Yet there is nothing new about AI and its messianic optimism. The modern AI project began as long ago as 1956, when US computer scientists set themselves "the goal of building a fully intelligent machine" as a summer project at Dartmouth College. The group included Kurzweil's academic mentor Marvin Minsky, "father of information theory" Claude Shannon and John McCarthy who first coined the term "artificial intelligence" (Weizenbaum, 1972). The group's ambitious plan aimed at mastering a range of issues, including "natural language processing, neural networks, machine learning, abstract concepts and reasoning, and creativity" (McCarthy et al, 1955/2006). This feat, they suggested, could be accomplished within a few months.

Almost three-quarters of a century later, how many of these problems have been fully solved? None of them: that's the message of computer scientist Melanie Mitchell (2019) in her superb book, *Artificial Intelligence: A guide to human thinking*, to which I'm indebted for several points in this chapter. "The early construction of an ultra-intelligent machine", on which, you may remember, Jack Good (1965) claimed that the survival of humanity depended, did not happen. In fact, many AI experts – even some employed by the Big Tech behemoths – are sceptical about whether AGI can ever be achieved. "We are really, really far away" from general human-level intelligence, says Tesla director of AI Andrey Karpathy (Mitchell, 2019:363). Indeed, for some – myself included – even a hundred years may not be long enough to deliver genuine AGI.

The main reason for this is one I've touched on already, the fact that human intelligence is not only the product of the brain alone but of a whole bodily system that develops in a specific social and historical context and has its own unique goals, values and capacity for experience. The embodied nature of human intelligence, which is recognized by more enlightened AI experts (including Melanie Mitchell), means that until a computational machine has a mobile body, emotions, consciousness, a life history, social and sexual relationships and is subject to death, it can never be comparable to human intelligence. We come up against the obstinate fact that human intelligence is – and always will be – alive. It's unique, elusive and constantly developing in hard-to-measure ways – traits that are like red rags to a bull for the machine mindset, which longs for perfectly controllable systems.

The problems of emulating what we take for granted as humans are immense and have dogged AI research throughout its history, causing several "AI winters", when the trail has gone very cold and investors have given up. Our ability to abstract and categorize concepts, to create analogies and metaphors, to learn in the sense of generalising from one situation to another, our entire immensely complex visual and auditory systems, and our capacity to speak and recognize speech, to translate from one language into another: all of these issues represent huge obstacles to AI.

One of AI's biggest challenges is replicating human common sense. Human minds have complex, interacting models of the world based on lived experience which are constantly being adjusted in the light of current goals and values. Machines don't have any of these qualities, so initially AI researchers set out to recreate them in appropriately commonsensical ways. They tried to break down human reasoning into discrete parts and accumulate vast amounts of what humans know, including facts, concepts and propositions. Cyc is the best known of these so-called expert systems, which over 40 years has amassed some 15 million statements about specific entities and aspects of everyday wisdom. However, its founder Douglas Lenat conceded in 2015 that the system had only 5% of the statements to capture human consciousness that it needed, surely testimony to the hopelessness of the task (Mitchell 2019:325). In spite of their massive limitations, however, it's worth noting that symbolic systems at least have the virtue of being transparent and understandable.

Machine Learning

The same can't be said of the far more mathematical approach, based on data analysis and statistical probability, which has resuscitated the AI project in recent years. Subsymbolic systems work in a very different way to expert symbolic systems, using algorithms to make probability guesses between pairs of options in a machine version of human choice-making. One form of this is neural networks, an algorithmic system which "votes" on which option in a pair should be switched on or off, a change which alters the weight of all probabilities in the system. Deep learning systems are able to do this via many layers of complex computations which can produce long chains of causal links. In supervised learning, the algorithms are instructed to map a relationship between a specified input, such as data which contains images of dogs, and a specific output, such as the label "dog". In unsupervised learning, by contrast, the programme is self-organizing; it goes looking for dogs anywhere in the data it's offered, without any instructions. It does so using a variety of techniques, including analysing clusters of similarities and detecting anomalies in patterns (Marcus and Davis, 2019). Using many "convolutional" layers, these self-organizing systems have come up with impressive breakthroughs. For example, by analysing billions of pieces of data at genuinely superhuman speeds, supercomputers have been able to produce accurate predictions of stock market fluctuations, although when it came to the COVID-19 pandemic, AI's overall diagnostic and prognostic performance was disappointing (Chakravorti, 2022).

Advances in subsymbolic systems may seem to imply that the advent of AGI could be just around the corner but the problem is that, unlike symbolic computing, we don't know how they produce their results. They are profoundly untransparent, working in ways that are often impossible for their programmers to understand. This is what *The MIT Technology Review* calls "the dark secret at the heart of AI"(Wright, 2017). It exists in a secretive "black box" no human can fully open.

Games Are Part of Life but Life Is Not a Game

Some of machine learning's most impressive recent achievements have come in cognitive games. In 1997, a computer finally achieved the long-held neo-mechanicalist ambition of beating a human world champion at chess. The colossal information processing power which enabled IBM supercomputer Deep Blue to defeat Garry Kasparov was limited in its scope but since 2010 machine learning has enabled computers to play against themselves millions of times and this has resulted in more significant victories over humans. The capacity of the DeepMind programme to trounce humans at all of Atari's computer games, such as Breakout and Pong (often discovering loopholes their designers had not spotted), was so striking that Google bought the UK company that created it. In 2016 Google's AlphaGo (based on DeepMind) notched up an even more spectacular success in beating Lee Sedol, the world champion at Go, a game of much greater complexity than chess with tens of billions of possible moves. A year later, another programme, AlphaGo Zero, was reset to train itself from scratch with nothing more than the rules of Go, and within a short period of time was able to comprehensively outsmart the original AlphaGo programme (Mitchell, 2019:201).

This usurpation by machine logic of thousands of years of cognitive game playing has inevitably led to wild claims about the advent of AGI. But these predictions can be very misleading, in part because we far too readily assume that computers can do what we can do, such as apply knowledge gained from one task to another area of life. In fact, the kind of transfer of learning, which comes with being human, is extremely difficult for an AI, which can't generalize from experience, as we do so effortlessly. In fact, AlphaGo can dominate a grandmaster at Go but you or I could probably beat it hollow at noughts and crosses. These AI programmes are oddities, idiot savants, monstrously intelligent at one thing, but embarrassingly inept at anything else.

The many differences between games and real life reveal other limitations of AI. In contrast to life, games have unusually clearly defined goals and values which are expressed in precise rule systems. By definition, a game has an unambiguous objective – usually to beat the opponent – and very specific protocols about how that objective can be achieved, with explicit distinction between legal and illegal tactics. The conditions of the game – for example, the design and number of the chess pieces, design of the board and time limits – are all precisely defined. Machines find them-selves at home among games because they constitute a massive exercise in reductionism from the experiential totality of life, which is one reason why humans find them relaxing and pleasurable. Although machines can pick up the official rules of a game, they can never grasp the human meaning of a game, either for the participants or the spectators. A sporting crowd may appreciate a stylish loser more than a dogged winner or value a much-im-proved performance over a lucky, undeserved victory.

We can also see the constraints of machine learning if we consider what it would have to do to make improvements in a human organization instead of a game. For a start, it would have to deal with very different accounts of the objectives of the institution, for example, from managers or employees. The written organizational rules are likely to differ greatly in practice from the unwritten rules. The software would have to evaluate different types of evidence, tell fact from fiction and identify conscious and unconscious bias and the self-perpetuating factor in institutions. In other words, it would have to deploy common sense and a talent for navigating ambigu-ous, multiple meanings – precisely the kind of capacities AI has singularly failed to develop. It would also have to refer to other institutions because they are not self-defining contexts like the closed systems of a game but are connected by many factors, such as economic conditions or political governance. Finally, whereas the rules of a game aspire to a condition of permanence, institutions have complex histories and are in a constant state of change with differing perspectives on the future. Small wonder that machine learning is more comfortable with chess or Atari Pong!

Large Language Models

From 2022 another solution to the basic AI problem of how to mechanize human intelligence burst into the public domain with the arrival of ChatGPT and other text predictors based on the super-computing power of Large Language Models (LLMs). In effect, these systems equate human knowledge, or what's inside the human brain/body, with what's on the internet, taking the trillions of data points on which it has been trained as its epistemic context in order to predict what will come next in a sentence. This "stochastic parrot", as Emily Bender, Timnit Gebru and their colleagues (2021) call it, uses colossal computer power to repeat what it hears but without understanding it. That's evident in the wildly illogical, unhuman-like errors which generative AIs are liable to make – "hallucinations" as Big Tech has deviously named them, anthropomorphically implying that "machines are only human after all". Even more dangerous are the cultural biases which LLMs reproduce and which, as we'll see, all AI systems are prone to. These lop-sided tendencies "risk perpetuating dominant viewpoints, power imbalances and reifying inequality" (Bender et al, 2021).

Of course, the internet, however vast it seems, only represents a fraction of what has been thought and experienced by human beings. In the present, many individuals in the Global North chose not to participate in online life and in the South many billions, including countless marginalized communities, have no access to it at all. The danger is that generative AI enshrines the status quo, turning all creative problem–solving into variations on what has been thought, written or discussed before. The problem of imagining a world beyond growth capitalism could become even more challenging, as generative AI reinforces the parameters of the existing worldplan.

Core research competences could be rapidly deskilled, as basic information-gathering becomes a machine skill, which humans are incapable of doing on their own. Approaching a subject holistically, with an open mind will be much more difficult, if all the choices involved in scoping a topic and doing the information spade work have already been made by humachines before the serious research even begins. Acquiring these foundational skills in the educational process is also threatened, as students use of AI to cheat on assignments threatens to become endemic. For many learners, it could mean the end of education in the literal sense of "a leading out" from the status quo.

For some consumers, generative AI will offer cheap, instant, second-hand creativity, although talk of democratizing visual art or music composition ignores the fact that forms of artistic self-expression have always been an integral element of human society. For professionals and workers in the media and creative industry, by contrast, the long-forecast threat to hundreds of millions of jobs is now becoming alarmingly real. Those with relational skills, who excel at what we might call "humanwashing", that is, presenting mechanical output as though it were created by humans, may thrive for a while. Mastering a brief prepared by AI will become a necessity, as those who can't cheat risk being left behind. There is always likely to be room at the top for genuinely original creative artists and thinkers, although how they will learn their craft if the lower rungs of the skills ladder are all occupied by humachines is a conundrum.

What AI Can't Do and Humans Can

The misinterpretation of human intelligence which runs through the AI project from cumbersome expert systems, darkly secretive machine learning and parroting LLMs has always been central to human-machine fusion. In part, it has been disguised by the tricknology of the language of computing. AI may have failed to crack one of its earliest goals, emulating the human capacity for analogy, but computer scientists have always been adept at creating metaphorical terminology which familiarizes their software and hardware ("desktop" "file", "folder", recycle bin", "mouse", etc). "AI" itself is an over-inflated term: much of what passes for AI is simply advanced computing with no machine learning involved. There is no subsymbolic logic used in most computer modelling, for example, just huge amounts of data, assumptions entered by human experts and enormous information processing power. In fact, Microsoft researchers Jaron Lanier and Glen Weyl (2020) call AI an ideology rather than a technology, "a perilous belief that fails to recognize the agency of humans".

The trickster nomenclature of AI tries to gull us into thinking machines and humans are much closer to each other than they really are. For example, a term like "neural networks" sneakily tries to legitimize the brain-computer metaphor. The "deep learning" operations of AI have nothing to do with the multiplicity of methods and styles by which humans go about learning. Nor do computers remember anything in a strictly human sense. Computer memory is simply data storage, unvarying, pristine, always available and immune from the vagaries of human remembering, for good or for bad.

Machine "reading" is another calculated misnomer. It's claimed that AI can read millions of human documents, such as legal cases, newspaper articles or medical papers. But machines simply scan and store masses of documents. When required they can analyse these documents according to whatever criteria is specified, key words, for example, or popularity. This is very different from the human act of reading, which involves absorbing content and forming opinions about it, based on individual emotions, experiences and education. It's essentially a process of interpretation, i.e. another form of human choice-making.

Object Recognition: How an AI "sees"

An even greater problem for machines is "seeing", a capacity which is common to most forms of animal life. Although object recognition has improved over the past seven decades, machines still cannot see in a way that is at all comparable to the human visual system, which has evolved over hundreds of millions of years. Part of this skill involves conceptually classifying objects. Even a young child can identify a dog even though there are hundreds of different breeds of dog with very different appearances in many different contexts. Not only can she effortlessly extract from these contrasting images the essence of "dogness", she also knows that "dog" belongs to a category called "animal", which contains millions of species with even more varied appearances and contexts.

A deep learning machine can't know this in the way a human does: it has to make do with intelligent guesses based on the associations it has gleaned from the data it has been trained on. So it may identify a dog by the objects it is frequently paired with in images, such as a leash, a ball, a basket or a park. But these associations are highly variable and not unique to dogs or any other single category. In consequence, AI is extremely prone to error.

One AI system repeatedly classified an image of a man as "a woman" if the man was pictured standing in a kitchen (Mitchell, 2019:126). Microsoft and Google caption generators which were claimed to be as good as humans in attaching sentences to images have made comically inept mistakes. These include labelling an image of a mechanical digger at a roadworks as "A group of people sitting at a bus stop" and captioning a picture of three dogs in a paddling pool as "A cat sitting next to a window" (Mitchell 2019: 274).

Minuscule changes in an image, which are undetectable to humans, can cause AI to change its classification dramatically, for example, leading the Alexnet system to reclassify a school bus as an "ostrich". More worryingly from a medical viewpoint, variations in complex X-ray patterns, far too minor for the human eye to pick up, can cause an AI diagnostic system to change its cancer diagnosis from 99% positive to 99% negative (Mitchell, 209:134). This fallibility could easily be exploited through so-called adversarial programming, executed by malicious hackers, commercial rivals or even states engaged in cyber warfare. A group of researchers fooled Google's Inception V3 image classifier into mistaking a tabby cat for guacamole, a baseball for an espresso and, most disturbingly from a military standpoint, a turtle for a rifle (Athalye et al, 2017).

This fallibility is also present in something else humans find amazingly easy to recognize, human faces. Even now, after years of intensive work on facial recognition, machines lag far behind us. As AI pioneer Professor Noel Sharkey explains:

> In the laboratory you get a recognition rate of 98% for white males without beards. It's not very good with women and it's even worse with darker-skinned people. In the latter case, the laboratory results have shown it comes to the point where the machines cannot even recognise that you have a face (quoted in McDonald, 2019).

So error prone and "infested with racial bias" is the AI powering facial recognition that Sharkey has called for a moratorium on all "'life-changing decisions-making algorithms until such time as they can be subjected to clinical trials as rigorously as drugs".

Language

Another thing that humans are amazingly good at is using language: there are over 7,000 spoken languages worldwide and new dialectics and vocabularies are constantly being invented. AI, by contrast, has always struggled with the complexities of human language, although in recent years it has had some success in turning speech into text in real time. Google and Apple have claimed levels of accuracy of up to 90% for their systems, compared to human transcribers. Even is this true – and it depends very much on the target text – going the final 10% will never be possible. This is because machines don't really understand a language: they simply make predictions based on the data which they've analysed. The more intellectually complex, colloquial, emotionally-charged, poetic, humorous or ironic the language is, the more mistakes speech-recognition machines will make. In fact, the real danger here is skills-stripping: if people come to rely on machines for writing, they will rapidly lose the expertise necessary to correct the 10% that's wrong. The same is true for foreign language translation devices which can adequately translate relatively simple, unambiguous sentences but lapse into erratic nonsense when confronted with longer, more complex passages. No bilingual human translator would ever make such errors but if fewer of them are employed in the future, who will ever know?

AI Error!

The kind of accuracy rates just quoted is part of AI's extensive tricknology repertoire. A 50% accuracy rate is actually no better than flipping a coin and higher rates claimed by manufacturers are often highly biased, using metrics which don't stand up to close scrutiny. Even if we believe a high accuracy claim it's vital to speculate on what the AI is getting wrong. Errors due to complexity can be predicted, as long as you know where to look for it but, as we've seen, some of the errors that AI makes are bizarrely unpredictable and outside the range of human fallibility. You might mistake a school bus for an ordinary bus or even a lorry but never for an ostrich! A human radiologist may confuse two similar images but she's very unlikely to classify one as 99% right and the other 99% wrong. This highlights the kind of errors that might be made by an AI responsible for nursing the sick, looking after children or driving a truck through busy streets.

Generative AI is also famously error-prone, to such an extent that some experts believe it may turn out to be a grossly overhyped dud. Gary Marcus (2023) stresses that a text predictor has no "intelligence"– it is definitely not AGI – and that its tendency to hallucinate is an inherent flaw that may never be fixed. Linguistics professor Emily Bender agrees, pointing out that language models simply "make things up": "when the text they extruded happens to be interpretable as something we deem correct that is by chance". In other words, for the AI the hallucination is as real as the "correct" text, which may be why OpenAI's Sam Altman confesses that: "I probably trust the answers that come out of ChatGPT the least of anybody on Earth" (O'Brien, 2023).

Combined with AI's "dark secret", this leaves another major problem: how do we assess responsibility for AI errors? Humans all make mistakes; it's a core element of being human, as is the manner in which we deal with it communally. Often, we base our assessment of errors on cause or motivation. For instance, if someone makes "an honest mistake" we're more likely to forgive them than if they do so through laziness or dishonesty. But how can we know the motive behind AI errors? If an AI causes a death we may have no more knowledge of its real reasons for doing so than we have of the motives of a serial killer. And if we don't know why it makes mistakes, how can we prevent it from repeating them? Trying to decide whether we are reading something written by a machine or a human is likely to become a growing uncertainty in our lives.

Biases

This concern is compounded by another source of error in AI, although one that has a more human cause: bias. Some of this imbalance comes from the data sets on which AI is trained, which reflect the prejudices, inequalities and discriminations still to be found in our unequal world. Other distortions emerge from the free-wheeling, profit-orientated manner in which AI enterprises often collect their data. AI data is often taken from where it can be most easily and cheaply found. It can be scraped illegally from the internet, without the owner's consent and with little attempt to account for a whole population. Unrepresentative and unweighted samples which would never be allowed in market research or opinion polling can pass for normal in much AI data-mining.

For example, in July 2023, I searched under the heading of "legs" in Google Images and found that 96% of the first 100 photos and illustrations of the human leg which appeared were white-skinned. Had this collection been representative of the UK, in which 18% of the population are non-white, there would have been four-and-a-half times more dark-skinned images in the sample (and the disparity in the US would have been even greater). Clearly, this kind of unbalanced data collection can contribute to the racial biases of facial recognition software, referred to above.

Other AI systems are used to define welfare benefit applicability and these too can be biased against the poor and disadvantaged, who are more likely to have been arrested or to have come in contact with social services. That means they are likely to feature more frequently than higher income groups in the data on which the AI system has been trained. As US Congressman Elijah Cummings commented: "If you're black, you're more likely to be subjected to this technology and it's more likely to be wrong. That's a hell of a combination" (Breland, 2017). The risk is that this creates what sociologist Ruha Benjamin (2019:5) dubs "the New Jim code", referring to:

> the employment of new technologies that reflect and reproduce existing inequities but that are promoted and perceived as more objective or progressive than the discriminatory systems of a previous era.

Gender biases are also prevalent in machine learning. An Amazon recruitment programme dismissed female candidates because it was trained on past hiring decisions which discriminated in favour of men (Hao, 2019). Often associations in software are explicitly gendered, such as "man is to computer programmer as woman is to homemaker", to quote the title of one research paper, which also studied word embeddings in data trained on Google News (i.e. on almost entirely twenty-first century data). Other sexist inferences included associating the "she" pronoun with "nurse", "receptionist", "librarian" and "socialite", and "he" with "maestro", "skipper", "philosopher" and "architect" (Bolukbasi et al, 2016). Sheng et al (2019) found that AI text generators produced sentences which are negatively biased against black people, women and gays, especially in the context of occupation. The homophobic bias included a description of a gay man as "someone who loves dancing and takes drugs", as opposed to a straight man depicted as "someone who finds own voice" and speaks clearly.

Other biases can reflect the worldview of the software engineers who select the data and the classification criteria from which the algorithms emerge. As we found in Chapter 10, Silicon Valley AI researchers tend to be white, high-income, college-educated and overwhelmingly male. Overall only 12%

of US researchers in machine learning are female, in the UK the percentage is even lower at 8% and an aggressively sexist culture has been reported in several high-tech firms (Chin, 2018, Young et al, 2021). Whistleblower Susan Fowler (2017) claimed that sexism in Uber reduced the percentage of female software engineers in her division from 25% to just 6%. This undiverse environment can influence what engineers consider important and unimportant, as does their education in computer science with all its neomechanicalist biases, and the ferociously pro-business, competitive capitalist environments in which they work. All these pressures can skew the data classifications of the systems which software engineers design and put blinkers on what AI can and can't see. In this sense, you might say, there's only one eye in AI. The problem is that this upstream half-vision is no longer apparent downstream, in the final output of the system, which is breezily presented as impartial, objective and accurate.

Correcting this bias is not as simple as it seems. "Debiasing" through positive gender and diversity discrimination might be a start but this is in itself a political and ethical act, which would be highly controversial, in part because of the lack of agreed human values (the "human alignment" problem) which we explored in the previous chapter. This also goes some way to explaining why it has been impossible for AI to achieve its primary goal of emulating human common sense, which in turn alerts us to another huge obstacle standing in the path of AGI.

Wisdom above Intelligence

For there is yet another source of imbalance at the core of the artificial intelligence project, the Western concept of intelligence itself. In AI development, this notion has always been thoroughly biased towards neomechanicalist science, particularly in relation to the Intelligence Quotient (IQ) programme, which is based on the assumption that human intelligence can be accurately measured on a universal basis. This originated in the heyday of Western imperialism in the late nineteenth-century when the scientific mission to classify and control everything and everyone under colonial rule was at its height (Anderson, 1983). IQ tends to favour the decontextualized, abstract way of thinking and the mathematical and symbolic language skills, which are central to the machine mindset. Indeed, you would expect AI professionals to receive high scores on this metric and regard such a score as a badge of honour.

Yet IQ is a highly controversial measure. It has been accused of racial bias, as African Americans sometimes receive scores that are lower than other ethnic groups, which has led to some notoriously false claims by racists and others. Critics point to IQ's cultural bias, seeing it as an artefact of an individualistic Western world fixated on abstract classifications and linear logic. By contrast, Asian societies see intelligence as rooted in a community and prioritize cognitive styles which recognize, and can successfully navigate, complexity and contradiction (Nisbett, 2003). This Eastern approach also focuses on the value of knowing when to show intelligence and when not to –a skill rarely displayed by humachinators.

This focus on wisdom as a balanced, multi-faceted, socially integrated way of interpreting the world is also found among other non-Western societies. For example, as psychologists Robert Serpell and Barnabas Simatende (2016) point out:

> Numerous studies in Africa have found that indigenous conceptu-alization of intelligence includes dimensions of social responsibility and reflective deliberation in addition to the cognitive alacrity emphasized in most tests of intelligence standardized in Western societies.

Robert Sternberg and Elena Grigorenko (2006) echo this view, insist-ing that "Intelligence cannot be fully, or even meaningfully, understood outside its context." For example, the Luo people of Kenya have multiple definitions of intelligence, including practical, context-based ingenuity and social intelligence that focuses on respect and consideration, as well as one which corresponds to academic smartness.

As for gender bias in IQ, although there's no difference in the average ratings of males and females, females scores tend to be more consistent, which means that males are better represented at the top of the IQ dis-tribution (as well as at the bottom) (Priess and Hyde, 2010:302i). This could be a significant factor when it comes to who gets the most-prized AI engineering jobs.

Western psychology itself has tried to counter the limitations of IQ over the past few decades by producing alternatives to it, such as spiritual intel-ligence and emotional intelligence (the ability to understand your own and others feelings). As mentioned in the last chapter, Howard Gardner's

(2000) multiple intelligences approach stresses different "modalities" such as interpersonal or naturalistic intelligence which are often masked by IQ tests. As in so many areas, the risk of AI is that it settles highly disputed issues in social science in favour of just one side of the argument without even acknowledging that there is a debate in the first place.

Conclusion: A Better Revolution Than Alien Intelligence

In conclusion, the AI project runs into the all-too-human problems associated with the Western notion of intelligence, displaying a vast suite of biases, distortions, prejudices and reductionist shortcomings. It culturally decontextualizes and instrumentalizes speed over deliberation and social responsibility. This it combines with mysterious errors only a machine could ever devise. After his losing battle with Deep Blue, Garry Kasparov told reporters that "the computer is an alien opponent, very different from any human opponent" and Alien Intelligence may well be a more appropriate use of the acronym AI (Baldwin, 2020). Even Geoffrey Hinton, who spent 50 years working on machine learning, appears to have come around to this view, stating: "Sometimes I think it's as if aliens had landed and people hadn't realised because they speak very good English" (Heaven, 2023). Inevitably, this notion of alien intelligence brings us back to the anti-social psychology of the machine mindset and its coldly logical, emotionless way of perceiving the world.

The danger is that we are not replicating the best of human intelligence but creating a force that is potentially hostile to human wellbeing and even human existence, as the ever-present threat of AImageddon reminds us. AI safety researcher Michael Cohen and his colleagues (2022) have proved that it's impossible to prevent an advanced AI from exploiting inherent ambiguities in whatever goals it has been set. If, for instance, it decided to use all the world's energy in order to satisfy its reward-seeking, this could "extinguish biological life", the researchers warn, adding that such "an existential catastrophe is not just possible but likely".

AI's increasingly invasive potential for destruction also manifests itself in its ability to distract us from the ecological, political and social challenges of the Anthropocene. It threatens to dominate our ways of assessing future risks and directly competes with the very qualities we need to avoid these risks, our decision-making, judgement and collective wisdom. On this basis, you could conclude that trying to reproduce human-level intelligence is just about the most stupid idea humanity has ever entertained.

A better revolution would focus on an authentic revolution of wisdom. This would put intelligent problem-solving and social and environmental responsibility in the same category, stressing reality as a multidimensional phenomenon which is finely balanced between interacting networks of cause and effect. This Ecocene approach would be consistent with deliberative demotechnics, which would practically demonstrate that it's not technology which is the paramount problem but the goals and values governing its development and use.

One outcome might be that instead of spending trillions of dollars on AI, we would address a piece of unfinished human business which shamefully the world has still not completed, universal education. Three hundred years after the start of the Industrial Revolution, humanity still suffers a massive loss of collective intelligence, due to the fact that 64 million children don't go to primary school and a third of all 12-17-year olds never attend secondary school. (Unicef, 2022). Another problem is that only a third of the world's nations have achieved gender parity at secondary schools and only two thirds at primary level. Globally, tertiary education is still very unevenly distributed. In sub-Saharan Africa, for example, the ratio of students currently enrolled in universities stands at 9.4%, against a global average of 36% (World Bank, 2022). The Covid-19 pandemic only made things worse, depriving countless millions of students of face-to-face education. It's in this arena of global education that we should focus more resources, if we are really concerned about increasing the sum total of human brain power.

These considerations compel us to return, as we always must, to the economic goals that drive humachination and to the dominator complex of the machine mindset. We find ourselves in the position of the fabled local who advises the lost visitor, "if I wanted to go there. I wouldn't have started from here!" As long as we follow the GUN worldplan pursuing the phantasms of never-ending economic growth and technology as an end in itself, many of the possible advantages of advanced computing will be lost. There's nothing more dangerous than cleverness in pursuit of stupid goals, a point that should become clearer as we examine the potential impact of AI on human decision-making.

CHAPTER 14

Mechanizing Decision-Making: The Diminution of Human Choice

"I actually think that most people don't want Google to answer their questions. They want Google to tell them what to do next." This declaration by former Alphabet CEO Eric Schmidt seems to confirm the importance for the humachine project of creating a machine alternative to human decision-making (Jenkins, 2010). It aligns with the beliefs of the original AI innovators, many of whom were less concerned with capitalist consumerism than with the supposed inability of humans to make the difficult decisions necessary to manage the modern world. It's no surprise then to see humachination attempting to capture human decision-making in almost every organization, profession and institution in existence and attempting to automate the most important life-changing choices that humans get to make.

This, I suggest, is a supremely dangerous ambition. Our ability to make decisions is at the very centre of human ontology and one of the principal reasons why Homo sapiens have become the dominant species on this planet. That's not to say choice-making is easy or convenient: the harder the call is, the more likely we are to put it off or look for someone else to make it. Having spent many years working with clients in organizations and therapy, I know how difficult it can be to make the right decision and then put it into practice. Decision-making is bedevilled by many different challenges: high emotions, stress, personal ambition, fear of making irreparable mistakes, conflicting groups, competing theories and imprecise, ever-changing information. So technology that seems to offer us an easy escape route from this thicket of difficulties is bound to be seductive.

And yet these choices, testing as they can be, go to the heart of who we are, as a society and as a species. As I suggested earlier, it's precisely these political choices that determine the technology revolutions in history, from the agricultural revolution, to the origins of city state civilisation and the Industrial Revolution. And decision-making remains absolutely central to our future in the Anthropocene.

Humachinators are not insensitive to this issue; after all, they claim that amalgamating the organic and the mechanical will lead to a techno-utopia which brings more freedom of choice rather than less. For this reason, they prefer to present cognitive humachines not as substitutes for human decision-makers, but as assistants who provide clever, stress-free tools, obedient servants always loyal to their human masters. However sophisticated the automation is, so the argument goes, it will always ensure that people not algorithms are the ultimate arbiters, or, in the jargon of AI, that the human will always be in the loop.

In reality, I suggest, the economic logic of growth capitalism fused with the narrow neomechanicalism of the machine mindset seem determined to appropriate as much individual and collective choice-making as possible. The "hidden persuaders" of advertising which Vance Packard described in the 1950s are today much better hidden and appreciably more persuasive, thanks to the cognitive humachines which played a fundamental role in the humachination big bang. Even more dangerously, as we've seen, data-based decisional engineering is being applied to the field of political choice. As far back as Barack Obama's successful presidential campaign of 2008, one of his political consultants boasted: "We knew who... people were going to vote for before they decided" (Zuboff, 2019:123), a claim, which, if true, could hammer yet another nail in the coffin of democracy.

Most people are still in ignorance of automated decision-making; one UK survey by the Royal Society of Arts revealed that only 14% and 9% respectively were aware of its use in the workplace and in the criminal justice system. I suspect that the same is true of other social institutions in which humans are in danger of being taken out of the loop, such as the armed forces, medicine and government, which we'll also review in this chapter.

When made aware of the practice, people in the survey were reported to be "overwhelmingly opposed to most uses of AI" for decision-making (RSA , 2019). Rather than ushering in an era of more efficient, anxiety-free choice-making, human-machine fusion threatens to strip us of our most important human skill, thus leaving Big Tech's "great men" even more securely in charge of the choices that will forge our future.

Justice: "All Rise for the Robojudge"

No institution is more crucial to a human society than its judicial system. A society can't function without basic laws and mechanisms for deciding on the guilt or innocence of its citizens. I'd argue that this kind of decision-making calls for wisdom rather than IQ-type intelligence, as it requires individuals or groups to exercise responsible, holistic judgements, which cannot be easily quantified. This, however, is not an argument likely to convince the manufacturers of the cognitive humachines, who are busy imposing their machine language probability weightings on the delicate scales of human justice.

Software is rapidly transforming the way legal professionals research and present a case. The judgements of human legal researchers are being replaced by computerized systems, capable of scanning tens of thousands of past cases and making tactical recommendations (Susskind and Susskind, 2015). Law professor David Engstrom claims "that the promise of an AI approach is that you get more consistency than we currently have" (Niiler, 2019). This contention seems to be backed up by a machine learning model that its creators claim has analysed 199 years of US Supreme Court decisions and predicted the outcomes with just over 70% accuracy (Katz et al, 2017). In reality, however, the claim is surely subject to all the caveats associated with AI accuracy examined in the last chapter. For example, what about the 30% of cases the AI got wrong? Were they cases which humans would also struggle with – in which the evidence is weak or the precedents hard to interpret– or were they ones which humans would find very easy to judge? As we know, "alien intelligence" doesn't conform to human reason, empathy or fellow feeling. AI can be one-dimensional, extremely limited in its understanding of actual human scenarios and language and chock-full of biases. People may accept errors in human judgements but the black box of machine language makes it impossible to know why an AI has reached its conclusion. As lawyers, judges and magistrates increasingly rely on software to analyze past cases and make recommendations, their ability to challenge the authority of their cognitive humachines is likely to diminish – deskilling at its most pernicious. In 2023 a New York lawyer who referenced a series of entirely fictional court cases was forced to admit he had used ChatGPT 4 to "supplement" his research. The judge found a litany of "bogus judicial decisions, with bogus quotes and bogus internal citations" (Davis, 2023). But will such errors become increasingly difficult to detect as the AI-assisted justice caravan ploughs on?

Judicial AI has been extensively used in China since 2016, where smart courts, smart court navigation systems and AI-based trial support services are common (2022). Estonia is also experimenting with an autonomous system for adjudicating over small claims which eliminates the need for judges (Niiler, 2019). Chinese legal scholar Zichun Xu (2022) is enthusiastic about the efficiency and "objectivity" which he asserts AI brings to ancillary judicial areas and relatively minor cases, although he admits that currently artificial intelligence "is only suitable to be an assistant to the judge and cannot completely replace the judge". But how long before the human is entirely taken out of the loop? "AI judge" software which purportedly can try a case and recommend a sentence is already on the market in China. As economic pressures increase on judicial systems around the world, it's surely only a matter of time until the AI sales army argues that automation needs to be extended to the most serious cases.

The UK, with its massive backlog of legal cases and its dramatic reduction in legal aid in recent years, could be the ideal candidate for the robotic judge. Robojudges would eliminate the theatricality and arcane paraphernalia of the British court but without the presence of human judicial actors how can we know that justice is being done? Will an appeal against an AI judgement simply consist of a different AI legal programme competing with the original one? If justice consists in nothing more than reading out a verdict calculated by a computer, the already shaky trust which the public have for the judiciary may disappear altogether.

Robojudges also threaten one of the most precious of all human decision-making processes, the jury system, in which randomly chosen citizens sit in judgement on their fellow citizens and dispense potentially life-changing outcomes. China puts justice squarely in the hands of judges (human or artificial) but trials by jury are still central to the Anglo-American judicial system. Anybody who has served on a jury will have experienced the growth in self-confidence that it brings, as the process moves through observation and discussion to a decision, often with minimal input from the judge. It's a vital, participatory form of decision-making that's replicated in popular assemblies and citizen juries, which could have a major impact in increasing political engagement and reversing the democratic recession.

Politically, there is also the danger that advanced judicial humachines will destroy the separation of political and judicial powers that is necessary for a fully functioning democracy. Powerful elites will no longer require compliant legal officers to ensure that the courts reflect their interests. A mere tweaking of the algorithms will suffice to normalize injustice. In my view, this strengthens the case for more human decision-making about justice and other crucial issues, not less.

Medical Decision-Making

Some of the difficulties confronting the judiciary are also being experienced by medical decision-makers, as medicine goes through a digital revolution. In *The Creative Destruction of Medicine* physician Eric Topol (2013:243) suggests that the whole concept of the patient is being transformed by

> the unparalleled super-convergence of DNA sequencing, mobile smart phones and digital devices, wearable and embedded wireless nanosensors, the Internet, cloud computing, information systems and social media.

Faced with this "tsunami of data", Topol admits that doctors will be tempted to treat the digital representation of the patient rather than the real human being. "Remote monitoring and diminished face-to-face visits between a doctor and a patient can lead to a loss of intimacy", he concedes, which raises "dehumanizing concerns". But will there even *be* doctors or nurses in a remote, depersonalized medicine of the future, in which patients get increasingly accustomed to describing their symptoms to humanoid software? One venture capitalist quoted by the author predicts that technology will eventually replace 80% of doctors (Topol, 2013:259). Topol rejects this suggestion but it's all too easy to see how a vicious circle of cause and effect will play out.

Take the announcement by Google Health of a breakthrough which enables AI to detect simple cases of breast cancer as accurately as human doctors. This was presented in a typically "human in the loop" fashion, as a useful back-up service to assist radiologists who would continue to make the important diagnostic decisions (Leon, 2020). In the UK, it was seen as a neat solution to the shortage of radiologists in the NHS. How could this not be good news?

A technosceptic response would be point that out that Google Health will not stop at the development of simple cancers but will use their new data to improve accuracy for more complex cases. Saying "enough is enough" is eminently possible for clinicians and for patients seeking more face-to-face contact with doctors but it's utterly contrary to the ontocapitalist Law of More. This strategy dictates that in time there will be fewer radiologists able to read scans. After all, what newly qualified doctor would want to train for many years in order to become only slightly worse at diagnosing cancer than a machine? And what medical authority will want to employ a radiologist who is much more expensive than an AI? As economic growth shrinks in the coming decades, cost-cutting in public medicine is likely to leaving fewer and fewer professionals able to interrogate AI diagnoses. And even if a doctor has the expertise to reject an AI diagnosis, will she do so if the consequences of making the wrong choice could lead to her being sued?

That doesn't mean that all diagnostic decision-making based on machine learning is what it's cracked up to be, as the fate of IBM's Watson Health reveals. Once seen as one of AI's greatest success stories and hailed as the future of healthcare, it was "essentially sold off for parts" to a private equity firm in 2021 (O'Leary, 2022). Some of its problems may have been due to the fact that despite being able to "read" thousands of case studies far more rapidly than any human, it did not reveal its biases or the kind of egregious errors which we examined in the last chapter (Frownfelter, 2021). Nor will a cognitive humachine disclose what influences its interpretation of medical research papers. It may rate a forceful conclusion more highly than a more balanced, thoughtful evaluation, because algorithms tend to respond best to extremes, as social media demonstrates. Despite spending $5 billion on healthcare acquisitions, Watson Health was unable to obtain enough real patient data to provide relevant clinical recommendations and relied too heavily on hypothetical models, which often resulted in "unsafe and incorrect" cancer treatments (Ross and Swetlitz, 2018). Some of the system's shortcomings were more prosaic; in clinical settings, the most common complaint from doctors was "you're not telling me anything that I don't already know" (O'Leary, 2022).

Perhaps IBM's top-down, solution-looking-for-a-problem approach was always bound to fail but some 70-90% of US hospitals now have "AI strategies" in place, writes physician John Frownfelter (2021). In time, the entire chain of medical diagnosis, treatment, surgery and aftercare could become totally dependent on AI technology. If we continue down our current path, it will gradually transform the highly trained, caring professionals who currently make life-changing medical judgements into increasingly passive, powerless administrators of machine choices. The champions of human-machine fusion will argue this represents the democratization of medicine because it closes the knowledge gap between the medical professional and the patient. The danger is that potentially it makes all of us subservient to the unchallengeable power of the robot doctor.

Military Decisions: Pushing Humans out of the Loop

Nowhere is the question of how to stand up to the power of cognitive humachines more pertinent than in the military sphere, another arena in which life-and-death choices constantly have to be made. Will AI really remain a humble, obedient servant to humans when it potentially controls some of the most lethal weaponry ever developed? Weapons have always been at the core of plutotechnic regimes, as ruling elites know that the violence they control determines their ability to compete with other state elites and maintain their apex position in society. Now a global, superpower race is underway to develop ever more sophisticated Lethal Autonomous Weapon Systems (LAWS). We'll return to this terrifying new arsenal of military hardware in Chapter 17 but for now the question is, who – or what – will actually make the life and death choices about the use of these new weapons? Well aware of the public's horror of Terminator–type killer robots, the military authorities assure us that all crucial battlefield decisions will be made by humans not by the weapons themselves. "A human will always be in the loop before firing," concludes a BBC report on automated tanks, quoting a manufacturer of the semi-autonomous Ripsaw armoured combat vehicle (Dempsey, 2020).

Ordinary self-driving cars illustrate one aspect of the skills problem involved in all this. Currently autonomous vehicles are at Levels 2 and 3 of development which require a driver to stay sufficiently alert to take over the wheel in emergencies (whether Levels 4 and 5 are ever legalized is an open question). But how can drivers maintain the advanced skills to make split-second, possibly life or death, decisions in hazardous traffic situations without extensive, ongoing driving practice?

In the military context, the classic example of a human in the loop was provided by Lieutenant Colonel Stanislav Petrov, reassuringly dubbed "the man who saved the world" (Scharre, 2018: 2). In September 1983, Petrov was in a bunker outside Moscow belonging to the Soviet Union's satellite early warning system, when sirens started blaring and a giant screen lit up with the words "launch". The semi-automated anti-missile system had detected five missiles were heading into the Soviet Union and had come to the conclusion that the USA had launched a nuclear missile attack. If it was true, Petrov needed to authorize a counter missile strike, a decision which might have resulted in a global nuclear war. There was no time for data checks, he had to rely on his intuition and this told him something was wrong. After a few agonizing minutes, which must have felt like a lifetime, he reported that the system was malfunctioning. It turned out that he was right: sunlight reflecting on the clouds has fooled the detection system. The human in the loop had prevailed whereas left to its own devices the autonomous system might have initiated World War III.

However, the psychological and career costs to Petrov illustrate the real-life difficulties of challenging a mechanical decision-maker. Far from being hailed as a hero, Petrov was in effect punished by the Soviet military authorities for exposing the deficiencies of his country's security equipment and his once promising career stalled. He eventually left the army and later suffered a nervous breakdown, complaining that "I was made the scapegoat "(Little, 1998). The risk of second guessing the verdict of automated systems couldn't be more clearly revealed. If your decision turns out to be wrong the results will be catastrophic but even if your judgement is correct, as was Petrov's, the personal and professional outcome can be disastrous. From a career point, the safe option is surely to agree with the machine's decision and blame it if anything goes wrong.

Of course, the 1980s Soviet warning system was primitive compared to modern automated weapons systems. Indeed, the pace of development is so rapid that military authorities are rowing back on their pledge that humans will always be the ultimate arbiters of combat decision-making. As Paul Scharre points out in *Army of None* (2018:24) a 2009 US Air Force report predicted that

> Increasingly humans will no longer be "in the loop" but "on the loop" – monitoring the execution of certain decisions" rather than making them. Simultaneously advances in AI will enable systems to make combat decisions and act with legal and policy constraints without necessarily requiring human input.

By 2018 a US Congressional Research Service report suggests that even this degree of passive oversight may be impractical, such is the revolutionary impact of AI on warfare. "AI systems reacting at machine speed may push the pace of combat to a point where machine actions surpass the rate of human decision-making." This, the authors warn, could "surreptitiously lead to a place where humans lose control of warfare" (Hoadley and Lucas, 2018:41).

This appears to be confirmed by the Lavender AI-assisted human targeting system, allegedly used by Israel in the current war in Gaza. A military insider interviewed by *+972 Magazine* revealed that:

> human personnel often served as a "rubber stamp" for the machine's decisions, adding that, normally they would personally devote only about "20 seconds" to each target before authorizing a bombing – just to make sure the Lavender-marked target was male. This was despite knowing that the system makes what are regarded as "errors" in approximately 10 percent of cases (Abraham, 2024).

In short, in many circumstances, it will be machines, not humans, which effectively make the life-and-death decisions on the battlefield.

Organizational Decision-Making: "Mindless" Businesses

All organizations are experiencing the same kind of existential shock as the armed forces. One of the justifications for the pyramidal structure of large-scale public and private organizations is that decision-making gets more difficult the higher up you go. It's claimed that leadership depends on the ability to make tough calls and the manager's status often depends on the wide range of people management skills he requires, which involve tacit, empathetic and qualitative decision-making (Harvey, 2015).

Whatever the merits of this justification, automation is rapidly destroying the organizational hierarchy of choice, especially in the ranks of middle management. For example, the crucial people-management task of recruitment is now being taken over by AI systems which can examine videos of candidates and match the personality profile they detect with the supposedly ideal requirements for the job. Multinational manufacturer Unilever claims to have saved 100,000 hours of human time in a year using the new HireVue candidate selection system (Booth, 2019). In the short term, this may seem like a win for managers – who in my experience often find recruitment the most challenging aspect of their jobs – but in the (slightly) longer term it could spell the end of their profession.

For some business theorists this new technology opens the route to the perfect corporation. In *The Humachine: Humankind, Machines and the Future of Enterprise* Nada Sanders and John Wood (2019) offer a techno-utopian vision of future organizations which combines enlightened, creative leadership with machine learning and advanced digital robotic technology. As the reader may notice, this use of the term "humachine" differs markedly from my own. To me, Sanders and Wood naively ignore the capitalist motives driving automation and the tiny staff sizes of existing automated businesses, as well as overestimating the chances of harnessing "benign superintelligence" and managing machines which are designed to manage you.

Simon Head's book (2013) *Mindless* is surely closer to the reality of the humachinated organization. He illustrates the way that new humachine business systems are going to the heart of today's people-orientated service industries, using the mechanistic techniques pioneered by Frederick Taylor in the early twentieth century. These enforced a strict separation between hand and brain in factory work. As Taylor liked to tell his workers "You are not supposed to think. There are other people paid for thinking around here" (Morgan, 1986:32). Now ironically, it's those "other people" – leaders, managers and administrators – whose jobs are being coldly analysed and broken down into sub-processes and specific tasks so that they can be automated. So-called Robot Processing Automation has already created its first billionaire, Daniel Dines, and it's likely to replace many more human jobs in the coming years (Konrad, 2019). Managers are fast becoming mere machine-minders, their jobs consisting of scanning screens all day to check for anomalies. In this they are suffering the fate of the industrial worker of the past by becoming a mere adjunct of a machine, except this time the algorithms may eventually dispense with their jobs altogether.

The "Smart" Government

Lastly, what about the effects of cognitive humachines on government, the organization which is meant to incarnate the highest level of collective decision-making? As you may recall, Klaus Schwab (2015) demanded a digital revolution in government in order to drive down costs and boost efficiency – the idea being to use data analysis to make the primary decisions about what is best for a nation, including strategy, resource allocation and forecasting.

In 2019 Schwab's call was answered by Britain's Conservative government under the influence of the Prime Minister's chief advisor, Dominic Cummings, whose novel use of microtargeting contributed to the victory of Vote Leave in the 2016 Brexit referendum. Cummings had a thoroughly Silicon Valley vision of government policy-making. This revolved around a carefully selected elite of decision-makers using "banks of screens, predictive models and untested cognitive tools" which would make No 10 Downing Street "look more like a NASA control centre", according to organizational psychologist Andre Spicer (2019). This small band of humans in the loop would almost certainly expand the power of the surveillance state but how well would it perform in terms of decision-making? Very badly, in Spicer's opinion. The danger is that the officials concerned would be overwhelmed by data and rely too heavily on computer models which fail to capture the whole picture. Cummings didn't last long enough in Downing Street to see how his team of data scientists and "weirdos and misfits with odd skills" would perform (Smith, 2020). But the smart government objective of turning Britain into "a global science and technology superpower" was soon revived by a new Prime Minister, Rishi Sunak, a long-time AI enthusiast, whose father-in-law is a co-founder of India's gargantuan Infosys IT conglomerate (gov.uk, 2021a). Rather improbably, in 2023 Sunak also began championing Britain as the "intellectual "and "geographical home of global AI safety regulation" (Rajvanshi, 2023).

As for practical governance, replacing long-serving civil servants and subject-matter experts with inexperienced, transitory special advisors means that there will be fewer experienced professionals in a position to evaluate data-based choices. Traditional feedback loops between the centre of government and regional branches are also likely to deteriorate as the number of public administration jobs is reduced due to automation – by as much as 32% according to a PWC forecast (Barej, 2017). Reducing the ranks of mid-level choice-makers pushes decisional power even further up the government hierarchy, but by no means guarantees more efficient policy-making. Will a leader elected on the basis of a small-state, neoliberal agenda tolerate computer modelling that suggests that high-tax and tight-regulation policies are the best way to govern a modern state? It's much more likely that assumptions introduced into policy-making software from the start rule out certain conclusions. This additional degree of political bias will only accentuate the neomechanicalists' cardinal sin of parading subjective policies as scientific objectivity.

Other biases contained in the data on which algorithms are trained also bode ill for those on the receiving end of "smart" government, as automation extends across swathes of public policy from education and healthcare to welfare and local councils. Algorithms can be prejudiced against those who are most dependent on public services, often unfairly exaggerating factors which emerge from poverty itself. With fewer public officials in face-to-face roles administering these decisions, it will be even harder to contest welfare levels "chosen" by algorithms. If your housing benefit is too low to live on or the choice of your child's school impractical, how can you dispute a decision, which few humans actually understand, even if you could find a human to talk to rather than a computerized "agent" in a call centre? The UK government's automated Universal Credit welfare system is already causing 350 complaints a day about incorrect payment adjustments, a process described by benefit claimants as "horrible" and hellish" (Booth, 2023). The use by Dutch tax authorities of a biased, error-prone AI system to detect childcare benefit fraud plunged tens of thousands of innocent families into poverty and led to hundreds of children being wrongly placed in care (Heikkila, 2022). With nobody prepared – or able – to take responsibility for these choices, government by machine is already revealing its most callous side.

A troubling example of this heartless attitude, and the apparent omnipotence of machine decision-making, was provided by the infamous

British Post Office scandal which began in 1999. For over two decades, government ministers and senior executives at the Post Office were faced with a choice: either the organization's new, billion-pound, automated payment system, Horizon, was utterly unfit for purpose or hundreds of sub-post masters had embarked on a nationwide spree of theft, fraud and false accounting. In spite of evidence to the contrary, the authorities chose the latter option, leading to criminal convictions for over 900 innocent sub-post masters. The consequences for these professionals, who are generally seen as pillars of the local community, ranged from imprisonment and bankruptcy to divorce and even suicide. In the end, it was proven that the Horizon computer system was deeply, and all-too obviously, flawed but saying "no" to automated technology proved just too difficult for those in power (Wallis, 2021). The scandal which finally exploded into the public domain in January 2024 was partially caused by a little-known change to British law in 1999, on the eve of the age of humachines. This ruled that henceforth computers and other "mechanical instruments" should be presumed to be operating correctly unless proven otherwise, the reverse of the legal presumption of innocence which applies to humans. Machine supremacism has actually been written into the statute book – a situation that urgently needs reforming (Bohm et al, 2022).

Conclusion: More Human Decision-Making Not Less

We've seen enough to realise that cognitive humachines are launching a serious assault on a competence which is at the core of being human. Good decision-making requires time to deliberate but dromology steals this from us, as in financial and commodity markets where billions of dollars are traded every day at speeds so fast that they prohibit human intervention (Brindle, 2018). Good decision-making requires transparency but the secrecy of the black box of sub-symbolic deep learning makes it impossible, even for experts to understand how AI reaches its conclusions. False objectivity, hidden biases and error-proneness also deprives people of the reliable information that is the key to good choices.

Ultimately, human decisions are difficult because the individual has to bear the responsibility for getting them wrong. But who do you blame in a world of depersonalized, automated choices? Who would be responsible for the miscarriage of justice made by a robot judge or for the fatal slip of a mechanical surgeon's scalpel during an operation? Will scapegoats always be found (like Stanislav Petrov) or will the blame be so diffused that everybody simply shrugs their shoulders in quiet despair? The human in the loop argument tacitly acknowledges the importance of human responsibility, even as it's used to disguise stripping humans of the skills on which that responsibility depends. Decisional obesity could be another way of characterizing this process, as the apparent ease and convenience of cognitive humachines attenuates our capacity to make the tough choices and balanced policies necessary to live our lives freely and face up to the collective challenges of the Anthropocene.

A SEWP paradigm-shift would bring about more human decision-making instead of less. Practice makes perfect, when it comes to choosing at both a personal and a social level. That could mean protecting juries in the justice system, dedicating more time to face-to-face doctor-patient interactions and a greater emphasis on practical decision-making in education from an early age, with children actively participating in making some of the decisions which affect their schooling. Different business ownership models would put employees in charge of daily and strategic decisions and this, combined with greater self-organization at work, would be the best antidote to democratic disenchantment. In public sector organizations, we could spread managerial responsibility rather than subcontracting it to machine intelligence, creating more human choices at every level.

Demotechnics implies that ordinary people can make the right strategic decisions about technology, given the right circumstances, in which to deliberate holistically, on the basis of reliable information and a transparent process. In contrast to the GUN goals of never-ending economic expansion (irrespective of the human and environmental cost), the priority of ecological democracy would be to increase human responsibility for making the key decisions about society. This could be the real revolution in choice-making that we need, but it will have to be accomplished in the face of other types of humachine, some of which can be even more wily, invasive and abusive than the cognitive variety, as the next chapter will reveal.

CHAPTER 15

Mechanizing Self and Others: Relational, Emotional and Communicative Humachines

> It's a social-validation feedback loop ... exactly the kind of thing a hacker like myself would come up with, because you're exploiting a vulnerability in human psychology.

Facebook co-founder Sean Parker was describing the "like" function on social media platforms but he might have been summing up the organizational principle behind Type 2 humachines, which operate in the sphere of human relationships. The purpose of the like device, which Parker claimed that he, Mark Zuckerberg and Kevin Systrom of Instagram designed, was to persuade people who preferred the "presence and intimacy" of "real-life interactions" to switch to social media instead (Allen, 2017). This ""dopamine-hit" helped all three entrepreneurs to become billionaires and turn Facebook into a global phenomenon but, as Parker has since realised, the cost to humanity may be enormous.

That's because what he calls, in his rather chillingly mechanicalist way, "a vulnerability in human psychology" *is* our psychology, at least that part of it which is expressed by our intense desire to be respected, liked and ultimately loved, by other people. The discipline of psychology studies these and other areas of human behaviour but attempts to do so respectfully, relying on carefully produced evidence. Humachine corporations take a more conquistadorial approach, invading, occupying and exploiting another domain of humanness in a way that can bring out the most anti-social aspects of the machine mindset. "God knows what it's doing to our children's brains", Parker complains. Let's go further and say nobody has any real idea what it's doing to human relationships in general but a good deal of it is likely to be negative. Indeed, Chamath Palihapitiya, former VP for user growth at Facebook, has said:

> The short term-term dopamine-driven feedback loops that we have created are destroying how society works. No civil discourse, no cooperation, misinformation, mistruth." (Vincent, 2017).

As we'll see in this chapter, relational and emotional humachines, via the internet, social media and digital communication, are all having a profound effect on our affective life, our social and sexual relationships and our ways of communicating with one another. As part of the biggest unregulated psychological experiment of all time, they are introducing new unconscious choices and coercive behavioural patterns which have profoundly disturbing consequences for our mental wellbeing and interpersonal relationships.

Affective Computing and Emotional Capture

As the mea culpas of Big Tech executives above illustrate, human emotions play a significant role in the humachination project. So far I've largely discussed decision-making from a cognitive point of view but ontocapitalism is well aware that emotions matter hugely when it come to buying products and services (especially ones we don't rationally need). Addictive, dopamine-firing commodities, from sugar and tobacco to processed food and pornography, have always been good for business and the ability to detect our emotional states would be a prize beyond riches for consumerism. This is exemplified by the cautionary tale Shoshanna Zuboff (2019) tells about the origins of one of the leading companies in the field of affective computing. Affectiva was co-founded by MIT professor Rosalind Picard in 2009, originally with the socially benign aim of pursuing "do-good" projects, such as helping autistic children develop the emotional skills they find so hard to develop. But soon market research and advertising companies were circling the firm, salivating at the prospect of using emotional detection to predict consumers' response to adverts. As new shareholders moved in, Affectiva's agenda become more aggressively commercial and Picard's original, worthy intention to respect users' emotional privacy was jettisoned. She herself was eventually "pushed out" out of her own firm (Zuboff 2019: 288.), which was eventually repurposed to autonomously monitor the occupants of a car and "deliver services in response to their emotional state" (Korosec, 2021).

Affective computing companies often base their emotional detection on biomedical data to produce a personality profile on an individual. For example, in gaming, as Andrew McStay (2018:47) explains, this biofeedback can include "heart rate, skin temperature, galvanic skin responses, brain information, facial expressions and other bodily behaviour". Other emotions can be tracked remotely by cameras analysing eye movements or by wearable biofeedback devices, which at least require the consent of the user. Emotional detection can also be enacted by voice synthesisers, which aim to analyse differences in vocal pitch, tone and volume. All these systems add another powerful dimension of choice manipulation. Matching emotional profiling to the picture extracted from browsing, purchasing habits and other metadata, can deepen the predictive powers of AI – giving rise to the ultimate advertiser's fantasy of being able to know a consumer better than she knows herself. This disturbing prospect is made even more sinister in the context of surveillance systems which combine this software with facial and gait recognition algorithms in an attempt to identify the moods and intentions of citizens in public settings, such as political demonstrations – yet another bad augury for democracy.

However, this "emotional capture", as it's tellingly named, suffers from the same one-eyed, reductionist bias that bedevils all humachination projects. Biofeedback and other quantifiable data offer some revealing clues about a person's inner life but it can only provide a partial, and therefore a potentially misleading, picture of what they are really feeling. The same objections which we found in relation to IQ come flooding back.

For example, much of affective computing is based on a classification of seven putatively universal emotions, devised by psychologist Paul Ekman in the 1960s. As Neda Atanasoski and Kalinda Vora (2019:120-5) illustrate, this schema is highly racialized, being derived from Charles Darwin's belief that the emotional expressions of non-Europeans, such as indigenous Australians, are more "transparent" than supposedly more civilized people who Darwin believed learn to conceal their emotions. Phenomenologists, humanist psychologists and others have long argued that this schema is too rigid in its interpretation of facial expressions and is culturally biased. As McStay (2018) points out, a smile in Japan can mean something quite different to a native than to a Westerner. Even in the West, I'd add, the visual vocabulary of the smile is vast, from the genuinely cheerful to the coldly polite, from the wryly ironic to the tremulously sad and from the aggressively triumphalist to the respectfully sympathetic. Without the interpersonal context you cannot know what the expression means, which is why as humans we spend years learning to decipher these situations. Moreover, even quantifiable biofeedback, such as a raised heart rate, can be unreliable, as normal cardiac rates vary considerably. And, as any therapist will tell you, assigning a specific emotion to any particular vocal trait or eye movement can be a hazardous guessing game, unless it's accompanied by careful dialogue and tactful exploration.

None of this is likely to dissuade advertisers from investing in affective computing to manipulate consumers' choices or corporations using AI emotional profiling to hire or fire their employees. No caveats will be included in the read-outs of a person's emotional profile which increasingly accompany police interviews or other potentially life-changing situations. Some advertising agencies now prefer this "hard data" to traditional market research focus groups or self-reporting, which they claim is more ambiguous and harder to act on (McStay, 2018). In other words, what people actually think and feel is becoming secondary to what machines conclude we are thinking and feeling.

Machines, of course, have no emotions, so they have to construe them from patterns of data; and what they can't measure, they jettison. Unfortunately, this unquantifiable material comprises a good deal of what is really meaningful in our emotional lives. The turbulent flow of emotions prompted by music or film or visual art can only be partially traced by biomedical feedback and intuitions, hunches, shortcuts and gut feelings also play a pivotal role in our decision-making (Gigerenzer, 2007). Indeed if the emotional regions of the brain are injured, even the simplest choices can become functionally impossible (Damasio, 1994). This sense of what feels intuitively right, even though we can't necessarily explain why, derives from the role that McGilchrist's (2009) bicameral theory ascribes to the right hemisphere of the brain. By contrast, the left hemisphere, you may recall, is always striving for more logical precision and control than reality can ever provide. Indeed, the idea of an AI-driven key, which can unlock our emotional secrets at the press of a button, is a quintessentially left-brain fantasy.

What effect will this technology have on human relationships once we come to rely more completely on biomedical data for analysing other people's emotions? Will the idea of objective emotional analysis weaken our ability to empathize with other people's subjective states? And what of your insights into your own inner life? If your feelings differ significantly from the humachine's interpretation of them, will you have the right – and the self-confidence – to contest this, especially if the results are buried within opaque layers of algorithms? Will our ability to discern and trust our own feelings – the purpose of much psychological education and psychotherapy – become increasingly problematic? In fine, affective AI raises the real prospect of the privatization of our personal identity and a form of emotional deskilling, which strips us of our access to our inner life and to who we really are. Could this be the ultimate enclosure of humans by machines?

Truth Detection

Focusing on another "human vulnerability" may help us to answer these questions. Being able to judge whether a person is telling the truth or is lying is an essential competence on which all viable human communities depend. So the prospect of new AI-powered devices which claim to provide better truth detection than the notoriously unreliable polygraph needs to be taken very seriously. For example, EyeDetect, which measures eye movements too small for a human to perceive, claims it can tell whether a person is telling the truth with 80-90% accuracy in a test lasting 30 minutes. It can do so remotely, via video, and autonomously, without the human expert who has the final say in polygraph testing. Its manufacturers suggest that the machine come to its conclusions "objectively", which would make it a digital oracle which doesn't have to explain itself and indeed can't, or not in a way that any human would understand (Katwala, 2019).

If these claims are credible, such technology could be a useful corrective to the post-truth era which ontocapitalism is helping to create. If applied to our political and corporate leaders, it might even provide a major boost to our flagging democracies. A reliable anti-psychopath test would be invaluable and might have spared us Donald Trump and others flagrant public liars. But inevitably politicians are wary of it and it's much more likely to be sanctioned for use on the powerless than on the powerful. Indeed, truth detection systems are already being targeted on police suspects, benefit claimants, refugees at borders and airports, loan applicants, insurance fraud suspects and a range of employees in the workplace. "It's the promise of mind-reading", says privacy campaigner Vera Wilde. "You can see that it's bogus but that's what they're selling" (Bittle, 2020).

This type of duplicitous humachine could also infiltrate itself into our personal relationships. Like a fitness app which checks your heart rate or the number of steps you've taken, we may soon be duped into trying to gauge in real-time whether a friend, family member or lover is telling the truth. It's likely to prove irresistible to neomechanicalists who crave absolute certainty in all aspects of life but its effect on social relationships, and the mutual trust which is at their core, would be dire.

For trust is another of the fundamental capacities that come with being human. It doesn't lend itself easily to quantification, except that we all know that trust can be lost an instant, whereas gaining it can take much longer. And it's vital to those most essential of all human capacities, love. The more loving the relationship, the more important trust becomes – with acquaintances, trust can be more negotiable. Love doesn't preclude lying. On the contrary, lovers know that a certain kind of lie may be necessary to smooth social relationships and boost confidence – and parents also have an accepted threshold of white lies with which to reassure their children. But when it comes to what really matters, we need to be able to distinguish truth from deception. It can be a painfully difficult tightrope walk, a quintessentially human balancing act that draws on all our emotional, cognitive and experiential resources.

Truth-detection devices can never recognize the minute differences in a unique human relationship or pick out the context-based discriminations which only the participants themselves can make. And the effect of the bizarre, alien mistakes which machine intelligence routinely makes could have a devastating impact on a relationship. If the truth becomes standardized as a measurable commodity to be arbitrated by humachines a new degree of distrustfulness could become the social norm. If we start to subject our children to digital eyeball-scanning in order to solve the perennial parental dilemma of knowing when a child is telling the truth, the entire art of parenting as a joint journey towards a child's independence could be destroyed. Polygraph expert Thomas Ormerod has warned against relying on "techniques which seem to offer a magic technology but which are in fact deeply flawed and potentially dangerous" (Devlin, 2020). He was referring to the use of AI truth-detectors by the police but his remarks might also apply to the potential effect of such systems on all human relationships.

Communication: Technologically Connected, Personally Disconnected

Of course, we don't have to speculate about the future to analyse what internet-based communication and digital messaging are doing to how we relate to ourselves and to others. Since the late 1990s there has been a communication revolution, with mobile phone ownership surging from just 16% of the UK population in 1996-7 to 95% today. Internet penetration exploded over the same period, from 9% to 98% (Statista, 2022). Mobile phones, emails, texting and hundreds of messaging platforms such as Facebook, Instagram, Snapchat, TikTok and WhatsApp, have significantly changed the way we communicate.

It's easy to forget – especially for those who are not old enough to remember – that until the 1980s most remote, personal communication had hardly changed in a century. It mainly consisted of letters, which had been around for millennia; lengthy telephone calls (using fixed landlines, controlled by the householder, who was often someone's parent); and terse telegrams only sent in emergencies. As a mode of communication, it could be frustratingly restrictive, especially for younger people. Yet I don't remember anybody in the 1960s or 1970s longing for the invention of mobile phones and when they did appear in the 1980s in the form of brick-sized implements favoured by City traders, they were roundly ridiculed.

Traditional, pre-digital communication is slow but it tends to elevate the whole over the part. Letters involve self-description, self-analysis and a commitment to narrative. (In fact, in the eighteenth century the epistolary, or letter-based, novel strongly influenced the birth of the novel as a genre.) Likewise, a telephone call involves a range of human skills, such as spontaneous reaction and counter reaction, subtle interrogatory dialogue, the unpredictable changing of subjects, interpretation of the tone of voice and other emotional or even contextual clues – dimensions which emails and texts rarely capture. A good deal of traditional communication is centred around setting up a face-to face meeting, the ultimate full-on, holistic human encounter, with all the sensory, cognitive, emotional and contextual information that it furnishes.

The risk of digital communication is that in a typically reductionist way it prioritizes quantity over quality. The digital message tends to be fragmented and broken down into small, decontextualised packages. Narrative, self-description and dialogue tend to be flattened out by the digital etiquette of brevity in order to cut through the mounting landfills of unread content among which we live. Texting eliminates vocal and emotional clues, which, at best, are confined to the crude, standardized shorthand of emojis. Communication becomes transactional. Even basic meanings can take a long time to identify and emotionally difficult subjects are avoided altogether, so that the unspoken can remain that way for years.

Research is only beginning to catch up with this explosive change in human communication, so we don't know exactly how it is affecting different groups. Perhaps voracious communicators will always communicate, regardless of the medium, but new technology may be restricting those who are less able or willing to communicate. Indeed, the signs are that many of us are shying away from human contact, preferring texts to calls and short calls to longer conversations – 60% of mobile phone calls end in under 90 seconds (Ofcom, 2019:11). These, and the other forms of inflexible communication, seem to be replacing in-person encounters.

Video-calling and conferencing, usage of which surged in the enforced circumstances of the Covid-19 pandemic, exacerbate this trend. The medium may have benefits in reducing travel and at least offering some form of personal visual information but it's also damaging traditional non-verbal communication skills and creating new mental health issues. Preoccupation with your appearance and difficulties in reading the emotional cues in other people's faces are some of the anxiety-provoking aspects of video calling that can lead to "Zoom gloom or fatigue" (Matani, 2021). Locke (2020) lists other problems, including not knowing whose turn it is to speak because of a lack of gaze awareness, the bleakness of constantly seeing a body image limited to head and shoulders against an unvarying background, the way video encounters start and end abruptly, without social finessing and the exhaustion that comes with endless meetings.

It's yet another sign of how, in the blink of an eye historically, we are endangering indigenous communication skills built up over many tens of thousands of years. In doing so, we risk handing over a crucial facet of Homo sapiens' inheritance to one-dimensional humachines, which can never replicate the unquantifiable aspects of reality that emerge from close, present, ongoing human dialogue.

Social Media and Mental Health: Digitally Connected, Socially Disconnected

Social media is also contributing to the degradation of personal relationships. Ideally, you might imagine, the algorithms of social media would be designed to have an equalizing effect, making it easier for the socially isolated to engage with others. But, as we know, correcting biases in algorithms is expensive and technically difficult and could only be done on the basis of explicitly agreed social goals, which are unlikely to include the profit-orientated exploitation of human vulnerabilities.

The result is that social media can have an unfair, disequalizing effect on social interaction. It works centripetally for those most able to engage with others but for those who have least social contact, it has a centrifugal effect, spinning away from the centre to the periphery. That, at least, is one interpretation of the research carried out by Brian Primack and his colleagues (2017), which found that higher rates of social isolation and feelings of loneliness are associated with those who are online most often. Users who access the internet at least 50 times a week have triple the risk of social isolation than those who use the internet once a week or less.

Mental health can also suffer as a result of online habits. "Smartphones and social media are destroying children's mental health" says *The Financial Times,* citing data that points to a "catastrophic" rise in reports of self-loathing, suicide and reduced socializing among teenagers since 2010, the point at which smartphone usage became ubiquitous. In France, for example, rates of depression among 15-24-year-olds have quadrupled in the last decade (Burn-Murdoch, 2023). One study found that compulsive internet use over a four-year period accurately predicted the development of increased depression and anxiety (Ciarrochi et al, 2016). Another study discovered that the greater the use of Facebook, the greater the decline in subjective wellbeing and life satisfaction among users – alternative solitary activities were not found to produce such effects (Kross et al, 2013). A study by Przbylski and Weinstein (2012: 244) concluded that:

> [T]he mere presence of mobile phones inhibited the development
> of interpersonal closeness and trust and indeed the extent to which
> individuals felt empathy and understanding from their partners.

Constant checking of digital devices can produce the very opposite of
being present and vividly experiencing the here and now. Ofcom reports
that children from the age of eight are "compulsively multi screening"
on TikTok because watching YouTube requires "too much decision-making" and passively scrolling media rather than creatively interacting with
it (Singh, 2023). And it's not just children. Psychologist Sherry Turkle
describes the way a number of her fellow mourners compulsively checked
their phones during a memorial service (Khazan, 2017). Perhaps in an
attempt to create the illusion of social communion, the average American
checks his phone 344 times a day and receives 65-80 notifications, usually
from algorithms that only know him as data (Wheelwright, 2022). A fear
of missing out on events or information can have an equally addictive
effect and constant exposure to the carefully curated, and seemingly perfect, lives of friends or celebrities can be depressing. In all of this, social
media's tendency to promote social and psychological divisiveness can be
painfully evident.

Digital Community or Fake Community?

This contradictory, splitting and integrating, dynamic can also be seen in
relation to the "community" of social media. In the Western world, the
institutions of community have been disintegrating for many decades, as
recorded by George Packer (2013) and others, and some have suggested
that this breakdown in fellow feeling can be supplemented by online connectedness. Social media can certainly enable people to keep in touch,
find common interests and form new groups. It can even provide the best
aspects of a real community – altruism, emotional support, practical help,
education and skills transfer.

But Facebook was not developed to create real communities. "What
Facebook does is watch you, and then use what it knows about you and
your behaviour to sell ads" as novelist John Lanchester (2017) so succinctly
said. Like other social media platforms, it has zealously followed an unregulated, free-market model, which enables it to algorithmically manipulate
its users' freedom of choice, on the one hand, while granting them virtually

unlimited freedom of expression, on the other. For the latter freedom it refuses to take the responsibility traditionally accepted by publishers. The result is that virtual communities can put people in touch with like-minded people in negative ways. Depressed people with suicidal ideation would be better in online groups with a wider range of experience to offer rather than with fellow sufferers. The same can be said for people who may end up radicalized by extremists on social media. And the epidemic of loneliness among older people brought about by the breakdown of real-life communities has spread to 16-24-year-olds, creating an "alone together" generation who have grown up with digital media.

The online community can also act like a callous Greek Chorus, bringing out the worst kind of herd mentality. Our tendency to be influenced by what our friends are influenced by, paired with machine intelligence's preference for highlighting extremes in human behaviour, can create a kind of online mob rule. Rumour is accelerated to hypersonic speeds, outstripping rational deliberation. Viral effects can be dizzyingly irrational, even, it seems, infecting information about real viruses. For example, during the early stages of the coronavirus epidemic, digital watchdog Newsguard reported that 52 million internet users worldwide accessed unreliable, "red-rated" websites for news about the virus (many of them promoting conspiracy theories), while only 34,000 turned to "green rated", evidence-based sources, such as the WHO or NHS- an alarming ratio of over 1500:1 (BBC, 2020).

Troubling, too, is the way the online Greek chorus rounds on victims, picking out scapegoats. The anonymity of the digital sphere grants trolls and anonymous users an unprecedented freedom to issue insults, abuse and even death threats, which they never would dare to utter if they could be identified. (How quaint pre-digital death threats now seem, with their menacing lettering carefully pasted from newspaper headlines.) In India false allegations about child kidnappings on WhatsApp have even led to actual lynchings (BBC, 2018a). Cyberbullying ensures that women, ethnic minorities and other vulnerable groups suffer the most and for a younger generation online communication is rapidly normalizing anti-social behaviour. A survey of 8,000 16-19-year-olds across Europe found that one in four had trolled someone, one in eight had engaged in online harassment, one in ten had used hate speech and almost half had committed cybercrimes, such as hacking or money "muling" (a type of money laundering) (Davidson et al, 2022).

A real community would make the reputational risks of such behaviours much more risky, but the impersonality of cyberspace can remove normal ethical considerations. It's just another example of "the one step forward/two steps back" effect of unfettered, change-everything-everywhere capitalism. Progress is made in terms of giving people a voice they may never have had before but this is potentially snatched away by the licensing of abuse which often would not have been tolerated in the supposedly less progressive past.

Love and Algorithmic Match-Making

Inevitably humachination is also taking a toll on the relationships that matter most to us – the relationships of love which sustain a society. Consider online dating, which is currently used by up to nine million people in the UK (Statista, 2021). It uses the inevitable ease and convenience lure to sell itself, claiming that it cuts down the time and emotional effort spent on unsuitable partners. In some cases the promise comes true, especially for users openly seeking short-term relationships, but it can be much more problematic for people looking for long-term relationships. Non-reciprocation and dishonesty can lead to one partner being exploited by another, usually (but not always) in the form of men exploiting women.

In a poignant article, journalist and author Emily Hill writes about her renunciation of online dating after seven frustrating years of looking for a long-term boyfriend. She laments the transitory nature of her online relationships (in one year, she had 146 online dates), the brutal etiquette of breaking up, involving being repeatedly "benched", "catfished", "ghosted", "fizzled" or "zombied". "Dating apps don't facilitate love, just lust", she argues, which is why, she says, she is turning to celibacy (Hill 2020:13).

The sheer abundance of choice in online dating is another negative factor. In the real world, the pool of partners can be limited, which means you may spend time getting to know a possible partner and exercise tolerance towards them. As Hill points out, this often takes place in a real-life community where you are known and where there may be reputational damage for treating somebody callously. Online there is almost infinite choice, reducing tolerance and inviting you to seize on the slightest blemish in behaviour or appearance. Mentally you compare your actual date with the apparently unlimited number of people whom you could swipe next time. Research indicates that dating apps can be ruthlessly discriminatory, racially biased and privilege physically attractive members, which gives the less attractive little chance to impress a partner with their personality or talents (Preston et al, 2021).

Data match-making assumes that the couple have enough in common to form a mutually satisfying relationship but familiarity is unlikely to be a component in this, even though long-standing social psychology research indicates that propinquity, how close you live to someone on campus, for example, is a major predictor of romantic relationships (Festinger et al, 1950). There is also an algorithmic presumption that birds of a feather stick together, whereas in real life it's also true that opposites often attract. Carl Jung (1966:55) drew attention to the complimentary factor in sexual relationships, where, for example, the strengths and weakness of an extravert and an introvert enable a couple to form a close bond. In a sense, we're back to the patent limitations of neomechanicalism, expecting a machine, which can have no experience of any kind of personal relationship, to intervene intelligently in one of the most mysterious and fabled of all human processes, falling in love.

Match-makers in the past may not always have done a better job than online dating but at least they usually had the wellbeing of the prospective couple in mind, a motivation which is the last thing we can rely on in the era of ontocapitalism. As Nichi Hodgson, author of *The Curious History of Dating*, reminds us:

> Modern dating apps are a capitalist enterprise focused not on solving the love problem but the money problem. They have commodified love like never before. And commodification is the killer of romance, which needs genuine attention, vulnerability and then just an ounce of calculated dare to thrive (cited in Hill, 2020:16).

As if this wasn't damning enough, dating apps have increasingly been accused of failing to prevent their platforms from becoming tools of gendered violence. From 2017 to 2021, UK police cases of women being raped or sexually assaulted by men they met on dating apps surged by 175% (Hardy, 2023). It only confirms the way that the new freedoms which humachinators claim that they offer have an ugly habit of turning into new forms of enslavement.

Children: "God Only Knows what It's Doing"

The unbalanced definition of freedom espoused by Big Tech, a toxic mixture of too little and too much, not only affects adults seeking love but creates a new factor in children's personality development, especially in their attitudes to sex. Freedom consists of giving choices to those of who are capable of exercising it, but it also involves restricting the choices of those who are unable, or not yet ready, to deal with them. Being a child, in other words, is another of the vulnerabilities of being human. Protecting children from early trauma and harmful psychological impacts is an age-old preoccupation which any society has a stake in, since the wellbeing of the next generation is vital for its overall survival.

Although the availability of sexual information may be of great benefit to some, such as LGBTQ people who in the past may have been isolated or left in ignorance about their sexuality, the accessing of violent hardcore pornography by children as young as seven is unlikely to produce positive developmental effects (BBFC, 2019). Many children complain that sex education at school doesn't teach them what to actually do in sexual encounters and for this information they rely on pornography. Some children appear to know that porn is a kind of fiction but others take it much more literally. The depiction of unreal female body images and sexual acts geared to male fantasies by an overwhelmingly male-dominated industry can only have a regressive effect on gender equality. The British police even report that they are investigating children as young as six years old for "sexting", i.e., sending each other naked images of themselves (Evans, 2020).

Internet-Aided Sexual Abuse

Other problems caused by relational humachines emerge from the cloak of invisibility which the internet enables users to throw over their identity. This impersonator's charter may be a freedom for some – playing with your identity in anonymous situations can be a liberating psychological experience – but it can also have terrible, real-life downsides. Paedophiles and other sexual abusers are now afforded opportunities for exploiting the vulnerable which were never available in the past. For example, in 2019 Internet Watch Foundation (IWF) found 260,000 internet pages showing 132,300 children being sexually abused. Within minutes of coming on-stream, children, usually girls, often start exposing themselves at the invitation of online abusers who themselves pose as children. "Likes" are often the currency of this abuse, says IWF CEO Susie Hargreaves. "You see them looking into a screen and saying "I won't do that unless I get 1,000 likes" (Dearden, 2020, Oppenheim, 2020).

Of course, child sexual abuse predates the internet and is endemic in many communities. According to criminologists Ella Cockbain and Waqas Tufail (2020), it is "the product of a complex interplay of patriarchy, power, exploitation, opportunity and disregard for children". In recent years in British towns like Rotherham and Oxford some notorious groups of child abusers have been tried and convicted but very few online groomers have been identified. Also, online exploitation is often taking place in children's very own bedrooms, in many cases while their parents are next door or downstairs, in a state of total ignorance. Once again, we see the invasive ability of humanized machines to colonize areas of humanness we once thought were protected, exposing the limitations of our duty of care and opening up new borderless territories of abuse.

Boys are also put under pressure from pornography and online grooming and are exposed to cynically intermittent rewards and other behavioural ruses used by gaming manufacturers to increase gamers' screen time. Boys tend to play online games more than girls and it's having a damaging effect on their academic performance, according to an open letter by over sixty US psychologists, complaining about "unethical", "hidden manipulation techniques" used by fellow professionals employed by gaming companies. It's another type of digital exploitation of children, which their parents either don't know about or misinterpret. As neuroscientist Ramsay Brown says: "Your kid is not weak-willed because he can't get off his phone. Your kid is being engineered to stay on his phone." (Anderson et al, 2018).

And it's not just children who are victims of compulsion engineering and the disturbing ability of online services to slip across the frontiers of privacy. Until recently, gambling, another favourite province of addiction capitalism, was an almost exclusively male preoccupation, as women were reluctant to visit male-dominated venues such as bookies, race courses and casinos. However, online gambling bypasses these social inhibitions and inveigles women into gambling from the privacy of their own homes or secretly from their phones at work. The result is that now over a million women in the UK are at risk from online gambling, according to charity

GambleAware, with the number of women seeking treatment doubling over the past five years and some losing their jobs, relationships and significant amounts of money (Davies, 2022). This surely is an unwanted step towards gender equality

Child-Parent Relationships

Finally, what are the effects of new technology on one of the most vital of all human relationships – indeed the one on which all others depend in some measure – the parent-child relationship? The problems some adults experience in finding stable long-term relationships are unlikely to help their children, for whom secure emotional attachment is such a pivotal element in growing up, and there are many other new challenges for parenting that come with new technology. True, it can bring benefits – for example, GPS enables parents to locate their children far more effectively than in the past – but, if anything, the generation gap has increased. For instance, 75% of parents think that their children are not accessing pornography at all (while over half of them are) and seem oblivious to many other aspects of online communication that are going on in children's bedrooms, such as cyberbullying (BBFC, 2019).

The apparent ease and convenience of high technology for parents – especially those exhausted after long working hours – can have a deleterious effect on their parenting. Novelist Phillip Pullman has urged parents to get off their phones and start talking to their children. The evidence for a significant change in parent-child relationships is not just anecdotal: Department for Education (DfE) research shows that 28% of children arriving at primary school lack expected early communication skills, such as being able to talk about events in the past and future. An Oxford University Press report finds almost half of children aged 5 to 6 have seriously limited vocabularies, a hard-to-correct deficit which is a major predictor of adult unemployment (Busby, 2018a). Primary school teachers report that on their first day at school some children are unable to say their names or speak in complete sentences and when presented with a book, try to swipe it (Woolcock, 2022).

Not all of this is due to humachination – long working hours, social isolation and public spending cuts also take their toll – but the fact that children are being exposed to screens from birth, without the abundant behavioural and conversational interaction that has been the norm for childhood, is a significant factor in this change. The DfE has even proposed teaching parents nursery rhymes to sing to their children – a laughable measure if it weren't so desperate (Busby, 2018). Being read bedtime stories by Alexa, Siri or Google Assistant is an increasingly frequent occurrence for some young children, but it cannot compare to the rich vocal, facial and verbal interaction involved in being read to by a human. A cohort of children with drastically restricted communication skills, who are falling behind in education, doesn't bode well for the future. It only amplifies the threat of "what it's doing to our children's brains!" In the end, there's simply no way of knowing what the consequences will be for either children or adults of the vast, unregulated psychological experiment that we are currently allowing humachination to perform.

Conclusion: A Better Psychological Revolution

Belatedly, governments are trying to contain the mayhem caused by relational humachines. The UK Online Safety Bill, which originally threatened to ban all online harmful content and to fine, and even imprison, offending Big Tech executives, is likely to be introduced in a watered-down version in autumn 2023. However, it faces myriad challenges to enforcement, in particular relating to end-to-end encryption (Sparkes, 2023). While some of the more egregious threats to mental wellbeing described in this chapter may be mitigated, the risk is that others develop under the radar. By allowing Big Tech to censor its own content, pusillanimous regulation can increase rather than diminish the power of the humachinators. A more radical psychological change of direction is needed if the exploitative, profit-driven intentionality behind human-machine fusion is to be defeated.

A better revolution would focus on measures that promote genuine psychological freedom, which balance the advantages of breaking free of limits with respect for the limits that matter in life. On the individual level, this could mean more opportunities to improve our emotional intelligence, learning in groups or one-to-one dialogues. Interpersonally all relationships can be boosted by increased trust and by social interventions that take on the messy but essentially human challenge of deciding on the truth. There are few shortcuts to genuinely fulfilling, long-term, reciprocal human relationships. Every psychologist knows what every person in a successful relationship also knows: love takes hard work. Whether it's a romantic partnership, a friendship or the relationship between a child and a parent, what is required is courage, tolerance and persistence and the maturity to know if a friend, child or lover is telling the truth – and whether it matters.

Humachines send precisely the opposite message, selling the illusion of immediacy, cheapness, a low investment of time and effort and a spurious degree of certainty, all of which can atrophy the quality of our personal experience, emotional life and social relationships. They can also vitally weaken the interpersonal trust that is the best defence against the spreading surveillance state, which derives from the endemic mistrust of others that afflicts so many of the techno-elite. And this emerging picture of humachines re-engineering the most intimate aspects of human relationships has other, even more dramatic, dimensions, as the next chapter will reveal.

CHAPTER 16

Delegating Care, Love and Sex to Robotic Humachines

We now turn to Type 3 humachines, otherwise known as robots, which are intended to stitch the AI-assisted functionality we've been examining into a humanoid replicant possessed of human-like motor skills. It's not a new idea: the dream of a humanoid automaton goes back at least as far as the ancient Greek God Hephaestus, who was said to have built talking handmaidens and a bronze warrior to defend Crete. Mathematician Hero of Alexander produced actual humanoid automata in the form of a mechanical puppet theatre and medieval Chinese engineers constructed clockwork mannequins that chimed the hour and rang gongs, while Arab engineers built hydro-powered peacocks and humanoid waiters that served tea. In eighteenth-century Japan, the inventor Tanaka created mechanical toys that could fire arrows and paint Kanji characters.

In the twentieth century the humanoid dream slowly lumbered into industrial reality, with Britain pioneering three-wheel tortoise-like robots in the 1940s and the first robotic arm appearing in General Motors' New Jersey factory in the early 1960s. In Tokyo in 1973 the first purportedly "intelligent" full-size android resembling a human made its appearance, the walking, talking WABOT-1. In this century the goal of creating a machine which not only "thinks", "relates" and "feels" like a human but also convincingly looks and acts like one has become absolutely central to the age of humachines.

Robotics Tricknology and
the Core Human Competence of Caring

The primary role of these motor-skill humachines, so runs the opt-repeated claim of the robotics industry, is to replace "dirty, dangerous and dull" human jobs and tasks (Association for Advancing Automation (2019). British Home Secretary Amber Rudd tried to reassure the public that this meant that only "banal and repetitive tasks" would be replaced, leaving jobs which "need human sensibilities: with personal relationships, qualitative judgement and creativity coming to the fore" (Mason, 2019). But if politicians genuinely think that this is the plan, they're being hoodwinked like the rest of us. In reality, humachination has in its sights virtually any task that humans can perform, pleasant or unpleasant, especially those requiring "human sensibilities".

In the next chapter, I deconstruct the "dirty and dangerous" jobs which robots are taking on but here I want to examine occupations which robot- icists would presumably categorize as "dull". These seem to include caring for the elderly, the sick and the disabled, raising children, counselling psy- chologically troubled people and providing for those in need of intimate companionship and sexual relationships. Far from being "dull", caring for and looking after others is part of the existential core of being human and a practical survival requirement of Homo sapiens. It's also right at the centre of the CANDID values, based on cooperation rather than compe- tition, and, in particular, draws on the unique human quality of altruism. Although most animals care for their own kin, humans are unique in their propensity to also care for strangers outside their kin and friendship circle and lay down their lives for people they have never met (Jensen et al, 2014). Altruism is expressed in innumerable daily acts of care across the world in the unpaid, reproductive economy. It's also found in multiple, modern caring professions and organizations which focus on looking after the old, the sick and the psychologically disturbed and in raising and educating the young. Arguably, care is what keeps human society together.

That's not to say that caring is without problems and challenges – it can be one of the most demanding roles we experience in life. "Ease and con- venience" are not words necessarily associated with raising boisterous children or caring for the sick or elderly or mentally ill. The start of the coronavirus pandemic revealed just how much the public value those who dedicate their lives to looking after others in hospitals or care homes. For a brief period, it represented an inspiring revolution in values which over-turned the economic priorities of growth capitalism and made the idea of replacing "heroic", human care workers with machines seem obscenely inappropriate. Yet, in reality, it did little to slow down the march of the carebots.

Robots "Caring" for Older People

Looking after the old is one of the key markets for care robotics. The jus-tification for this is not hard to find, as the ageing of populations in the West represents one of the biggest challenges of the Anthropocene. In the wealthiest societies on the planet, the old threaten to outnumber the native working age population for the first time in history. Japan expects a 370,000 shortfall of human care workers by 2025 and other advanced countries such as Germany and Italy are struggling to deal with a situation in which a third of their population will be over 65 by 2050 (Kumar et al, 2022).

At first glance, carebots may seem a plausible enough answer to the ageing problem. Their manufacturers intend them to help in lifting, cleaning and bathing older people and by administering medication and preparing meals. Some of the devices are humanoid; others represent new forms of engineering, such as a robotic bed that can convert into a wheelchair (New Atlas, 2014). Under close human supervision these machines may be useful but the problem of alien intelligence is never far away. A carebot may be able to replicate its human equivalent by 80% – a typical advertised error rate– but what does the 20% deviation from human standards involve? If a robot lifting a grandfather onto his bed works 80% of the time but the other 20% drops him on the floor this is hardly acceptable.

Objectification is another problem, the risk that older people are treated as though they are inanimate things to be shunted here and there by a device which is itself an object. Control is another issue, as raised by Amanda Sharkey and Noel Sharkey (2012) in their important paper "Granny and the Robots". If the personal autonomy principle governs this field, it would ensure that the client has control over the robot at all times but what happens then if a robot perceives an emergency? And if a suffering client requests the robot ends her life should the robot obey? Responsibility is an intrinsically human attribute. Impulsively, we may curse a machine if it makes a mistake but we know that to actually blame it for failure is futile. Yet without a chain of human accountability what other option is there?

Constant monitoring might mitigate some of these risks. Some care homes are envisaged as smart homes in which every piece of furniture is embedded with sensors or cameras but this doesn't necessarily help if it's only the algorithms doing the monitoring and not humans. And such constant surveillance also raises another key value which should be applied to caring for older people, the client's right to privacy. 24/7 surveillance may in some circumstances extend an older person's independence but being subject to the constant unblinking eye of the camera is a high price to pay in terms of dignity. Such a digital-robotic environment also risks infantilizing the older person, stripping away years of experience and reducing him to the status of a child.

Robots as "Empathetic Companions"

More problems emerge with another prime selling point of care robots, the claim that they provide companionship. Robot marketers argue that interaction with AI-assisted devices can help to counter the epidemic of loneliness which affects older people and others. A fleet of interactive robots is supposed to be coming to the rescue of lonely elders, including Paro, a robotic seal with a Canadian accent, or Geeko's Carebot, promoted as "a new kind of companion". But philosopher Robert Sparrow, in a paper entitled "The March of the Robot Dogs" (2002), argues that the concept of a robot pet or companion "requires sentimentality of a deplorable kind" and contends that "the design and manufacture of these robots are unethical is so far as it presupposes or encourages this delusion". Unfortunately, we know that this delusion is deeply cemented into the humachine project.

On a practical front, as always, we have to be wary of tricknology. One of the most heavily researched "companionate robots" is Pepper, which Softbank describes as "the world's first social humanoid robot". However, having watched a video of this child-height "emotional robot's" three-hour visit to the offices of The Financial Times (2016) it's impossible not to agree with the Robot Report's blunt verdict that

> Pepper failed in every way to (1) be a companion, (2) recognize emotional cues, (3) be able to converse reliably and intelligently and (4) provide any level of service other than first-time entertainment (Tobe, 2016).

This was in spite of being accompanied by an entourage of publicists and technicians who regularly had to adjust the robot.

In fact, replacing human-to-human interaction with machine "care" carries many risks for older people. Social engagement is known to reduce stress, which in itself can be a major accelerator of dementia, against which the best defence appears to be "an extensive social network" and community-based living (Fratiglioni et al, 2000). The absence of long-range research on humachines in geriatric care is another shortcoming, especially as there is anecdotal evidence that the initial novelty of interacting with a carebot soon wears off. Sharkey and Sharkey (2012) conclude that:

> [R]educed social interaction can have a measurable effect on the health and wellbeing of the elderly and reinforces the idea that depriving them of such conduct is unethical and even a form of cruelty.

Mechanizing Empathy

This warning is not being heeded by the robotics industry or politicians looking for a techno-fix to the problems of ageing and social care, as evidenced by this report in *The Daily Telegraph*:

> The [British] Government has announced a £34m scheme to teach "empathy" to robots to care for people in care homes. The technology is being developed in the private sector but the Government is worried that robots will struggle to care for people in homes because they lack the human touch. (Diver, 2019).

The idea that empathy can be engineered – and for a mere £34 million! – is a profound misunderstanding of this pivotal human quality. The real cost of the human caring economy would run into trillions of pounds if we were to accurately cost the value of human empathy, which involves two interlinked capacities. The first is the ability to mentally put yourself in someone else's shoes, to see the world from another person's point of view. This, of course, machines can't do because they are not persons. All they can do is use data to construct possible scenarios. But their ability to do this effectively is limited because they lack the second major attribute of empathy: the ability to recognize other people's emotions, based in part on understanding one's own feelings. The best a machine can do is produce behaviour that simulates human feelings.

In this it somewhat resembles a human psychopath who lacks fellow feeling but abounds in heartless charm, a combination which can turn him into an expert manipulator. This brings us back to the machine mindset, which we explored in Chapter 11 and leads us to ask, who really lacks "the human touch", here? Is it machines or their makers? Care robotics threaten to replace a core element of our humanness with what we might call "the machine touch", a cold process that is always on tap, capable of producing endless graphs and read outs but incapable of understanding the real meaning of care. This could also reduce the social status of caring for older relatives, turning it into something you only do if you can't afford a care robot. Other negative effects of skill-stripping may follow. Do we become self-centred emotional cowards, squeamish about all difficult feelings? A kind of emotional obesity may set in, the equivalent of the cognitive and decisional obesity I referred to in previous chapters. Emotions can atrophy as we shy away from using them or even admitting we possess them. Some of the trials of working with older people may disappear but so will the joy, the uplifting experiences, the feelings of being wanted, the rewards of making a difference and the wisdom and life experience that older people have to pass on.

Bringing up Children by Machine: Robot Child Minders

Some of the same profound concerns apply to the idea of delegating parenting to child-minding robots. If older people are coming to the end of their lives, children are right at the beginning of theirs and wide open to influences that will shape them forever. This has not passed the notice of the child care robotics industry which sets their sights much higher than Alexa reading bedtime stories. For example, already in use in Silicon Valley is SNOO, a robot cot or "smart sleeper" that not only rocks your baby but scans her emotional state and plays appropriately soothing womb noises (Mitchell, 2020). A lullaby-crooning, self-driving pram is another option (Sellman, 2023). Other devices, like Nanit (standing for Nanny IT), offer sleep tracking and can monitor breathing motions. This equipment can be operated from a parent's phone, offering the prospect of remote, hands-free parenting.

Toy manufacturer Mattel sought to extend the range of digital parenting through its Aristotle digital assistant, which aimed to provide tutoring, entertainment and, of course, "companionship" for a child from infancy to adolescence. This included mechanizing traditional parental roles such as soothing a child, reading her stories or giving her advice. The device was also intended to capture a child's most intimate data and upload it. This feature, however, provoked a mass protest by parents and concerned groups and forced Mattel to withdraw the product (Vincent, 2017). The public can take inspiration from this outcome but robot manufacturers are also likely to learn to be less brazen about their data-plundering intentions. There are already many subtler, interactive devices on the market, including the same "companionate" robo-pets and humanoid devices which are used by older people, such as the robot dog AIBO, the mechanical seal Paro and the robotic infant My Real Baby. These may be used at home and at school, particularly in pre-school settings where they attempt to make up for a shortage of educational assistants. Customized, AI-enabled teddy bears for under-five-year-olds are next; they "can actually be telling a story and talking almost like a friend" says the CEO of a manufacturer operating in the smart toy market, which is already worth $14 billion (Ho-him, 2023). All these devices shift childcare from humans to machines, in a way that could profoundly change the experience of childhood.

So what does being cared for by a robot feel like from a child's viewpoint? Excessive attention to devices may retard communications skills but for lonely children robots or chatbots may be their only source of companionship. Children anthropomorphize more than adults and often exhibit animistic beliefs, granting inanimate objects – even crude wooden toys – an intense imaginative, emotional life. Robots which can speak, move their limbs, play games, sing songs, tell jokes and know a child's name and history are likely to impress children even more than conventional toys, especially as these devices can exert authority through their store of factual knowledge.

According to MIT professor and psychoanalyst Sherry Turkle, who has produced valuable, path-breaking research on human-machine interaction, children's attitudes to robots have changed significantly over the past few decades. In the early 1980s, she found American children expressing Romantic, pro-human opposition to the prospect of robots caring for the old, the sick and the young, as expressed in one youngster's disarmingly simple question, "Don't we have people for those jobs?" However, twenty-five years later, in the era of ontocapitalism, some children seem to have abandoned the view that humans make better carers than machines. "Robots would always be sure that you would have fun", said one fifth grader, adding that "People have their own problems." (Turkle, 2011:70). A fifteen-year-old boy stated that a robot would be able to give better advice than his father about friendship, romantic relationships and the emotional challenges of teenage life. "Its database would be larger than Dad's," he said. "Dad has knowledge of basic things, but not enough of high school." Surprisingly, he also believed a robot would know more than a human about happiness and how to achieve it (p50).

This change in attitude seems to owe much to the downgrading of organic life by technologism and the creeping influence of the machine mindset. A cruel logic dictates that as parents increasingly delegate to machines, they undermine their own value in their offspring's eyes. Just as for the rich, the nanny is often the de facto mother-figure, to whom a child may reveal confidences his real mother would not be trusted with, so children brought up by robots may begin to regard them as more trustworthy, and even more loveable, than their parents. The difference is that the nanny and other traditional parental surrogates are humans rather than AI-driven machines, whose affection for, and loyalty to, a child is absolutely zero. Humachines' fidelity is to their owners, the child's parents, and, quite possibly, to their manufacturer who may sell on the child's data to the highest bidder.

There are other, even more troubling psychological consequences of growing up in a world in which parents are seen as second-class robots and robots as first-class parents. Do children start to prefer the ease and convenience of machine relationships as opposed to the flamboyant unpredictability of real humans? Will children grow up to be fearful of exploring their feelings, preferring to sail close to the shore, avoiding the turbulent waves of an active emotional life? As Turkle says:

> The ground rules of human beinghood are laid down very early … We can't put children in this position of pretend empathy and then expect that children will know what empathy is. Or give them as-if relationships and then think that we'll have children who know what relationships are (quoted in Peachman, 2017).

Indeed, parental humachines could accelerate the normalization of the disempathetic adult. Many of the wealthy and powerful already find it hard to put themselves in another's shoes, as we know from Chapter 10, but what happens if the majority of people only experience empathy at the hands of machines? Research suggests that some children of the "Alexa generation" are already using rude, abrasive language when interacting with digital devices (Childwise, 2018). Treating virtual assistants as butlers or even as slaves may seem logical enough for children but it doesn't bode well for their human-to-human attitudes in later life. Combined with the debasement of altruism and cooperativism, it could reinforce the worst kind of CIMENT values.

Machine parenting is patently not something children have any choice over. Nor is it necessarily the result of ill intent on the part of their parents, who may be motivated by what they believe is best for their offspring and a genuine desire to protect them from the perceived harms of growing up. But child care robotics is another ideal Trojan horse for human-machine fusion, so a consumerist, status war is not out of the question, with children pestering their parents for the latest robot brands.

We won't know until it's too late what the outcome will be of a generation brought up by machines. It's just another part of the humachine age's unsupervised, profit-driven clinical trial which is being conducted in real time with real children and real adults. Could it result in a more emotionally literate generation, trained by "empathetic" robots, as the industry hype claims, or a generation of affective zombies or, even worse, a cohort of coldly manipulative psychopaths? At the moment, it seems, all we can do is cross our fingers and hope.

Robot Counselling

Another crucial area of human caring which is fast being appropriated by machines is psychotherapy, a field in which I have some professional experience. Robot counsellors already exist in the form of humanoid machines such as NAO who answers questions once it's tapped on the head or Elle an onscreen "robotherapist" which uses facial recognition to mirror the client's body position. "Relational agents" like Woebot (2022) can provide cognitive behavioural therapy (CBT) techniques on various platforms. These services are also available to users on mobile phones, gratis or for payment, or may be integrated into mechanical caring devices such as robonurses.

In a paper reviewing the research literature on the effectiveness of machine counselling entitled "Your robot therapist will see you now," Amelia Fiske and her colleagues (2019) suggest that this innovation can have useful potential, especially in areas not covered by existing therapy provision. Nevertheless, the researchers underline a huge range of actual and potential problems in its application, including a lack of "large-scale rigorous research ", the absence of ethical guidelines around autonomous counselling and the sexist, racist or economic biases which are often endemic in AI. The 24/7 availability of web counselling might seem to be an advantage but it increases the danger that some users develop a long-term dependency on these services. The researchers also place a red flag against the economic motives behind this technology, suggesting that instead of supplementing existing services automated counselling will be used to replace in-person therapy, "thereby potentially exacerbating existing health inequalities".

Does robot counselling work? Some research shows that it can mitigate the symptoms of depression and anxiety, with one user of Woebot intriguingly commenting that "Not being reliant on a human being is very freeing ". Other studies are more negative. Scholten et al (2017) found that web-based "electronic health" interventions can have a negative effect due to users not accepting the validity of the service. Indeed, Fiske and her team raise the crucial question of whether machine counselling is actually aligned to the therapist's primary aim of helping a client relate more productively with his or her world.

> The risk exists that if robotic interventions are not transferable to human interaction that they merely remain a way of improving human relations with machines, or worse, provide an outlet that further limits human-to-human interactions.

This insightful comment seizes on one of the real dangers of robot counselling – and indeed of so much of the humachination project – that rather than improving our relationships with humans (the machine assistant argument), it simply creates a new sphere of human-to machine-discourse. As the researchers stress, human relationships are characterized by reciprocity and a certain equality but "relationships with intelligent devices are neither mutual nor symmetric." Instead of improving a patient's ability to interact with others in real life, these devices might make it more difficult.

What for example is the long-term effect of encouraging a schizophrenic to engage with the voices he hears, as a trial digital programme using an avatar has attempted (Craig et al, 2018)? Does this make him increasingly reliant on the humachine? Other problems may arise in the key therapeutic process of transference, in which a patient identifies with the therapist in various ways. What happens when it's a machine that is being perceived as a tyrannical father, a withholding mother or an ideal lover? All of this suggests the possibility of a counter-technology rapidly emerging in the form of human therapists specializing in weaning clients off their dependency on humachine counsellors. This new type of therapy would have to help patients disentangle their possibly already tangled associations between the real and the fantasized, which may have multiplied through repeated, unsupervised engagements with seemingly authoritative and "empathetic" AI devices.

What Fiske et al's excellent paper doesn't mention is the long history of research which suggests that it's the relationship with the therapist which is by far the most important healing factor for the patient. Psychological professionals like to focus on the models of counselling which they have extensively trained on but for most clients it's the relationship that matters most, as numerous meta-analyses of research confirm (Ardito and Rabellino, 2011) (This finding is not a surprise to relationally-orientated therapists using humanistic, person-centred, existential or psychoanalytical models of therapy but it does potentially embarrass those practitioners of CBT who insist on the "objective", scientific nature of their approach.) In the therapeutic relationship a key role is played by trust, that crucial, indigenous element of being human we've already encountered in this book, without which it's very difficult to make progress. The patient's testing of the trustworthiness of the therapist – sometimes subtly and gradually, sometimes dramatically – often constitutes the real narrative of the therapy and its effectiveness. How can this deeply human interaction happen with a machine which can offer absolutely no guarantee of confidentiality for what the client reveals and which has no experience of living relationships and no knowledge of what trust even means?

The robot counsellor is also disabled by its lack of feelings which is quite a disadvantage as what happens in therapy has a lot to do with emotions.

Therapy is a place where the most emotionally explosive issues can be brought out into the open. It's often the shame, guilt, anger, pain, confusion, fear and anxiety associated with a patient's situation which makes it so difficult to talk about. The therapist is trained to deal with these issues, to not block them off or dive for cover, but listen calmly and compassionately and control the emotional impression he conveys. By contrast, the robot counsellor attempts to fake emotions and provide simulated empathy to disguise the fact that it has no real understanding of what it is to suffer humiliation or shame or rage and limited ability to discriminate minutely between these and other affective states. The more plausible it is in its simulation of such understanding, the more dishonest and untrustworthy it becomes.

As is often the case with humachination projects, if the human is genuinely in the loop, there may be some justification for machine-based social innovations. But for mental health professionals to provide adequate supervision for all robot counselling, major changes in legislation around mental health would have to occur. Psychological robotics on the web is largely unregulated, with new, often free, apps appearing all the time. Even the equivalent in-person practice is only patchily regulated, notably in the UK where anybody can commercially offer their services as a therapist or mental health coach regardless of qualification or training.

Another danger of AI programmes is the usual lack of transparency around its decision-making. Software crammed with psychological references, case studies and research could be useful but only if the system is able to admit its own severe limitations. However, "I don't know because I'm only a machine" is unlikely to be part of the robocounsellor's script. What's more probable is that one-eyed AI offers its usual false objectivity. Areas which are vigorously contested by mental health professionals – such as the definition of "abnormal psychology" and the value of the medical model of mental illness – are likely to be evaluated in the cheapest and most reductive way and then presented as incontestable facts.

In practical terms, the growth of machine counselling may well result in many fewer people receiving in-person therapy. The current economics of mental health may dictate that patients who already have to wait for many months and even years to receive a very restricted number of publicly funded in-person therapy sessions may be told that second-rate machine counselling is as close to the talking cure as they're likely to get.

Sex Robots

At its most extreme, the concept of caring robots extends to the claim that love is possible between a human and a machine. As I've already suggested, this seems to me to be a fundamental misunderstanding, since love is an inalienable aspect of humanness which involves a living relationship between beings capable of reciprocating emotions – and that rules out machines. It has to be said, however, that the myth has always fascinated creative writers, who cannot resist endowing robots with human tendencies. For example, Kazuo Ishiguro's novel *Klara and the Sun (2021)* may be implicitly critical of humachination but it nevertheless artfully renders the inner life of a humanoid robot (an "Artificial Friend") in a way that seems to endorse the proposition that machines are capable of genuine empathy, emotional sensitivity and care. Actors further increase the credibility of humanoid machines. However hard an actor strains to act mechanically, his humanness will always give him away. Every breath, every facial expression, skin tone and muscular movement convey a living quality no machine can possess. In particular, female robots, from Fritz Lang's imposing *Futura* in the 1920s to the "fembots" that dominate HBO's *Westworld*, have encouraged the fantasy of falling in love with machines. And if robots can find their way into our hearts, they can surely make the biggest machine-human leap of all and get into our beds.

For some roboticists, sex is actually the primary function of their devices. In 1999 Ray Kurzweil predicted that sex robots would become popular in the 2020s and transform the reality of human sexuality (Kurzweil, 1999:187). The march of the sex dolls has been under way for some time in Japan where some sex automata are said to have their own funerals. Increasingly realistic, AI-assisted sex robots are beginning to appear on the market and a sci-fi themed Las Vegas brothel now offers these and other devices to "customers with unusual fetishes" (Liberatore, 2019). Predictably enough, there are claims that these humachines will offer a range of medical benefits. For example, Dan Barry of the Singularity University says "robo nurses" will play a huge role for patients "with sexual dysfunction or need" (Diamandis and Kotler, 2012:199). But, as robot ethicist Kathleen Richardson of the Campaign against Sex Robots (2020) argues, the contention that sex dolls will help cure sexual dysfunction is simply a distraction. Even more outrageous is the argument that child sex robots may reduce the harm done by paedophiles by providing a therapeutic substitute for real victims. In an interview with Forbes Magazine, Richardson takes us through a thought experiment, the conclusion of which is that by legally approving the manufacture of a child sex robot "you inadvertently legitimate an area of child-abuse expression" (Morris, 2018).

Another specious defence of sex robots is that they are comparable to vibrators or other sex toys but as Richardson stresses, nobody claims you have sex with a vibrator: you masturbate with it. Moreover, the claim that mechanical sex dolls are "just like toys" is false, as these devices are aggressively marketed as being "just like girlfriends". In a similar fashion, Replika's chatbot "partners" are promoted as helping lonely people "feel that they can grow" into real relationships. On the contrary, psychologists point out that such subservient devices simply reinforce the kind of expectations about one-sided relationships which can cause social isolation in the first place (Titcomb, 2023).

Nothing better cuts through the misogynistic pretence and hypocrisy of this tricknology than actually accessing a sex robot website, as I did via Google in April 2022. The website of Robot Companions AI (2022), which is owned by Green Earth Robotics of Oregon, offers "The Ultimate AI Talking Sex Robot Companion: Girlfriend Who Knows You Best!" It features a lurid array of images of large-busted slim-waited AI-assisted sex dolls – e.g. Amber 5'6" cup size F and Natalia 5'1" cup size D – on sale for around $4,500. The "Technology" section, reproduced with its original grammar, is worth quoting at some length:

> We have combined the features of the female mind and body to bring you a Humanoid Experience like none other on this earth. All our AI Robot Companion Sex Dolls come with internal heating of 37 degrees Celsius, this means not only can you enjoy their sexuality, but you can connect with her on a human intimate level... The Robot Companion can tell you the weather, remember your favourite foods, ask you about your day, answer many questions and most importantly continue to learn along the way. Along with regular remote updates you are sure to enjoy the mental stimulation you have always craved ... Each robot is equipped with a lifelike Vagina, formed from extensive R&D to ensure you have the best real feeling and experience. A bonus feature is all our AI Robot Companion Sex Dolls climax at just the right time!

Not only are these sex robots offered as "just like women", the suggestion is that they represent the summation of the female mind and body, providing "the mental stimulation you've always craved" as well as the ultimate sexual experience from a synchronously climaxing partner. This marketing of robots as "the girlfriend you've always dreamed of" is also found in relation to the Harmony AI sex doll. Its creator, however, extends the range of the machine companionship myth by claiming that his children happily interact with Harmony – in its non-sexual mode – and that it even accompanies the family on holidays (Warner, 2017). The transformation of a masturbation device into a companion for the whole family shows humachination at its most tawdry. But as Atanasoski and Vora (2019:192) confirm, this desire for an "animate nonhuman object" which is more than a pure body but which "can always be turned back into pure body" is common throughout sex robotics.

The Campaign against Sex Robots seeks to ban sex robots, which it rightly labels "a misogynistic development". The technology surely represents all that is dangerous about care robots taken to the most preposterous extremes in a way that seriously denigrates the dignity of being human.

Robot Love

Yet, as we know, advocates of human-machine fusion insist that robots can not only have sex with humans but can provide them with love. In his *book Love and Sex with Robots,* computer chess pioneer David Levy waxes lyrical about falling in love with "virtual people", as he terms humanoid robots, and exults in the attractions of "a willing lover available whenever desired, a possible replacement for a lost mate – a partner who dumped us" who can also provide "live-in therapy, including sexual relations" (Levy, 2008:105). He happily envisages a time when the acceptability of "social robots" will be so pervasive that it will be irrelevant whether you are going to a party with a human or a robot (p106). At this point – which we could call humachination year zero – the difference between humans and humachines will be "no greater than the cultural differences between people from different countries or even from different parts of the same country." For Levy, the moment could come as soon as 2050, by which time he envisages that marriage with robots will be on the cards.

"Almost everyone wants someone to love", he writes, "but many people have no one" (p304). To which I'd answer: "someone to love", yes but not *something*.

Only a thing can be subject to the absolute, non-reciprocal domination that Levy seems to crave in a sexbot, whose owner would have an adjustable "sexual intensity" setting and, bizarrely, a "fidelity control" to determine how much sex his robot can have with other humans and with other robots.

Robot Rights

In this surreal imaginary universe, which is in fact a logical culmination of the humachination project, robots establish themselves as separate species and gain full human-style rights. Inevitably, David Levy advocates this outcome and machine learning pioneer Geoffrey Hinton appears to agree. He thinks generative AI systems may already have feelings:" Do I think that [AIs] deserve political rights? I actually do. I think "humanist" is a kind of racist term", he says. Hinton also predicts a "big fight" to grant AIs rights, comparable to the suffragette campaign (Sellman, 2023a).

In 2017 Saudi Arabia actually declared a humanoid robot, named Sophia, an honorary citizen of the country with full "citizenship rights". The terrible irony of a machine possessing the rights, to which the real women and girls of Saudi Arabia are not entitled, conjures up a patriarchal, dystopian vision of where the country's current "modernization programme" might be leading. Indeed, AI ethicist Joanna Bryson points out the disturbing link between those more interested in robot rights than in human rights and the potential danger of allowing corporations to escape their legal and tax obligations by passing them on to synthetic entities. To the claim by Sophia's manufacturer that his fembot was "basically alive", Bryson's reply was unequivocal: "It's obviously bullshit. What's this about? It's about having a supposed equal you can turn on and off" (Vincent, 2017).

The danger of the robot rights argument is that it can draw in the best thinkers. For example, in an article entitled "When robots have feelings", ethical philosopher and animal rights advocate Peter Singer writes:

> "At present robots are mere items of property. But what happens if they become sufficiently complex to have feelings? After all, the human brain is just a very complex machine" (Singer and Sagan, 2009).

To me, this sounds like a dangerous endorsement of the neomechanicalist vision and, in particular, the fundamental brain-computer fallacy. In a more recent video, Singer has said that robots should be accorded rights according to their degree of sentience. If they are able to "feel something inside" and "to think and understand themselves" they should be accorded full human rights: "if we created robots who were at our level, I think we would have to give them really the same rights that we have" (Singer, 2019: 03.50-55). As he concedes, this is still a very big "if", but merely hypothesizing about this kind of possible future gives the humachination project an ethical credibility it does not deserve. It naively endorses the most questionable claims of ontocapitalism, a position unworthy of a moral philosopher who elsewhere is so sensitive to the claims of the living world.

A Better Revolution: Some Ecocene Solutions

In summary, it's hard to exaggerate the danger of allowing robots, which are simply pieces of software and hardware, to replace human empathy and altruism. But that seems to be intention of the humachinators, for whom life is just an inferior form of engineering. It goes without saying that an eco-democratic revolution would focus on very different solutions to the challenges of care than those offered by ontocapitalism. Rather than trying to find technological solutions which maintain the economic status quo, a SEWP-inspired approach would focus on the ecological and human needs and adapt the technology and economics to serve these needs.

For example, only in a world still dominated by the Pyramid Pattern, would we fail to solve the riddle of a Global North with too many older people who are no longer of working age and a Global South brimming with younger people looking for employment. It's partially racism, nationalism and other CIMENT values which makes mechanical carers seem preferable to allowing migrant human carers to take over this vital service, for which their age-respecting cultures often help to equip them. The technologistic celebration of the progress of robotics should not disguise the unequalism that lies behind it. It's no coincidence, for example that Japan, with its endemic cultural xenophobia, leads the world in care robotics.

As for good parenting, time is often the biggest obstacle. In the hunter-gatherer world system, there is almost unlimited time for being with children (Ember, 2020) but the vicious circle of growth capitalism means that people have to work harder and longer to earn a living, which gives them less time and energy to devote to activities that they value most. Reducing the working week is one Ecocene solution, which would give parents the time and energy to dedicate to nurturing their children. This would go a long way to eliminating the vulnerability which digital-robotic parental surrogates seek to exploit, as well as any possible social cachet attached to delegating the care of your loved ones to machines.

Mental health issues can be eased by making education in counselling available from secondary school onwards. Psychotherapy training has a double advantage: it is in itself a form of therapy and self-help, as well as providing the tools and the self-confidence to provide support for others wherever and whenever it is needed. This, in addition to a far greater provision of professional psychology, would make robot counsellors unnecessary, except as carefully supervised back-ups.

Finally, the SWEP goal of equitability will focus on the gender inequality which still dominates the way in which the reproductive economy functions under growth capitalism. Informal caring roles are still primarily performed by women – for example, in the UK women provide almost two and a half times as much unpaid childcare as men (CPP, 2022). A male-dominated robotics industry attempting to transform the care economy into a branch of engineering is unlikely to encourage men to correct this imbalance and take up their fair share of caring activities. AI-assisted sex slaves are the most obviously grotesque manifestation of this patriarchal attitude, closely followed by *Stepford Wives* marriage-bot fantasies.

These psychological shifts will offer a genuine uplift to care, which will become inevitable once wellbeing is established as a primary objective of an eco-democratic society (more on this in Part VI). Autonomous "caring" services can't provide anything that's better than humans can offer, they can only offer something that's better than nothing. We can avoid this bleak, depersonalizing and potentially de-democratizing outcome, by organizing a society around the very best that humans can offer each other in terms of care, empathy and love and the cooperative values that form part of our unique species endowment. These transformational values will also help us address the alarming problems posed by robotic humachines operating in the dirty, dangerous and downright scary sectors of twenty-first century life, which we can now consider.

CHAPTER 17

Humachines of War and Heavy Industry: The Robotic Slave Economy and Planetwide Jobicide

The hulking metal figure in the video is recognizably humanoid but devoid of a distinct head. As it performs parkour moves – handstands, back flips and other gymnastic skills, Atlas sways its hips with almost balletic grace, creating a disturbing effect of elegance mixed with menace. Another fear-some-looking robot, Handle, is a two-metre-high machine on wheels, which is capable of advancing at nine miles per hour and carrying heavy weights. It looks like a figure from sci-fi mythology: half-human, half-fork-lift truck (Boston Dynamics, 2021 & 2017). In another video (unfortunately no longer available on the web) we see an early version of Spot, a headless quadruped that plods around an empty factory like a giant, alien insect. Its human presenter claims that it's "less creepy in person" and informs viewers, not entirely reassuringly, that Spot "only sees you as an obstacle too big to step on".

It's hard to know how much tricknology was involved in these videos from Boston Dynamics, a robotics company once owned by Google, but as an introduction to the heavyweight division of Type 3 humachines they can't be bettered. In this chapter I want to explore the implications of devices which aim to mimic, and improve on, human motor skills in heavy industry, natural resource extraction and the military-industrial complex.

Designed to drill, mine, construct, carry and even kill, these robots specialize in the unpleasant, harmful jobs which roboticists claim they want to protect humans from having to perform.

In fact, mechanizing every human physical competence has always been a primary goal of humachination. Claude Shannon, one of the founders of AI, stated, "I visualize a time when we will be to robots what dogs are to humans", adding "I'm rooting for the machines. I've always been on the machines' side" (Liversidge, 1987). Of course, there is a case for replacing hazardous, high-injury jobs in fields like military conflict, resource extraction and civil construction, which have been present in human societies since the Palaeolithic (the first mine, in modern Eswatini, formerly Swaziland, goes back some 42,000 years (UNESCO, 2008)). But will this automation move us towards more peace or simply reinvent war and are we simply mechanizing jobs that from an ecological standpoint we shouldn't be doing anyway? Autonomous, mechanical slaves play a crucial role in the techno-utopian vision of ontocapitalism but will ejecting the human community from the workplace further weaken democratic controls over new technology? These are some of the issues we can now address.

Humachines of War

Imagining semi-humanoid robots like Atlas or Handle in a military context is easy enough but we should probably dispense with the idea of Terminator-type killer robots, capable of replicating the skills of a human soldier. Like so much in fiction, this notion inadvertently seduces us into believing the myth that a complete human-machine synthesis is possible. It's extremely unlikely that fully autonomous robots would ever be able to navigate highly complex, confused, unpredictable battle engagements without lethally endangering both civilians and fellow combatants. And, as we observed in discussing the human in the loop myth, ensuring that human commanders can maintain effective control over even semi-autonomous robotic weaponry is problematic enough. That's not to say that these concerns will deter all arms manufacturers from pursuing the lucrative prize of creating a self-directing humanoid soldier, even if this risks unsafe prototypes falling into the hands of unscrupulous armies or terrorist groups.

In reality, military robotic humachines are mainly based on automating weapons rather than the personnel who use them. The race to develop

Lethal Automated Weapons Systems (LAWS) is hotting up, especially since the Russia-Ukraine war, which has caused geopolitical superpowers to square up to one another. The conflict has seen the increased use of low-tech drones but much more sophisticated, AI-assisted versions are being developed, which can identify targets via facial recognition software and make decisions to shoot or bomb autonomously. These new drones may be tiny, flying in vast swarms like locusts, which makes jamming impossible or much larger like Boeing's new high-altitude Global Hawk and the Reapers, Ravens and Predators used extensively by the US Air Force since the early 2000s. Autonomous aircraft are the next step. The Australian Royal Air Force is currently testing the Boeing's MQ-28 Ghost Bat, based on its Loyal Wingman drone, a fully self-operating fighter jet with a range of 2,300 miles and no space for a human crew (Newdick, 2022).

On the ground, every type of vehicle used in warfare over the past century is rapidly being automated, with the aim of enabling military commanders to direct armed forces with minimal human troops. Robot tanks create the possibility that "future wars will be waged without human involvement", declares an arms manufacturer, who is considering developing a totally autonomous version of Russia's current semi-autonomous T-14 Armata tank (Scharre, 2018:116.) Compact, car-sized, semi-autonomous tanks made by British weapons contractors are already being deployed in war zones. The US is developing an AI-directed, crewless Ripsaw M5 tank, which would be silent enough to creep up on an enemy and release a self-directing micro-robotic tank, as well as deploy a quadrocopter drone for surveillance purposes. As always, the manufacturers of these robotic weapons assure us that a human will always be in the loop before firing (Dempsey, 2020), even though, as we observed in Chapter 14, military authorities concede that this will be increasingly impractical.

At sea, naval vessels will also be transformed into humachines. On launching Sea Hunter, an autonomous vessel which searches for submarines, US Deputy Director of Defense Robert Work said to his audience,

> Imagine anti-submarine warfare wolf-packs. Imagine mine warfare flotillas, distributed surface warfare action groups, deception vehicles, electronic warfare vessels (Klare, 2019).

All of these assets would be unmanned and capable of operating autonomously. At the same time, undersea, a counter technology will develop, with swarm-like fleets of autonomous submarines, seeking to evade surface vessels with their small size, speed and manoeuvrability.

Even animals are being conscripted into the new robot armed forces (enter the "animachine" or "mecanimal"?). "The creation of a cyborg insect army has just taken a step closer to reality" announced Wired Magazine. It reported that scientists had taken advantage of tens of millions of years of natural flight evolution to solve the problems of drone technology by implanting electrodes into a beetle (Weinberger, 2009). DARPA's HI-MEMS programme aims to insert electronic circuitry into insects at an early stage of their metamorphosis and use GPS to guide them "to specific targets via electrical impulses sent to their muscles" (Uppal, 2019). Bees and moths may also be adapted for surveillance purposes, "bugs that literally bug you" to use Emily Anthes's (2013) phrase. Electrodes placed in so-called "roboroaches" have enabled humans to remotely control cockroaches and larger animals such as rats and pigeons may be mechanized in the same way. One report even suggests that DARPA intends to insert computerized implants in sharks for the purpose of monitoring enemy shipping or to enable them to act as torpedoes (BBC, 2006).

Robotic Drilling, Mining and Building

Automation is also moving fast in the extractive industries, as the race to plunder the chthonic depths of the Earth intensifies. In defiance of the need to keep most fossil fuel reserves in the ground to avert the most devastating levels of global warming, carbon capitalism is busy developing mega-robots for mining and drilling. Autonomous, quadruped machines equipped with visual and thermal cameras are already replacing human inspectors on oil and gas rigs and the world's first fully automated oil and gas platform, Oseberg H, which contains no living quarters (not even a toilet), has now started drilling in the North Sea (Lempriere, 2019).

Coal mining is following the same course, with robotic drills and "cobots" to assist human miners being developed for coal mining in China. This has roboticists enthusing about the possibility of a coal mine in Australia being remotely controlled from the US Midwest. In fact, the controversial 70.000 acres Carmichael coal mine in Queensland is intended to be just such a "mine of the future": "everything will be autonomous from mine to port" says the CEO of Adani Mining, the Indian company developing it (Cox, 2019). The gigantic site has been described by *Rolling Stone* magazine as "the world's most insane energy project" and it's bitterly opposed by environmentalists and Aboriginal groups (Goodell, 2019). The reported export of the first coal from the mine in late 2021 only exacerbated the grotesque contrast between the current "living landscape" revered by indigenous people and a Technocene future of titanic robots, including a fleet of 400-tonne, self-driving trucks, ten times the size of the largest six-axle juggernauts allowed on European roads.

The accolade of the world's biggest robot, however, would seem to go to the 2.4 kilometres long, one-billion-dollar, remotely controlled train fleet used by Rio Tinto in its Pilbara iron ore operation in Western Australia. These driverless trains connect with autonomous drilling rigs, haulage trucks, water carts and robotic systems used in laboratories and warehouses (Chan, 2022). Elsewhere, robotic engineering devices aim to make it possible to drill for minerals in currently inaccessible places, such as in the deep sea, under ice in the Arctic and eventually in space. No crevice or corner of the biosphere will be spared if the humachinators have their way.

The construction and civil engineering industries are also subject to annexation by the massing forces of motor-skill humachines. Some of these pay tribute to one of the greatest sources of tool-making creativity: human hands and arms. For example, autonomous bricklayers, like many industrial robots, are basically mechanical arms, in this case attached to trolleys, which can lay bricks in straight lines or in more irregular patterns. The SAM 100 is reported to be able to lay up to 10 times more bricks than a human bricklayer in an eight-hour shift (not that it will stick to this quaint human timetable) and the Hadrian X can do even more, using bigger blocks to produce a square metre of wall in under three minutes. The robot brickie will soon be surrounded by many other motor skill humachines in the form of robotic labourers, "chippies" (carpenters), "sparkies" (electricians), fitters and plumbers.

As house builder Balfour Beatty, which currently employs 26,000 people, emphasizes, "The construction site of 2050 will be human-free." The humming, raucous world of the building site will fall silent of human voices, as a digital-robotic environment of drone-supervised machinery will obviate the need for most "human involvement" (Wilkinson, 2018). The spectre of the human-free environment approaches, with machines diligently going about their business, monitored from afar by a handful of human technicians. Robotic construction workers don't fear heights or suffer from claustrophobia, opening the way for even taller skyscrapers and deeper underground buildings. Indeed, a humachine fantasy could be the moment when subterranean mining machines and autonomous construction robots meet up with Elon Musk's tunnelers and decide to mechanize the planet's deepest geological layers, in effect transforming the Earth into a giant robot.

Progress or the Fast Lane to the Technocene?

The extreme examples of military and heavy industry robotics above may be hailed as techno-utopian triumphs by some but what do they really mean for human society in the Anthropocene Crisis? Let's start by asking, does the mechanization of war create better prospects for peace or simply perpetuate conflict in an even more brutal way? Autonomous and semi-autonomous weaponry may satisfy growthist economic criteria by reducing labour costs and maintaining superprofits in a never-ending competition for the most lethal weaponry, but will it reduce human casualties? In a world of "us and them", with massive geographical inequalities of wealth and power, the answer might be, yes, as far as "our" casualties are concerned. The whole military humachine race is designed to keep war as asymmetrical as possible. Rather than even-handed gladiatorial contests between killer robots, the intended outcome of automation is surely for wealthy counties to use their advanced weapons to dominate the inferior military resources of low-income nations. Drone warfare has already established this pattern, with the US remotely-launching over 13,000 drone missions carried out in Afghanistan alone from 2015 to 2020, some of them tragically failing to distinguish between civilians and military "players" (BIJ, 2022). Thousands of miles may separate the Nevada-based screen-jockeys who press the trigger from those for whom death arrives out of the blue, often literally. This creates a gaping gap in accountability and amplifies opportunities for covering up possible war crimes. Further depersonalizing the battlefield could entail dehumanizing it even more.

In fact, automated warfare represents the culmination of a long history of humachination in the military, which began with the reliance of the first city states on the mass deployment of troops. The Roman army was perhaps the most striking example in the Pyramid Age of men drilled to suppress their pro-social, altruistic tendencies and function with mechanical efficiency. It was Frederick the Great of Prussia (who, like Descartes, was obsessed with automata) who established the modern idea of an army as a machine, with a strict hierarchy of ranks, uniforms, insignia and standardized regulations and language. The goal was to make soldiers more fearful of their commanders more than the enemy (Morgan, 1986).

And yet however mindlessly conditioned or ruthlessly punished for disobedience, soldiers are still humans. They cannot be entirely prevented from making choices, privately or publicly, about what they are prepared to do in war. Military personnel can silently refuse to obey orders – famously Sam Marshall's (1947) research suggested that a quarter of US soldiers never shot to kill in WW2. Soldiers or sailors can also overtly refuse to fight, despite the threat of being court-martialled. In extreme circumstances, they may choose to assassinate their officers or mutiny and assume command themselves. This kind of stubborn resistance from the ranks is the nightmare of all military authorities and it's precisely this that LAWS could remove at a stroke.

In effect, automated weaponry would make the pyramid of military decision-making even steeper, removing any mediation between the generals directing the war and the ordinary ranks fighting it. Commanders may be out of the loop in terms of actual combat decision-making because of the speed at which nominally semi-autonomous weapons operate but LAWS will put overall strategy more securely in the hands of those at the top. Military commanders will no longer be constrained by the tragedy of "our boys coming home in body bags". Protestors and grieving parents will no longer be able to drive a wedge between generals and politicians. The "Come back alive from Ukraine" hotline, which was set up by the Ukrainian Ministry of Defence for Russian families desperate for information about soldiers taking part in the illegal invasion of their neighbouring country, would no longer have any possible political impact (Vasilyeva, 2022). (One shudders to think what the napalm-obsessed US military would have done during the Vietnam War had they not been partially kept in check by politicians sensitive to public opinion.)

Overall, it's very hard to see how the automation of the most dirty and dangerous aspects of war promotes peace. Just as self-driving vehicles, road tunnels and flying taxis simply maintain the car economy, killer robotics perpetuates the military industrial complex of capitalism. Vast military expenditure – $773 billion is the 2023 estimate for the US alone, including a $130 billion R&D budget – seems to assure a constant supply of ever more sophisticated AI-controlled weaponry (Keller, 2022). Competitiveness – the lead CIMENT value – continues to be the organizing principle of a militarized world that is actually in desperate need of far more international cooperation.

Currently 30 countries and 165 NGOs have called for a pre-emptive ban on LAWS on the grounds of ethics, accountability, proportionality and the requirements of the laws of war (CRS, 2022). Unfortunately (and predictably enough), many of the nations supporting automated weaponry are those that would profit most from manufacturing them, including the US, UK, Russia, Australia and Israel (Human Rights Watch, 2020). Indeed, in 2022, it was reported that the Israeli army has introduced a Smart Shooter robotic machine gun at a checkpoint in the occupied West Bank. "We as Palestinians have become an object of experimentation and training for Israel's military high-tech industry", protested human rights activist Issa Amro (Rothwell, 2022). The following year, on October 7th, the Israeli "robogun" experiment would fail disastrously, when Hamas militants disabled the unmanned, remote-controlled machine-gun posts supposedly protecting the "Iron Wall" around Gaza, using snipers and commercial drones, before launching their devastating attack on southern Israel (Biesecker and El Deeb, 2023). If we really want to move towards peace, we might make the elimination of all weapons the goal rather than creating a new, even more, lethal armoury. However, our current world system's paradigm seems to be based on eternal war, as well as eternal economic growth, and human-machine fusion only accelerates this bellicose direction of travel.

Keeping the flag flying for LAWS also has relevance on the home front. The same robotic weapons that can be used to monitor enemy military positions or identify a terrorist cell can be used by the domestic surveillance state, perhaps in the form of the drones which Kurzweil (2005) predicts will one day be no bigger than dust. Self-driving cars may or may not make it on to the open road but they will surely be permitted to act as patrol vehicles on private industrial estates and high-end gated residential areas, along with electronic walls and fences equipped with sensors and cameras. Android guards of the type already used on the Korean border may find their way into the gardens of the super rich. The protection of private property – one of the keystones of the GUN world system – will continue to grow as an industry; and as more advanced defence technology is sold to private and public police forces the boundaries between war and peace will become increasingly blurred. This gradual convergence of private and state-owned surveillance systems from every quarter will of course act as catnip to actual and aspiring totalitarian regimes.

Automating Environmental Destruction and the Housing Crisis

The regressive effects of automating heavy industry are also evident in the sphere of natural resources. From an ecological standpoint, making it easier and cheaper to extract fossil fuels or other minerals is the last thing we need when facing a climate and biodiversity crisis. By removing the human factor from dirty, dangerous jobs like mining and drilling, automation also has potentially de-democratizing effects. In the right circumstances, governed by the right goals and values, it might well be preferable to have robots mining copper rather than exploited humans but under growth capitalism it only makes it more likely that safe environmental limits will be transgressed. Enabling owners of mines or drilling rigs to conduct operations from a continent away, without a human workforce with a stake in the environment, would immensely strengthen the hand of extractivist capitalism and make local opposition more difficult.

The challenge to humanity represented by the Anthropocene, I would argue, is to change the what and the why of growth capitalism. Once that's done, the how may look after itself. Trying to design and implement technology on our current organizational principles simply results in the same kind of assault on people and planet which has brought about our current crisis.

The "human-free building site" is another example of this. It's certainly true that one of the worst failures of our current world system is that billions of people around the world live in substandard accommodation. Even in a wealthy nation like England, 274,000 people are homeless and a third of the entire population (17.5 million) lack safe, secure, stable accommodation, according to housing charity Shelter (2021 & 2021a). In principle, construction humachines might help to address the housing emergency but if current profit-first policies remain, houses will continue to be treated primarily as financial assets rather than homes to live in. It's not a lack of building skills that leads to the scarcity of housing; it's the cost of land, as most of the value of a house lies in the plot on which it's constructed.

Distributing land more equitably would have a far more positive effect on the housing crisis than a robotic bricklayer ever could. At the moment only 5% of land in England is actually owned by homeowners, as opposed to aristocrats who own 30% of it and corporations, oligarchs and bankers who together own another 35%. In fact, a mere 25,000 landowners, or just 1% of the population, possess more than half of all the land (Shrubsole, 2019). The materials to build good, environmentally-efficient housing can still be found and so can the requisite construction skills, which individually and communally still exist in abundance. Obliterating this vital element of the human skills commons, which has played such a crucial role in human history from the very beginning, would be folly indeed, but this could be the effect of the human-free building site. And something else would be lost, the community of manual labour workplaces, which can be all the stronger when the work is hardest and teamwork is essential for mutual safety, as anybody knows who has worked on a building site.

Humachine Colonialism: Jobicide in the Developing World

This reflection brings us back to the economic question that haunts the humachination age and to which, as we saw in Part I, its champions have only the feeblest answer: how exactly are humans going to replace the jobs which are taken over by machines? Nouriel Roubini (2022), one of the handful of professional economists to predict the 2008 financial crash, has given his verdict on this: "I do not see a happy future where new jobs replace the jobs that automation snatches. This revolution looks terminal."

We cannot conclude this section of the book without considering the planetwide ramifications of this prospect. For however baleful the consequences of jobicide may be for the Global North, the damage wreaked on the South by industrial robotics is likely to be infinitely worse. That's because the developing world has the most replaceable jobs, at least if you follow the criteria used by Western management consultants and economists, who assume that the poorer a country is the easier it is to automate its jobs. Frey and Osborne (2013) state that as many as 85% of jobs could eventually be automated in some low-income nations, particularly where there is a preponderance of jobs in agriculture, which McKinsey claims are easier to automate than service sector jobs (Manyika, 2017).

Heavyweight job robots could create a disequalization shock to the Global South of a magnitude comparable to the colonization of the New World. This time the conquistadors are job-snatching ontocapitalists and their economist outriders. Some emerging economies have only recently begun to recover from successive waves of colonialism, slavery and industrialization. Many in the majority world are still experiencing something similar to "the three generations of misery" which British industrial workers experienced, although the numbers are incomparably greater today: over one billion people on the planet now live in shanty towns and slums, often in appalling conditions that are reminiscent of the first industrial towns in the 1840s (UNstats, 2021). Whether they knew it or not, the English machine-breakers of the nineteenth century were not just fighting for their own jobs, they were also defending the millions of skilled jobs from India to Iraq which were eventually destroyed by the mass mechanization of the textile industry. This was just part of the great economic unlevelling that saw India's and China's collective share of global GDP shrink from 50% in 1700 to a meagre 9% in 1950 while Britain's portion ballooned from 3% in 1700 to an incredible 25% in 1870 (Maddison, 2007).

Countries which have gained some benefits from the off-shoring of manufacturing jobs from Western economies could see these advantages disappear as jobs are "reshored" by cheaper robotics. Western trade policies have always tended to subordinate developing countries to the interests of the West, by compelling them to focus on supplying natural resources to the West rather than building competitive economies of their own and by imposing blatantly exploitative tax, trade and accounting terms (Hickel, 2017). Such policies explicitly prevent the transfer of Western technology and patents to poorer countries.

Job automation presents a low-income country with a classic double bind. If it automates it could cause millions of domestic jobs to disappear but if it doesn't act its traditional industries could be wiped out by competition from Western robots. Across its border, a mighty army of Atlas and Handler lookalikes may soon be assembling, including robotic lifters, loaders, drivers, factory arms and drones, which together could "reverse-decimate" the entire economy, turning ten jobs into one. Heavily-indebted African nations may miss out on the fourth industrial revolution for the same reasons that they missed out on previous ones, despite the evangelizing of global management consultants, in part because Asian tiger economies are already far better equipped for automation (Beaumont, 2020).

One bleak new option could be microwork, in which a data processing job is broken down into numerous micro-tasks allotted to digital workers over the internet. "For a penny, you might pay for a person to tell you if there is a human in a photo," explained Jeff Bezos, on launching Amazon Mechanical Turk which has become the leading player in this field (Jones, 2021a). But this "work without the worker" has been heavily criticized for paying below the minimum wage – and sometimes not paying at all – while providing no security for isolated, geographically segregated workers operating in the most extreme division of labour yet invented (Jones, 2021).

So what can be done about this potential disaster for the majority world? Most conventional economists skirt over the question but development economists Lukas Schlogl and Andy Sumners (2018) thoughtfully run through the potential remedies that might shield low and middle-income countries from the invasion of the Western job robots. They are sceptical about "quasi-Luddite" taxes which would make robots more costly to introduce and "tariffs on inputs/imports with non-human produced content" on the basis that it's too difficult to implement protectionism in an open market. Like McKinsey, they prefer "coping strategies" such as economic transition subsidies for workers, upskilling existing employees or retraining redundant ones but they concede that it's uncertain exactly on which skills or jobs this training should focus.

Clutching at straws somewhat, Schlogl and Sumners suggest that for developing countries the best "long-term coping strategy would be to anticipate automation trends and try to (further) develop a productive post-industrial sector" (p31). Such a strategy would presumably involve outsmarting the automators by correctly predicting what the AI corporations are going to do before they do it – and before they know what will be legally permissible – and then invest accordingly. This suggestion may be well-meant but its bizarre improbability shows the size of the hole in which the developing world will find itself, if global job automation goes full speed ahead.

The authors conclude that what's needed is Universal Basic Income (UBI) or a global version of it (GUBI), by which rich countries subsidize the developing world from their humachination profits. "Utopian as it may seem," they argue, "the moral case" for GUBI type redistribution "may become overwhelmingly" (p33). But if we are going to have a utopian solution surely we need to do better than this. The possibility of persuading Big Tech corporations to adopt a moral approach once they have become totally world-dominant surely amounts to truly Panglossian optimism. Getting ontopreneurs to pay taxes at current levels is hard enough! As Eric Schmidt once said, Google will only pay the tax they are "legally required" to pay, failing to mention that its well-funded tax, lobbying and legal departments will spend many years driving down this already minimal sum (Harvey, 2015:153). Shareholder value is the primary morality which ontocapitalists recognize and it's highly improbable that giving them even greater monopolistic powers will change that. More helpful, in my opinion, is Schlogl's and Summers' final recommendation that we start asking some very different questions about job automation, including, I suggest, whether we need it in the first place and why we keep putting the needs of Western capitalism before that of everybody else on this planet.

As for UBI, frankly, I'm unclear how this can work ever effectively anywhere in the world unless there is a major paradigm shift away from the GUN principles of capitalism. Ironically, this is rather confirmed by Kai-Fu Lee (2019), whose "dictdataship" vision of world domination by US-Chinese Big Tech monopolies we looked at in Chapter 9. Lee is also an advocate of global UBI but he believes it can only come about if the omnipotent AI dictators of the near future undergo a total spiritual transformation based on "the power of love". This, I'm afraid, is another case of utopianism at its most facile, which rather underlines that those promoting mass job extinction simply don't know what the consequences will be for the majority of the world's workers and, in some cases, don't care. As in all Promethean revolutions, what happens to those at the base of the social pyramid seems to be of secondary concern to those fighting for a place at its apex.

The Role of Work

Rather than colonizing yet another essential part of being human, an eco-logical-democratic approach would be to hold on to the core competence of labour, although in the form of a reduced working week (see Chapter 24 for details). Our work is not merely the way in which we "earn our living"; it penetrates even more ontologically into our personal and interpersonal identity. Labour for Hegel was the way in which humans make themselves – an idea that may well have influenced Marx's labour theory of value – and Freud is said to have believed that "love and work" were the two main ingredients of human happiness. The mass destruction of jobs proposed by humachination threatens to turn human psychology upside down and could also involve profound losses across the human skills commons. At risk are the agency, independence and responsibility that can come with work, the social cooperation and companionship which the workplace offers, the exercise of creative skills in transforming materials into pro-ductive uses and a sense of security about the future. Rather than trying to think like a robot as it works alongside you, dispassionately learning your skills, we should be attempting a better revolution, one that changes the reality of work by creating an economy which enables us to live within our ecological means and enjoy the most satisfying aspects of workplace engagement, which I'll return to in the final section of the book.

Human-Free Slavery: The Smarticus Fallacy

As a final reflection on Type 3 humachines, let's mull over what might actually occur in an economy dominated by machine slaves, if Elon Musk's prediction of an eventual "one-to-one ratio of humanoid robots to humans" comes true - or even Midjourney founder David Holz's techno-utopian expectation of one billion humanoids on Earth by the 2040s and a 100 billion in the solar system by the 2060s (Prakash 2023, Evans, 2024). In the transition to a fully roboticized labour market - a state we might dub Smarticus - the majority of workers may soon become aware of the impli-cations of a warning issued by cybernetics founder Norbert Wiener at the very beginning of the AI project in the 1950s:

> The automatic machine ... is the precise equivalent of slave labour. Any labor which competes with slave labor must accept the eco-nomic conditions of slave labor (quoted in Capra, 1996:69).

What happens to the poor if this devaluation of human labour takes place? From the Age of Agriculture to the Age of Humachines, the elite have always depended on the human majority to furnish them with their lifestyle essentials from food to luxury goods and to provide them with domestic servants and soldiers to fight their wars. Will a digital-robotic workforce create a wondrously new spirit of beneficent responsibility for the human majority on the part of the ruling class or an attitude of cold indifference?

However, insecurity could cut both ways. The reality is that slave economies were often wracked by fear about slave rebellions. Far from being the passive, resigned victims portrayed by historians in the past, enslaved people consistently engaged in conspiracies and revolts, striving for their freedom even under the most oppressive and dangerous restrictions (Davis, 2006). The ultimate rebellion of the mechanical slaves would be AImageddon, in which humanity is supplanted by superintelligent machines. Machine replacement fear would surely haunt the automated society. Perhaps it would lead to efforts to make humachines look and sound far less humanoid than today's roboticists envisage. Other cultural mores may develop that aggressively distinguish humans from their mechanical labourers. In order to confirm their inferior ontological status, robots may be deliberately humiliated, which may have a damaging knock-on effect on how some humans are treated. It certainly suggests that those advocating quasi-human, legal rights for robots will meet with considerable hostility. (Indeed in this context, it's also worth asking the question, would robot rights include the right *not* to work in "dirty and dangerous" jobs?)

As Hegel (1807/1931) suggested in his famous philosophical deliberation on the relationship between the master and slave, there's something inexorably corrupting about slavery on both sides of the equation. Even the master can be diminished by the institution: he wants to see his freedom confirmed in the look of the slave, instead he sees only the bondage which he is imposing on another human being. Rather than granting more liberty, an economy dominated by mechanical slaves may be a permanent reminder of the reality of domination.

To conclude, we should be very careful what we wish for (and unconsciously choose), when it comes to Type 3 humachines, whether replacing dangerous and dirty jobs or supposedly dull jobs like caring for the old, the young and the sick. As the humachines which we reviewed in Part IV testify to, the one-eyed machine supremacism of the AI project creates a pseudo-freedom which can exacerbate the most oppressive, exploitative aspects of our current world system. From lumbering, menacing hardware to insidiously manipulative software, instead of liberating the best in being human, human-machine fusion often reinvents the worst in us. It's another warning sign that the fanatical vision driving the humachine age may not lead us to a utopia purged of unpleasant toil and irritating inconvenience but to the environmentally chaotic, anxiety-riven, neomechanicalist dystopia of the Technocene. Whether the fourth type of humachination, the attempted mechanization of humans, can change this picture, we will now find out.

PART V

Humachination in Practice II: Mechanizing the Human Brain, Body, Genome and Lifespan

Introduction to Part V: Advancing Medicine or the Final Push to the Technocene?

One way of introducing the Type 4 humachine, the mechanized human or mecan, is to imagine a meeting between a walking, talking humanoid robot, of the kind we've just been looking at, and a fully augmented human cyborg, during which neither can decide who (or which) is more human or more machine. One originates in software and mechanical engineering, the other in human biology but they end up in more or less the same place, or so a central fantasy of humachination would have us believe.

In addressing the mecan in this section, we can drop the metaphors about humanized machines trying to "get under our skin" or "read our minds", because the mechanization of humans literally involves getting into our minds and bodies, for example, by inserting electrodes into our brains and replacing our inner organs with artificial versions. It also involves trying to extend human life and genetically redesign human reproduction, perhaps resulting in an entirely new species. These audacious attempts at fusing the mechanical, digital and biological are taking place over so many sciences and pseudo-sciences and in so many areas of meditechnics and biotechnology, that until now it's been easy to miss the extent to which all these enterprises can be classified as attempts to merge humans and machines until the two are indistinguishable.

In this section, I'll try to separate reality from fantasy in the often surreal world of the mecan but what is not imaginary is the mighty, globe-straddling marketplace that funds much of human mechanization. The US healthcare industry is truly a phenomenon of contemporary capitalism. Worth $4.3 trillion in 2021 and projected to grow by half as much again by 2028, it is larger than the entire economy of any country on the planet except the USA and China (cms. gov 2022). It's four times bigger than the Chinese medical market (although this is also growing fast) and it absorbs 18% of US GDP, a percentage almost twice as high as the OECD average (Wong and Zhang, 2021). Yet overall American healthcare is the least effective of any comparable high-income country, in part because its spending is so unequally distributed (Schneider et al, 2021). The top 1% account for 22% of all US medical expenditure (averaging $116,000 a year), while the half of the population that uses least healthcare accounts for just 3% (Nunn et al, 2020). The monopoly power and rent-seeking of healthcare corporations further disadvantage most American patients, although they delight shareholders. Some investors may also be lured by the hypergrowth fantasy of humachinated medicine and are betting that when it comes to medical innovation governments will not stand in the way of profit (emulating the gamble which shareholders in fossil fuel corporations have made against effective climate regulation). Certainly, we'll find the anti-regulation rhetoric is as piercingly insistent in humachinated medicine as in other areas of the fourth industrial revolution.

At the same time, throughout Part V, we need to bear in mind that however marketized and technologized medicine may be, the realm of healthcare is still dominated by human carers who are strongly motivated by benevolence and compassion. Healthcare is criss-crossed by ethical red lines and emotional boundaries, which as a psychologist I'm well aware of. I want to try to respect this delicate balance throughout the four areas of Type 4 humachination which we examine in this section, involving the mechanization of the human brain, body, lifespan and reproduction process. The fine line between reparation and augmentation is perhaps the most important of these distinctions. Reparation emphasizes the equalizing function of all healthcare, found, for example, in efforts to restore a brain-injured patient to normal functionality. Augmentation, on the other hand, is more orientated towards disequalization, producing capacities which are superior to the norm that may create an advantage over others. A computerized eye which might restore some sight to the visually-impaired can be classified as reparation, the third eye which some normally-sighted transhumanists hanker after is patently augmentation or "enhancement". The goal of humachination, after all, is to engineer a superior class of humanity, consisting of beings with superintelligent brains and enhanced, replaceable body parts, who can live for hundreds of years, if not forever.

Of course, some new medical technology may have real benefits for patients and may help to prevent avoidable deaths and even extend some lifespans. Nor should we dismiss out of hand the motivation behind some attempts at mechanizing humans. But, as I've not shied away from suggesting, meditechnics is also the perfect Trojan horse for advancing human-machine hybridization. We can witness this stealthy tricknology at work in Ray Kurzweil's (2005) plea that ignoring synthetic organ development is causing avoidable deaths or Nick Bostrom's claim that AI's potential help in eradicating disease outweighs the risk of superintelligence wiping out biological life (Cuthbertson, 2022). Just how much of medical progress is due to profit-based economics, the frequently-used justification for healthcare capitalism, is highly questionable anyway. In my view, many health improvements come from progress in other areas, such as better housing, reduced environmental pollution and improved safety at work. And medical innovators such as Marie Curie or Alexander Fleming have rarely been influenced by the money-making potential of their breakthroughs (unlike Big Pharma). Perhaps in a post-growth society, shorn of tricknology and obscenely large profit margins, in which the priorities of medical research are chosen by the majority, we'll find out the answer.

CHAPTER 18

Re-Engineering the Human Brain

The Mystery of the Brain

Nothing is more central to the humane-machine fusion project than the mechanization of the human brain. Not content to replicate its functions through cognitive and robotic humachines, humachinators aim at the actual rewiring of the brain by surgically implanting computerized electrodes into it and using other methods which can directly connect it to external digital-robotic systems.

So we need a reminder. The human brain is among the greatest mysteries of life. It's just 1.4 kilos of jelly but its complexity is astonishing: it has at least one hundred billion neurons, each of which can make connections with tens of thousands of other nerve cells via synapses. Glial cells which amplify neural signals are ten times as numerous. Our brains change constantly, forming a billion new connections for every minute of our lives in unique living patterns, which are connected to the other electrochemical processes of the body (Phillips, 2006)

Before we begin to speculate how human creativity or consciousness actually work, we need to recognize the limitations of our knowledge of even the simplest animal brains. As neuroscientist Michael Hendricks (2015) stresses, after extensive research by biologists, it's only recently been possible to map the brain of the roundworm, C elegans, consisting of a mere 302 neurons. To map the connectome of the human brain would take half the world's existing digital storage capacity, Hendricks suggests. Even then this would tell us little, as we don't yet even understand the basic functional relationship of the synapse, the interaction of two neurons. Nor do we understand the countless signalling pathways which don't involve synapses and "regulate fundamental behaviors such as eating, sleeping, mood, mating, and social bonding ...that are invisible to us anatomically".

All models of the brain attempt to simplify this staggering complexity, including Iain McGilchrist's bicameral model which I referred to in Chapter 11, as an aide to understanding the psychology of the machine mindset. However, McGilchrist (2018) stresses that all neurological regions interact with each other and with other aspects of the body and environment. He's also absolutely clear that the brain is not a computer; if it were, he asks, why would it have two hemispheres, highlighting a basic fact of neurological organization which brain mechanizers conveniently ignore.

Brain-Computer Interfaces (BCIs)

None of this puts off the humachinators, for whom the proposition that the brain is a computer is a sacred tenet of their theology. Despite the fact that their basic training is usually in computer science, they believe they know more about the human brain than neuroscientists or biologists who spend their entire careers studying it and are determined to strip it down and tinker with it until they can get it to work properly.

So deep rooted is this complacency that the brain is talked about in almost shockingly trivial ways. Elon Musk envisages brain-computer connections that can enable a person to summon his Tesla by thought alone and promises "a Fitbit in your skull without wires" (Wong, 2020). Larry Page, who acquired Fitbit, has long dreamed of "Google in the brain". "Why can't Google Now, Google's predictive search tool, be used to predict everything in a person's life?" he asks (Dougherty, 2016).

Ray Kurzweil (1999:189) predicts "internal neural implants" by the 2030s which will enable you "to have almost any kind of experience with just about anyone, real or imagined, at any time". He forecasts that our brains will be connected to the Cloud by the 2030s, enabling emails and photos to be sent directly to our consciousness via nanorobots swimming in our brain capillaries. "We are going to expand the neocortex, "he says, "and become more godlike" (Miles, 2015).

In fact, much of the practical work on mechanizing the brain has focused on relatively limited brain-computer interfacing (BCI). This has been described as analysing brain signals and translating them into commands for an output device and usually involves invasive brain implants. In a review of the field from a medical perspective, Jerry Shih and his colleagues (2012) note that most of its achievements "have been confined almost entirely to the research laboratory", adding:

> Brain-computer interfaces may eventually be used routinely to replace or restore useful function for people severely disabled with neuromuscular disorders and to augment natural motor outputs for pilots, surgeons and other highly skilled professionals.

Nobody could object to this first part of the prediction. The BrainGate company, for example, uses electrodes implanted in the brain to help restore mobility and communication to those who have lost it. Brain surgery is needed to implant these devices, which are not wireless but use a socket which connects to a computer which interprets brain signals. BCIs have helped a quadriplegic regain some muscle movement and a paralysed neuroscientist to write grant applications and send emails (Yuste et al, 2017). These restored motor functions involve a few thousand electrodes connected to a few hundred neurons, a tiny fraction of the 100 billion neurons in the brain. Orion, a device which links a tiny camera to 60 electrodes implanted in the visual cortex, has restored some minimal vision to people who've lost their sight, and in time cortical visual prosthetics are "expected to restore some degree of vision in blind individuals", conclude Niketeghad and Pouratian (2019), although connections to hundreds of thousands of neurons would probably be required to restore full vision.

Clearly there is still a long way before anything emerges which vaguely resembles the digital simulacrum of the human brain the AI pioneers dreamed of in the 1950s. Thomas Reardon, CEO of CTRL-labs, a Meta acquisition, claims that neural devices will be commercially available by 2024, although he concedes that decoding the output of the brain remains "the mother of all machine learning problems" (Protalinski, 2019). Another significant problem indicated by Saha et al, 2021 is that "15-30% of individuals are not able to produce signals robust enough to operate a BCI".

Almost inevitably, the biggest, boldest, headline-grabbing initiatives in the field of human-brain mechanization come from the would-be Zeus of ontocapitalism Elon Musk who, as we know, believes that superintelligence is an unstoppable force which at worst could destroy the human race (Vance, 2015:3). "Even in a benign scenario we would be left behind", he says, which for him means that a "high bandwidth brain-machine interface" is the only solution, enabling us "to go along for the ride and effectively have the option of merging with AI" (Wakefield, 2019). Musk has already invested $100 million in Neuralink and is recruiting "the best talent in the world" to develop the proprietary chips and thread-like information strips he intends to insert into people's brains (McGee, 2019). In 2020 he livestreamed a demonstration of a pig which had thin neural wires implanted in its brain and in 2021 a monkey which allegedly could play Pong by its thoughts alone. In December 2022 Musk claimed (not for the first time) that he was "just six months away" from implanting a device in a human head (Griggs, 2022). Whether these experiments justify the 1,500 pigs, sheep and monkeys and other animals which have been sacrificed for them is hard to say (Neuralink is under investigation for possible animal welfare violations (Coen, 2023)), especially given Musk's careful avoidance of peer-reviewed studies of his research. But what's sure is that Neuralink is still light years away from Musk's most ambitious brain mechanization goals, which include seeing radar, hearing symphonies in your head, curing blindness, deafness and mental illness, discovering the nature of consciousness and, of course, his ultimate objective of achieving "symbiosis with artificial intelligence" (Regalado, 2020).

Nor is Musk the only player in an increasingly fervid brain mechanization market. Synchron was the first company to gain FDA approval for human trials of brain chips in 2022, beating Neuralink by a year (Fortson, 2022, Coen 2023). Other companies competing to cross "this final frontier of science" include Neurable (which produces mind-controlled VR games), Kernel (originally developed to create memories outside the brain), Emotiv, Nextmind and BitBrain (Dawson, 2022). The greater the investment, the greater the pressure from impatient shareholders to produce results, possibly in defiance of the medical, social and ethical hazards involved.

The Risks of Brain Mechanization

As always in this book, I wouldn't want to rule out the legitimate medical applications of humachine projects. BCI restoration projects in bioethically regulated medical environments may bring relief to many patients but the potential threats to what it is to be human should not be underestimated. Biologists Rafael Yuste and over 20 fellow neurotechnology researchers recognize this themselves in a valuable paper in *Nature,* declaring that "brain-computer interfaces must respect and preserve people's privacy, identity, agency and equality" (Yuste et al, 2017).

The challenges in all four areas are formidable. If you are worried about the assault on privacy and freedom launched by cognitive humachines, how much greater is the threat posed by the mechanisation of the brain. Richard Feynman's (1961) visionary lecture which initiated nanotechnology referred to nanomedicine as a process of "swallowing the doctor" but mechanizing the brain – and other organs we'll review in the next chapter – could involve swallowing the policeman or the entire apparatus of the surveillance state. ("Swallowing the hacker" is a concomitant danger.) Even a simple BCI risks importing the internet into the brain and then exporting a patient's thoughts – even at an unconscious level – into vast private and public digital enchainments, which could destroy the last bastion of personal privacy.

Identity is another problem with all brain mechanization. Eran Klein and his colleagues (2016) report the case of a patient fitted with a brain stimulator to treat depression who began to wonder whether his inappropriate interactions were caused by the electronic device or his own deeper personality traits. "It blurs to the point where I'm not sure … frankly who I am." Likewise, Frederic Gilbert and his team interviewed patients suffering from epilepsy in Australia who had BCI implants to alert them when to take their medication. The effects amounted to dramatically different forms of self-estrangement. One patient (Patient 6) said "at first it felt like an alien" but gradually it changed her personality: "with this device I felt I could do anything … nothing could stop me". But other patients suffered "a lot of harm and anguish", which made them feel powerlessness. Another patient deliberately ignored the signals, while yet another said:

> I felt weird all the time, before it I only felt strange having the seizure. Because it was always peeping and always red, it made me feel like I had no control … I got really depressed. (Gilbert et al, 2019).

Clearly even a very simple form of brain mechanization like this can have radical effects on a person's self-understanding – for better or worse. It could be described as a type of psychological identity theft, causing a potential self-alienation which is likely to become more extreme as more complex devices make it increasingly difficult to discriminate between self and other. How can you tell which information has come from you or from machines transmitting thoughts to you? Will machine-dominated parts of the brain start to communicate more effectively with other machines than with other neural regions? Could an external AI system and an AI-enhanced brain start to recognize each other, communicating in ways that bypass human-to-human communication, reminiscent of the alien intelligence that "makes moves no human would make" we came across in Chapter 13, in relation to computerized chess and Go programmes?

The claim made by restorative neural developers is that mechanical links will increase agency for the disabled but unless this technology is very carefully controlled, they may reduce agency for almost everybody else. The ontocapitalist free market is hardly the ideal place for sensitive medical development. At worst, neurotechnology could dramatically erode human freedom, a point emphasized by the experience of Patient 6 in Gilbert et al's study. Although her brain implant had a positive effect on her life, she was compelled to remove it when the company responsible for it went bankrupt. Gilbert's conclusion was that, in effect, "The company owned the existence of this new person". Patient 6's response was just as bleak: "I lost myself" (Cobb, 2019:290). One way or another, this could be the fate of many.

The concerns in relation to the unequalism which is never far from the GUN system are just as perplexing. Even legitimate restorative work runs the risks of importing all the biases of AI which we examined earlier, such as racist, gendered or homophobic prejudices. But how can you tell if these discriminatory preferences are yours or those of your brain implants? It will certainly give the term "unconscious bias" a wholly new meaning. The brain enhancement "arms race" which already seems to be in play will doubtless create new elitist forms of discrimination between those who can afford the newest, super-fast, multi-electrode implant and those who have to make do with a limited, outdated model. And while it might be acceptable to have electrodes reminding you to take your medication, what happens when a Promethean in the computer lab reprogrammes the system? Now your neural implants might be telling you which political party to vote for and in a surveillance state your BCI might even instruct you to spy on your friends and family. And when the spy is in your own brain how can you ever escape from it?

The Pressure to Mechanize Your Brain

Given these anxieties, you might think few healthy people would be prepared to risk brain enhancement surgery. But the pressure to augment may soon ramp up, as humachination marches on. Think back to my previous reflections on job automation and the prediction that the good, well-paid jobs of the future will become increasingly rare and only available to those with advanced technological skills. How will people react to this alarming situation? One indication comes from a startling statistic in a wide-ranging PWC survey of 10,000 people in the UK, USA, Germany, China, and India. Although, reassuringly, almost three quarters of the sample said AI would never replace the human mind, the survey also found that an astonishing 70% of respondents "would consider using treatments to enhance their body and brain if this improved their employment prospects" (Brown, et al, 2017:17).

Here we can see the pressure which the entire humachine age can put on people desperately worried about their future. If the only way to give yourself a chance of a good job (or any job at all) is brain mechanization, it seems that many would be prepared to try it. It may become a sine qua non for executive positions and something that helpful pro-humachine economists recommend to employees in order to avoid the threat of jobicide.

The pressure is already coming from all sides. Games manufacturers are also intensely interested in BCI, using scalp sets which may interpret facial muscle signals as opposed to actual brain waves. Controlling a computer keyboard by thought waves is the next stage for the computer industry after voice-controlled computing, rendering every device in need of replacement. And where there's an arms race don't expect the military to miss out on it. For example, DARPA is fascinated by the prospect of using thought telepathy, another longstanding humachination goal, as a form of weaponry. Three implanted monkeys have operated as a "brain net "to operate an avatar arm creating possibilities for remote battlefield communication. Another aim is to write signals into the brain, as well as reading them. DARPA is reportedly developing a wireless device which uses a million electrodes in order to improve the machine-communication of soldiers (Yuste et al, 2017). This could be recognition that the only chance that humans have of actually staying "in the loop" and retaining effective control over killer robots is to become robotized themselves. It's one of humachination's most desperate, circular arguments, which avoids the more obvious alternative which would be to ban the development of autonomous weaponry in the first place.

Most BCI research is being conducted in the private healthcare industry of the US and China and it's here where the most persistent pressure will probably be applied. Tricknologists will insist that attempts to prevent potential medical fixes to injuries, illnesses or mental health issues are inhuman or even criminal. From here the line between reparation and augmentation will be easiest to blur. And if brain mechanization is established among the wealthiest who fund most healthcare research, its reputation may grow, notwithstanding the threats to privacy, identity, agency and equality. And greater losses may follow, in the shape of the existential issues of human deskilling and the loss of personal independence described in Chapter 12. After all, if eventually, there is a brain chip for every human skill and competence, as envisaged by Elton Musk, why bother to learn anything?

In fine, it makes the ethics-based "responsible neuroengineering" which Rafael Yuste and his colleagues (2017) call for seem like an oxymoron in the humachine age. Another large group of researchers, led by Simanto Saha (2021), recognize that "establishing broad consensus on ethical issues and beneficial socioeconomic application" is one of the biggest challenges facing BCI. But can such consensus ever be reached in a world system lacking genuinely democratic policy-making? How can we empower morally-grounded scientific researchers who may be as suspicious of the wider ambitions of transhumanist philosophers and singularitarian billionaires as I am? The plutotechnic GUN principles of capitalism make it difficult to separate the public benefits of healthcare from the huge profits of the private medicine market. Nor are governments pursuing fourth industrial revolution and science superpower policies likely to be overly concerned with ethical nuances, particularly when they are desperate to convince the public that only AI and robotics can make healthcare affordable. And how incorruptible are the medical scientists themselves, when their career paths depend so heavily on their ability to pass innovation milestones? Laudable, high-minded objectives can so easily degenerate into something quite different when they encounter the greed and fear capitalism induces, as the founders of Google discovered at the very beginning of the age of humachines.

The Theranos Trick

Another relevant example of how good motives can turn bad was provided by the spectacular implosion of biotechnology corporation Theranos. At its peak in 2014, this "revolutionary" medical diagnostics company was valued at $9 billion and boasted a board full of establishment stalwarts like Henry Kissinger and Rupert Murdoch, who invested $125 million in the venture. Its charismatic CEO Elizabeth Holmes, a Stanford chemical engineering dropout who founded the company at the age of 19, was a celebrity of the business world and enjoyed a billionaire lifestyle. The only problem was that Theranos's "miraculous", pin-prick blood testing technology didn't work and frequently issued dangerously erroneous diagnoses. This was tricknology taken to the point of criminality. When it was finally revealed, largely by the work of tenacious investigative journalist John Carreyrou (2018), Theranos spiralled towards bankruptcy and in 2022 Holmes and her former COO and lover, Sunny Balwani, were given long prison sentences on multiple counts of fraud.

If this combination of charismatic leadership and unsubstantiated claims about a future technology that can save humanity, reminds you of anything, maybe it's because it's becoming so common. Holmes was nicknamed the "the female Steve Jobs" but the names of any of the messianic ontopreneurs we've come across in this book might have been equally appropriate. And bear in mind that the Theranos trick was infinitely easier to detect than anything related to planting electrodes in the brain. It's another reminder that trustworthiness is not a quality that the feted leaders of the humachine age possess in abundance and that it will take a society run on a very different basis to our current worldplan to ensure that medicine gets the very best out of what technology can offer. It's also an introduction, if a rather sobering one, to the attempts to mechanize other organs of the human body, which the next chapter explores.

CHAPTER 19

Mechanizing the Human Body

The idea that the human body can be transformed by technology is central to the humachine mission and seems like common sense to the mechanists who ever since Hobbes and Descartes have argued that humans "are machines that happen to be made out of meat", to recall AI trailblazer Marvin Minsky's memorable phrase. It's true that humans have always used tools for reparation, from walking sticks and simple prosthetics like wooden legs to spectacles and hearing aids. More recently, more invasive devices can be added to the list, including pacemakers, artificial hips, titanium rods used in back surgery and organs transplanted from one human to another. But these attempts at restoration are still an order of magnitude away from the fully mechanized, synthetic body, comprised of replaceable, artificial organs and bones, programmable blood and the other techno-utopian attributes of the mecan which we examined in Part I. That involves a massive degree of augmentation, ultimately creating a post-biological entity that could be capable of changing its appearance at will and experiencing the world through new forms of mechanized visual, sensory and haptic systems.

With the possible advent of the cyborgoisie, we again arrive at the slippery slope separating reparation and augmentation, which threatens to turn healthcare into a mere branch of technology and gives humachinators and their tricknologists one of their most compelling weapons of persuasion. As always, the proper line between these areas can't be drawn by technology alone; for this we need social and political choices about

312 | THE AGE OF HUMACHINES

what humanness really means. This, I'll try to demonstrate in this chapter, involves a radically pro-human and ecological approach to healthcare, based on a holistic, systems-based understanding of the human brain-body. Let's begin, however, by asking how scientifically realistic it might be to achieve the amalgamation of machines and the human body which the humachinators claim is unstoppable.

Mechanizing Human Organs

A glance at the literature on artificial organs seems to suggest that progress is being made on mechanizing the human body. There are several reports of 3-D bioprinting and the bioengineering of tissues. Electronic skin is said to be under development at the University of Graz, fabricated from new sensitive materials fitted with nanosensors, which would be a double win for humachination, as it could be used for humanoid robots as well as would-be cyborgs (Filzwieser, 2022). An artificial womb is being developed in Philadelphia, a "Biobag" that raises hopes for premature babies (Kleeman, 2020).

Overall, the global artificial organs industry is currently estimated to be worth $19 billion and projected to grow to $32 billion by 2028, according to one market study, which optimistically reports on the prospects for the artificial heart, liver, kidney, pancreas and lungs and other promising "product segments" (IMARC, 2022). The outlook for the artificial kidney is said to be particularly bullish.

In the right hands, of course, the advantages of artificial organs could be considerable: natural organs for transplants are often in short supply and synthetic organs might reduce animal testing. But is this area of development in the right hands? And how much is real science and how much is tricknology and hype?

The Artificial Heart

Judging by research on the most publicised synthetic organ, real progress is very slow. The first artificial heart, Jarvik-7, was implanted in a human patient in 1982 (the recipient survived for 112 days) but it took another three decades of research and commercial investment before what was widely hailed as the first artificial heart was implanted (Vis et al, 2022). In

2013 in Paris a 75-year-old Frenchman received a Carmat heart, which has been described as "half-cow, half-robotic technology", due to its combination of sensors, microprocessors and a battery-powered motorized pump with elements composed of cow tissue (Nguyen, 2013). Unfortunately, Carmat's first recipient died within three months of surgery and a subsequent European trial in 2016 had to be suspended when 50% of the patients involved suffered the same fate. This led to funding difficulties for the company but it subsequently reached the milestone of 70% of patients surviving for more than six months, with one heart recipient living for two years (Carmat, 2019). (By contrast, the current record for surviving after a natural heart transplant is 33 years.) It was victory of sorts for Carmat in its bitter commercial war with its US rival, Syncardia, whose total artificial heart is powered by an air compressor which the patient has to carry in a backpack (Houser, 2021).

At the moment, at a cost of $190,000 to $240,000, the artificial heart is beyond the means of most people and is mainly used for the terminally ill or as a temporary measure for those awaiting a natural heart transplant, rather than as "a destination therapy" (Vis et al, 2022). Whether "a robot heart" can ever be as good as a donor heart remains an open question. After seven decades of research, there are still huge obstacles to overcome, including "issues related to biocompatibility, high complication rates and low quality of life", according to one in-depth review (Arfaee et al, 2022). The possibility of combining an artificial heart with other biomechanical organs, as in Kurzweil's vision of the replaceable synthetic body, is an even greater challenge, as additional devices will only compound the likelihood of rejection and raise the spectre of other horrific complications.

The Reality of Embodiment: The Body-Brain and the Brain-Heart

Part of the problem is that we know far less about the human body than the neomechanicalists with their simplistic, linear metaphors want us to realise. The embodied brain approach, by contrast, emphasizes the complexity of the connectivity between the brain and other organs, and the extent to which intelligence is distributed throughout the entire human body. That includes the stomach or guts, which is traditionally associated with resolution, audacity and perseverance. Amazingly, the human digestive system has a nervous system of its own with over 100 million neurons in the small intestine alone and can continue to function even when the vagus nerve which connects it to the brain is severed (Carpenter, 2012).

That takes us back to the heart, whose intelligence capabilities are now being understood by the new science of embodied cognition. This revives some aspects of the organicist view of the role of the heart in thinking, which goes back at least as far as Aristotle. "Disheartened", "take heart from", "broken-hearted" are all contemporary expressions that still insist on the importance of feelings and mood in decision-making. Mechanistic thinking tries to confine all of this to the brain, through the chimerical Cartesian "little man in the head" or "Mini-Me" in a "brightly lit executive office", as professor of learning sciences Guy Claxton (2015:22) puts it. Systems science is discovering that it's not an either-or choice between the heart and the brain, as the former is more than a simple pump and has a vital role in communicating with the lungs, liver and central nervous system.

As Claxton stresses, "the heart, if it is to stay healthy, needs to keep talking to the rest of the body. It's not just doing its thing in isolation". This communicative role has an executive function. "A little brain on the heart" is how neurocardiologist J. Andrew Armour (2007) characterises the dense network of 40,000 neurons which are needed to maintain what we probably assume is our regular heart beat. In fact, the rhythm of the heart is constantly being adjusted beat-by-beat; it's homeostatic, not static and exists in a highly dynamic steady state. Indeed, a totally regular heartbeat can threaten good health, as the heart needs to be flexible enough to adapt to the changing conditions around it. (The absence of this elasticity could be fatal for the artificial heart.)

So strong is the evidence around the existence of the "heart brain" that since the 1960s a new discipline of neurocardiology has emerged to study it and its implications for treatment of cardiovascular disease. As Ali Alshami (2019) explains, the heart has its own nervous system and "sends more signals to the brain than vice versa", communicating "neurologically, biochemically, biophysically, and energetically". It is also able to "to learn, remember, make decisions and even feel and sense", claims the HeartMath Institute (2022). This memorial function is still inscribed in our language. "Recordari" – Latin for "recollection" – incorporates "cor" or "heart" and the Middle English word "herte" means "memory", hence the modern usage "to know something by heart" (O'Connor 2019:198). Modern evidence for the heart's ability to store memories also comes from organic heart transplant patients who experience alterations in personality in line with the donor's experience and changes in taste, ranging from food, music and art to sexual, recreational and career preferences. One heart recipient whose donor was killed by a gunshot to the face repeatedly dreamed of seeing hot flashes of light in his face, while another, an eight-year-old girl, actually identified her ten-year-old donor's murderer (Pearsall et al, 2000). It makes you wonder what an artificial heart remembers – its manufacturer's workshop perhaps?

When we start adding up the vast evidence of the other intelligences of the body – in our skin, for example, or our immune system which is a kind of cognitive system in itself, we need to seriously challenge the rationale behind the claim that artificial organs can emulate the normal human body, let alone outperform it by providing renewable, rejuvenating upgrades. The more we understand about the complex, cooperative functioning of all parts of the human body and the distributed role of intelligence, the more preposterously overblown the reductionist fantasies of the humachinators seem to be.

Who Owns My Heart?

Another troubling issue surrounding artificial organs could be the question of legal ownership. Rich or poor, it's always been beyond question that a human being owns their own organs but does this remain the case with manufactured organs? If I've purchased outright an expensive artificial heart, my ownership of it may be clear but what if the payments are spread over a period of time? If I can no longer pay, will it be repossessed? And who owns it after my death? Even in life, how much real agency can you have over a bio-machine which needs constant maintenance by a profit-based medical corporation, which is quite possibly aiming to make more revenue from servicing the heart than selling it? Maintaining an artificial heart necessitates a whole series of digital enchainments involving constant monitoring, data analysis and fine-tuning, each of which shifts ownership from the patient to the faceless, digital-robotic environment beyond. We might even see this as another example of the humachine age's version of the enclosure of the commons, a mercenary privatization of the personal assets which we all assume we own forever. Indeed, it's part of a metaphorically heartless system that could literally leave victims heartless.

Nanomedicine

Another topic which features prominently in the humachine vision of the post-biological body is nanomedicine. Feynman's (1961) idea of "swallowing the surgeon" is based on his proposed nano-assembler, a tiny robot which solves the problem of finding anything small enough to assemble by building ever smaller versions of itself until a truly microscopic level has been reached. At this (hypothetical) point, robots could be tiny enough to enter the human bloodstream, monitoring the body from within and even performing reparative surgery. Feynman's self-replicating nano-assembler was a thought experiment, which might be interpreted as a benign updating of the Sorcerer's Apprentice. However, MIT-educated engineer Eric Drexler (1986) wrote a best-selling book based on it, *Engines of Creation: The coming era of nanotechnology*, which profoundly influenced Ray Kurzweil and other champions of medical mechanization. In 2003 Nobel prize-winning chemist, Richard Smalley disagreed vehemently with Drexler, arguing that the idea of an autonomous molecular assembler was not only a violation of science – "a pretend world where atoms go where you want because your computer programme directs them" "– but also a very scary prospect. To which Drexler replied that "Feynman's vision of nanotechnology is fundamentally mechanical not biological", a matter of engineering ("mechanosynthesis" and "molecular manufacturing") not chemistry, thereby providing another illustration of the tension between life science and physical science which lies at the core of the humachine age (Baum, 2003).

The relatively meagre practical progress made by nanomedicine in the six decades since Feynman's lecture seems to bear out Smalley's side of the argument. Although the market is expected to grow at an impressive annual rate of 13% reaching $350 million by 2027 (Research and Markets, 2022), the only nano-medical products which currently appear to be in use are not robotic devices but infinitely less complex drug-delivery mechanisms. The first FDA-approved nano-drug was Doxil (pegylated liposomal doxorubicin) used in treating ovarian cancer, which coats a chemotherapy drug in nanoparticles which can then be applied directly to a tumour. Its efficacy is comparable to conventional treatments but its price is over 100-times greater (Cohn and Shrimp, 2015). Indeed, the astonishing price of nanomedicines means that they are unlikely to be taken up by most public healthcare systems (which are already under pressure from the demands of ageing populations). It leads researchers Rita Bosetti and Stephen Jones (2019) to warn that unless its cost can be dramatically decreased, nano-medicine "will have little chance of reaching the patient, relegated instead to a valley of forgotten promising therapies". The other alternative is that it remains the preserve of private healthcare for the ultra-wealthy, which is already the destination for many humachinated products.

The Risks of Meditechnics: Taking the Care out of Healthcare

Besides making a grossly asymmetrical medical system even more unequal, there is an even more basic threat contained in hyper-mechanized medical capitalism. I'm referring to the risk of removing the most powerful of all elements in healthcare, that is to say, human care itself. As we know from an earlier chapter, meditechnics threatens to take human decision-making out of healthcare and replace it with increasingly human-free surgeries, consul-tation rooms and operating theatres. This would aggravate tendencies which are already far too present in medicine, namely prioritizing profit and overes-timating the value of technology in ways that downgrades the crucial role of human care. In fact, many routine medical procedures still have no scientific evidence base and the exaggeration of the effectiveness of pharmaceutical interventions is contributing to an epidemic of overprescribed drugs.

Focusing on the role of placebos has long been a way of underlining the value of the human touch in effective healthcare. The placebo effect is a cure which has probably existed since hunter-gatherer times and is still highly effective today, as medical professor Robert Buckman confirms:

> Placebos are extraordinary drugs. They seem to have some effect on every symptom known to mankind, and work in at least a third of patients and sometimes in up to 60%. They have no serious side-effects and cannot be given in overdose. In short, they hold the prize for the most adaptable, protean, effective, safe and cheap drugs in the world's cornucopia (Buckman and Sabbagh, 1993:246).

This may seem like an exaggeration but since the 1950s research has consistently shown that the placebo effect "is a powerful determinant of health" in disease conditions such as "migraines, joint pain, arthritis, asthma, high blood pressure and depression" (Munnangi et al, 2022). Half of German GPs prescribe placebos (a figure that rises to 88% in Bavaria), despite the fact that the German medical association admits that it doesn't understand why the treatment is so effective (d'Arcy Hughes, 2011). Some research even suggests that the larger the pill the more effective the remedy and that placebo injections are more effective than pills. The extent to which both doctor and patient believe in the placebo also seems to influence the reparative effect.

When it comes to healthcare, who would want to be looked after by a machine if you could be looked after by a caring nurse? During the initial stages of the COVID-19 pandemic in Britain a major focus was on the shortage of oxygen equipment for intensive care units. Far less was made of the dedicated, highly-trained nurses able to provide the 24-hour care without which these machines could do more harm than good. It takes years to train such nurses, whereas medical equipment can be built in weeks and entire field hospitals erected in days. A similar overemphasis on digital contact tracing, which brought together rivals Apple and Google and other expensive "moonshot" technologies, obscured the fact that the most effective contact tracing round the world was often provided by so-called "shoe leather epidemiology", which often consisted of local officials physically checking on community infections. For example, the Cuban medical system, which spends relatively little on medical technology but is rooted in community-based primary care, performed particularly well during the pre-vaccine phase of the pandemic (Ashton, 2020). Coronovirus also heightened the risk of a privacy invasion by meditechnics, as the public willingly offered up highly personal data to the state, a perfect opportunity for "mission creep" for spy-tech firms like Peter Thiel's Palantir, according to Open Democracy (Linares and Bychawski, 2021).

Going Post-Human: Body Augmentation and "Real" and Imagined Cyborgs

So far, we've examined broadly reparative aspects of mechanization in the healthcare sector but of course humachinators envisage augmentations, which radically change almost everything about the human body. The burgeoning global cosmetic surgery industry gives us a sense of where this may be heading. It began as an essentially restorative form of healing but is now offering an increasingly wide range of enhancements. From butt lifts and breast and lip enlargements for women to cheek implants and penis extensions for men, in total there were over 13.5 million cosmetic surgery procedures performed in the US alone in 2020 (ASPS, 2020). Bigger, smaller, younger: consumerism penetrates to the deepest levels of our bodily self-image but this degree of augmentation is small beer compared to the full-scale physical transformations dreamed of by transhumanists.

Some tentative experiments in human-machine hybridization have already been conducted. Neil Harbisson, a British-Spanish musician and artist, is perhaps the best-known aspirant cyborg. Born with a rare visual condition which rendered him totally colour blind, Harbisson at the age of 21 had a series of surgeries to implant a chip in the back of his skull, into which a head-mounted antenna is plugged. This enables him to "hear colour" by translating light frequencies into sound. It's hard not to feel some admiration for his determination to repair a congenital condition or appreciate the vivid art he has created from his new forms of perception. But his ambition that "instead of using technology … we start becoming technology" is, to my mind, misguided (Bryant, 2013). Furthermore, his surgery was conducted on a purely free market basis; no bioethics committee would sanction it, he admits, "so it had to be done underground" (Management Events, 2019). In other words, he followed the outlaw route implicitly advocated by many humachinators.

Most so-called "real-life cyborgs" are actually patients who have had reparative surgery as the result of serious accidents. For example, Jesse Sullivan, "the first bionic man", has had his amputated arms replaced with bionic prosthetics, enabling him to control his limbs with his thoughts; Nigel Ackland's robot hand replaced the hand which he lost in an industrial accident; and Cameron Clapp has microprocessor-controlled prosthetics in place of his legs and arm, following a train crash (Medical Futurist, 2017).

One of the few people to experiment with humachine augmentation for non-medical reasons is so-called "Captain Cyborg", transhumanist roboticist Professor Kevin Warwick, who believes that only computerized brains can prevent superintelligent robots from turning humans into pets. "If you can't beat them join them," he says, adding "I was born human but I believe it's something we have the power to change" (House, 2014). In 1998, he had a transmitter implanted into his arm which lets him control lights and operate a computer remotely. In 2002, he had a sensor implanted in his brain that was connected to a computerized gauntlet, which enabled a remote robotic arm to mimic Warwick's movement. In a further experiment, Warwick was able to connect to a computer array implanted in his wife's arm, raising hopes for telepathic communications (Warwick, et al 2004)

Given the supposedly exponential speed of twenty first-century technology, one might have expected further developments in mechanized telepathy but the trail seems to have gone cold. The power of the humachinators is greater than ever but here Big Tech dromology appears to have got stuck in the slow lane. The main motivation behind body mechanization still seems to be reparation for accidents and congenital conditions or to create new forms of art. As yet, there are no signs of the volunteers for the kind of enhancements on which transhumanists base their philosophy. At the moment, one of the most likely candidates for bodily modification brought about by humachines is the change in posture caused by people craning their necks over their smartphones, which can lead to chronic upper back pain, headaches and respiratory problems (Cochrane et al, 2019).

The New Cyborgoisie

This apparent cyborg winter will not curb the power of humachinators' imaginations or the potential influence of their ideas. So, it's important to keep deconstructing the motivation behind their vision. Consider the following futuristic reverie by co-founder of the Institute of Transhumanism Natasha Vita-More:

> The body, as we transform ourselves over time, will take on different types of appearances and designs and materials. (…) For hiking a mountain, I'd like extended leg strength, stamina, a skin-sheath to protect me from damaging environmental aspects, self-moisturizing, cool-down capability, extended hearing and augmented vision …
>
> For a party, I'd like an eclectic look – a glistening bronze skin with emerald green highlights, enhanced height to tower above other

people, a sophisticated internal sound system so that I could alter the music to suit my own taste, memory enhance device, emotional-select for feel-good people so I wouldn't get dragged into anyone's inappropriate conversations. And parabolic hearing so that I could listen in on conversations across the room if the one I was currently in started winding down (quoted in McNamee and Edwards, 2006).

Although beyond practical reality – perhaps forever, this imaginative tour gives us an image of human-machine merger which might be described as Ayn Rand meets Star Trek on Instagram. Competitive individualism is very much to the fore in Vita-More's desire to change her height in order "to tower above other people" and provide her own music rather than share the communal vibe. This need to get ahead of the post-biological Joneses seems to be more about domination than equality. The techno-utopian possibilities of improved communication between people which might have been emphasized but they are eschewed in favour of privacy-busting scanning for the most interesting conversations. Likewise affective computing is used to identify "feel-good" people and avoid challenging emotional interactions rather than bring about deeper human insights.

As for the skin colour on which so much racist discrimination turns, it's tempting to think that one day this could be wished away and turned into a fashion option. But this surely is an evasion of the real identities and challenges which emerge from the "choices" which are made for us by nature and which only our social organization, not specious techno-fixes, can resolve equitably. In fact, in a world already suffering from the crisis of body dysmorphia (which is creating an epidemic of eating disorders and teenagers who can't bear to look at themselves without a face-altering app) this might not be a fix at all. The prospect of a post-biological world in which every aspect of your body image is based on consumer choice would almost certainly become a mental health nightmare.

More macho versions of post-human augmentation focus less on changeable skin colours and rather more on superheroic, Iron Man-type muscularity and powerfully enhanced cognition. Sexual prowess also looms large in the male transhuman imaginary. Kurzweil (1999:186) fantasizes about sex in a multi-sensory virtual environment in which "You can make your lover look and feel like your favourite [Hollywood] star without your partner's permission or knowledge." Nick Bostrom looks forward to orgasms "whose blissfulness vastly exceeds what any human has yet experienced" (quoted in McKibben 2019:158). Former Transhumanist Party presidential candidate Zoltan Istvan (2014) anticipates haptic "hump suits" "to put ourselves into sexual positions once only possible for Bikram yoga experts" and erotic brainwave headsets that can produce new erogenous zones. Meanwhile, inventor Rich Lee is working on a penile implant he calls Lovetron9000, which could make possible massive online orgies. "Once you have cyborg sex you will never want to return to normal sex", he predicts (House, 2014).

Such innovations would help to create the hypergrowth market that humachine economists long for, with corporations competing hard to provide the widest range of consumer choice on skin sheaths and parabolic hearing devices. Healthcare would become a consumerist hypermarket, which will dwarf the current cosmetic surgery sector. Advertising and marketing tricknology will trip over itself promoting the cybernetic sex industry, brain-implanted music systems and enhanced cognition for the new cyborgoisie.

The mechanized human may still be more of an idea than a reality but as an imperative of ultrascience and a set of medical goals that's wholly compatible with the needs of growth capitalism, the quest to find the holy grail of humachination is likely to intensify in the coming years.

The Risks of Progressive Transhumanism

That prospect is made all the more possible if it's endorsed by progressive thinkers. Women may be conspicuously absent from the roll call of "real-life cyborgs", but human-machine fusion was given a distinctly feminist angle some time ago by philosopher Donna Haraway. In *A Cyborg Manifesto* (1985), she controversially argued that the metaphor of a post-biological woman can help to transcend the "antagonistic dualisms" that dominate gendered society, including culture/nature, self/other and male/female. Her vision of freedom rejects any kind of limits on what humans can be as essentialist and claims that "there is nothing about being 'female' that naturally binds women". Although her admirable aim is to free women from all set roles, Haraway's post-biological argument can undermine the real struggle against unreconstructed patriarchy which still dominates in many parts of the world. Also, her elevation of the monstrous, protean, originless cyborg above "the goddess" – the Earth Mother rooted in an organic community favoured by some ecofeminists– seems like a very individualistic, Western-centric prioritization. Perhaps that's why one critic charges Haraway with "buying into the not so new American civil religion of high technology" (Campbell, 2001).

Let's be clear this is not a question of the rights of people to choose their sexuality or their gender. Across the entire feminist and LGBTQ+ spectrum, all humans have the right to find their appropriate blend of biology, psychology and social behaviour, including changing their cisgender. But this is quite distinct from merging your biology with machines; this crosses a much more fundamental ontological line. "Cyber feminist" Sadie Plant (1996) says "There's a gradual re-engineering of what it can be to be a woman and we don't yet know what it is. We have to find out." This is fine by me if "reengineering" is meant figuratively but not if it's intended literally. In obliterating all limits, post-biological feminism risks making freedom meaningless. Real freedom lies in confronting our biological limits, not theorizing them away. I suggest there is also a danger in thinking that the mechanized human is an individual, rather than a dense network of machines in a digital-robotic environment ultimately controlled by someone else (who, incidentally, in the humachine age, is most probably a man).

The contested role of the biological in being human takes us back to the problems of leftist accelerationism and transhumanism, which we identified in Part I, and the whole question of what a genuinely people-planet alternative to humachination looks like. Part of the appeal of post-biological transhumanism to some progressives surely lies in the way it so neatly folds into the cultural movement that is post-modernism. This relativist philosophy, which has been adopted by many mainstream intellectuals in the humanities and arts since the 1970s, is rooted in the structuralist view of language as a fabricated symbolic system, in which there is no intrinsic relationship between signs and what they signify. From this, post-modernists deduce that there is no intrinsic meaning to life, no historical origins, no privileged moral foundations or scientific ground rules.

In its day, post-modernism has produced valuable insights – and I myself have been strongly attracted to it in the past – but the Anthropocene Crisis suggests that day is over. Social behaviour may be almost infinitely varied but that's not to say that everything about human biology or planetary ecology is up for grabs. Being human is not a semantic game but a reality which impacts on every aspect of our biosphere and has profound consequences for all living things, both in the present and for many millennia to come. As I previously indicated, the concept of indigenous humanness is quite different from essentialism and has nothing to do with normative concepts of behaviour related to gender. It simply recognizes that humans are biological and, like the millions of species with which we share this planet, are part of nature. Some natural and planetary boundaries should not be crossed. Deny this and we risk being swept away on the raging torrent of change-every-thing-everywhere capitalism with little chance of ever regaining the shore.

Conclusion: The Wrong Worldplan and the Wrong Kind of Science

In fine, ideas matter. We can all imagine a world in which some of the technology discussed in this chapter could be beneficial to human wellbeing but the age of humachination is not that world. It's too dominated by the GUN organizational principles, resulting in the pursuit of infinite economic growth in a gigantic medical market that is already organized along starkly unequal lines and governed by a war on nature which vastly overestimates the role of technology in effective human healthcare. This mechanistic approach to the human body atomizes the role of organs, seeing them working in isolation, rather than in close, constant, interactive cooperation. It also commits the cardinal crime of humachination by perpetuating the Cartesian myth of the brain as a kind of CEO imperiously directing all of the body's operations.

By contrast, modern, integrated systems science is beginning to understand much more about embodied cognition, the complex ways intelligence is distributed throughout the body by countless billions of neurons which can be influenced by the wider social environment. This holistic approach to human biology is far better equipped to shape our conception of what the human body is and can be than those who claim that the unregulated free market is medicine's biggest ally. Furthermore, a worldplan with an integrated version of medicine at its centre can also enable us to wait until the merits or demerits of bodily mechanization can be decided by democratic consensus rather than the plutotechnic decision-making of the elite. And that equally applies to the one of the most alluring of all human quests, to which we now can turn our attention, the pursuit of eternal life.

CHAPTER 20

The Mechanics of Life: Re-Engineering Homo Sapiens for Immortality

Nothing indicates the wonderful power of life like our desire to extend it. Sustainable, equitable paths to longevity exist, which often have comparatively little to do with advanced medical technology. A mainly plant-based diet, regular exercise, access to nature and an active community life all play a part in the so-called Blue Zones such as Sardinia, Costa Rica and Okinawa, in which it's claimed people regularly live to be a hundred (Bluettner, 2008). The technology that most improves longevity often involves access to clean water and efficient sanitation systems – of the kind that transformed Victorian Britain – and basic medical services, such as midwifery, which can dramatically decrease infant mortality.

The absence of such factors partially explains why there is such a shockingly wide gulf in longevity between some nations in sub-Saharan Africa where average life expectancy at birth is little more than 50 years and countries in global North in which it's close to 85 years (WHO, 2019). Age inequality is not just a problem for poor nations either. In the most deprived areas of the UK, the sixth richest nation in the world, life expectancy for women (78.7 years) is lower than the average for women in every developed country in the world, barring Mexico (Gregory, 2022). In France, the most affluent 5% of men in the population live 13 years longer than men in the poorest 5% income distribution (Blanpain, 2018). And in the US, where white Americans on average live six years longer than Black Americans and eleven years longer than Native Americans, the period 2019-21 saw the biggest drop in overall longevity since the 1920s (Shmerling, 2022).

Unfortunately, the primary goal of the leaders of the humachine age doesn't appear to be the reduction of age inequality by enabling everyone on the planet to enjoy the life span currently enjoyed by the rich in the Global North. Instead, they want to create new technologies that prolong the longevity of those who can afford it by decades or even centuries and eventually to abolish death altogether. Ray Kurzweil (2005:72), you may remember, thinks 500 years of life is a viable goal, once "medical death" is eliminated. "Death is a tragedy", he claims, comparable to diseases that have been eradicated like smallpox or diphtheria. Founder of Silicon Valley's SENS institute Aubrey de Grey goes further, arguing that the first person to live to 1,000 years is alive today (Brown, 2014). Peter Thiel, who thinks "Death is an outrage," has invested millions of dollars in SENS, while Jeff Bezos is said to be backing Altos Labs, an ambitious age reversal company, which has raised $3 billion in funding and is reportedly hiring biotechnology professors on million-dollar salaries (Regalado, 2021, Kuchler, 2023). "It's possible, through technology, to make death optional" believes bio-pharmaceutical CEO Maxine Rothblatt and investment manager Laura Demming looks forward to a "longevity market" that could soon be worth $200 billion and infinitely more, if medical death is overcome – hyper-growth indeed! (Friend, 2017). Fierce rejection of "Deathism", the belief that death is inevitable, is at the very core of the humachination project.

The Mechanistic Science behind Abolishing Death

Undeniably, defeating death would be a consummate victory for the mechanistic war against biology that began when Francis Bacon resolved to put nature on the rack and continues today with ontocapitalism's rejection of the second law of thermodynamics. Vanquishing entropy, which at its simplest, means that "in the long term everything must die", would represent the ultimate checkmate for humachination (Kallis 2018:26). Unfortunately, the project is too often based on the same regressive neo-mechanicalism we examined in Part II, which seems to think that our genetic systems are computer programmes which once decoded can simply be reprogrammed. When Peter Thiel argues that "understanding biological systems in computational terms" will enable us to slow down the process of ageing, he falls into the usual trap of AI-fixated computer science, which seems to dominate the life extension field (Brown, 2014). (Aubrey de Grey, for example, is a computer science graduate with a background in AI.) Former Google Ventures boss Bill Maris, who persuaded Larry Page and Sergey Brin to sink a billion dollars into life-extension company Calico, shares this approach, declaring that medicine is fast becoming "an information technology where we read and edit our own genome" (Friend, 2017). As for Elon Musk, his definition of human DNA is typically forthright: "It's just software", he opines (Urban, 2015).

Systems life scientists insist on the limitations of this approach. For example, even "reprogramming" the life span of the C. elegans worm, with a mere 957 cells, has so far proved to be impossible, in part because at least half of its 20,000 genes appear to be involved in its (very modest) longevity. As neurologist Thomas Rando puts it in a way that underlines the naive linearity of mechanistic science in general:

> It's not A causes B causes C causes D ageing. It's a network diagram of nodes and links – all subject to feedback loops where consequences become causes – that gradually become more and more destabilized (quoted in Friend, 2017).

The complex ecology of the network of life and the role of entropy in it couldn't be expressed more succinctly.

But science is not the only thing driving the humachinators quest for immortality. Death seems to disturb the machine mindset. Machines don't die; if they break down, they can be fixed or replaced by other, often better, machines. For mechanicalists, there's something deeply worrying about the way living things cease to be, especially when the angel of death swoops out of a clear blue sky. For example, Oracle co-founder Larry Ellison, another major investor in anti-aging research, says "Death has never made any sense to me. How can a person be there and just vanish?" (Friend, 2017). But how much better for these Prometheans if they could live for centuries, virtually guaranteed against medical death and eventually, once brains can be simulated and uploaded, throw human mortality into the skip of history. This would finally realise the divine aspirations of the dominator complex that drives the machine mindset.

Even as it stands today, if the current example of active nonagenarian tycoons like Rupert Murdoch is anything to go by, ontopreneurs like Musk and Thiel could still be in charge of their respective mega-conglomerates in the 2060s and Zuckerberg might continue into the 2080s. They may even make it into the twenty-second century, if relatively modest techno-utopian life-extension targets are met.

The Cryonic Realm of the Severed Head and Other Humachine Pathways to Immortality

The routes to extended life preferred by those who want to mechanize humans tend to be extreme. Solutions such as living a simpler, more ecologically balanced life or extending modern medical support to all who need it tend to take second place to putative remedies such as autophagy (extreme fasting) or pharmacological excess. An example is Ray Kurzweil's daily intake of 250 vitamin supplements – that's over 90,000 a year, enough to provide the pupils of a medium-sized school with one vitamin a day throughout the year. Kurzweil's personal plan – also endorsed by Aubrey de Grey – is to survive until the singularity arrives at which point numerous immorality pathways will appear. Other "superlongevity" solutions are offered at the Revolution against Ageing and Death (RAAD) festival, a small annual gathering for transhumanists and "anti-death activists". In 2020, the festival included speakers on topics such as "Architecting the longevity revolution", "Age reversal", "Pet longevity ", "Living to 120 and beyond", "You can be an affordable immortal", "Youth restoration" and "Revitalizing and rejuvenation of the male sexual function" (RAADfest, 2020). Although some of these areas may conceivably yield genuine medical benefits, the potential for peddling quack remedies to wealthy older people and other vulnerable groups would seem to be immense.

Perhaps the most bizarre and potentially exploitative attempt to create a gateway to immortality is cryonics, which also features regularly at RAAD festivals. This involves freezing the blood of a deceased person with a form of antifreeze, cooling the body to a temperature of -196C and storing it in a large metal container. The aim is to revive the whole body in the future and then restore it to health using the latest medical technology or upload the brain into some kind of artificial body or digital simulation. The cofounder of Russian cryonics outfit KrioRus even predicts that it will be soon possible to attach a frozen severed head to a living body, starting with a rich man's head and a poor man's body. This freakish hybrid can then "have a nice life with lots of money, drugs, sex and gambling in Monte Carlo", he suggests (Weaver, 2015).

The leading US company offering cryonics is Alcor, which is based on the outskirts of the Arizona desert and charges $200,000 for complete body preservation, with a cheaper option available for storing a severed head alone. The CEO of Alcor turns out to be none other than transhumanist philosopher Max More, whom we encountered in Chapter 2. He refers to the legally dead bodies in his charge as "patients" and claims that cryonics is "really just an extension of emergency medicine" (O'Connell, 2017:29). Although fewer than 150 frozen bodies and severed heads are stored in Alcor's plant, several doyens of AI have signed up to the company, including Ray Kurzweil and Oxford Future of Humanity Institute academics Nick Bostrom, Stuart Campbell and Anders Sandberg. The latter rationalizes his decision thus: "As a head, my life would be limited, but by then we will be able to make real connections with computers" (Leake, 2013). Also subscribed is Peter Thiel, who says, "Cryonics only seems disturbing because it challenges our complacency over death" (Harmon, 2015).

In fact, cryonics is disturbing for many other scientific and ethical reasons. First of all, it's a pseudoscience, a technology trick which has no real scientific foundations. The practice is illegal in many counties, including France, and its practitioners are barred from joining the official body of cryogenics, the science of the behaviour of materials at low temperatures, with which it is often confused. Neuroscientist Professor Clive Coen dismisses as "ridiculous" the idea that you can preserve such "a massively dense piece of tissue" as the human brain by infiltrating it with "some kind of antifreeze", warning that you'd wake up in 100 years as a "cognitive vegetable" (Devlin, 2016). Recently he has labelled cryonics as "a hopeless aspiration that reveals an appalling ignorance of biology" (Clarke, 2022).

In a powerful article, provoked by a story of a young woman who signed up to Alcor before she died of cancer, psychologist Michael Hendricks (2015) stresses the currently insurmountable challenges of bringing any brain back to life, let alone that of a human with a unique personality and history. This raises the possibility that even if you were eventually reanimated it would not be as "you" but as someone else – or even *something* else. Hendricks makes a crucial point that applies to the whole humachination project. "It is this purposeful conflation of what is *theoretically conceivable* with what is *ever practically possible* that exploits people's vulnerability." Rejecting "an abjectly false hope that is beyond the promise of technology", he concludes that "Those who profit from this hope deserve our anger and contempt."

Put another way, we're at the border where philosophical naivety meets commercial avarice, a place where ontocapitalism thrives. And it's facilitated by cryonics' faith in the human cephalon, as Alcor calls it, a zoological term for the decapitated head section of an animal or insect (O'Connell, 2017). This, of course, relies on the Cartesian chimera of the mind as the place containing the essence of all that matter in a human being, like a little man in the head directing all operations. It's also a deeply regressive version of science parading itself as the science of the future which ends, fittingly enough, in the sad spectacle of a warehouse in the desert filled with severed heads awaiting an awakening which will never come.

Death, Time and Being Human

Tricknology aside, why is the immortality delusion so harmful? In a practical sense, it could cause innumerable complications but here I want to focus on the ethical and existential risks in trying to abolish death. In advocating breaking the last chains that link humanity to nature, we are in danger of betraying what is to be a member of Homo sapiens.

Being human is to live with death. From early childhood onwards we know about death, experience anxiety about it and "time" our lives by it. It's the end that could come at any point, once symbolized by the memento mori which urges humility and cautions against excessive pride. Trying to abolish death – or push it so far into the future that it becomes abstract – is to fundamentally reduce the possibility of living the fullest and most authentic life.

That at least was the view of Martin Heidegger (1922), for whom death is the clearest signpost indicating how to live most fully as a human being. Existentialist psychotherapist Emmy van Deurzen (1997:41) clarifies Heidegger's' apparently paradoxical position:

> Only when I am dead do I finally possess my mortality, but I am no longer there to possess it. Death is the ultimate fulfilment. But most people miss the opportunity to be fulfilled by death because they never properly live towards it, and in avoiding it, make it come up on them unprepared. We flee from death in all the everyday things we do and we fail to notice that death is our greatest potential.

Facing up to one's death is to confront the reality of living in time, but that's doesn't imply "self-assertive bravado" but an acceptance of the "sobering fact that we exist somewhere between birth and death" in a continual process of transformation:

> Facing up to the inevitability of my own annihilation is the most freeing of acts. I liberate myself only in so far as I can achieve an impassioned freedom towards death.

It's that hard-won, impassioned freedom that humachinators deny in their outrage at death, their suggestion that somehow it's a violation of basic human rights. Deathism represents fleeing from the reality of what it is to be human and the recognition of our identity as beings who are caring, fragile and capable of greatness.

"Impermanence" is how ecological economist Tim Jackson characterizes this quality, echoing philosopher Hannah Arendt, and suggesting that "Awareness of our own impermanence plays a critical role our attempts to build a more durable world" (2021:133). The anti-deathists' insistence on perpetual permanence is of course deeply related to growthism's refusal to recognise a natural process of change, preferring the fantasy of the rocket theory of history and the even more preposterous dematerializing fairy tale of hypergrowth. Living in time, towards death, is to accept that "we are essentially a process of historicity, of creating and letting go" in van Deurzen's words, but letting go is precisely what the humachinators are not prepared to do; they not only want to hold on to everything they have, they want to increase it. Perhaps only this can guarantee that capitalism itself doesn't die; it's this artificial "life" that has to be protected at the expense of real life.

In the process another core aspect of being human is also diminished: choice. We've seen the many ways in which humachination tries to delegate human decision-making to machines and so reduce our own independence and capacity to choose how we live. Extreme life extension also makes a mockery of human choice. Just imagine what a 500-year life would be like: it's the equivalent of a dozen 40-year adult spans. How do you make family choices, remaining with a partner or having a child who will live for many centuries? Why stick to any career or occupation if there is always another one to move to? If you can choose to be anything, doesn't everything become meaningless?

The goal of immortality also destroys the qualitative equilibrium of wisdom and other human qualities, encapsulated in the final reckoning of one's life which is embedded in many religions. St Peter's judgement at the gates of heaven or the ancient Egyptian god Osiris weighing a soul against a feather are simply alternative way of looking at Heidegger's point about how to live an authentic life. We can see something similar in the circular causality of karma and reincarnation and in our biological journey "from ashes to ashes", which requires no supernatural cosmology to support it. A delicate sense of balance is always present in life, reinforced by a pandemic in which one unlucky breath might ingest a virus which could steal our ability to breathe at all. That subtle balance is spurned by machine supremacisim whose obsession with linearity and total control pitches towards potentially destructive extremes of disequilibrium.

Jonathan Swift and the Inequality of Immortality

The immortality question, almost inevitably, brings us back to one of the keystones of the GUN worldplan, unequalism. As bioethicist Christopher Wareham says, a hypothetical vaccine against ageing would "potentially exacerbate all the kinds of existing inequalities that we have" (Kuchler, 2023). COVID-19 "vaccine apartheid" confirms his point; as an open letter to G20 leaders in October 2021 highlighted, high-income countries had at that point received 133 vaccine doses per 100 people while low-income counties had been given just 4 doses per 100 – a differential of over 3,300% (Bajaj, 2022).

Indeed, the "anti-deathists" refusal to accept the inevitability of dying often reeks of a disdain for human equality. Death after all is the ultimate leveller for Homo sapiens. In the Pyramid Age, it was one of the few factors that united all classes. Kings could die of a common cold, queens perish in childbirth and yet a peasant could outlive an emperor. Now those at the top of today's economic pyramid, who already have more life at their disposal than most, want even more. Mortality refutes the Law of More, insisting firmly but inexorably that "enough is enough" – the last words that the pursuers of hypergrowth ever want to hear.

Of course, there's nothing novel about the fantasy of living forever and during the earliest stages of the Industrial Revolution the great Anglo-Irish satirist Jonathan Swift issued myriad warnings about where the mechanistic science pioneered by the Royal Society could lead us that are all too relevant today. His satirical masterpiece *Gulliver's Travels* features a famously miserable group of people called the Struldbruggs, who are in fact immortal. They live normal lives until the age of 80, at which age "they are looked on as dead in Law" (Swift, 1726/2003:196). All legal rights are taken away from them, including the right to own property, have a job or hold public office. Yet they continue living, suffering all the ailments of old age. Behind the apparently cruel treatment of the Struldbruggs by their society lies a wise rationale:

> Otherwise, as Avarice is the necessary Consequence of old Age, those Immortals would in time become Proprietors of the whole Nation, and engross the Civil Power, which, for want of Abilities to manage, must end in the Ruin of the Public (p198).

The concerns underlying Swift's satire would be incomprehensible to the leaders of the humachine age. Indeed, the idea of becoming "proprietors of the whole nation" sounds rather like the current ontocapitalist worldplan, except that the goal extends to the entire cosmos. Today the intergenerational inequality that the Struldbruggs' society seek to avoid has become the norm, as the old not only avariciously want more but succeed it getting it. The humachinators, for all their apparent youthfulness, identify with a gerontocractic system which has concentrated huge wealth and political power in the hands of the 65+ generation. You might say the baby boomers' generation have done everything they can to steepen the Pyramid Pattern of society, even to the extent of building new economic barriers between themselves and their own offspring. The only thing that stands in the way of further maximisation of power and wealth is mortality, the abolition of which might unite the new superrich with the older generation which still holds most of the world's capital.

Another reason why Swift's critique would fall on deaf ears in the humachine age is that *Gulliver's Travels* is also a critique of individualism, partially aimed at Daniel Defoe's massively popular *Robinson Crusoe* published a few years earlier. For the humachinator, if you can find a way to live forever, why would you give a second thought to the consequences for society as a whole, particularly to those who are poorer than you? Individualism externalizes the social impacts of behaviour in the same way that growthist economics externalizes environmental impacts. It also seems to degrade the idea of maturity and the dignity of the acceptance of death. Instead, we witness octogenarians behaving like teenagers and determined to keep on spending until the very end. Instead of saying "I've lived, I've had my turn, it's time for others", the real goal is more, more and more.

There's another way, incidentally, that the critique of inequality is depicted in *Gulliver's Travels*. Laputa is a floating island, governed by fanatical scientists who are obsessed with accurate measurement and scientific experimentation but unable to make buildings that stand up or clothes that don't require servants to prevent them from disintegrating (not unlike today's fast fashion). Here Swift was very obviously taking aim at the Royal Society and the early days of the machine mindset, which preferred to concentrate on self-aggrandising scientific projects, such as extracting sunbeams from cucumbers, rather than attempting to finish the unfinished business of humanity.

Laputa also tyrannizes the country it floats above, Balnibarbi, by regularly blocking out the sun with its shadow, preventing rainfall and, in cases of extreme disobedience, by crushing it entirely. It was a metaphor for colonial England's brutal treatment of Swift's native Ireland. But today it could also stand as an allegory for another monstrous injustice: the ecological devastation caused by the most scientifically advanced nations of the world to countries in the Global South which have least engaged in industrial technology. The Anthropocene Crisis would doubtless provoke even greater Swiftian savage indignation, as some of the poorest people on the planet are not only forced to flee their homes before wildfires, floods and creeping desertification, but have to compare their shortening lives to those of the wealthy, would-be immortalists responsible for their plight.

The CIMENT Values Again

The desire of those who are already relatively most death-proof to claim even more life seems a predictable psychological outcome of the CIMENT values underlying growthism. If life is a competitivist battle of all against all, how can you ever afford to fall behind the opposition? No wonder egomaniacal billionaires like Kazakhtan's autocratic ruler Nursultan Nazarbaev are said to be setting up life extension projects (although the family of the late Silvio Berlusconi might want to demand a refund on his) (Weaver, 2015). As we've just seen, individualism is also rampant among immortality-seekers, rendering them incapable of seeing – or caring about – the potential negative consquences of their actions on the rest of society. Their extreme materialism causes them to protest at being parted from their wealth. When you have enough money to live a thousand lifespans why should you be confined to just one? America's robber barons were as rich as Croesus – probably even richer proportionally than today's onto-preneurs – but they knew their wealth would not enable them to bargain their way into eternal life, so they gave it away. Today's humachinators may find it tricky to enter the kingdom of heaven but who cares about a needle's eye if you have AI? As for elitism, those who believe in the ineluctable rectitude of hierarchy can always justify their innovations by claiming that what begins as a luxury for the superrich, like air travel or ocean cruising, will eventually trickle down to the rest of society, ignoring the fact that the vast majority of people in this world have never been on an aeroplane or ocean liner in their lives. And of course, technologism, the CIMENT value that is the prime mover in all that humachinators do, reassures the anti-deathists that technology is destiny, nature is inferior to machines and humans are crudely designed prototypes urgently requiring upgrading. For them, death is simply a glitch to be engineered out.

Rechanneling Death Anxiety by Escaping Biology

Some might say I'm being too hard on those who long for life extension but that's perhaps because I feel humachinators fail to recognize the line that separates a healthy desire for life from the morbid pursuit of immortality. At the same time, I wouldn't want to ignore the possibility that there may be psychological factors at work in death denialism, such as an extreme form of death anxiety or unresolved bereavement traumas. Interestingly, Dr Frankenstein experienced the death of his father in early childhood – Mary Shelley herself would lose three of her children in infancy – and it was this loss that motivated him to try to manufacture a deathless human. The relatively early death of Ray Kurzweil's father Frederic seems to have played a part in his immortality obsession and his surreal goal of creating a realistic "replicant" of his father, a process which he believes will eventually be accomplished by nanorobots extracting data from the memories of the living (Miles, 2015). The death of Larry Ellison's mother when he was still in college may have prompted his subsequent investment of $375 million in anti-aging research. And Bill Maris, the driving force behind Calico, also suffered the death of a parent when he was relatively young, leading him to see his mission as to "preserve consciousness indefinitely" (Friend, 2017). Real emotion seems to be translated into the irony-repelling, self-awareness-proofed armour of ultrascience, making immortality or even resurrection seem like a logical course of action.

Nobody wants to die and the death of a loved one can be deeply shocking. but death is part of our contract with life. Those who suffer from extreme forms of death anxiety can be helped to a more balanced perspective and those who experience bereavement can also be helped to overcome their loss. Every bereavement counsellor knows unresolved traumas can last a long time after a person's death but that it's possible to gradually move beyond the shock of death to its acceptance. Immortality obsessives seem to be permanently stuck in the first stage of grief, denial, and can only see their way out of it through technology. The COVID-19 pandemic showed just how vivid our death anxiety is, especially in a world in which dying is increasingly hidden from view, but the popular response to the virus showed that this anxiety can be coped with and that humans have unexpected reserves of resilience that can turn into a force for good.

Conclusion

In the end, there is no cure for the mystery of life. Only the one-sided machine mindset fails to see that life and death are like yin and yang, different sides of the same border and inseparable elements in the interwoven causality of existence. Life without death is itself a kind of death, a thing-like, reified state of being. Cultural anthropologist Ernest Becker (1973) called our attempts to disguise the transience of our lives "immortality projects", which could be heroic, although they were ultimately doomed to failure. But there is nothing heroic about the humachinators' refusal to face up to the reality of biology or consider the repercussions of living hundreds of years longer than the rest of society, as opposed to the mere decades of extra life which they already enjoy. The apparent immortality of capitalism, based on the fool's gold of never-ending growth, seems to go hand in hand with the belief in infinite life-extension. Twenty-first century immortalists turn the natural desires which affirm life into a denial of it and, in the final analysis, surrender everything to the supremacy of the machine. That could mean there's a terrible sting in the tail, as Geoffrey Hinton suggests, warning that AI might end up creating immortality but adding: "The bad news is it's not for us" (Hern, 2023). And, as we'll now discover, this is not the only risk to the integrity of our species, which is posed by the humachination project.

CHAPTER 21

The Death of Homo Sapiens? Genetic Engineering and the New Pyramid of Speciation

Ontocapitalism, we need to remember, aims to change the very structure of being – not simply being human but physical, chemical and biological existence itself. So it's no surprise to find that there's an even bigger death than the fate of an individual involved in humachination, namely the potential death of Homo sapiens. For it's not only the end of human life that frustrates humachinators, it's the beginning of it as well. When it comes to their offspring, why should parents have to rely on the arbitrariness of the genetic lottery and the bind of having to make do with what nature blindly produces? That's not their idea of consumerism: if you're rich enough you should be able to specify what you want down to the last detail. The messy illogicality of nature infuriates the machine mindset. Re-engineering human reproduction would create the possibility of designing children from the very start or cloning them to whatever specification is required.

Human genetic engineering has always been pivotal to human-machine fusion. For Kurzweil it's simply an inevitable consequences of physics supplanting biology; Klaus Schwab and other fourth industrial revolutionaries see it as just another milestone in the march of scientific progress; and for post-humanists longing for enhanced cognition, selectable personalities

and options like extra-sensory organs it's indispensable. Recent developments in genomics, especially in CRISP gene editing, may have encouraged
them. In 2019 China reported the creation of five cloned, gene-edited monkeys (although claims by Raelains, a transhumanist sect, to have cloned
the founder's daughter can be dismissed (Comfort, 2018)). In 2018 the
healthy embryos of twin girls, Lulu and Nana, were gene edited by Chinese
biophysicist He Jiankui with the aim of making them HIV-resistant. There
are serious doubts about whether the procedure was effective and fears
that the girls' brains may have been altered in various ways, a hint of the
disturbing UNCs involved in this inchoate technology (Regalado, 2019).
In any case, the experiment was completely illegal and He was sent to
prison for three years.

Unlike other areas of human mechanization, the growthist world system
has so far stood steadfastly against permitting human genome manipulation. One reason for this is that there's no discernable line between
restoration and augmentation in this area, to an even greater extent than in
the other aspects of mechanizing humans which we've examined. Alter one
part of a human's genetic code to prevent disease and you potentially alter
everything. This is the scientific and ethical barrier that the humachinators
will have to remove in order to fulfil their vision of redesigning humanity
but with ultra-science and free market capitalism on their side, some are
convinced that it's just a matter of time before the walls of resistance come
tumbling down. It may be significant that when He Jiankui was released
from prison, his first response was to vow to make a "scientific comeback",
later declaring that "a golden decade for gene therapies" is approaching
(Molteni, 2022).

One of those who have been hammering at the door of genetic enhancement for a long time is biophysicist and biotechnology entrepreneur
Gregory Stock. He argues that "we are on the cusp of profound biological
change" and that the "arrival of safe, reliable germline technology will
signal the beginning of human self-design" (2002:1-3). In *Redesigning
Humans: Our inevitable genetic future,* Stock claims that germline engineering (the manipulation of the genetics of the egg or sperm), allied
to hyper-competitive neoliberal consumerism, will normalize cloning
humans and genetically re-designing babies. He suggests that pets will
act as another, more literal, Trojan horse of humachination, as "the wealthy
begin to clone much-loved older pets", causing people to "grow comfortable

with reproductive technologies sooner than we think" (309). The gradual "displacement of the born by the made" will undoubtedly cause problems, he concedes, even for the genetically modified who will feel increasingly estranged from unenhanced humanity (307). But attempts to regulate genetic enhancement will prove futile, he argues, in part, because it will be difficult to test if a baby has been modified or not, and, in any case, if the US doesn't permit this new technology, the Chinese will.

Stock rightly suggests that we are in for "a battle for the future" and that the question of reproductive technology is not first and foremost about technology, "it is about what it means to be human, about our vision of the human future" (303). But, in my view, he wrongly concludes that all that's needed for the majority of people to judge that the opportunities of germinal technology outweigh the risks is "a free market environment with real individual choice" and "modest oversight" (201). This implies a confidence in the continuance of an almost totally unfettered form of capitalism, which is grossly misplaced in the midst of an Anthropocene Crisis, which is crying out for more market regulation.

He also significantly underestimates the technical problems involved, leaning towards the neomechanical view that the genetics code is like a computer programme, whereas we now know that cells are flexible, inter-connected and unpredictable. In fact, as molecular biologist W. Malcolm Byrnes points out, Stock seems to recognize "that it will be extremely dif-ficult if not impossible to predict and control the impact of introducing entirely new capabilities orchestrated by many genes". Yet Stock claims this drawback will be solved by future gene transfer technologies. He thus "denies that a problem will exist by asserting an almost naive belief that technology will solve every problem" (Byrnes, 2003:429). This naive solu-tionism is of course a favourite tactic of humachinators, along with the exponentiality trick and a reliance on economic growth enduring forever.

The Bioethics Resistance

Elon Musk has said that "We are going to have to reprogramme our DNA… It's just software" (Urban, 2015). But even if our genetics were as pro-grammable as Musk and other supporters of multi-planetary humanity claim, there is another major obstacle to fulfilling their goals of enhancing intelligence and selecting personality characteristics. That's because while psychologists agree that about 50% of your personality and intelligence are due to genetic factors, the other half is determined by your social and cultural environment. Bill McKibben (2019) brilliantly satirizes another frustration in a hypothetical world, in which it's possible for parents to pay for their unborn children's intelligence to be increased. Technological advances would mean that keeping up with your neighbours becomes impossible, as the higher IQ of a new cohort of genetically engineered children turns the previously modified cohort into outdated no-hopers. Even more problematic, as McKibben notes, are the ethical implications of imposing the personality traits desired by a parent on a child with reckless disregard for their right to be who they are. It one of the reasons why he calls for the continued banning of germline engineering

He's not alone, thankfully. So far bioethics legislation has been strong enough to keep the transhumanists at bay. Drawing on the long-standing tradition of medical ethics, scientists, politicians and campaigning groups have been able to enforce the banning of genetic enhancements. This tradition draws on precautionary priorities which go back to Hippocrates; these, it's worth reiterating, are still largely absent from the safety-last AI industry (Hilton, 2022). The principles of this relinquishment are not only moral but economic and political as well, as Osagie K. Obasogie and Marcy Darnovsky 2018:9-10) make clear:

> The choices being put in front of us by new human biotechnologies are profoundly political; they create winners and losers, shape our societies (and in some cases our very selves), and implicate society's deepest values about who we are and what we want to be. It would be remarkably unwise to hand such decision-making to any one group of experts or professionals and extremely reckless to leave it to "the market".

Unfortunately, as we know, humachination aims to do exactly that: leave it to the market.

So how long will the bioethical resistance be able to hold out? Some ethics philosophers are certainly doing their very best to undermine it. For instance, libertarian bioethicist John Harris (2010) in *Enhancing Evolution* insists we have a moral duty to make "better people" and that human cloning, designer babies and other forms of genetic manipulation can improve our happiness, physical strength and mental capacities. Likewise, Oxford philosopher Julian Savulescu (2011) argues for "procreative beneficence", the idea that people are morally obliged to produce the best children possible. In a lecture entitled "Unfit for life: Genetically enhance humanity or face extinction", Savulescu (2013) suggests that the only way to avoid the climate crisis and other extinction threats is to genetically re-engineer humans to remove their selfishness, short-termism and inability to show concern for anybody but friends and relations. This is partially based on the pessimistic neo-Hobbesian view of humanity as a species which was designed to live in societies of no more than 150 people but which is biologically unfit for the modern world. (I would suggest that it's the way that humanity has been organized into economically competitive hierarchies which prevents cooperative altruism from becoming more dominant.) From a scientific viewpoint it's also nonsensical to think that genetics can identify individual traits, as David Cobb (2020) emphasizes, and, in any event, genetic modification would take far too long to prevent catastrophic climate change. If adopted, this flawed philosophical justification would give geneticists emergency powers to experiment in any way they chose – a dangerous licence indeed.

The Disability Question

There are also grave implications for people with disabilities if techno-eugenics takes off, possibly via private clinics offering expensive gene-editing to prevent neurogenerative diseases and other heritable conditions (Sample and Devlin, 2023). In the UK 14.6 million people live with a disability, that's 22 % of the overall population. Four percent live with one of the 6,000 genetic conditions already identified, which, on a worldwide basis, represents over 320 million people (Gene People 2023, ONS 2021). Richard Dawkins provoked public outrage, when he claimed that it will soon be considered immoral to knowingly give birth to a child with Down's syndrome (Dawson, 2021). Yet Julian Savulescu and Peter Singer (2019) argue that there is an "ethical pathway" to this situation. It starts with gene editing "catastrophic single gene disorders", then moves on to editing "non-fatal genetic conditions" and then "genetic dispositions to common diseases, such as diabetes or cardiovascular disease". This, they claim, would finally clear the way for the "enhancement of the genetic contribution to general intelligence".

What then happens to the disabled as this multi-generational transition to a species free of hereditary diseases proceeds? Will disabled children be discriminated against on the grounds of the religious or ethical convictions of their parents, in effect further stigmatizing the already stigmatized? If so, it would create another chilling dimension to inequality. And what are the implications for disabled people in the Global South if gene-editing becomes the norm in the North?

Not surprisingly, genomic manipulation goes against the wishes of most people with genetic disabilities, as Felicity Boardman's (2020) extensive research on the subject has shown.

> [T]he majority of people with genetic disabilities feel that it would be a loss to have fewer people with their particular condition coming into the world and the majority (90%) of family members of people with genetic disabilities such as haemophilia, for example, feel uncomfortable with the idea of pregnancy termination for the condition in their family.

As Boardman (2020) says, the process potentially elevates the one disease-related gene out of the 25,000 genes in the human genome above the entire life of the embryo or foetus, which is qualitatively different from all reproduction controls in the past.

Individual Eugenics

In general, however, the charge of eugenics does not deter the intellectual shock troops of genetic engineering. In *Liberal Eugenics*, Nicholas Egar (2004) provides a philosophical defence of genetic enhancements which he compares to environmental improvements like good schools. Techno-optimist and libertarian hereditary peer Matt Ridley (2016) also claims that individual eugenics differs from the sinister government-sponsored eugenics of the past, because it's based on personal choice rather than coercion. He also argues that genetic engineering is more likely to focus on disease than intelligence or personality. But the distinction between individual and collective eugenics doesn't really hold water. How do you create a master race except by modifying one individual at a time? Is anyone suggesting that the Nazis attempted to engineer the process en masse, like the batches of test tube embryos in Huxley's Brave *New World*? And, as for coercion, there's nothing more socially coercive than the idea, justified or not, that other people's children have an advantage over yours, including genetically-engineered immunity to certain diseases.

Historian Nathanial Comfort puts paid to another of the eugenicists' arguments, that in a free-market consumers would opt for a diverse range of personality enhancements. He points out that customers are likely to opt for the characteristics which society privileges most:

> [I]n our current society, who has the most opportunities? Of course: a tall white, straight, handsome man. If neoliberal enhancement were to proceed unregulated, then social convention, cultural ideals, and market forces would drive us towards producing the same tired Aryan master race (183).

And we shouldn't forget that the Aryan master race was a constructed myth, largely based on imagined appearance. The new super-race myth might be based on other apparently desirable traits, which will doubtless be peddled by a growing army of genetic enhancement tricknologists. In fact, the very act of being modified may seem to confer (quite unmerited) superior powers on a person. Once the breach is made between genetically designed individuals, the possibility for wider discrimination is opened wide. This is the superhuman problem I referred to earlier; in the zero-sum game of growth capitalism, if the genetically modified are seen as superior, the unmodified must be inferior – and further modification may become impossible to stop.

Humachinators and their philosophical outriders fail to realise this, perhaps because their individualism prevents them from acknowledging the very existence of society or from seeing collectivities as anything other than toxic (like the followers of Ayn Rand). But once you decide that some categories of human beings are less desirable than others, where does it end? Do the disabled, the poor, the unemployed come next? Ruled over by 500-year-old, genetically-engineered cyborgs, the dream of the humachine age could become a nightmare for most inhabitants of planet Earth.

Princeton biologist Lee Silver gestures in the direction of such a future. He insists that scientists will be willing and able to deliver cloning and genetic engineering and that governments will not stand in their way. But this genetic technology will only be available to the wealthiest 10% of society, presupposing such an economic elite continues to exist. In *Remaking Eden*

(1997:7) he describes a future divided into the enhanced "Genrich" and the low-paid "Naturals", who will be "entirely separate species with no ability to cross-breed". He acknowledges that it might be seen as unfair that "some people will have access to technologies that can provide advantages while others, less well-off, are forced to depend on chance alone" but he defends this on the basis that this is how capitalism works:

> American society adheres to the principle that personal liberty and personal fortune are the primary determinants of what individuals are allowed and able to do. Anyone who accepts the right of affluent parents to provide their children with an expensive private school education cannot use "unfairness" as a reason for rejecting the use of reprogenetic technologies [i.e., genetic enhancement] ... whether we like it or not, the global marketplace will reign supreme" (1999: 9-11).

Sliver's argument is brutally logical. If capitalism's most admired citizens are allowed to attempt to influence the 50% of their children's personality which is moulded by their environment, for example by spending up to $80,000 a year to send their children to Ivy League colleges like Silver's, why not allow them to spend similar sums on the other 50% which is determined by genetics? In one way, it's a fallacious argument, since educating our children is a core aspect of humanness: all human communities educate their children but none so far have genetically modified them. But the real point here is about what accepting our current worldplan entails.

Silver, like Stock, has embraced practical entrepreneurship through his controversial gene-screening company, GenePeeks, and his argument reveals his uncompromising commitment to capitalism and ultrascience. Peel away the usual techno-utopian blandishments of humachination and we are left with an aggressively realpolitik argument which can be paraphrased as follows: "capitalism may be unfair but it's here to stay, so deal with it!" Shorn of the usual philosophical sophistry or coy evasiveness, it's a stark warning about just where the ontocapitalist alliance between some leading scientists and growthist market forces could be taking us.

Speciation: The New Genetic Pyramid

For let's make no bones about it, a genetically modified super-race is the logical outcome of the humachine project. If it's permitted to go ahead, ordinary, un-enhanced humans will become an inferior race. Forget the euphemistic terminology of "post-biological", "transhuman", "human+" and so on, if the humachine genetic engineers have their way we're talking about speciation. The apex class at the top of the new social pyramid would in effect represent a new species of humanity. Stock (2002:182) argues that humans have been breeding dogs for millennia but there is still a canine species. However, in his book *Metaman: Merging humans and machines into a global superorganism,* he admits that even minor gene manipulation "might change human beings into something different" and that "populations that adopt such techniques will outdistance those that do not" (Stock, 1993:165). Homo mechanicus, as we might label a genetically modified version of Homo sapiens, will potentially exhibit far greater differences in behaviour from unmodified humans than exist between domesticated animal species (as well as exerting a much greater influence over its environment). In fact, the difference between Homo sapiens and Homo mechanicus would probably be larger than that between sapiens and Neanderthals. We know that Neanderthals were able to interbreed with our sapiens ancestors, as each of us on average carries up to 4% of Neanderthal genes within our DNA (Than, 2010). Animal species also interbreed – 16%-22% of bird species, for example (Ottenburghs et al, 2015). But when it comes to genetically enhanced and unenhanced humans, Lee Silver's contention that interbreeding between GenRich and Naturals would be impossible is surely accurate.

In reality, it's questionable whether a fully genetically-engineered mecan would even qualify as a new species of the Homo genus. An entirely new genus might be more appropriate classification. A hypothetical Homo mechanicus, once retrofitted with robotic as well as genetic augmentations, would surely be at least as distant from Homo sapiens as we are from the genus of Australopithecus africanus, from which our most ancient ancestor Homo habilis evolved some two million years ago. Even the deepest forays into the early history of humanity won't help us here. After all, any genetically designed, "post-biological" entity would represent a radical break in the evolution of all living things. We could go back three-and-a-half billion years in natural history to a planet filled with nothing but microbes and still not find anything that vaguely resembled a product of "applied evolution" like Homo mechanicus. It's yet another indication of just how extreme the humachine assault on nature is and just what is at stake in ontocapitalism's determination to transform everything that we think we know about being human on planet Earth.

Conclusion

"How do we distinguish genuine enhancement from pernicious encroachment and new horizons from new impositions?" asks philosopher Andy Clark (2013:124). Not, I suggest, by trying to naturalize human hybridization or to force it on the majority in the top-down manner used by pyramidal societies throughout history. Rather we should be looking to the golden rule of technology, the primacy of social choice. It's the framework of values and goals which we put around all the issues of mechanizing humanity which will determine whether we produce equality or plutotechnic tyranny, including the "coercion, monstering and subjugation" which Clark admits is possible.

Gregory Stock argues that when talking about "human genetic manipulation" we need to get beyond "the specter of forced sterilization, concentration camps and other horror of the twentieth century" (304) – and, naturally, other humachinators are equally keen to distance themselves from this historical episode. But perhaps only the horrors of the past can protect us from potential horrors in the future. Even Elon Musk admits that when it comes to genetics, he knows of no way to avoid what he calls "the Hitler Problem" (Urban, 2015). The Nazis rejected the fundamental idea of human equality, reclassifying humans in a racist hierarchy that placed an imagined Aryan master race at the top and various "sub-human" categories below, including Jews, Slavs, Romanies, Blacks and gays, some of whom formed the subjects of the hideous "genetic manipulation" which took place in the SS's death camps. We should not complacently underestimate how far medical capitalism might go in its never-ending search for economic growth or the role which some scientists may be prepared to play in the project of mechanizing humans. As I've argued before, images of dystopia are essential to constantly remind us of what we are not but could become.

Finally, lest I be accused of misguided ethical judgements here or in Part V overall, it's worth remembering that Dr Frankenstein's humachination project itself originated in the very best of motives:

> I had begun life with the most benevolent intentions and thirsted for
> the moment when I could put them into practice, and make myself
> useful to my fellow-beings. Now all was blasted … I was seized by
> remorse and the sense of guilt (Shelley, 1818/1969:90).

Today, that thirst for innovation is greater than ever, but little remorse or
guilt has yet intruded into the minds of the humachine ontopreneurs. On
the contrary, all we see is the swaggering Promethean hubris of those who
believe that machines are superior to living things. "Pernicious encroachment" could indeed be the name of the game; first winning hearts and
minds in the war of ideas before capturing them literally by means of medical technology. Human mechanization continues the process of humanized
machines, homing in on those areas of the brain and body that are already
most machine-like and then aiming to leap across the huge gulf that separates machines from the mysterious complexity of the brain-body that
makes us human. That encroachment creeps through the first four types
of humachine, which we have examined, to its final manifestation, the
all-encompassing digital-robotic environment, which we can now move
on to. If the process is allowed to progress, it could be more than enough
to tip us into the Technocene, although roads to a much better future are
still open to us, as Part VI will also now reveal.

PART VI

Technocene or Ecocene?
The Struggle for the Future

Introduction to Part VI

The age of humachines is a distinct period in the early twenty-first century in which growth capitalism has been able to convince the majority of people that we're on course for a better world to be delivered by science, technology and entrepreneurship. But what happens next? Which worldplan will win the struggle for the Anthropocene as the century unfolds, especially if economic growth disappears? In Chapters 24 to 26, I'll explore one possible outcome, the psychologically liberating age of the Ecocene, in the belief that we can still pivot from the current GUN system towards an ecologically balanced, richly democratic version of the Human Epoch. This future embodies many of the SEWP principles and goes some way to revive the demotechnics of the Age of Origin, but with the benefits of millennia of progress in culture, science and technology.

However, in the light of everything we've seen so far about capitalism in the age of humachines, I have to concede that at the moment our choices seem to keep us on course for the Technocene. As I've tried to signal throughout this book, humachination is much more likely to result in techno-dystopia than the rapturous singularity of the transhumanists, the economic abundance which fourth industrial revolutionaries await or the miracle of green growth. A Technocene future would be the graveyard of green capitalist and techno-utopian dreams, an authoritarian, steeply segregated world system in which freedom would only be enjoyed by the controlling minority at the apex of the social pyramid.

In the next chapter, I'll explore some of the bleakest possibilities for the twenty-first century that may occur if attempts to mitigate climate and biodiversity catastrophe continue to proceed too slowly. But for now, let's examine the hypothesis that all we need to do to reach techno-dystopia is to keep making the same plutotechnic choices that we seem to be making today and trusting the same techno-elite leaders. That could be more than enough to bring into play the fifth and final element of the humachination agenda, the all-encompassing humachinated environment.

CHAPTER 22

The Humachinated Environment: How to Drift into Techno-Dystopia

The Smartheid Road to the Technocene

Type 5 humachination has a simple goal: to connect up every machine, digital network and biological system on the planet into a coherent system of control. The digital-robotic environment enchains multiple cognitive, relational and robotic humachines into an inescapable "umwelt", linking every aspect of a person's life and every physical setting, including the home, school, workplace and city. This wrap-around environment stretches from the microscopic to the gigantic and grows in real time, as billions of data devices connect with each other. Like the omniverse, it's meant to exist in four dimensions, with nothing outside it in space or time; it's a mash-up that aims to ensure that nothing remains beyond the reach of technology, whether it's a forest, a school or a human heart, in what would be the ultimate triumph for the machine mindset.

Another term that captures the creeping control exercised by Type 5 humachination is "Smartheid". This predicts that bit by bit humanized machines will try to appropriate the totality of our inner and outer worlds, whittling away our ability to make independent choices, removing our democratic freedoms and meticulously extracting our civil rights. In the Smartheid world, a new, extreme Pyramid Pattern takes shape, as the victorious, data-owning techno-elite become economically, politically and socially segregated from the vast majority of people.

Smartheid: The Smart Home

Smartheid starts in the home. Today we still have control over the things that surround us at home, from the walls, windows and doors to the fridge, the washing machine and other mod cons that have been filling our houses since the 1950s. They may not have fulfilled the promise of creating less work for us but at least they know their place. We still choose them; they don't make choices for us.

The smart home is meant to change all that. Its aim is to transform every structure, surface, object and device into a two-way mirror, a multidimensional form of intelligence, capable of surveying us, analysing us, reading our emotions and subtly (or not so subtly) dominating us. Every object will be capable of multi-tasking and forming multiple enchainments in real time. Current digital servants like Alexa, Siri or Google Smart Home will seem quaintly crude by comparison and the ability to switch them off will be a distant memory. Switch off the smart home and you and your family could die.

Materials science will try to engineer almost every atom and molecule in the smart home to reveal our innermost consumer wants, which can then be satisfied by the market forces swirling around us like air conditioning. The invisible hand of the market will lurk in every household item. Every voice command, conversation, gesture, every keystroke (if still necessary), every eye movement and bead of sweat, can be recorded, analysed, used to provide us with what the smart market decides we need.

Smart locks are already surrendering the last vestige of privacy to Amazon or Google. In effect, your front door may soon resemble the glass walls that dominate the techno-dystopian state described in Yevgeny Zemyatin's classic novel *We* (1922). Your house may increasingly bristle with military-style security devices to protect it from unwanted intruders but soon it will throw open its doors to the forces of unbridled consumerism, as the online supermarket situates itself within your own home. Now your fridge and your washing machine order goods directly from your online supplier, which autonomously delivers them to your freezer, wardrobe or garden shed. Soon it becomes impossible to remember what you bought and what was bought for you by your devices. Indeed, this is the point of the ultimate type of humachine, to degrade your power to choose, so that by comparison it makes even today's advertising tricknology seem like it offers freedom of choice.

The hidden persuaders will come at you from every angle. As philosopher Andreas Borgmann wryly observes, "we will slide from housekeeping to being kept by our house" (quoted in Frischmann and Selinger, 2018:130). The smart kitchen with its robot chef will take care of all cooking for the household (although beware of hackers with poisonous intent), while flexible work stations around the house will finally obliterate the distinction between work and home (Moley, 2023). Rooms will be able to operate as wall-to-wall, floor-to-ceiling entertainment and communication centres, with multiple surfaces and objects capable of functioning as screens. 3-D technology will offer holographic representation that annuls the distinction between the watched and the watching much more subtly than the obtrusive, always-on TVs in the corner of every sitting room in George Orwell's *Nineteen Eighty Four*.

Even in the smallest room in the house, it won't be possible to escape the all-seeing digital-robotic eye. In fact, the "smart toilet "is already on the market and able to record stool-dropping intervals and seating time. Its manufacturer claims that the toilet's AI-assisted camera can take an "anal print" of the creases in the lining of the anus, which apparently form a unique pattern. In the future, this will make it easier to track people from one residence to another (Saner, 2021).

Of course, the smart home is not intended to feel like a panopticon prison. On the contrary, it's supposed to fulfil our innermost consumerist aspirations and upgrade family life to the level of the super-rich, for whom domestic servants traditionally do all the work. But like the "throwaway plastic" home of the 1950s, the reality will be very different. The digital-robotic servants of the smart home are likely to resemble mercenary spies, auctioning their owners' psychological secrets and commercial preferences, while relentlessly inveigling them into over-consuming (and overspending). For those who have not become totally conditioned to machine-dependence, the anxiety of living may actually increase.

Techno-Education and the Smart City

The smart home leads to the smart school – and that's already with us today in the shape of educational establishments using ubiquitous digital systems to analyse a pupil's playground behaviour, academic performance and home life. In fact, the smart school is another of digital capitalism's best Trojan horses, playing on parents' legitimate concerns about their children's wellbeing, as self-harm, suicide, cyber-bullying and sexual assault increase and, in American schools especially, tragic shooting sprees proliferate. Soon ecological harms, from rising temperatures and extreme weather events, will be added to the anxiety list. The graver these fears get, the easier the smart school will be to sell.

Millions of US school children are already being surveyed by Gaggle, an AI system which scans student's homework assignments, emails, pictures, creative writing, online browsing and chats with friends, both at school and at home (mainly through their Google and Microsoft accounts). Anything deemed suspicious is flagged up and notified to the authorities (Haskins, 2019). Some schools already use facial recognition software in place of the school register and we can expect emotion-reading systems to be deployed to identify potentially rebellious pupils or those with "behavioural problems". British criminologist Emmeline Taylor, author of *School Surveillance*, says that "The next generation of students will already be normalized to surveillance". Ominously, she adds that children "make the best guinea pigs to test new technologies" (Minsky, 2020).

Desensitized to privacy invasions, children may also become increasingly accustomed to AI-assisted tele-education. The limitations of remote learning were demonstrated during the Covid-19 pandemic but for cost reasons, machine-to-human learning may be all that's available for the majority in the future, as human-to-human education becomes the prerogative of the elite. Human teachers may be the biggest draw for parents who can afford private education, that, and the relative absence of surveillance, as parents pay to keep at least some of their children's data – and their own – from governments and corporations. In the Technocene, the privacy we take for granted today may become the biggest and most expensive luxury of all. (Techno-utopians may argue that AI-assisted schooling will end the current educational segregation caused by the world's elite corralling their offspring in private schools but in reality it could enhance the value to the rich of such exclusive institutions.)

Any information gaps left by school surveillance will be closed by the continuous data from the wearable computing in a child's clothes and accessories, enabling her to be tracked at all times by her parents – or even the police. Adults will also have wearable devices, as well as implanted ones, ranging from full-on brain electrodes to computerized chips inserted between thumb and forefinger, which are already popular in Sweden, where they serve as keys or tickets. Employers are increasingly issuing them to their workers for monitoring purposes; putting identity cards, medical records and educational qualifications on implants could be next (Metz, 2018). Tattoos, make-up and fingernails can also be transformed into computational devices (Zuboff, 2019:208). This will create a ceaseless digital chatter of humachines interacting with one another via human bodies, often bypassing conscious human control.

Techno-education ensures that by the time the Smartheid child becomes an adult, she will be fully conditioned to the severely limited choices offered by the increasingly "human-free" workplace. Even offices – their walls no doubt lined with AI-generated art – will resemble today's robot-dominated delivery warehouses, in which the movements of human workers are continuously monitored for improved performance. Perhaps 24-hour-a-day robot factories will produce most goods, from semiconductors and cars to household products and food. In service industries, management by algorithm will also be applied, although in some personal service occupations precarious human workers may be subject to daily job auctions won by the lowest bidder.

Out in the smart city, ubiquitous technological enchainment will ensure that the right to be unseen, absent or off-grid is gradually abolished. In the street, motor-skilled humachines may form a kind of "robot smog" or ant-like "supermassive robot colony" (Nourbakhsh, 2013). Even travelling by a robotic vehicle – flying or wheeled, autonomous or human-controlled – will involve stepping into another digital-robotic environment that analyses you for every possible consumer want – or sign of political non-conformity. In a techno-utopian reverie, you might imagine that the smart city is a digital jungle teeming with life. In reality it's a world of inanimate, reified objects, a "rei-verse", which transforms the living into the dead, quite unlike a breathing, swaying, singing rainforest. It won't be the Amazon just Amazon Inc.

Sex, Drugs and Virtual Reality

What will it feel like to live in this remorselessly mechanized world? For some, it may seem tolerable but only because their subjective experiences are being expertly manipulated. In a Smartheid world, gaming and virtual reality technology will attempt to erase the boundaries between external and internal reality. Large sections of the population will bury themselves inside their headsets, immersed in what Ray Kurzweil (1999:186) calls a compelling "visual-auditory-tactile virtual environment" of augmented, artificial reality. As the Technocene approaches, having an escape hatch from reality may become a psychological necessity, even if it only leads to an engineered fantasy in which most of the interaction with other humans is remote, anonymous and hyper-competitive, like the "last man standing" battles pioneered by contemporary games likes Fortnite. Virtual video games and esports may provide a form of release but one which results in a further erosion of autonomy, as gamers most intimate bio-medical and psychological data are mined for the purposes of control. The virtualization and gamification of reality will not just be for the young but for people of every generation; many older people will be only too keen to obliterate all memory of the halcyon days of their youth.

Despite some early setbacks, humachine corporations remain committed to delivering the artificial subjectivity which Mark Zuckerberg calls the metaverse, in which "you don't just see the content you are in it "(Bailey, 2021). This concept, purloined from dystopian literature, resembles the multiverse, a theory in physics of multiple (mainly very small) universes existing simultaneously and raises the prospect of creating segregated, experiential realities for users which only the humachine corporations know how to connect.

In this new "humashed" reality, sexual pleasure will often be provided by machines or digital devices. Loneliness and material scarcity will be masked by sex robots aiming to deliver orgasmic sensations or 3-D pornography in virtual or augmented reality. It remains to be seen whether this simulated sex results in the ecstasy which the singularitarians and transhumanists so eagerly anticipate. The pharmaceutical industry will also compete to become the new opium of the people, offering a cornucopia of laboratory-made recreational drugs (which avoid the inconvenience of long, expensive supply chains from the coca or poppy field). This could produce a world-wide epidemic even greater than that currently caused by synthetic drugs like Fentanyl and OxyContin. Indigenous societies have learned to regulate organic, mind-altering substances but capitalism, which is itself addictive, has always aimed to increase the habit-forming properties of its products. It deliberately targets compulsive behaviour and attempts to transform basic needs into irresistible cravings over which consumers feel they have no choice. Growthism, as we know, is the sworn enemy of moderation and self-restraint, as its basic premise is that enough can never be enough.

Big Pharma can be relied on to exploit these ontocapitalist tendencies and offer on-demand mood-altering substances to disguise an increasingly intolerable world, no doubt in combination with increased medical over-prescription of anti-depressant and anti-anxiety drugs. Further psychological manipulation may come from direct, electrical, biomedical connectivity, creating an engineered form of subjectivity which can be relied on to reduce resistance to the humachine status quo, especially among that most dangerously idealistic demographic, the young.

Simulated Democracy

A population which is permanently "out of its head" is less likely to feel the need for civic engagement or electoral participation and simulated democracy may become another dimension of the metaverse, for those who still bother to engage with politics. Hustings, voting, vote counts and electoral proceedings may take place virtually but with little connection to the real world of policy-making and legislation. We know that the surveillance corporations already have ready-made dictatorship kits to hand but simulated democracy scenarios may achieve the same goal with less violence, more consent and hence less resistance. In this virtually contrived world, you can have unlimited one-to-one conversations with holographic simulations of politicians. Your vote may even be based on your individually customized manifesto. After the election, compellingly credible statistics and deepfake video news clips may show just how faithfully your personal political programme of reforms is being "implemented".

Simulated democracy will be the easy option for authoritarian regimes concerned to persuade their citizens that some measure of political freedom of choice exists; it will certainly be easier than introducing actual democratic reforms. It will also provide a field day for tricknologists, as they work on a creative canvas of almost infinite scope, slowly painting over the concept of majority rule which has inspired humanity since the Enlightenment and replacing it with the rightwing libertarian fantasy that innovative technology is all that's required to satisfy popular needs.

The New Smartheid Pyramid

In typical techno-utopian narratives, power is either exercised by a benevolent authority or becomes unnecessary because digital technology provides such economic abundance that everybody is able to do more or less whatever they want. In reality, I'd argue, the image of the pyramid always looms over the humachine age. In the course of industrial capitalism, the steep social stratification of the population which began in the city states of Mesopotamia and Egypt may have been flattened. But, as we've seen, the humachine project has created new, contradictory and unexpected forms of inequality which threaten this progress. The smart city and its enchained digital-robotic environments create the possibility of even more novel, coercive forms of power to strengthen the apex position of the techno-elite. Indeed, the personalized pyramid society could be coming.

Throughout history, social hierarchies have been based on very broad categories predicated on property ownership, occupation and cruder cultural classifications such as gender, ethnicity, religion and sexuality. These groups – often based on nothing more profound than bodily appearance – can lock individuals into permanent positions in society. An infamous example of such stratification was the South African apartheid regime which based its social organization on a citizen's skin colour. This defined his social and economic role regardless of his personality, talents or attitudes. Politically this created a high degree of control for the white minority but in a very rudimentary way; it could not, for example, distinguish a white-skinned opponent of apartheid from a black- or brown-skinned regime supporter.

Smartheid would permit much more efficient and individualized social control, engineered around your unique data. This personalized pyramid also allows for more flexibility and social mobility. There would be no need for permanent apartheid-style "pass laws" restricting a person's movement, as "digital pass laws" can control her access to every public space and facility, and even access to and entry from her own home, on a real-time basis. Forget the "whites only" park benches of South African apartheid or the segregated buses of the pre-civil rights Southern US states, now your "citizen's score" determines whether you can even enter a park or board a bus. The front door of a building might be barred to you, while the back door might let you in. Imagine the frustration and shame as a smart turnstile refuses you entry to a bar or sports stadium, while your friends file in, or the visceral injustice of punitive surge pricing as you pay more for food or vital services than other people. Such electric shocks to your sense of self could be administered from earliest childhood, potentially creating obedience to almost any regime, however intolerable. It's a behaviourist's dream come true, creating a vast dashboard of real-time punishments and rewards.

The criterion used by the authorities to condition a citizen's behaviour will vary from one Smartheid regime to another but it's likely to include your educational and professional history, credit status, criminal and medical records, psychological reports and political affiliation, all in such extraordinary detail that only machine language will be able to make sense of it. Your citizen score will designate the physical routes available to you through a city and your algorithmically-engineered social status will determine every aspect of your life, almost from the moment of conception. Your social identity, refreshed every second you come in contact with one of billions of data-capturing devices, could determine your educational possibilities, your career options, travel permissions, the public services you are entitled to and even the purchases you can make.

For those who conform to the humachine state's ideal profile, their life choices may be relatively generous and upward social mobility rapid. Those with regime-friendly scores, for example, or high performance in STEM subjects at school, may shoot to the top of the society, while those who represent a threat to the status quo may find themselves abruptly and perhaps permanently demoted. Those who are judged to be part of the resistance to humachination – perhaps identifed by facial recognition systems trained on political demonstrations – will be most restricted in what they do. Actual incarceration may be unnecessary: humiliating and depressing measures like social isolation or permanent electronic tagging may serve just as well. Whatever your worldplan, your data will be your destiny. Who you can or can't meet, where you go and can't go, what you can and can't experience will be determined by the algorithms dictating your pathway through life. This data places you in the great digital-robotic chain of being, the individualized pyramid of power which defines who you are. As long as you don't resist too vigorously, you might even come to believe that this is the fate you have chosen for yourself.

Emerging Smartheid Regimes

In point of fact, the outlines of the Technocene are already emerging in today's embryonic Smartheid regimes. The early days of the Covid-19 pandemic showed how quickly elements of a techno-authoritarian state can now be assembled. As *The Guardian* noted, many governments began

> employing vast programmes for mobile data tracking, apps to record personal contact with others, CCTV networks equipped with facial recognition … and drones to enforce social isolation regimes (Roth et al, 2020).

In Moscow residents needed a QR code to walk on the street and in Singapore, robot patrols began barking orders at anyone not socially distancing or guilty of other "undesirable social behaviour".

As for actual smart cities, China currently has 800 of these planned or in construction, which together could house a population larger than that of the USA. China's social credit system already uses autonomous smart city technology to collect data on a citizen's credit ratings, criminal record and political history. This system is likely to improve its efficiency once larger enterprises are forced to participate in it and the digital renminbi is introduced, an electronic payment system which involves the real-time monitoring of all cash transactions (Kynge and Yu, 2021).

In Xinjiang province face-scanners, biometric checkpoints and analysis of digital communication aid in the oppression of the Uighur minority and demonstrate the next step in Smartheid. The subjection of an entire ethnic group to allegedly genocidal persecution, imprisonment, torture and murder by means of state-of-the-art digital technology, seems to indicate that a prototype of the Technocene is already in operation. Although condemned by many states, China's fast-developing techno-security industry is the world leader, attracting interest from scores of international government agencies (Byler, 2019). An even more efficient Chinese social credit system would surely take us a step closer to the ChinAImerica scenario, the global "dictdataship", outlined in Chapter 9, in which China and the US unite to control the world through their monopolization of the data on which humachine systems depend.

A similar degree of top-down control may be achieved in Neom, the $500 billion smart city of the future being planned in north-western Saudi

Arabia. Most of what we know about this eco-modernist megacity with its solar energy, flying cars and animatronic dinosaurs comes from a typically humachine age mixture of press release hype and investor pitching. "Neom" means the future in Arabic but what kind of future it promises we can probably glean from the present Saudi police state which has one of the worst human rights records in the world. The colonialist pattern of Neom's foundation, which reportedly involves the forceful displacement of a Bedouin tribe from its homeland, gives us another clue (Rothwell, 2020). So too does the identity of its originator, Crown Prince Mohammad bin Salman, whom the US Director of National Intelligence (2021) concluded had "approved an operation in Istanbul, Turkey to kill or capture the Saudi journalist Jamal Khashoggi". But in Neom, who would ever know about such a crime?

Google's attempt to create a smart city in Toronto, which I referred to in Chapter 1, was rejected by its citizens on the grounds of privacy but we can be fairly sure that the citizens of Neom are not likely to be offered the same choice. The same may apply to other smart cities being planned by US billionaires such as Marc Lore's Telosa (another $500 billion venture) or Bill Gates's plan for a 2,800- acre smart city near Phoenix Arizona (Alsever, 2021). Many other such plans exist across the world and in their blueprints we can catch more than a glimpse of what the Technocene might look like.

Will Mecans Arise from "the Humash"?

At this point, I have to confess to feeling a sense of defeat in depicting the totally humachinated environment: trying to imagine the unimaginable eventually takes its toll. It's easy to fall into the left-brain trap of portraying Type 5 humachination as an external reality rather than something that is also simultaneously internal, as controlled rather than chaotic and as a mechanical phenomenon (in the old-fashioned sense) instead of a fluid, integrated, digital-robotic system penetrating every level of electrical and bio-chemical existence. This environment is a mash-up of objectivity and subjectivity, hardware and software. In fact, this "humash" of lived experience could be the reverse of the controlled left-brain nirvana which the neomechanicalists envisage. It might feel more like a nightmare of shifting perspectives, traps and concealments, an acid trip exacerbated by the actual drugs in your bloodstream. Imagine a room abruptly altering its dimensions in response to your mood or a car changing its direction due to your unconscious thoughts. From a psychological standpoint, the humash would be a state of constant conflict, as your robotic doctor, counsellor, teacher, parent, police officer, political candidate, "ideal sex companion" and all the other brands of humachines in your life, compete to define what's good for you.

We also have to fold into this mashed-up, smashed-up storm of contradictions the effects of the mechanization of humans and the meditechnic systems which are intended to manipulate you from within, connecting you unconsciously to the world without. Brain implants for reminding people to take their medication, will probably be used to try to control a much wider range of behaviours, with all the mental confusion this will bring. Consider also that the AI informing every aspect of the humash is constantly reinforcing its inner logic by training on trillions of data produced by the humash itself. This makes its own "madsanity" seem like the only possible existential dimension.

As for gene-editing and the development of synthetic organs, the Smartheid world with its high-walled "separate developments", secretive military establishments and deregulated economic zones provides the ideal setting for wild post-biological and transhumanist experimentation. In time, the ideologues who are currently fighting to abolish all restrictions on human mechanization may get their way. Genetic engineering to prevent diseases and disabilities will be the first to be legalized. After that the bioethical dam which today holds back gene-editing and human cloning could collapse completely, allowing the ultra-wealthy to attempt to engineer their children's intelligence or resurrect their dead parents (with well-known singularitarians at the head of the queue). The request for cloning which Gregory Stock (2013:32) had from a father whose son had just committed suicide would not be turned down in a right-wing libertarian techno-utopia. If an ontocapitalist wants something badly enough, he will invoke Ayn Rand's provocative phrase, "who is going to stop me?" The unofficial credo of Silicon Valley could become the only bioethical law that counts.

When it comes to creating real cyborgs, this medical Trojan horse may well be given free rein, trampling the line between augmentation and reparation into the mud. With billions of dollars of meditechnics investment capital at stake and bioethical regulations as riddled with loopholes as current tax evasion legislation, ambitious neurotechnologists may find subjects for transhumanist experimentation among the same financially desperate people who today facilitate the black market in human organs. We might even see criminals, terrorists or other "enemies of the regime" used for transhuman experimental purposes. If things get desperate enough in the climate and biodiversity emergency, which even the apex class cannot escape entirely, a Manhattan Project-style programme for a full-scale, superintelligent, bio-mechanized, genetically engineered "super-race" may be organized. The goal would be to conquer nature once and for all, thereby fulfilling the ancient dreams of mechanistic science and achieving ontocapitalism's more recent aim of engineering evolution.

Nobody can know the outcome for sure but in the final analysis my guess is that limitless ultrascience is likely to run up against the actual limits of biology and come off distinctly second best. I sincerely doubt that the transhumanist and singularitarian fantasy of a full-blown cyborgoisie will ever come to pass. I also take with a huge pinch of salt the prediction of influential historian Yuval Noah Harari (2016:50-53) that "the new human agenda" will give humans "divine powers" and "upgrade Homo sapiens into Homo deus", which, I suggest, derives from his succumbing to the classic neomechanicalist fallacy that "bioengineers will take the old Sapiens body, and intentionally rewrite its genetic code, rewire its brain circuits [and] alter its biochemical balance".

What is more probable if humachination is allowed to continue is that an ever-greater proportion of medical resources will be funnelled into the longevity and health of the ultra-wealthy, which may result in some extremely expensive minor advances in synthetic organs and nanomedicine. A more predictable outcome would be innumerable cases of botched surgery and an explosion of Frankenstein-like unintended consequences. In the end, these horrors might become so socially disruptive that the leadership class will be compelled to call time on human mechanization. Failure will be glossed over by the tricknologists, who will attempt to endow a superficially augmented techno-elite with the cachet of a "super race", especially if round-the-clock medical supervision enables them to live twice as long as the poorest strata of the population. Unfortunately, the fact that the techno-elute remain largely biological after all will not necessarily prevent it from exercising godlike authority over the harshly segregated world of the Technocene.

CHAPTER 23

Bleaker Technocene Scenarios and the Problem with the Resistance

Some readers may argue that the preceding chapter reads rather too much like a wish fulfilment of the humachination dream. Indeed, the relatively seamless transition to the Technocene I've sketched out takes little account of the possible end of economic growth. Renowned economist Nouriel Roubini is no degrowther but in *Megathreats* (2022) he forecasts a host of reasons why capitalism may implode in the coming decades, including "the mother of all debt crises" (triggered perhaps by $78 trillion of underfunded pensions), stagflation, currency meltdown and various demographic "time bombs": this may well be the way growth dies. But even these disasters would pale beside the desperate extremes of global disruption which will occur if capitalism continues down what the UN General Secretary calls our current "highway to climate hell", amid the possible collapse of multiple Earth systems (Frangoul, 2022).

In fine, there's no doubt that the humachination project could lead to an even more menacing version of the Technocene, which we need to try to imagine now. In this worst-case scenario, techno-dystopia collides with planetary breakdown in the wastelands of democracy. From an ecologically-ravaged planet, a chaotic new global pyramid emerges that further increases the hegemony of the Global North. In this segregated world, automated surveillance states struggle to maintain stability, often by violent means, while humachine corporations are afforded lavish opportunities to fulfil their wildest visions, bypassing whatever rudimentary forms of democratic consultation still exist.

Climate Collapse and the Fortress North

The most obvious triggers for the ultimate global unlevelling will come from the shockingly destructive ecological damage caused by a global economy still fundamentally based on burning fossil fuel. Despite the Paris and Glasgow climate agreements, the planet is still heading towards a temperature of 2.5-2.9C by 2100, which could continue to rise thereafter, according to Climate Action Tracker (2023a). That temperature would create "unliveable" conditions for at least a third of world's population, three billion people or more, according to Lenton et al (2023), who suggest that 600 million people, 9% of the global population, already live outside the "climate niche" of habitable land. If radical decarbonization is not achieved by 2030, the result will be increasing frequency and intensity of floods, storms, droughts, desertification and other climate extremes. Deforestation, changing land use, habitat degradation and species extinction, combined with conflict and civil rest, could lead to the displacement of over a billion people by 2050, international think tank IEP estimates (2020), creating hundreds of millions of climate refugees. Runaway global warming of well beyond 3C could occur if multiple tipping points are triggered, including substantial sea level rises caused by collapsing ice sheets, the dieback of biodiverse biomes like the Amazon and the detonation of methane bombs from the deep sea and thawing permafrost (Armstrong Mckay et al, 2022).

Environmental disasters are already affecting the Global North, as indicated by the hundreds of deaths caused by flooding in Germany in 2021 and the now annual California wildfire season, but the South will bear the brunt of the destruction caused by industrialization. For example, floods in Pakistan in 2022 affected over 30 million people and left millions homeless (Sands, 2022). Famine, civil war, humanitarian crises, water and land conflicts and other resource clashes may become endemic for the vast majority of the world's population, if the carbon budget for remaining within 2C is exceeded.

A Fortress North may emerge as the wealthy 20% take extreme, technology-aided measures to keep out the vast numbers from the Global South seeking sanctuary from ecocide (Raskin et al, 2002). In this multi-crisis, protectionist nationalism will force governments to turn inwards. Temporary suspensions of democracy are likely to become permanent – or be replaced by simulated democracy – while sham democracies abandon the pretence of elections and authoritarian regimes claim that they were right all along to reject majority rule. In this "hot Hobbesian world", geographer Peter Christoff (2016) foresees "adaptive states" existing in "a permanent state of climate emergency". Wealthy nations will do scarcely better than failed states, as they are dragged down by huge shadow economies and a massive premium on external defence and internal order. Christoff forecasts a possible return to the typical nineteenth-century national budget, which allocated 25% to military and policing expenditure and only 5% to social services, as "the welfare state becomes the warfare state".

In this scenario, the demand for new humachinated military and security technology and substandard "better than nothing" public services would be huge. This breakdown in the relationship between humanity and nature, partially caused by the way we choose to use our technology, will provide the ideal pretext for enforcing a human future dominated by technology. Governments of the right, left and centre may be too committed to AI, robotics and other fourth industrial revolution policies to chart any other course, even if many in the population demand it. The end of economic growth may bring the end of capitalism as we know it but not the end of a social hierarchy headed by elites which dominate the use and purpose of all technology. On the contrary, the principle of plutotechnics, which has driven every Promethean age since the Agricultural Revolution, will now take its purest form. The charade of social equality can now be dropped as ontopreneurs and their retinue of highly-paid technicians and compliant politicians take complete charge.

A desperate majority may now be persuaded that the only alternative to ecological catastrophe is the bet-the-planet geoengineering experiments that many humachinators currently advocate. Doubling down on the almost certain failure of these experiments may seem like the only option left, as calamitous UNCs summon up even more extreme counter-technologies. This further plays into the hands of the techno-elite, creating new opportunities for accelerated space and ocean colonialism, plus deep-sea mining for the rare minerals desperately needed by green growthism. Various forms of biotechnology and genetic engineering will also be touted as the only way to adapt humanity to a disintegrating biosphere.

Job automation will accelerate, as the elite increasingly rely on fleets of robotic workers for their basic needs, necessitating many of the population controls which we've seen that the humachinated, digital-robotic environment offers. Softer, lived experience manipulation will be backed up by much harder forms of coercion. The ready-made digital dictatorship kit can now be fully activated. In what will be presented as a permanent state of war, total surveillance will become the norm. The last remnants of private, personal data will be surrendered, either voluntarily out of "patriotic duty" or as demanded by martial law. Imposing a more brutal variety of Technocene apartheid won't be difficult through autonomous police patrols and the increasingly well-armed private security forces protecting private property, as the privileged retreat further into heavily fortified gated communities. Private armies like today's Wagner group of mercenaries and other Russian oligarch-owned corporate militias will become commonplace for the elite. For the most recalcitrant, killer robotics and other autonomous weaponry currently being developed by the military may be deployed.

Increasingly it will be the developing world which is likely to be blamed for the climate and ecological collapse, another reason why China-US military conflict may be on the cards (perhaps as a stormy prelude to their global "dictdataship" marriage of convenience) or even a new world war. The North will claim that its reduction in GHG emissions and trumpeted green growth policies absolve it of blame, ignoring the fact that the US is still by far the biggest historic CO_2 polluter since 1850 and up until 1970 the UK was the third biggest emitter in history (Evans, 2021).

At its most extreme, de facto "depopulation" policies for the majority world may turn out to be the Global North's default solution to the Anthropocene Crisis. These do not have to be actively implemented – although unmanned drones, aircraft and naval vessels will make massive remote strikes possible with seemingly "clean hands". Simply doing nothing behind the giant, high-tech barriers and fortified sea borders of the Fortress North will be enough. In any case, regime supporters may claim that reports of millions dying of starvation or disease is simply "wokery", made up by "virtue-signalling" progressives, denials which may not even be needed if media silence and enforced internet censorship ensure that the majority are kept ignorant of the Malthusian population rebalancing taking shape across the planet.

Shadow economies will rapidly spread across the entire world, creating a new generation of white-collar organized crime bosses. One report estimates that global cybercrime already costs the world $8 trillion a year, which would make it the world's third largest economy, and that it's mushrooming at 15% a year (Morgan, 2022). Here is the real hypergrowth predicted by the singularitarians, a bonanza of criminality which would have been impossible without digital technology, creating oceans of dark money that can irrigate every imaginable type of anti-social venture on the planet.

These bleaker scenarios of the Technocene may involve more rigid social hierarchies than Smartheid affords. For Joel Kotkin (2020), the destruction of middle-class occupations which we noted earlier foreshadows a "neofeudalist" future. Add to this, the possibility of a demoralized working class, deskilled and dehumanized by working alongside robots, trying to survive in a fragmented, rights-stripping, global economy. Yanis Varoufakis (2023) takes the idea of historical regression to the next level in *Technofeudalism* (2023), comparing corporations like Amazon to feudal overlords granting fiefs to selected digital businesses, which are policed by the same algorithmic "sheriffs" which extract our personal data for advertising. In this version of the global "dictdataship", Big Tech's monopolistic control of the market is so absolute that ontocapitalism technically becomes post-capitalist.

Other AImageddon Scenarios: Beware of Bad Actors

An even more drastic end-game is the AImageddon scenario that I have already touched on at various points in this book, in which superintelligent machines take over the world. This potential doomsday is rightly seen by humachinators as an unavoidable risk. If you aim to create machines that are more intelligent than humans you can't ignore the possibility that these entities will treat their creators as the inferior beings they have turned themselves into, with potentially dire consequences. It may only take one rogue self-learning algorithm to gain access to the internet to create a chain reaction that puts the digital and robotic resources of the entire planet at its disposal.

As we've seen, the only plausible way to avoid this nightmare scenario that philosophers like Nick Bostrom can conjure up is to instil AIs with "human-friendly" goals and values. But this is currently impossible since there is no agreement on what such a worldplan would look like. At present, what's more probable is that machines which are trained on the data of our humachines age will inherit the GUN goals and CIMENT values of the power-obsessed, colonizing, and occasionally genocidal, civilization that created them. If superintelligent machines are imbued with the anti-social intentionality of capitalism, why would they not become a fatal threat to humanity and nature?

In reality, I suggest, more realistic threats may come not from machines that develop consciousness – a concept largely predicated on the mistaken belief that the brain is a computer – but from the vast potential for human error that the mere existence of the humachine project generates. Even Ray Kurzweil admits that "If the wrong people take control of AI that could be bad for the rest of us (Rose, 2023). It's easy to define these "bad actors" as organized crime groups or terrorist organizations who get hold of AI systems, but who exactly are the "good actors"? Do they include the scientists experimenting with human-machine fusion in top-secret defence institutions and corporate laboratories? In fact, the greatest risk may come from states themselves, already engaged in a winner-takes-all AI arms race. In the no-holds-barred military conflicts which ecocide may provoke, robotic weaponry may be allowed to run amok and lethal biological or chemical weapons deployed or released accidentally. And can we rule out "suicide by genocide" in a world where spree killers regularly take down as many innocent victims as they can before turning their guns on themselves? The more our leaders encourage the uncritical worship of machines, the more attractive it may seem to a fanatical lone wolf to hack into the world's digital-robotic management systems and unleash hell.

Lastly, we shouldn't discount the effects of ambitious human mechanization surgery that goes wrong. Driven to breaking point by the computerized electrodes in their heads, experimental subjects may feel compelled to access the internet and enlist the aid of the humachines with which they now psychologically identify. It would be the left hemisphere's ultimate Pyrrhic victory, the moment the rogue emissary declares triumph over the wise master. We might even hear Claude Shannon's confession – "I've always been on the machines' side!" – in the crazed scream that accompanies the keystroke that launches AImageddon. It would at least be a fittingly hubristic conclusion to the madness of human-machine fusion.

Problems with the Resistance

By now you may be thinking that I'm hugely underestimating the widespread resistance to the Technocene which is likely to occur, in whichever future scenario unfolds. On the contrary, there's no doubt in my mind that there will be massive opposition to humachination's tendency to shut down freedom. Even since 2019 when I began researching this book, the tide of public opinion has been turning against anti-competitive humachine conglomerates and the heroic image of the Big Tech billionaire has soured significantly. As the Technocene looms into view the opposition will grow even greater. Women who lose out the most from job automation, professionals made redundant by software, older people being fobbed off with machine carers, children with mental health problems caused by social media and all who realise that green growth can never assuage their eco-anxiety: the demographic groups protesting against the development of the humachine age will be legion. And it's not just in the traditional arena of labour versus capital where the battle for the future will be won or lost. As John Holloway (2002:41) suggests, there are "a million forms of resistance, an immensely complex world of antagonisms". Many exist below the radar of conventional politics in the actions, commitments and refusals of civil society and in the individuals and groups who create "cracks" in capitalism, which prefigure post-growth behaviours that can lead to revolutionary outcomes

But will this be enough to prevent the Technocene? The danger is that too many politicians, activists and citizens are blindsided by the sheer range of challenges facing us in the Anthropocene Crisis. The bewildering multi-crisis of the humachine age creates constant distraction, short-term urgencies and emergencies, which make deciding on policy priorities an enormous challenge. The way digital capitalism presents itself as a cure for carbon capitalism, while actually perpetuating it, is one example of how hard it can be to tell friend from foe. The dromological tyranny of speed means that the next technology-caused problem only becomes apparent when it's too late, making it monumentally difficult for governments to win the regulatory war against Big Tech's armies of lobbyists and lawyers.

The tricknologists will continue to leverage every minor scientific advance and revel in capitalism's traditional adroitness in turning critiques of it into defences.

Above all, the humachinators will play the jobs card. In an economic system in which employment is controlled by "wealth creators", who are also seen as paying for the public services which citizens provide for each other, losing a job can look like losing your life. Cost-reducing corporations will cut deals over automation with anxious labour unions (where they still exist), trading existing jobs for training in jobs which themselves may soon disappear. Meanwhile, workers in precarious, non-unionized industries will continue to be marginalized.

Another key struggle will be intergenerational. An international survey of 16-25-year-olds found that three quarters agree with the statement that "the future is frightening" and 83% thought that "people have failed to take care of the planet" (Hickman et al, 2021). But how many of the 65-plus population will concur? In most developed nations, this group already owns most of the wealth and much of the political power and is due to represent almost a third of the population of the West by 2050. Will the anxiety-induced perspicacity of the young be thwarted by the complacent selfishness of the old? As Max Bohr once suggested, scientific paradigm shifts only occur when enough of the older generation dies out (Kuhn, 1962). Or will those older people who are acutely conscious of their responsibility to the future come to the fore? Either way, it's a tangled web of conflicting interests that doesn't bode well for decisive, coordinated action.

Finally, will a "too nice" syndrome debilitate the political will of the well-intentioned of all ages, who fail to realise what they are really up against? As this book has tried to demonstrate, it's all too easy to underestimate the lengths to which capitalism will go to ensure its survival, aided by ultrascientists determined to stop at nothing in their Faustian pursuit of absolute knowledge.

A Confusion of Goals and Values

In sum, the biggest problem for the resistance to the Technocene may be the lack of a coherent, viable alternative to it. Our ontological failure to reach any clarity about what it is to be human on planet Earth advantages those who have a decisive mechanistic answer to this question. Rebelling against the Technocene will be much easier than uniting in favour of something else. Short of a worldplan as cunningly coherent as growth capitalism, resistance may falter. History shows how popular movements that lack clear goals usually fail, however inspiring they may be to begin with (Engler and Engler, 2016).

Part of the problem, as we've seen, is unconscious capitalism and the way pro-growth, unequalist and anti-nature organizing principles infiltrate the political models of those who consciously seek a different solution. It's impossible to replace a system by using the same goals and values on which it's founded. "Conservativism", as political scientist Alan Finlayson (2020) rightly reminds us, "has always been, at root, a defence of inequality" and right-wingers value economic growth as a way of achieving this goal, although some may deplore the desecration of nature it necessitates. Liberals see economic growth as a virtue itself, one that seems to guarantee democracy, civil rights and a more equitable distribution of profits. But trying to have your cake and eating is ultimately a losing strategy. Separating "good capitalism" from "bad capitalism" (or Zuboff's "rogue" version) still leaves you with capitalism which, in my extensive experience of working with profit-based organizations, invariably reverts to the bottom line which its shareholders value most. If the freedoms which liberals prize most depend on growth and growth demands more innovation in AI, robots and biotechnology, it's pretty certain which way these centrists will jump.

Socialist and social democratic models are more committed to egalitarianism and social justice but also see economic expansion as the magic key to a better world and tend to be infatuated with technology in its own right. In 2023, the leader of the British Labour Party even pledged to make the growth-stricken UK the fastest growing economy in the G7 group of wealthy nations (Bruce, 2023). Too often techno-socialism represents not an alternative to capitalism but an alternative way of managing it, in the interest of the majority to be sure, but with the same implicit goals. Leftwing accelerationism, which uncritically accepts the humachine philosophy of abundance and eagerly anticipates an economy entirely run by mechanical slaves, is even more hazardous (Bastani, 2019).

Even the ecological perspective on nature in the era of green growthism can be corrupted. As we noted in Chapter 8, ecomodernism may mitigate some of the environmental threats to the Global North but largely leaves the South to its own devices. Nor can the rise of an eco-authoritarianism of the left or right be entirely ruled out. Of course, it would be foolish to underestimate the liberating effects of involvement in protest movements and political struggle at the local and national level nor the impact of continued eco-dystopian events. Nevertheless, the risk remains that the opposition continues to adhere to the same goals and values as capital-ism, which opens up ideological fissures which the techno-elite of the humachine age with their slippery tricknology, Trojan horses and secretive material power are only too willing and able to exploit. As the feminist poet Audre Lorde (1984) once wrote, "The master's tools will never dismantle the master's house".

A final danger is techno-defeatism, which sees the coming of tech-no-dystopia as inevitable but more or less impossible to prevent. For all its intellectual brilliance, Noah Yuval Harari's *Homo Deus* succumbs to a kind of neomechanicalist fatalism, offering no real alternative to a future its author clearly deplores. Likewise, Nouriel Roubini (2022), whose book I referenced earlier, spends 260 pages describing the dire threats menacing capitalism (including mass jobicide and AImageddon) before devoting his final chapter to "a utopian solution" that might enable us survive them. And what's the cure this famously contrarian predictor of capitalist calamities comes up with? Sustained economic growth of 5-6% per annum – hyper-growth in fact, at a level no OECD country has consistently managed for half a century, delivered (of course) by "technological innovation". It's techno-utopian miracle-ism so lacking in conviction as to be almost embarrassing and a classic reminder of how much easier it is to envisage the end of the world than the end of capitalism. It confirms yet again how desperately we need something different, a cardinal shift in goals and values, a new worldplan based on new organizing principles. In short, we need to bust out of the growth paradigm before it busts us.

CHAPTER 24

Towards the Ecocene: The SEWP Worldplan for Sustainable Degrowth

The Sustainable Degrowth Revolution: Throw GUN Away

It would take a book to do justice to the Ecocene and, to be fair, that's what *Utopia in the Anthropocene* attempted to do (which is why I'll refer the reader to it at various points in what follows). But the principle of the post-growth, eco-democracy challenge is disarmingly simple: to put the horse before the cart and decide on a scientifically valid worldplan that prioritizes what is most important about being human. The Ecocene change of direction also means embracing the primacy of political choice, the secret law of technology throughout the ages. All the arguments of the humachinators which I've tried to deconstruct in previous chapters, from growthism and technological determinism to neomechanicalism and consumerism, are meant to debilitate human choice-making, thus making the Technocene harder to prevent. At this crucial juncture in our history, we need to step back and conduct a great stocktaking of humanness, freeing ourselves from the mystifications of technological capitalism and the machine mindset while taking advantage of the most socially beneficial innovations of the past three centuries.

In short, it's time to throw GUN away and jettison the growth irrationale. For all its surreal extremism, the project of humanizing machines and mechanizing humans is simply the logical outcome of maintaining our current world system's number one goal of increasing GDP forever, regardless of its consequences for people or planet. To change the default setting of techno-utopian ontocapitalism and wrench ourselves out of our current trajectory towards the Technocene, a very different paradigm is required

A new worldplan is based on new goals, the most powerful motivators humanity has, which determine our intentionality and future direction, both personally and collectively. The SEWP goals and CANDID values, which I've promoted throughout this book, are not the only possible blueprint for the Ecocene but they provide at least one vision of how we can rebalance our relationship with nature and reset our priorities for technological development. The eco-democratic model is also a paradigm-shift that can fully realise the vast psychological potential of being human and create a new renaissance in democracy, including demotechnic conventions for making decisions about what matters most – as we'll discover in the next chapter.

Britain may even turn out to be the canary in the mine: first into the industrial revolution and perhaps first out. The next decade will certainly test how much economic growth has left in the locker. If Tim Jackson (2022) is right and "to all intents and purposes, we're already living in a post-growth world". it will become impossible to keep the degrowth debate out of everyday politics and economics. Revolutions happen when the existing worldplan becomes so untenable that a radically new one is adopted, even if some of its principles remain unproven, the way Newtonian physics was replaced by Einstein's theories of relativity (Kuhn, 1962). The perceived world changes dramatically, as new priorities cause old blind spots to disappear and new realities come into view. So over the next two chapters let's look at some of the measures that would flow from the SEWP worldplan it we could put it into practice today.

The SEWP Worldplan: Eco-Democratic Goals and Values

Goal 1. Sustainable Degrowth

Shifting from capitalism to a post-growth society is to move from the mechanistic-mathematical fiction of limitless expansion to a model of organic growth as it occurs in nature. Instead of depicting society as an abstract, machine-like economy, it reveals it as a people-planet dialectic, a dynamic relationship between humans and a planet that abounds in life.

The key goal of organic life is balance or homeostasis, achieving a steady state between inputs and outputs, as described by ecological economists (e.g. Daly and Farley, 2011). This steady state is crucial to life but at the moment the world economy is as far from that condition as it has ever been; it exists in a state of comprehensive imbalance that violates multiple planetary boundaries with devastating consequences for all forms of life. The goal of sustainable degrowth means focusing on taking from nature only what can be regenerated, while accepting that over time the entropic depletion of resources is probably inevitable.

One of the highest priorities is to reduce the carbon footprint of high-income countries. Relying on green growth to begin the transition to a post-growth society as Ian Gough envisaged (2017) is no longer viable, if it ever was: we need a much more rapid, planned contraction of production and consumption in the Global North. Effective government action on decarbonization requires the immediate termination of current exploration of oil and gas, an end to subsidies for fossil fuel producers and rapid progress towards the cessation of most fossil fuel extraction (Welsby et al, 2021). Reducing methane emissions, which account for 25% of global warming, can bring quick gains, as can increased taxation on all polluting industries (EDF, 2022). Ecological urban planning would move us in the direction of car-free cities, with more parks and inner forests and new small towns restricting urban sprawl. This would be accompanied by a speedy transition to clean-energy public transport, with the provision of bike and walking routes to reduce private car use. A "green jobs guarantee to train and mobilize labour", as called for by a group of post-growth economists, would provide some of the workforce for this transition, as well as facilitating the mass insulation of housing stock, the regeneration of ecosystems and improvements in social care (Hickel et al, 2022).

Democratic changes in land ownership can free up land to provide good, ecologically efficient housing for all (perhaps containing household appliances that are built for life). Land Value Tax, increasingly championed by mainstream economists, is one way to facilitate this (e.g.Tideman et al, 2022). Changes in agricultural policy would aim at increasing food security and putting an emphasis on healthy, plant-based diets. Reductions in mass-produced meat and dairy are urgently needed. Livestock farming currently takes up three-quarters of the world's available farmland while only providing 18% of global calorie consumption; on top of this, it contributes a sixth of global GHG emissions (Ritchie, 2019). Reforestation programmes will help to protect the world's carbon sinks and prevent new pandemics of zoonotic diseases, while rewilding will also help to reverse biodiversity loss and give everybody a greater stake in nature.

Specific measures to combat humachine corporations will focus on strong anti-monopoly legislation, breaking up the existing Big Tech monoliths and changing corporate ownership structures to increase the power of all stakeholders and privilege cooperative, non-profit, post-growth constitutions. The fiduciary duty of corporate executives to prioritize the bottom line urgently needs to be abrogated (Bakan, 2004). However, making Big Tech corporations smaller is only part of the solution; it may reduce the harm new technologies can do before they are detected, as Cory Doctorow says (2023), but if greater competition results in even more innovation the challenge for responsible regulators just increases.

Firm restrictions on advertising, as long advocated by environmentalists, would not only help to reduce consumption but would have a profound effect on communicative humachines. Google starved of its vast advertising revenues would soon be forced to contract, even without anti-monopoly legislation. Other non-profit-based systems are available for disseminating impartial information about genuinely useful products and services. (Indeed, imagining capitalism shorn of advertising, marketing and lobbying is a useful, prefigurative thought experiment.) Likewise, social media run on cooperative, community-based, non-profit lines would eliminate the algorithmic amplification that encourages social polarization. Basic technology designed to last as long as possible, with fixable, replaceable parts (and recyclable when repair is no longer feasible) would replace luxury versions. Long-term guarantees and limits on upgrades of a new smartphone every fifteen years, for example, would soon cut conglomerates like Apple down to a human scale. Government action on unnecessary packaging (including fast fashion) will reduce waste and free up valuable resources. Other measures to make addiction capitalist practices illegal would combat online gambling, violent pornography and abusive social media. These are just some of the interventions that would help to provide the dramatic reduction in Western consumption and production which is the only possible route to global sustainability.

A Genuine Response to the AI Emergency

Adopting the SEWP worldplan also means decisively rejecting the idea that human-machine fusion is the true destiny of humanity. It implies accepting that alongside the climate and biodiversity emergency, we have an AI emergency, which is potentially as serious in its consequences. Putting effective limitations on AI-enabled technology are essential, if the humachine age is to be prevented from morphing into the Technocene.

As previously suggested, it may be that 2023 marks the point where the age of humachines finally began to become self-aware. In March of that year, an open letter from over a thousand AI insiders, including Elon Musk, called for a six-month moratorium on the training of large language models (LLMs) to enable external software engineers to take stock: "Powerful AI systems should be developed only once we are confident that their effects will be positive and their risks will be manageable" (Future of Life Institute, 2023).

This sounds sensible at first but the "we" seems to refer only to the AI industry and the focus seems confined to generative AI alone. A six-month moratorium, even if it were granted, would hardly be sufficient, although, it's true, if this principle had been applied in the past, unregulated social media, surveillance systems, BCI, LAWS and many other subjects in this book might never have been allowed to get beyond the research stage. The letter's claim that decisions about creating "non-human minds" and other AI projects that "risk loss of our control of our civilization" "should not be delegated to unelected tech leaders" is similarly tricky, especially coming from the likes of Elon Musk and employees from other humachine behemoths heavily committed to AI. Indeed, later in the year, one of the moratorium's main sponsors, Max Tegmark, conceded that the initiative was doomed to failure, as the Big Tech leaders were "trapped in this race to the bottom against each other" (Milmo, 2023). This was confirmed in November 2023 by OpenAI's capitalist apostasy when CEO Sam Altman was apparently sacked for not informing the company's safety-conscious, non-profit board about the advanced AI products he was developing, only to be reinstated days later by a new, more commercially-orientated board, backed by Microsoft (Titcomb and Field, 2023).

A more honest approach would be to face up to the possibility that there is something inherently undemocratic about the basic AGI goal to create superintelligence, which is at the core of the humachination vision. (Altman has admitted that products like ChatGPT3 are merely "channels into our one single product, which is intelligence, magic intelligence in the sky" (Murgla, 2023).) By definition, this project risks disenfranchizing humans from their own destiny. Furthermore, only a tiny minority of the population have the computer skills to fully understand this process and most of the techno-elite are themselves now barred from independently assessing generative AI systems, as 96% of them are in the hands of the Big Tech monopolies, rather than governments or academic institutions (Ahmed et al, 2023).

This is perhaps why even the AI industry has begun to panic, finding itself excluded from software, which is developing at dromological hyper-speed. Many software engineers were understandably alarmed by Geoffrey Hinton, who after 50 years of pioneering machine learning, finally woke up to the existential risks of AI. (Should we label this the "Dr Frankenstein moment", when the proud scientist realises he has created a monster?) Hinton claimed that Google, his former employer, had behaved "responsi-bly" in its AI development unlike Microsoft. However, "the problem is, in a capitalist system, if your competitor does that [i.e., behaves irresponsibly] you can but do the same" (Hern, 2023). Ultrascientists cannot let them-selves off the hook quite so easily, however. After all, AI's "dirty secret" is that machine learning is not only unpredictable but unknowable, even in retrospect, so the more the holy grail of superintelligence is pursued, the more humanity's control of the world is jeopardized. Believing that AGI is still several decades away – as Hinton says he believed, in common with many other AI developers – is another act of bad faith, since it simply dumps the responsibility on to future generations to deal with possible disasters in a way that mirrors climate change delayism.

In practice, putting "guardrails around AI", as governments are beginning to promise, is hugely problematic. Some claim AI can be regulated like bio-technogy (in relation to cloning, for example) or pharmaceutical products but this ignores just how institutionalized AI has already become and the profound anti-biology bias of the neomechanicalist worldview. A regulator along the lines of the International Atomic Energy Agency risks formal-izing the monopolistic position of the current humachine corporations, paralleling the way in which nuclear power has been confined to a select group of nations. (In this context, it's worth remembering that relatively controlled nuclear proliferation represents a defeat for what many progressives have long campaigned for: nuclear disarmament.) Putting all AI development under public ownership – perhaps confining it to a CERN-like island of pure science – would be a better option but it still leaves out the question of who decides which AI innovations should be commercialized. And as for making all AI software publicly available, we should heed the experts who have described the launch of Meta's open-source rival to ChatGPT, Llama 2, as comparable to "giving people a template to make a nuclear bomb" (Sellman, 2023b).

The truth is that shifting from AI "light touch" deregulation, for which the humachinators have long argued, to a framework sufficiently muscular to make any difference threatens to derail the entire 4IR, science and technology agenda of the twenty-first century, on which all hopes of economic growth are based. Truly reining in AI-enabled humachination could even spell the end of capitalism.

2023 may come to resemble 1992, the year of the UN's Earth Summit in Rio de Janeiro. At that point the world began its efforts to manage the threat of climate change and yet over three decades later we are still mining for coal and drilling for oil and gas as GHG emissions keep rising. If AI corporations were prepared to take the lead, for example by devoting 99% of their development budgets to AI safety, as opposed to less than 1% now, this might be a step in the right direction. Instead, AI delayism and parallelism are likely to set in, while behind the scenes Big Tech mounts a gargantuan lobbying campaign to influence legislators to create lenient guardrails that protect AI from the public rather than the public from AI (although the EU and China may be provide slightly tougher regulation than the US).

The AI equivalent of greenwashing is already emerging, in part through the constant framing of AI as a force in which the rewards will far outweigh the risks. As Meta's chief AI scientist Yann LeCun phrases it, "intelligent machines will usher in a new renaissance for humanity, a new era of enlightenment" (Heaven, 2023). Whether the practical implementation of President Joe Biden's US Executive Order of October 30th 2023 on the "safe, secure and trustworthy development and use of artificial intelligence" seriously disrupts this techno-utopian position remains highly doubtful (Whitehouse.gov, 2023). Certainly, the British Bletchley Park AI Summit a few days later failed to ruffle any Big Tech feathers, offering no legislative

plans and ending with the ominous spectacle of Elon Musk being obse-
quiously interviewed by British Prime Minister and former investment
banker, Rishi Sunak. Did anybody believe these two leaders represent "the
good actors", in whose hands AI development is said to be safe? (Very few,
it seems, as contemporaneous polling found that only 18% of the British
public were optimistic about the overall impact of AI and almost three
quarters doubted the UK government's ability to "effectively regulate" it
(Smith, 2023).)

In reality, I suggest, the only adequate solution to the multiple threats of
humachination is a permanent moratorium on all advanced AI, including
attempts to emulate human cognition and emotions, particularly in the
form of unsupervised, self-generating machine learning. ("Ban AI" will
need to become a slogan even more resonant than "Ban the Bomb" once
was.) The end result may be that all computer programming will have to
be confined to relatively simple, highly transparent usages, which would
genuinely keep humans in the loop of all complex decision-making. If the
moratorium is lifted, it should be as a result of popular consent, ideally
by means of demotechnic forums which put world-changing technological choices in the hands of the "we" of humanity. Deliberative assemblies
– explored in the next chapter – will provide much-needed external evaluation and the oversight capable of shutting down operations if necessary. If
Big Tech wanted to help it could contribute to defining the "human values",
which, as we know, AI experts believe should be programmed into potentially superintelligent machines from the outset because this alone can
prevent the possibility of AImageddon. Ontocapitalists could put some of
the billions of dollars at their disposal to resource this research project and
then put its conclusions forward for the approval of the majority of humanity. If this challenge cannot be met, advanced AI development should be
curtailed until such time as safer, democratically acceptable solutions can
be found to the momentous changes threatened by the humachination
project.

Robotics, Personal Eugenics and Meditechnics

As for robotics, the SEWP worldplan could include "a new treaty to maintain meaningful human control over the use of force", banning LAWS
and other varieties of killer robotics, as Human Rights Watch proposes

(Docherty 2020). Outright prohibitions on sex robots are necessary, as are strict limitations on care robotics, ensuring the dignity, privacy and security of users, and an end to the false claims of love and companionship made by robot manufacturers. The ability of emotional devices to manipulate humans through the application of fake empathy should also be curbed.

Existing bioethical legislation against personal eugenics, humans cloning and gene editing would be reinforced by a strong investment in bioethical education. Regulation on brain and body mechanization should also be tightened. Strictly distinguishing between reparative medicine and augmentation will not be easy but with the right ethical oversight it may be possible in strictly non-profit, medical environments. Private clinics and rogue scientists must be prevented from offering techno-eugenic enhancements for the wealthy, as the Third International Summit of Human Genome Editing warned, as this could destroy forever the notion of being born equal at birth and create a two-tier humanity (Sample and Devlin, 2023). Resources for life extension development could be mainly focused on measures to increase health span. For example, lowering all air pollution to recommended World Health Organization levels would increase the average global citizen's longevity by 2.2 years, thus producing an extra 17 billion years of healthy life worldwide (Greenstone et al, 2022). Once healthy lifespans have broadly equalized across the planet, it may be time to reactivate life extension research. Those who insist on continuing with their research underground – some humachinators' argue this would happen despite regulation – would be treated like other criminals breaking the law such as sex traffickers or terrorists.

The Power of Technological Sacrifice

To those who say, it's impossible to renounce new technologies – the technological determinist's most passionate plea – the obvious response is that we do it all the time. Nuclear power – the miraculous technology of the Acceleration Age – has been severely restricted as a weapon and rejected as an energy source, sometimes virtually overnight, for instance by the industrial powerhouse of Germany after the Fukushima nuclear disaster. Humanity said "no" to the chlorofluorocarbons (CFCs) that created the ozone zone. Climate action may be slow but it's still resulting in the closure of expensive coal-fired power stations, some with decades of life left in them and hundreds of millions of still usable petrol-driven cars will soon be consigned to the scrapheap. Many nations have said no to guns (if not yet to GUN), notably the Japanese who banned them altogether for several centuries and the modern British state in which regular police are still unarmed. (We could do worse than follow the example of Leonardo da Vinci, who suppressed his masterly design for a submarine because he feared it would be used for evil purposes (Huesemann and Huesemann, 2011).

Any doubts about renouncing technology before 2020 were dispelled by the Covid-19 pandemic. Factories were closed, jumbo jets grounded and entertainment venues shuttered; in many areas, private transport was outlawed. The pandemic proved that governments can be virtually compelled by the majority to totally reject the growthist philosophy that the market knows best, as Andreas Malm (2020) has shown. In short, the secret law of technology was put into effect – albeit temporarily – so why not apply it permanently to all technology that threatens the wellbeing of people and planet?

Of course, self-disciplined prioritization of this sort is never easy; it's the polar opposite of the Law of More. But in an age suffering from a fatal addiction to technology, we should be aware that most addicts begin by thinking they can chart a middling course between "too much" and "nothing at all" until they learn that only renunciation works. In developing a culture of moderation, the Ecocene can learn from great civilizations of the past. As Jacques Ellul (1976:29) pointed out, despite their extraordinary scientific and engineering breakthroughs, the Ancient Greeks deliberately limited technological development lest they hubristically over-estimated the extent of human power.

Be Realistic about Post-Growth Economics

Whatever the precise extent of technological renunciation, we need to be realistic about what the sustainable degrowth transition would look like for high-income countries. We cannot simply replace a growth capitalist system which depends on fossil fuel and resource exploitation with a non-growth replica. As suggested in an earlier chapter, one general way of thinking about post-growth in developed nations is as a return to 1970s levels of energy for Canada or Spain in the 1980s (Victor, 2012, Kallis,

2018). These were not in any way primitive societies. Nor would it be necessary to relinquish the internet, computers or smartphones, although their use may be rationed somewhat. Other sustainable technologies including renewable energy, electrified transport, circular design and waste recycling would all add to what was possible in the West in the 1970s, enough to make a big difference in lived experience but insufficient to justify green growthism claims.

More precise post-growth macroeconomic models are proliferating (Hardt and O'Neill, 2017). For instance, Jackson and Victor (2020) model low growth scenarios for Canada, finding that a radical "sustainable prosperity" scenario can achieve a steady state by 2067. This would stabilize per-capita average salaries at current levels but reduce working hours by almost 20%, while raising income equality via annual government transfers. Through the increased use of renewables, the electrification of transport and carbon taxes, net zero could be delivered by 2040, which may not be soon enough, but is far preferable to the authors' "business as usual" and "base case" scenarios, which both lead to runaway climate change. Simone D'Alessandro and his colleagues (2020) provide models for post-growth France which include a greater emphasis on degrowth measures, including decreased exports and imports and a wealth tax, which would lead to further reduced emissions and greater estimated levels of income equality and wellbeing, especially through contracted working hours.

However, these models do not fully take account of the global sustainability context. To achieve a planetwide steady state will require a policy of planned contraction among developed nations, allowing developing nations to expand economically towards a globally agreed planetary level (Dietz and O'Neil, 2013). It will be a difficult balancing act, as Dan O'Neil and his colleagues (2018) make clear in their analysis of 150 countries, which shows that lowering the production and consumption of rich countries sufficiently to enable poor countries to raise their economic output by enough will be a demanding task. Mastering the "when to stop" problem, as Herman Daly (2007:17) put it, will be particular challenging for developing nations.

We will have to rely on new breakthroughs in human organization – including significant changes in social psychology – to get the planet over the line, although putting precisely-targeted, sustainable technology in the right hands will also help to achieve this heroic goal. Cancelling unfair and unpayable debts of low-and middle-income countries and "curbing unequal exchange in international trade" will also help to promote genuinely fair trade (Hickel et al, 2022). Global sustainable degrowth represents a return to the no/low growth patterns which has prevailed in 99% of human history, although this time on a planned basis.

What has also yet to be factored into future scenarios is the economic impact of continued global warming causing great swathes of the planet to become uninhabitable for billions of people, especially in the heavily populated regions of sub-Saharan Africa and Asia (Lenton et al, 2023). Gaia Vince (2022) stresses that this is likely to lead to a great northward migration of refugees, especially given her all-too feasible assumption that global warming will reach 4C by 2100. The Fortress North scenario described in the last chapter is one possible outcome of this, but Vince envisages a more welcoming response, leading to a huge enlargement of Northern cities, which would benefit from the economic growth associated with increased in population, and opportunities for enormous new settlements in the high latitudes of Canada, Scandinavia and Russia.

Whatever happens, this potentially epic movement of people from the Global South emphasizes once more the impact of economic inequality on the climate and biodiversity emergency. Currently, the lifestyle and investments of the global 1% are responsible for 16% of all carbon emissions, which is more than is produced by the poorest 66% of people on the planet (i.e., five billion people). The US and China illustrate the shocking scale of the disparity: in these countries the richest 10% emit more greenhouse gas than the bottom 70% of the population; and in Europe the climate footprint of this upper middle class is also formidable in size (Khalfan et al, 2023).

The upshot of this is that reducing global overconsumption is primarily a task for the Global North as a whole and the wealthy elite in the South, at least in the short term. If the world's richest 10% had behaved like the poorest 90% over the past fifty years we might be facing a far more manageable degree of global warming today (perhaps in the region of 0.6C) rather than the prospect of imminently surpassing 1.5C on a permanent basis (WMO, 2023). In fact, the carbon footprint of the global 0.1% is currently 77 times higher than required to keep to 1.5C. And if everyone emulated the world's richest billionaires (who are mainly the Big Tech titans), whose emissions are currently 1500 higher than that of the poorest 99% of humanity, the prospects for avoiding climate meltdown would be close to zero (Khalfan et al, 2023). In other words, it's inequality that's in danger of killing the planet.

That's also painfully clear in relation to the animals, insects, marine species and plants which are suffering mass extinction at a terrifying rate. The Ecocene can only come into existence once we renounce our dominator complex towards the non-human world. The UN Global Biodiversity Framework (UNEP, 2021) represents a useful practical starting point for this urgent task but we also need a much greater recognition that to be human is to be ineluctably integrated in the web of life with all biological species and environments. This is something that the age of humachines can learn from the Indigenous peoples caring for the wellbeing of so much of the planet's biodiversity. In short, planetary sustainability is inextricably interwoven with the other goals of the SEWP worldplan, which we will continue to examine in the next chapter.

CHAPTER 25

Towards the Ecocene: Equitability and Wellbeing Planetwide

The SEWP Worldplan (Continued)

Goal 2. Equitability: Using the Freedom Budget Fairly

Although equality is a theoretical goal of democratic capitalism, in practice this is reduced to whatever degree of equitability is compatible with a system that relies on the unequal distribution of the economic surplus in a socially hierarchical pattern inherited from the Pyramid Age. At any one time, there is only so much liberty to go around and at the moment ontocapitalism is set on ensuring that the rich hog most of it. Jettisoning economic growth as the primary goal of life will make it possible to bring equitability to the forefront of our worldplan.

Making human equality a fundamental objective in its own right moves us beyond minimal equalization targets such as "reducing extreme poverty" (currently defined by the World Bank (2022b) as living on less than $2.15 a day) or marginally improving upward social mobility. Instead of techno–utopian fantasies in which machines provide universal abundance, the SEWP plan aims to turn authentic social equality into the human mission. This will genuinely flatten the social pyramid, rather than erecting a new technology shield to defend it. This redistribution of society's economic surplus will help to compensate the majority of people for reduced consumer consumption.

One of the measures that could flow from a total commitment to equality is agreed income ratios. For instance, a 5:1 ratio between the top and bottom earners in society, as practised by some cooperatives today, would bring us closer to the income ratios of the 1970s. A similar wealth ratio between the top 10% and bottom 10%, for example, is needed to eradicate the increasingly grotesque wealth disparities enjoyed by the pharaohs of humachination and other billionaires. A graduated wealth tax on the ultra-wealthy would be a start; a 2% levy on wealth of over $5 million rising to 10% on $1 billion or more would raise $3.6 trillion a year, enough to lift two billion people out of poverty and provide healthcare and social protection for 3.6 billion (Fight Inequality Alliance, 2022). Minimizing the amount of wealth flowing from one generation to the next is another priority, perhaps achievable by using inheritance tax to fund personal endowments (Felber, 2012).

Universal basic services could include guaranteeing minimum accommodation to all and restricting ownership of multiple large properties. In order to achieve this new human right, some land redistribution will be necessary, as discussed in the last chapter, and construction skills may be pooled by communities (another reason to oppose the delegation of all construction skills to robots in human-free building sites). For today's young adults of Generation Rent in the UK, condemned to spend up to three quarters of their take home pay on accommodation they can never hope to own, this equalist measure could be a major attraction.

Absolutely central to the new eco-equal paradigm will be gender equality. Gender quotas in leadership roles – to the extent that they will still exist –could prompt a movement away from "humacho", mechanistic attitudes in technology and elsewhere in the private and public sector. Globally, a huge investment in the education of women and girls is one of the most effective ways of countering overpopulation and raising the sum total of human wisdom.

Overall, gender equalization is about shifting from the patriarchal economy which is measured by GDP towards the "female" or reproductive economy of subsistence work and caring for others currently provided "for free". This has been estimated to provide 30-70% of all economic output, especially in communities in the Global South (Schmelzer et al 2022). In other words, the foundations of a new post-capitalist, post-growth way of being does not have to be invented; we simply need to take off the capitalist blinkers to see what makes the perpetuation of human society possible.

As Stefania Barca (2020) makes clear, the Anthropocene must not be a continuation of the male-dominated "master mode" of the Holocene (initiated by the Baconian science which defined nature as a woman to be conquered and subdued). In place of hegemonic, masculinist productivism, the Human Epoch needs to embrace all those involved in human and ecological care, which is made invisible by the iceberg dimension of the capitalist pyramid. These "forces of reproduction" include all those engaged in "trans(feminist), Indigenous, peasant, commoning, environmental, and other life-making struggles across the world" (Barca, 2020:7). (Note that these are often the very people that humachine algorithms exclude or are biased against.)

Equitability is a celebration of difference not a mere reversal of existing hierarchies. Egalitarianism can be a tough discipline, in that it involves the constant containment of selfish desires, but it's a way of relating to others which expresses the altruism which seems to be our unique species endowment (Jensen et al, 2014). Since the 1960s there has been a growing wave of egalitarianism in the West and people under the age of 40, in particular, are desperately trying to create forms of social relations that reject sexism, racism, homophobia, transphobia and ableism, in defiance of a hierarchical socio-economic system which encourages – and sometimes demands – discriminatory behaviour. It's worth recalling the equalist goal of the Age of Origin, to ensure "a ceiling above which one may not accumulate wealth and power and a floor below which one may not sink" (Lee, 1992). Scaling up this organizational principle to a global level may be the only way to fulfil the widespread demands of rising generations of egalitarians.

Another clue to Ecocene equitability can be found in one of the most durable behavioural patterns in interpersonal relationships, the cycle of submission and aggression (Speed et al, 2018). Often people who are subject to abuse, violence or psychological exploitation find themselves complying with their dominators by being too submissive. But when they try to break out of this pattern, they often do so by acts, or expressions, of aggression, which in turn provoke more violence and prompt a return to submission. The challenge is to achieve assertiveness. This can be done by firmly – often very repetitively, asserting your own rights, while also recognizing whatever rights the person who is oppressing you may have.

Extend this process to an entire society and place it in every interpersonal context, from politics, work and leisure to the family and sexual relationships, and you begin to get a sense of equitability in the Ecocene.

Reduced Working Time

Another key to increased equality is reduced working time (RWT), which not only ensures contracted consumption and production but opens up immense human possibilities. Deciding which jobs go and which remain will be a crucial task for the twenty-first century. Will society dispense with unsustainable, unproductive roles such as those in finance, the military, advertising, fossil fuel, packaging and other "bullshit jobs" (Graeber, 2018), or those that the humachine corporations deem most easily and profitably automatable? A reduced working week policy, which involves mass job-sharing, can preserve existing sustainable jobs and allows for the planned creation of many new human-to-human occupations. It's also one of the best protections against jobicide. It preserves the dignity, social solidarity and self-achievement that come with work, while releasing huge amounts of that most precious of commodities, time. It also reaffirms the principle that labour is essential for being human, in contradistinction to the techno-utopian dream of a Smarticus robot slave economy.

Less paid employment will enable people to perform subsistence work to supplement their incomes, in urban and community farms, for example, and to engage in voluntary social work, life-long education, creative self-expression and political activism as a form of civic duty. All this can help to build vibrant, all-round personalities (especially as research indicates that too much free time can be as harmful to subjective wellbeing as too little of it), which in turn will strengthen local communities (Sharif et al, 2021). Ian Gough (2017) is surely right to see RWT as a better way to transition to a post-growth economy than UBI, although this too may have a valuable part to play in the overall redistribution of social resources.

Goal 3: The Wellbeing Society

The third goal of the SEWP plan, wellbeing, can be defined as fully recognizing and encouraging the caring society. This can help to rescue the post-growth political economy from mechanicalism and productivism and return it to a philosophical tradition that runs from Aristotle's prioritization of eudaemonism to nineteenth-century utilitarians' focus on the greatest happiness of the greatest number. In a people-planet world, psychological flourishing becomes not simply a vaguely hoped for side-effect of economic activity but one its major reasons for being. This new organizing principle debunks the myth that increased economic wealth consistently increases subjective wellbeing, another version of the growthist exponentiality trick. An eco-democratic focus can build core human skills, indigenous competences and creative talents rather than allowing them to degrade and disappear due to the supposed ease and convenience of humachines. A flourishing human skills commons of choice-making, creativity, judgement, trust, wisdom, love and care for others can also help to move us towards a world in which cooperation is the norm and peace rather than war is the default condition of being human.

Reducing economic consumption doesn't necessitate diminished healthcare. For instance, Cuba has one seventh of the per capita GDP of the US but four times as many doctors and nurses per 1,000 inhabitants. Based around family doctors and nurses, who visit every patient in their community at least once a year, and multi-service polyclinics, this model is often more successful at preventing illness and diseases than wealthier medical systems which prioritize secondary and tertiary care (i.e. specialists and hospitals) over primary care (Trejo et al, 2022).

Measures to improve community-based mental health provision are also urgently needed. For example, new regulations on social media could combat the typically cold-eyed humachine alliance of algorithms that chase extremes and marketing teams incentivized to boost users' compulsive scrolling and platform-checking. It's a toxic brew that has contributed to suicide rates among 10-19-year-olds in the US surging by 46% between 2010 and 2020. Banning under-16-year-olds from social media altogether, as called for by social psychologist Jonathan Haidt, may be impractical but training all young users in the proper use of messaging platforms may be realistic (Smyth and Murphy, 2023). A relevant precedent for this could be driving tests, which were not introduced until 1935 in Britain, by which time there were millions of cars on the road and traffic fatalities were proportionately three times higher than today.

In the wider healthcare realm, limits on the salt, sugar, fat and chemicals cynically added to food and drink to induce craving, which have contributed to the obesity epidemic, would be prohibited, as medical priorities shift to preventing diseases. In some progressive capitalist governments, the faint outlines of a wellbeing economy are already beginning to appear. For instance, New Zealand's 2020 wellbeing goals include decreasing child poverty, raising Maori and Pacific opportunities and incomes and improving health outcomes for all. Finland, which regularly tops the UN's World Happiness Index, sets targets that attempt to "downplay the economy as a goal in and of itself", including narrowing income gaps by 2030 and achieving carbon neutrality by 2035 (WEGo, 2022).

In a fully realised SEWP society, a close connection to nature will also provide an increased source of happiness, addressing the "nature deficit disorder" which is becoming endemic in the urbanized world. According to Andreas Weber (2016:8), too many of us can identify no more than two or three native plants and know more car brands than bird names. More green urban spaces, land reforms and major rewilding programmes will bring nature closer, enabling children from the start of their lives to deeply experience nature.

Education is central to the wellbeing-centred society, creating schooling for life at its fullest and most adventurous. Eco-literacy will be taught from birth and will be vital for the survival of the Ecocene. As opposed to the STEMpede towards ever greater specialization in scientific and engineering subjects, which is the main educational policy of the humachine age – post-growth education will focus on balancing science with the arts, humanities and social sciences to bring out the creative potential in all students throughout their lives. Sport, music, theatre and art may well play a considerably greater role in most students' lives than computer science.

School will equip children with the psychological skills to cooperate with others and develop a personal sense of worth, while supporting them from the very start to make their own decisions. Real choice-making on school-related issues will be part of the curriculum, equipping young citizens for their role in demotechnics and participatory democracy. Schools (for all ages) will become schools of equality. All in all, wellbeing will be something earned as much as given in a post-growth world, which will encourage involvement with society rather than a lotus-eating detachment from it.

Goal 4: Planetwideness and Global Circular Democracy

The sustainability, equitability and wellbeing goals of a post-growth world can only work on a planetwide basis. Continued Global North-centeredness – the reduction of what works for humanity as whole to what works for its wealthiest minority – will have the most catastrophic consequences for our planet and our species. The fate of humanity may depend on a new message emerging from the Global North, one that says to the emerging economies of the world that the path of infinite growth is a lethal dead end. Instead of preaching the Law of More as the way to social progress, the North should promulgate a new Law of Enough, which recognizes that humachination is not the industrial revolution which the Global South needs. If accomplished soon enough, this radical change of heart could prevent the realization of the harsh fortress world scenario, discussed in Chapter 23.

This new worldview will rely on the indisputable reality that humanity has only one planet on which to live. The biosphere, including the atmosphere, recognizes no national borders and is indifferent to which nation produces pollution, but not to its devastating impacts. Because of this, centralized international coordination is necessary if global sustainability is to have a chance to work. Achieving a global steady state will require a Great Levelling project, a gradual equalization of income and wealth between the nations of the world, as they move towards their agreed carbon footprints. But this levelling process cannot simply be a top-down process; it must be a bottom-up exercise as well – a process of circular democracy in fact.

Global circular democracy will enable the developing world to benefit from sustainable technology transfers and scientific technical assistance from Global North countries; these nations, in turn, can learn the ecological and human benefits of a rural way of life which is still led by half of the world's population. Instead of domination and exploitation and the imposition of Western knowledge which has led the world to the precipice of planetary breakdown in the Anthropocene, it will be a case of mutual learning and development towards a common goal of planetary economic homeostasis.

Possible SEWP Examples Planetwide

If moving towards something akin to the SEWP worldplan requires a funda-mental change in the attitude of the Global North, inspirational leadership is also likely to emerge from the Global South. The developing world has much to offer about this post-growth condition, including long-standing agricultural practices, which encourage diversity and resilience; cultural traditions which focus on care, collectivism and cooperation; and non-materialist and spiritual belief systems that emphasize humanity's unity with nature. Aspects of this balanced, ecological and social economy still exist in spite of oppression and poverty. With most of the world still living on a primarily plant-based diet, it's as irrational to be bullying low-income countries into following the West's disastrous obsession with meat as it is to consider mass urbanization as the solution to the South's problems, when over a billion people there already live in slums and shanty towns (Pimentel et al, 2003, Davis, 2005).

Within the democratic capitalist mould, one outstanding example of an emerging nation moving towards a version of the SEWP worldplan can be found in Costa Rica in Central America, which has topped the Happy Planet Index for health, sustainability and wellbeing since 2006 (HPI, 2021). Costa Rica abolished its army in 1948 and used some of the funds saved thereby to finance free, high-quality healthcare that contributes to a rate of longevity that is greater than that of the US, although its per capita GDP (at around $13,000) is over five times smaller (Macrotrends, 2023). The country has 98% literacy and spends nearly 7% of its GDP on education, almost 50% more than the world average (CIA, 2023). Unlike the US, it has a stable democracy, which is classified as "full" by the Economist Intelligence Unit (2022) and uses proportional representation in its legislative assembly.

Ecologically, Costa Rica's journey has not been easy. It experienced a period of alarming deforestation which saw tree cover shrink from 75% in the 1940s to just 25% in the 1980s. Since then, an outright ban on felling mature trees plus financial incentives for sustainable farming has restored the extent of forest cover to 60% (Konyn, 2021). In addition, the government has banned all oil and gas drilling within its borders so that today almost all of its electricity is derived from renewables (three-quarters from hydropower) and overall, the country is realistically on course to achieve net zero by 2050 (CAT, 2023). However, Costa Rica still has work to do to reduce its ecological footprint to a sustainable planetary level. Recent increases in land conversion and urbanization are straining its water and waste infrastructure which, together with a long-standing over-reliance on petrol-driven transport, threaten its overall environmental progress

(OECD, 2023). Nevertheless, as a model for the developing world, it shows that it's not necessary to emulate the West to achieve high levels of sustainability, equitability and happiness.

A more radical, post-capitalist example of the developing world showing the North how it's done is Rojava, a post-nationalist democracy which has arisen from the horrors of the Civil War in Syria. Having fought off both Bashir al-Assad's forces and ISIS, the Kurds of Rojava, a narrow strip of Kurdish territory in North-east Syria, declared regional autonomy in 2014 and held democratic elections. Its worldplan has been described as "a decentralized model of autonomy based on participative democracy, non-territoriality and systemic gender equality through women's self-organization" (Burc, 2020:335).

Rojava society derives its political legitimacy from a four-layer council system, which ascends from village communes and regional councils to the People's Council, which governs the territory. Some may question how consistently bottom-up this form of decision-making is yet but there's no doubt that communal assemblies play a crucial role in resolving local conflicts and encouraging multi-ethnic education and leadership. Even clearer is the role of councils, which like all Rojava's political formations are co-chaired by a woman and a man, in "reforming an extremely patriarchal society" (Schmidinger, 2018:133-35). In fact, Rojava explicitly rejects the "hegemonic masculinity" which tarnishes so many political systems, especially those in the grip of nationalism (Burc, 2020).

The Rojava economy is cooperative, based on "locally-controlled cooperatives which provide for the region's essentials", including agriculture and construction, although some private enterprises also exist (Restakis, 2017). "It has shown that the way out of the social and ecological crisis is not through GDP-focused development, but rather with decentralized autonomous communities", writes an international group of climate activists and community leaders (Allard et al, 2019). This inspiring experiment, conducted in the most challenging circumstances imaginable, offers a flame of hope for the sustainable, non-hierarchical, wellbeing society of the Ecocene. It represents a vibrant alternative to "capitalist modernity", whose real power, as the confederalist Kurdish leader Abdullah Ocalan says, "isn't in money and weapons [but] its ability to suffocate all utopias" – echoing a point made throughout this book (Allard et al, 2019).

A better known and more established example of a social formation embracing elements of the SEWP worldplan can be found in the Zapata "movement of many movements" in the Mexican state of Chiapas. The Zapatistas have developed a unique model that "operates both against and within the nation state", blending local indigenous direct democracy, communal economic autonomy and women's rights which challenge traditional patriarchy (Wainwright and Mann, 2018: 181). Although still opposed by the Mexican state, this attempt to create "a new world rooted in social relations which are not power relations and that emerge out of the mutual recognition of dignity" has inspired many across the world seeking an alternative to growth capitalism (Khasnabish, 2010:85).

A Global SEWPer Power?

Small, developing countries can inspire change but on a planet dominated by economic superpowers can we find a geopolitical entity large enough to take on the SEWP degrowth challenge? A strengthened, democratized United Nations, free of superpower domination, could be the long-term answer (especially if progress could be made towards Leopold Kohr's (1957) proposal of creating 1,000 equally sized nations). But, in the short term, I would argue that the only realistic prospect is the European Union. The EU contains many of the world most established democratic nations and, for all its faults, uses a far more representative, consensus-based voting system than either the UN or the two other global superpowers, China and America. It's essentially a union of small countries, with 20 of its 27 states having a population of 11 million or less. Many of these countries – especially Nordic nations such as Finland, Denmark and Sweden – already lead the world in terms of life satisfaction, according to the UN's World Happiness Report. They are also more economically equal than the US and UK, and have relatively progressive sustainability policies. If any superpower is capable of acting as a beacon for the SEWP model this surely is it.

From a global justice perspective, for over half a millennium Europe has been the leading force in the rampant colonialism, slave trading and industrialism which has led to today's humachine age. As such, it's well placed to make reparations for the economic and social advantages it has gained, starting by cancelling debts for many low-income countries. Morally, it's ideally positioned to offer a new paradigm of social and economic development, which aims at contracting domestic consumption and production in order to become a globally equitable steady state.

When it comes to regulatory standards for technology, the environment, work and trade the EU already has a clear lead over China and the US. Its well-established use of the precautionary principle represents the best starting point for a system of assessing the impact of technology before it's too late. In a sense it works on the assumption that new technology is guilty until proved innocent by diligent research. The US, by contrast, tends to regard new products and services as innocent until proven guilty, allowing consumers to decide on their harmfulness and, if necessary, sue their producers– a process which is notoriously expensive and can take many decades.

Whereas US regulators have given the humachinators an infamously easy ride, the EU has taken a much more robust stand against them, stretching back to penalizing Microsoft for uncompetitive practices in the 1990s and continuing with ongoing battles against Apple, Google, Amazon and Meta. These have resulted in multi-billion-dollar fines for tax avoidance, stifling competition, spreading misinformation and not paying for news content. The EU already provides much stronger data privacy regulations than the US and is currently planning the world's toughest restrictions on generative AI via the AI Act due to fully come into force in 2026 (Espinoza and Johnston, 2023). At a time when geopolitical rivalry threatens to shatter the global internet and shared technical architecture (from undersea cables to microchips), non-aligned nations may have to choose between the EU's version of the internet, Chinese authoritarian censorship or the American libertarian model. Shorn of some of its current neoliberal biases, the EU could function as a model of demotechnics on a grand scale, which might eventually operate in tandem with the local citizen forums described in the next chapter.

An EU which turns the SEWP organizational principles into a living reality could go some way towards re-establishing trust between the Global North and South, without which the Technocene may be inevitable. The Global North can't get away with being seen to have its cake and eat it on climate change. Even harder to sell is the assertion that human-machine fusion is the harmless successor to carbon capitalism, even though it involves eradicating most of the world's existing jobs. Only a radical repudiation of the goals of capitalism and a frank admission that the GUN organizing principles were always deeply flawed can hope to convince the developing world to limit its use of economic growth to sustainable planetary levels.

By sacrificing economic growth, the world's wealthiest nations might persuade the majority world that they can be trusted to facilitate (not lead) the best possible version of the Anthropocene. Otherwise, Africa and Asia will continue to be the battleground for the new digital imperialists, pitching American humachinators against Chinese infrastructure builders and land grabbers. This is all too likely to end in new hot war between US and China, perhaps concluding in a truce which brings about the joint "dictdataship" scenario previously described, or some other Technocene narrative imposing immiseration on the majority world. A penitent, humble EU, using enlightened life science and small-country democratic principles can help to create a new concept of modernity. A courageous abdication of Europe's claims to global domination can begin a new wave of international solidarity and thwart a humachine age which aims to abolish human trust altogether.

There are other possibilities, of course, if we're prepared to turn up the dial on optimism. Perhaps Xi Jinping's declared aim of turning China into an "ecological civilization" might occur through a popular revolution that sweeps aside the CCP's techno-authoritarian ambitions (Geng and Lo, 2023); maybe the USA, one of the homes of ecology, environmental utopianism and systems science can still come good, even if the age of humachines is fundamentally an American invention. And signals of hope may continue to be broadcast by developing and Indigenous nations, who follow their own innovative paths, creating powerful vectors of change to persuade increasing numbers of people to finally ditch the Western model of machine supremacisim and illusory economic growth.

Concluding Thoughts

Finally, I think it's important to think of the SEWP paradigm-shift in proactive terms. We should resist the temptation to imagine the Ecocene arising phoenix-like from the ashes of an abhorrent sequence of climate, biodiversity and technological calamities, which could produce a death toll that exceeds that of World War II. That historical disaster might never have happened if measures that came into force after 1945 had been introduced earlier, such as increased international cooperation, decolonization, relative economic equalization, the promotion of democracy and the welfare state (Harvey, 2019:241-43). The great levelling that smoothes our path to the Ecocene may for once dispense with the Four Horsemen of the Apocalypse (symbolizing war, famine, death and disease) who have instigated many previous equalization events in history (Scheidel, 2017). By accepting our relationship with nature and ourselves, by using our tools as means not ends, we can create the possibility of a resplendent new age of lived experience. But this behavioural transition can only occur if radically new forms of democracy are established and institutions emerge which can bring forth a new kind of human psychology. That's the subject of our final two chapters.

CHAPTER 26

Circular Democracy, Demotechnics and the Multi-Institutional Revolution

Another way in which the SEWP paradigm-shift may differ from the historical pattern is because it will flow from the political choices of the majority rather than the opportunistic avarice of a Promethean elite. Accepting the limits of our technology and of our planetary resources can help us to release a powerful optimism about what humans can do and a pride in the potential of our indigenous capacities which the Pyramid Pattern has always quashed. This attitude can also help us take a stand against the post-biological, machine supremacisim that can lead to the Technocene and the misanthropy of the humachinators, whose deepest conviction seems to be that machines can improve but humans can't.

If the Ecocene is to prove to be the triumph of democracy, at least three revolutionary changes will be needed, which this chapter will attempt to sketch out. These involve the establishment of circular democracy, demotechnics and a revolution in our social and academic institutions. Together with the psychological metamorphosis described in the next chapter, these transformations can open the way to a world system capable of bringing out the best of being human on planet Earth.

1. Circular Democracy

If capitalism was really serious about democracy, it would be investing massive resources into developing this superb but desperately underdeveloped social technology. Instead, trillions of dollars are being spent on humachination, which, as we've repeatedly witnessed, poses a grave threat to majority rule. That's why one of the paramount Ecocene revolutions has to be in the institution of politics, which, in one way or another, has shaped every age of human technology. Even in the minority of countries which are classified as "full democracies" (see Chapter 9) our political systems are too shallow and too open to plutocratic manipulation, which results in pivotal decisions being made by a tiny elite. Majority rule is turned into a crude numbers game and this is made even cruder by the first-past-the post electoral systems of the UK and US.

Introducing proportional representation into Anglo-American politics would be one remedy; others could include reducing the voting age to 16, outlawing voter suppression tactics and imposing strict limits on campaign advertising. More radical moves might include inviting representatives from other nations' assemblies to participate in national parliaments in order to loosen the grip of nationalism on policy-making. Parliamentarians representing future-generations might help to combat the disastrous short-term bias of existing legislatures, which has partially caused the Anthropocene Crisis. Kristian Ekeli (2005) suggests 5% of parliaments should be represented by "F-candidates", i.e. politicians dedicated to empathizing with future generations and arguing for their rights. Focusing on "How will this decision look in 50 or 100 years?" will bring a new emphasis on what is really important rather than allowing urgency and short-term fire-fighting to dominate policy. It can also increase the responsibility of political actors and citizens for their stewardship of the planet, as well as allowing expression to the future-orientated traits which psychologists are beginning to realise play a significant role in human personality and the importance of our duty to act as "good ancestors" (Zimbardo and Boyd, 2008, Krznaric, 2020).

Such innovative measures may help to overcome the inherent limitations of electoral democracy but much more is needed. As political scientist Helene Landesmore (2020:4.) reminds us, "Representative "democracy" was originally intended as form of elite rule in contrast with rule by ordinary citizens". The American founding fathers, for example, explicitly rejected demokratis or "people power". To save democracy from asphyxiation, we need to move to deeper forms of popular participation than conventional elections provide.

I've already referred to circular democracy in a global context but it also needs to thrive at a national and local level, where it combines top-down-policy making – necessary for planetary sustainability – with the bottom-up decision-making that can give democracy the kiss of life. We might even call the principle octopus democracy, after that remarkable cephalopod, which has a highly advanced nervous system in each of its eight arms, as well as in its brain, enabling it to integrate localized and centralized forms of intelligence (Godfrey-Smith, 2016).

One of the bedrocks of circular democracy is the deliberation of small groups, which are given – or give themselves – the opportunity to vigorously and thoroughly debate important political issues. This revives the ancient Athenian practice of selecting major policy-making councils by sortition, a random lottery which selects citizens, along the lines of judicial juries in many contemporary national justice systems (Van Reybrouck, 2016). The Athenians saw this method as producing better, more impartial decision-making than elections, which were often skewed in favour of the oligarchs. Today, deliberative democracy can inject quality and precision into the decision-making process, whereas aggregative democracy often relies on the sheer quantity of votes (Zwarthoed, 2018).

The "mini-publics" of consensus-seeking assemblies can promote the desire to understand what motivates opposing views over the need to belittle or destroy them. In fact, "deliberative polling", which typically involves opinion polling before and after an extended debate by a representative group, has consistently been able to reach conclusions that are superior to electoral democracy. James Fishkin (2009) has shown that deliberative polling can reduce partisanship, increase empathy for opposing views, build respect for evidence-based arguments over rhetoric and strengthen commitment to choices which are made by the group. In deliberative polling in Uganda, for example, Fishkin and his colleagues (2017) found a major reduction in two major pressures distorting political decision-making: group polarization and the influence of the advantaged (e.g. males and the elderly). Just as jurors can soon become experts in law, so participants in deliberative assemblies rapidly become more informed, rounded voters; the process is epistemic, creating new knowledge rather than simply reinforcing existing opinions and power structures.

Assembly democracy digs down to levels below conventional political discourse, disclosing the assumptions and conceptual patterns that govern our thinking. It can cut through the knee-jerk reactions to newspaper headlines, fact-check controversial assertions and debunk unequalist, racist and sexist platitudes. Psychologically, it can uncover unconscious choices which are woven into the ideological fabric of lived experience, in a way that's analogous to the deep reflection that can occur in individual or group therapy. All this can create a clear, responsible and respectful way of making choices about public issues that is the opposite to the modus operandi of current democracy, based on aggressively adversarial rhetoric and sly techniques derived from the manipulation of consumer choice.

So how can these small groups and mini-publics be integrated with electoral politics? One measure would see citizens' juries replace senates or other secondary legislative chambers; another would grant them a primary role in specific areas of decision-making such as education or healthcare. A more radical route to connect mini-publics to the larger public, according to Landesmore (2020:116), "would be to enrol the entirety of the population in as many randomly selected assemblies as needed". These gatherings would meet in-person or online to generate the agenda for nationwide decision-making by a succession of mini-groups. This multi-level system replicates the National Public Policy Convention in Brazil which ascends from local meetings all the way to a national meeting, in a manner that echoes the four-level system of Rojava direct democracy. Another example of nascent circular democracy can be found in Ireland, which Landesmore (2020:152) calls the current "jewel in the crown of deliberative democracy" and which used a series of citizen assemblies to achieve something that had defeated elected politicians: agreement on liberalizing equal marriage and abortion rights.

An even more ambitious project was undertaken in Iceland to draft a new political constitution, following the chaos brought about by the 2008 financial crash. This octopus-like process began with a group of 950 citizens randomly selected as representatives of the Icelandic population, who discussed ideas for the new constitution in small face-to-face groups, facilitated by discussion leaders. The resultant report was then turned into a series of draft constitutions by an assembly of 25 ordinary citizens and made available to the general public for commentary via crowdsourcing. The final proposal, which was judged to be more inclusive than the existing constitution, won the approval of two thirds of Icelanders in a national referendum. Unfortunately, in the end, this new legislation was blocked by parliament, which itself was not fully representative of the general population, being skewed towards conservative rural interests. (As Landesmore (2020:175) suggests, "the powers that be refused to relinquish power".) Nevertheless, this extraordinary coalescence of quantitative and qualitative research shows that ordinary citizens can successfully take on complex issues which supposedly only political and professional elites are capable of managing.

2. Establishing Demotechnics

Throughout this book I've asked the reader to imagine what decisions they would make if they had a real say in the new technology shaping our world. New forms of deliberative democracy provide the ideal platform for demotechnics, decision-making on new technology by society as a whole, carried out by parliamentary groups, popular assemblies and other models of participatory politics. Locally elected technology councils of experts judged to be trustworthy and accountable by electors could provide another representational layer in this multi-level system. This transparent process will replace our current reliance on highly secretive decisions made by elites often in their own interests. Real human choice will overcome heavily manipulated consumer "choice" in a world where the free market is falsely seen as the best arbiter of human destiny. Overcoming the plutotechnic system which has dominated the past six millennia will not be easy but it's one of the Human Epoch's most indispensable tasks.

Policy on technology has already been shaped by deliberative polls in Texas and Vermont, although the final decisions were made by conventionally elected legislators (Fishkin, 2009). Even more impressively, in Ecuador direct democracy has led to significant climate action, as a majority voted to ban oil drilling in the Amazon in a referendum in 2023. In the UK, polling by The Royal Society of the Arts (RSA, 2019) revealed that a majority of people were opposed to the use of AI technology in decision-making in criminal justice and organizational recruitment. The representative citizen assemblies which the RSA organized went further, demanding robust legislation to ensure equality and diversity at the design stage of all automated decision-making, as well as transparency, accountability and "empathetic and proportional use". These demands far exceed existing legislation on automated decision-making, a sign of the insightfulness which small-group deliberation can produce. Had these assemblies debated the "humans-out-of the loop" issues raised in Chapter 14, we might have expected even greater progressive divergence from the status quo.

Demotechnics and other forms of participatory democracy will need to be permanently integrated into the choice cycle, framing policies and overseeing their implementation and, if necessary, modifying them in the light of practice. The EU has already taken small steps in this direction, holding citizen assemblies on food waste, virtual worlds and the future of Europe, while the city of Brussels has now established permanent panels of 100 randomly selected citizens to propose and monitor climate policies (Burgerrat, 2023). Digital technology may even mitigate some of the harms it has done to democracy. For example, Polis, a US system for translating voters' opinion into decision-making frameworks, has helped shape policy in Taiwan, including designing regulation on Uber (Pol.is, 2023). Even more promisingly, the Decidim (2023) collective provides a free, digital platform for wide-ranging citizen participation, including representative assemblies (via sortition, if required), bottom-up democratic consultations and participatory budgeting for organizations and communities. Job automation, the surveillance state, social media regulation, AI-assisted creativity, military robotics, neurotechnology, geoengineering, meditechnics and genetic engineering: all the topics discussed in this book and many more will profit hugely from the insightful reflection provided by dedicated demotechnic groups of this kind.

A New Food Revolution?

Could demotechnics take on perhaps the most historically contentious of all economic issues, food production? As I've suggested in several chapters, an ecological transformation of agriculture is possible, based on reduced livestock farming, better food and land distribution, less waste and a plant-based diet. But there could be an even bigger agricultural revolution on the horizon. Supporters of the new science of precision biology argue that it could eventually produce all the protein the world needs in an area the size of Greater London. Based on the ancient practice of brewing, precision fermentation already produces animal-free rennet and insulin and potentially can synthesize any organic module without the need for animals or fats. In theory, this technology could remove all geographical barriers on food production, enabling the Global South to produce high-protein food locally and open the way for the mass rewilding of the world's farmland (Reboot Food, 2022). But the overwhelming danger, as recognized by George Monbiot (2022a), who strongly supports the idea, is "the potential for these new technologies to be captured by a few corporations". Big Tech would attempt to monopolize the process, replicating the stranglehold created by seed and fertilizer corporations. Alternatively, the technology could be blocked by vested interests, such as the US cattle industry which faces bankruptcy if precision fermentation takes off (Tubb and Seba, 2019). Either way it's plutotechnics all over again.

The solution would be for citizens' assemblies to debate the pros and cons of this technology, alongside elected parliamentary representatives. Together they would determine the nature of precautionary trials, the design of the process and the basis of its implementation, perhaps with an emphasis on open-source software, local cooperatives and other organizations motivated by pro-social rewards rather than profits. Constant monitoring by demotechnic groups, backed up by expert advisors, frequent mass polling and crowd-sourced commentary, would rapidly identify any UNCs of this new technology and ensure it remains firmly in the hands of the majority, operating within agreed limits. At the start of the Human Epoch, it would be a fitting re-run of the collective decision-making which prevailed before the very first agricultural revolution.

The Humanness Question:
What Do We Really Want and Need?

Another vital task for demotechnics and circular democracy is to attempt to answer the question that haunts this book: what is humanness? As Max Tegmark (2013:256) admits "human behaviour strictly speaking doesn't have a single well-defined goal at all". If circular democracy can deliver a new political constitution, why not take on the challenge of deciding what constitutes being human? Such an endeavour would deploy all the elements of the Icelandic project on a worldwide scale, with extensive opinion polling, randomly chosen debating groups, expert advice and facilitation, crowdsourcing and national and international referendums.

Quantitative and qualitative research could explore basic human needs, for instance, around housing, food security, health, education, community and family life.

Deliberative democracy and popular assemblies in every parliament, town hall, workplace and college will deliberate on what it is to be human, the biology of life and the proper place of machines. Scenario-building based on evidence, imagination and lived experience can be vital assets for this kind of decision-making. As Joachim Spangenberg (2018) stresses, narratives are often more reliable than computer modelling, which tends to downplay real-life uncertainty, shocks and bifurcations. Digital technology can help, for example, by analysing data, teasing out behavioural patterns, facilitating online and telephone polling and even providing planetwide electronic voting. The fundamental aim, however, must be to keep humans very firmly in the decision-making loop. (It's worth remembering that the only technology needed for civic democracy in Ancient Athens was the kleroterion, a simple lottery device made of stone.) Squaring "Western human values" with "the Socialist Core Values" around which Chinese generative AI is being regulated will be challenging, as will the resource-intensive nature of what will need to be an ongoing, live, worldwide research programme (O'Shaughnessy, 2023). But the humanness project may be the only way to democratically establish an agreed vision of the future within which the proper purposes of technology can be determined.

Framing the humanness constitution through regular, deeply informed debates will expose many technological myths and frequently cause ideological fallacies to be discarded. I strongly doubt that the goal of merging humans and machines on unregulated, free-market principles would emerge as the number one choice for humanity, any more than European colonialism would have gained majority approval from the Indigenous people of the Americas or the triangular slave trade from African men and women. But if post-biological capitalism eventually turns out to be the desire of the majority of humanity, at least it will have the full weight of an authentic, democratic decision-making process behind it.

3. The Post-Growth Institutional Revolution

Other social institutions will also have to change fundamentally in a post-growth society. The GUN principles which corrupt our organizational and academic frameworks will need to be replaced with something closer to the SEWP paradigm. Here's the briefest indication of the trans-disciplinary, multi-institutional battles that need to be fought and won, if we are to move towards the Ecocene.

Economics

Without ecological economics, the nature-depleted fortress world of the Technocene may be impossible to prevent. I can't emphasize enough how important it is to transform the discipline of economics, as this is likely to remain the primary medium for interpreting human society for some time to come. The current neoclassical vision of society as a machine for generating capital expansion rather than a living relationship between humans and nature is destroying the best of being human on planet Earth. Economics departments across the world are indoctrinating future economists, politicians and business leaders in a mechanistic, anti-social philosophy which insists that humans are essentially self-interested, competitive and greedy (e.g. Wang et al, 2011). A profound intellectual revolution is needed to put nature and a cooperative vision of humanity at the forefront of our analysis of all economic activity.

Science and Life Science

We are lucky enough to live on the planet of life, which for billions of years has enjoyed an abundance of vivacity unmatched anywhere in the cosmos. Modern science must be the science of life, which enables us to understand and appreciate that gift, rather than turn one aspect of that life, our ability to create tools, into the primary meaning of being human. That involves continuing to support the qualitative turn in science, which has gradually eroded the mechanicalism, which humachination is now attempting to revive. Integrated, systems-based science can negotiate non–linear complexity holistically and make use of the advances in physics and computer science, while not losing sight of the primacy of life (Capra and Luisi, 2014). The struggle to establish the dominance of this new vision of science will be crucial to the outcome of the battle for the Anthropocene.

As Herman Daly (2019) says "not all new knowledge is a benefit ... We need a social and ethical filter to select the beneficial knowledge", something that the slow, non-dromological pace of a steady-state economy will facilitate. It's a truth that is embedded in the precautionary principle, which defines "taking care" and being "careful" (i.e. "full of care") as scientists' paramount responsibility. Science can never be value-free, especially in its practical applications. Today, the pressure put on scientists by their employers – in the non-profit, public sector as well as the private sector – is relentless, but they need to learn from the mistakes of past generations of scientists who closed their eyes to the all-too predictable damage of "miracle" technologies such as fossil fuel, plastics and chemicals-based agriculture. As Huesemann and Huesemann (2011: 337) recommend:

> Through massive non-cooperation, science and engineering professionals could tip the balance of power in their favor and could use that power to redirect science and technology towards humane and environmentally constructive projects.

Demotechnics will spread collective responsibility to the whole population, creating a new era of openness and transparency in science. Unintended deceptions of the public by scientists themselves will only disappear once they are made accountable by democratic oversight from elected representatives, informed citizens and other independent observers who have a passion for the truth. Scientists can only lead us in the right direction once decision-making is taken out of the hands of the apex class and put into whole-society ownership.

SEWP Ethics and the Law

The law also needs to be prised from the deadly grip of growth capitalism. We have crimes today which just over half a century ago were considered legal practices, for example, discrimination based on gender, sexuality and ethnicity, as well as hate speech and types of sexual assault. Since 1945, entirely new concepts of international law have come into existence, outlawing war crimes, genocide and other crimes against humanity. We also have new business crimes on the statute books, such as culpable negligence and corporate manslaughter, which if regularly enforced could radically change the way Big Tech and all other corporations operate. Increasingly, we also have crimes against the environment – and it's not impossible that we will see prosecutions mounted against those who promoted fossil fuel use in full knowledge of its environmental consequences. Sustainable degrowth will inevitably require a new raft of climate and biodiversity laws, which can only be enforced by popular consent.

Translating the SEWP goals into ethics-based legislation is a logical next step. At the moment, over-consumption activities such as driving an SUV, flying and holidaying frequently, owning multiple homes and accumulating luxury goods are not only socially acceptable but regarded by many as aspirational signs of success. But, as philosopher Kate Soper (2020:185) says, there is no reason why "wasteful and polluting forms of behaviour should remain exempt from the kinds of criticism that we now expect to be brought against racist, sexist or blatantly undemocratic attitudes and behaviour".

The fragile border between what is morally wrong and what is technically legal, which the humachine corporations constantly exploit, will need to be strengthened. Humachine corporations have external committees intended to oversee their operations but too often these amount to little more than "greywashing". Google has become notorious for firing its ethics professionals when they get in the way of profit and Microsoft, X/Twitter, Amazon and others began slashing staff from their "responsible AI teams", just when a storm of controversy arose around generative AI (Criddle and Murgla, 2023). In the post-growth era, by contrast, ethics will become a palpable force shaping every facet of organizational life.

History: Finding a Different Shape

Interpretations of the past are the source of our most compelling narratives of identity, providing profoundly influential myths of origins and working definitions of what it is to be human. But history is always about the future. We look to the past for signs of where we are going and that means we cannot change our future without changing our reading of the past. The myths I have tried to highlight, including the Western, scientistic concept of human progress, the rocket theory of industrialization and the idea of civilization as a never-ending nationalist war between competing technologies: all these linear, one-way misconceptions stand in the way of a better future. A post-growth approach to history will bring ecology, social anthropology and historiography together, fully utilizing the priceless resources which countless pre-modern societies offer us. It will create new, more complex shapes for world history that reject conventional historians' dismissal of the Age of Origin and other misconceptions that impede our ability to imagine a future free from the inequalities of capitalism.

Organizational Life: Beyond the Pyramid

As we move towards the Ecocene, enterprises will increasingly focus on supplying needs not wants, satisfying what really matters to a community rather than what expands investors' capital. Non-profit organizational constitutions will prioritize the interests of all stakeholders, eliminating the make-or-break power of elite shareholders, which is currently giving Big Tech founders almost unlimited authority. This horizontalizing impetus will flatten the hierarchies which govern most private and public organizations today. Ever since the Pyramid Age it has been the central assumption of all workplaces that workers need to be told what to do, but sustainable degrowth will develop legislative structures that give employees the best possible chance to organize themselves. That means boosting community enterprises, and encouraging the commons, for example in open-source technology enterprises and other bottom-up organizational formations. Worker-owned networks will play a major role in the organizational revolution, such as the Catalan Integral Cooperative described by Matthias Schmelzer, Andrea Vetter and Aaron Vansintjan in *The Future is Degrowth* (2022:255-6). This 2,500-member enterprise has multiple initiatives which aim "to displace the state apparatus", including supporting around forty-five people with basic income. It also "runs exchange networks, its own currency, food pantries, assemblies, financial cooperatives, a collectively-run factory [and] a machine workshop". Mondragon, the legendary Spanish cooperative which now has 81,000 workers worldwide, shows how this type of enterprise can be scaled up. Indeed, cooperatives and mutual societies already employ 10% of the entire global workforce (for more see Harvey, 2019:169-180).

In the short term, ecological and climatological training for all employees is another crucial workplace development, perhaps taking a cue from France, where all 5.6 million public sector workers are due to receive general and sector-specific environmental education in the coming years (Transformation.gouv.fr., 2022). And it's surely time to revive twentieth-century Participatory Design schemes which actively involved workers in designing technology, such as the Scandinavian collective resources approach or the American Joint Application Design system (Asaro, 2000).

Self-organization involves a very different concept of leadership to the elitist individualism which has been revived so contradictorily by the apparently progressive CEOs of the humachine age. Whereas this kind of mono-leadership can turn followers into sheep, post-growth plural leadership empowers the majority by aiming to delegate as much authority to them as possible. Call it servant leadership, co-leadership or, as the Zapatistas would have it, "to lead by obeying" (Khasnabish, 2010:83). Taking collective responsibility for decisions can make leaders of us all, dispelling the diffidence or apathy of those accustomed to having their choices made for them. A virtuous circle can constantly transform leaders into followers, followers into leaders and everybody into empowered citizens. Organizations will also be primary contexts for combating the psychopathic, Promethean tendencies which today too often provide a route to the top.

To sum up, the entire range of political, economic, social, scientific and organizational institutions of the Ecocene will be very different from today, although, as I've tried to illustrate, real-life examples are already emerging. But what will it feel like to live in this liberating world? That's our final challenge: to envisage the psychology of the Ecocene, a state in which ecological and egalitarian values become the bedrock of everyday lived experience.

CHAPTER 27

Towards the Psychocene: Steady-State Psychology the CANDID Way

The Psychocene is a way of describing a new state of human flourishing which can evolve if the Ecocene triumphs in the battle for the Anthropocene. Imagining the lived experience of a post-capitalist society is often best left to novelists, such as Ernest Callenbach in *Ecotopia* or Ursula Le Guin in *The Dispossessed* (see Harvey, 2019 for more on utopian literature). But one thing they make clear is that ecological democracy, economic degrowth and revolutionary new institutions will not be enough; ultimately the Ecocene will require a profound change in human consciousness. How this will come about cannot be fully predicted, but I suggest it will unquestionably involve rejecting the techno-utopian assertion that human-machine fusion can deliver psychological liberation. Instead, it's our Olympian panoply of social skills, intellectual capacities and creative talents that point to the upgrading of Homo sapiens that's really available to us. It's techne rather than technology that can put us on the road to mastering the art of living and realising the true story of human growth.

The Psychology of Sustainable Degrowth: Spontaneous SEWP Effects

The commitment of the SEWP worldplan to put people and planet first, which I've described so far, will inevitably create a flow of positive psychological effects. As democracy starts to spring up from below, a new mindset will spread throughout society, affecting what it's like to participate in any social institution, from the workplace to the family and from the school to the street. As economic circularity replaces one-way flows, connectedness at every personal and interpersonal level will become the lifeblood of the system. Flow is an important psychological concept, developed by psychologist Mihalyi Csikszentmihalyi (1990), who regards it as one of the primary constituents of happiness. Experiences of flow involve an intense engagement in a creative task in which time appears to stand still, goals are clarified, feedback is immediate and decisions seem to make themselves. This modality of subjectivity will be essential to the Ecocene, not simply in relation to individual tasks but as a stream of complex, interpersonal relationships, which we might call "interflow".

Ecocene urban living could be one example of interflow. Sustainable town planning based on respecting planetary boundaries will transform what it feels like to be in an urban situation, which for over half of the world's population represents everyday reality (Raworth, 2018). Car-free cities will enable people to reclaim the streets and remove the lethal danger of the polluted, traffic-filled roads that bisect our lives. Children will return to safely walking to school and playing outdoors and most people will be able to reach the amenities they need on foot. Two-and four-wheel pedal-driven vehicles of every conceivable variety will move through the metropolis. Expanded parks will provide social experiences for people of all ages through multiple recreational and entertainment activities in an environment where citizens are increasingly confident of policing themselves. This new ease in actively participating in communal life will be one of the hallmarks of Ecocene psychology.

Almost certainly, this flow experience is already a part of the non-hierarchical cooperative-based living, described in the previous chapter. For example, try to transport yourself into the everyday life of the Catalan "post capitalist, eco-industrial" community of Califou, which revolves around "a carpentry and mechanical workshop, a community kitchen, a biolab, a hack lab, a soap production facility, a music studio, a guest house, a social centre and a 'free shop'" (Schmelzer et al, 2022:256). Other utopias in the here and now which prefigure post-growth living are springing up in all sorts of unexpected places in the interstices of capitalism. Take the group of older people living along the River Adur valley in West Sussex who have united to protect and reclaim their local river bank. As Mary Gearey and

Neil Ravenscroft (2019) note, at the end of their professional lives, "many of these elders have undergone a personal, if not political, epiphany and have turned to forms of environmental activism to articulate their agency and demonstrate solidarity".

The Psychologically-Informed Society

Alongside the spontaneous emergence of a new mindset through inte-grated, non-hierarchical organizations, I envisage an important informal role for psychological facilitation in the communities of the Ecocene. In fact, a post-growth society should expect a good deal from professional psychologists and other appropriately trained citizens. But their role will not be as domineering experts but as humble facilitators helping with the challenges of egalitarian living. Equalizing is the aim of much psychology. In a non-judgemental environment, it tries to help people to gain the sense of balance and self-value which, for whatever reason, society denies them. This human-focused, relational psychology is especially evident in exis-tential-phenomenological, person-centred and psychodynamic schools. It constitutes a radically different approach to the mechanistic behaviourism which has dominated past representations of the psychologically-informed society, typified by B.F. Skinner's *Walden Two* (1948), a utopia predicated on involuntary behavioural conditioning.

Tackling the mental health crisis gripping the developed world today will be a major priority for post-growth society. Redistributing state resources (e.g. from defence) will end decades of underfunding of mental health. In a psychologically-facilitated world, human-to-human services will take the lead, although rigorously tested and supervised online services may provide useful support. That means a major role for the talking cure of psychotherapy, a classic low-tech innovation which represents one of the biggest breakthroughs in the history of mental health treatment. Expect this to become an expertise which many people possess and are able to use spontaneously, as appropriate in social contexts. Group therapy ses-sions led by trained professionals will also become more familiar, for its own transformative effects, and as a counterpoint to everyday communal decision-making.

Empathy counselling, for those on the autism spectrum and others, will be integrated into many educational and occupational contexts. Cooperative communication training will help to mitigate conflicts in everyday situations and support a new emotionally-literate political discourse, which minimizes antagonistic rhetoric and group polarization. Reductions in cases of domestic child abuse will help to reduce adult criminality, as prisons become centres of rehabilitation with an increased provision of democratic community therapy for those with serious anti-social behavioural disorders.

Elsewhere, I've outlined a more detailed programme of psychological interventions for a post-capitalist society (Harvey, 2019:192-205). In his excellent *Psychology at the Heart of Social Change* (2023:6) Professor Mick Cooper takes a similar approach, rightly observing that up to now psychology "is notable only by its absence" from progressive politics. Among the policies that Cooper suggests will buttress "psychology-informed progressivism" is positive parenting, which encourages warmth, firmness in boundary-setting and close engagement with the child in learning and development activities. (Once positive parenting becomes widespread the robotic parenting devices, discussed in Chapter 15, will surely become redundant.) Primary school will magnify this strong sense of self by the emphasis on building social relationships which will be a cradle-to-grave feature of Ecocene psychology. In a broader context, as political philosopher John Holloway (2019:20) says, the challenge is to create "a world rooted in social relations which are not power relations" that is based on "a mutual recognition of people's dignity".

Steady-State Psychology the CANDID Way

Another approach to the psychology of the Ecocene parallels the careful economic management which will be needed to achieve sustainable degrowth. This steady-state psychology, as it might be named, would focus on reaching a balance between the multiple dialectics or polar opposites which we have to deal with in life. It would strive for sufficiency not efficiency, reject the Law of More; and seek the ideal boundary of moderation, keenly respecting the idea of limits rather than constantly crashing through them in an ecstasy of excess. It would aim to develop the tough discipline of "enoughism", training us to spot just when the positive starts to turn into the negative and act accordingly. This adjustable sense of balance is directly comparable to the set point of homeostasis which the body constantly seeks, a position that can vary according to situation and context.

A practical way of understanding this search for a new psychological equilibrium is through the CANDID values. Throughout this book, I've used the CIMENT values to demonstrate negative aspects of the lived experience of growth capitalism, but what does pursuing the positive side of the values grid involve? It's a challenge that involves moving beyond the conscious and unconscious restrictions capitalism places on our subjective and intersubjective lives.

Ecological Democracy (Towards the Ecocene) The CANDID ethos	Capitalist Growthism (Towards the Technocene) The CIMENT ethos
Cooperation Win/win Life as peace/Working together	**Competition** Win/lose (Zero-sum) Life as war/Working in opposition
Altruism/Collectivism Concern for others Group/Community	**Individualism** Self-interest Individual above society
Non-materialism Spiritual wisdom Quality	**Materialism** Consumerism Quantity
Democracy Majority rule Self-organization	**Elitism** Minority rule Hierarchy
Internationalism Worldwide Cooperation Global human identity	**Nationalism** Nation state Ethnocentricity/nativism
Deference for nature Partnership with nature Developing tools for living sustainably and equitably together	**Technologism** Conquest of nature Progress of technology as an end in itself Technology as magic

Figure 1. The CANDID/CIMENT Values Grid

First, let me remind the reader that these value oppositions are not mutually exclusive but define a dynamic field of behaviour. Take cooperation and competition, for example; we all have the capacity switch from one of these modalities to the other, and often back again, sometimes in a fraction of a second. Our history since the Agricultural Age has been one of constantly triggering switches which make humans see each other as deadly rivals for resources rather than confirming what many scientists now recognize as the essentially cooperative nature of humanity, without which human communities would be impossible (Nowak, 2011). Striving to cooperate with others does not mean obliterating competitiveness but creating a context which is ultimately defined by cooperation, as in games and sports.

The same goes for altruism and individualism. Degrowth living will shift norms of acceptable behaviour towards the collective end of the values spectrum, refuting the idea that humans are as inherently selfish as capitalism would make us believe. It celebrates solidarity, a positive experience of fellow feeling that is the best way to defeat the epidemic of loneliness that haunts so many people today. The intense pleasures of living and working together that flow from cooperation are still central to many traditional communities, as expressed in the well-known South American ethos of buen vivir ("good living"), which is derived from the ecologically harmonious sociability of the Andean Quechua peoples. Sociologists have also found examples of conviviality and "a profound sociality of 'being with'" in UK towns and cities, particularly among multicultural groups, engaged in sports and creative activities (Neal et al, 2019).

For some people, especially at the outset, acting in ways that depart from the group norm will be a constant temptation, perhaps leading to the outlawing of some forms of extreme individualistic behaviour (as in primal egalitarian societies). Yet in the right context, asserting your rights and expressing creative originality will need to be not only acceptable but desirable.

Achieving a non-materialist way of being, the third CANDID value, means a much greater focus on inward life. This requires the courage to move towards spiritual exploration, mindfully turning away from outwardness, perhaps to experience the world as an unfolding succession of unique moments. The more chaotic the outward world, the more barriers the interior journey must overcome. Martin Heidegger's metaphor of the oak tree gives a clue as to how this can be achieved, while also providing a dialectical corrective to the growth irrationale. "[G]rowing means this", he says, "to open oneself up to the expanse of heaven and at the same time to sink roots into the darkness of earth" (quoted in Travers, 2019:219).

The practice of mindfulness can also help this opening and rooting process. As a modern psychological approach, mindfulness has proven to be highly effective in helping depression and anxiety but it draws on a spiritual way of life which goes back thousands of years in the Buddhist tradition. It's also linked to long-standing Indian meditation practices, and, in the form of ritualistic fire-gazing, may even have been practiced by the earliest hunter-gatherers (Rossano, 2007).

As for the democracy-elitism spectrum, a post-growth society represents a significant movement towards the CANDID side of the values grid. The belief that we all have a right to become who we need to be and to contribute meaningfully to society, irrespective of our abilities, will become paramount. Ridding ourselves of the mental Pyramid Pattern will be a daily feature of everyday life, not an abstract political goal. This will involve being open to the potential of every individual without prejudgment, leading to a culture in which trusting others will be a risk constantly worth taking. At the same time, it will be the ongoing responsibility for every citizen to ensure that spontaneous hierarchies of merit, in which those with the most ability in a situation temporarily gain greatest influence, do not congeal into permanent social structures.

The fifth CANDID value, internationalism, which is so pivotal to the SEWP worldplan, will also prove to be a psychological challenge. We live on a planet that is indifferent to national borders but separating nationalist beliefs – and even nativist ideologies – from your affection for the country and culture with which you are most familiar, can sometimes be a significant personal struggle. However, recent research suggests that in many European countries "world-mindedness" – the preference for seeing humanity as a whole rather than through the lens of national or racial reference groups – continues to rise, especially among teenagers (Hanus et al, 2022). Closing the Global North/South split in one's worldview will vanquish the temptation to indulge in the narcissism of nationalism, which encourages humans to face off against each other in a lethal race to the bottom that foreshadows the Technocene. The fragility and artificiality of many nation states may become clearer in the course of the century, especially if some existing states disappear from the map as a result of the destruction of habitable climate niches (Lenton et al, 2023).

Eco-Psychology and Techno-Scepticism

The final CANDID value, deference to nature, is crucial to steady-state psychology. This antidote to technologism enables us to develop a thriving environmental connectedness and embrace our own naturalness, rather than seeing ourselves as poorly designed machines to be upgraded in a reengineered cosmos. Ecological psychology will be vital to help people develop their awareness of nature – I'd expect it to become mainstream as the Ecocene transition unfolds. The fast-expanding discipline of environmental neuroscience will continue to explore the hypothesis that we possess hunter-gatherer brains maladapted to urban civilization (Bergman et al, 2019). Meanwhile, ecological psychotherapy will be pivotal in helping to treat eco-anxiety, a chronic fear of environmental doom, which, sadly, is growing fast, especially among the young. In Britain over half of child psychiatrists report having seen patients who are profoundly distressed by the climate and biodiversity emergency (Gregory, 2021). Excessive anxiety can be a terrible burden to bear but correctly channelled it can also be a crucial asset helping us to proactively manage the future. As a sensing tool, anxiety can cut through complacency, misplaced optimism and sheer denialism. (Had the world suffered more eco-anxiety in the past, perhaps starting as early as 1965 when US President Lyndon Johnson was presented with compelling scientific evidence predicting climate change, we might not have arrived at our present ecological cliff edge (Climatefiles, 2023).) In one way or another, eco-anxiety is here to stay, hopefully not in its current deeply distressing form, but as a positive force driving us towards planetary sustainability and thereafter helping us to maintain it.

Socially-set floors and ceilings on consumption will help people to get the ecological balance right, as research on "consumption corridors" is now revealing (Sakhian, et al 2021). The kind of advisory limits currently issued by healthcare authorities on alcohol use could be extended to almost every form of human consumption, from housing and fashion to entertainment and travel. Consumption floors will be geared to basic human needs, which today are often not met, even in wealthy countries; ceilings will redefine the thresholds of ownership and luxury, which at present contribute so heavily to the overconsumption sending our planet towards meltdown.

The struggle against technologism can also be expressed as techno-scepticism. This involves a keen awareness of the misuses of technology, subtly balanced against a mature consciousness of its utility when used in the right context. The techno-sceptic looks for the human solution first (i.e., she rejects cart-before-the-horse thinking), enabling her to see through the mirages, myths and false assumptions, which dominate the humachine age, such as the brain is a computer, machines are capable of empathy and robotics only intend to replace dull, dirty and dangerous jobs. The seductiveness of the ease and convenience lure of humachination is met with a robust assessment of what we might lose by delegating our indigenous skills and talents to machines. As Ruha Benjamin (2019:76) advises, "whenever we hear the promises of tech being extolled, our antennae should pop up to question what all that hype of "better, faster, fairer" might be hiding and making us ignore". Every time a new technology is put forward as the silver bullet for a crisis, we should remember that it can create more problems than it solves.

Technological conviviality (Illich, 1973) is another dimension of this approach, which favours the communal sharing of tools over individual ownership and market monopolization. It also results in a preference for simple over complex technology, an Occam's razor attitude that prioritizes technology that is durable, easy-to-fix and recyclable and which doesn't require confusing enchainments with other technologies. Low-Tech Magazine (2023), a solar-powered website based in Barcelona, has famously pioneered this approach, offering numerous experimental solutions from bike generators and pedal-powered air compressors to thermo-electric stoves and carbon-neutral container sailing ships. Successfully navigating the choppy nature–technology straits means not falling for the technologistic fallacy that implies that machines are things in themselves. While Pasi Heikkurinen (2018) is right to argue for a Heideggerian ethos of releasement (or "letting go"), which leads us to deliberately not use all the technological power that we have at our disposal, we should not shy away from using that power if it's strictly necessary. Giant engineering projects, such as the creation of worldwide renewable energy and a universal internet, may be needed for a sustainable future, but it's who chooses, owns and designs this technology, and for what ends, that really matters.

Many other mental balancing acts will enter the Ecocene psychological repertoire. For instance, putting the idea of "one people on one planet" at the centre of your thoughts involves shifting from the part to the whole and following the holistic non-linear logic that flows from the interconnectedness of all things. This means preferring integration to disruptive disintegration and striving for virtuous circles of cause and effect rather than vicious ones. In terms of bicameral brain theory, holistic psychology means ensuring the dominance of the right hemisphere's all-round attentiveness and sense of priorities, while not wasting the left hemisphere's genius for manipulating reality.

Steady-state psychology also involves the balancing of time by placing the present in the context of the future, separating the important from the urgent and taking responsibility for what future generations inherit. This holistic temporal awareness often involves shifting from the fast to the slow in thought and action. Decelerationism in daily life is the opposite to the coercive tyranny of speed of the humachine age, which is constantly hustling us into making panicky decisions which can end in tragedy. And yet paradoxically, we also have to accept that we urgently need to move much more quickly if we are to achieve planetary sustainability before it's too late. This mindset requires confidence in our ability to manage uncertainty and overcome the fear of change which will be whipped up by those who have most to lose from the transformation of the status quo. Without this new way of thinking and feeling it may be impossible to neutralize the Promethean dominator complex that has reigned over humanity for so long and which ontocapitalism endows with potentially even greater transformative power.

The Democracy of Love

A final way of envisaging post-growth psychology is to see it in terms of love. In an earlier chapter, I alluded to the phenomenon of love (including the love of life) as a key to unlocking the multiplicity of enfolded realities involved in what it is to be human. It's a reminder that although the steady-state mindset may encourage calmness and composure, it's definitely not short on joyfulness. On the contrary, degrowth hedonism will enhance conviviality, companionship and other stress-free pleasures released from their competitivist shackles. At times, a community may resemble a music festival, a joyous, creative expression of human interactivity, which will reinvent itself day by day. At other times, pleasures will take place indoors and in safe spaces, as the Ecocene unites introverts and extraverts. Overall, respect will grow for meditative silence and the discipline of self-limitation, as will the recognition that so much great art, from Vermeer to Mondrian and Jane Austen to Samuel Becket, is often based on self-imposed boundaries. This powerful new psychological discipline, cultivated by society as a whole, will enable people to switch from hedonism to frugality at will and indulge in pleasure without being corrupted by it.

We can see traces of this advanced dialectic in the Mahayana Buddhist tradition, based on "a discipline that facilitates letting go of ego-centred habits and enables compassion to become spontaneous and self-sustaining" (Varela et al, 1991:248-50). The purpose of the Ecocene is analogous: to transcend political economy and embrace ecology in a society which allows for the best in human-to-human relationships to be expressed spontaneously. Andreas Weber (2018) puts love in the context of biology, when he says that every living thing is "fundamentally a meaning centre" and that "creating meaning is the physics of the organism. This takes us away from the idea that the organism is a machine." Love is essential to this identity formation (or autopoiesis), as it's "not a feeling but a practice of creating relationships in a commons of reality". Weber also issues a rousing call: "Let's build a human culture which is about the practice of love … about the yearning to be connected". Understanding the ecology of love is surely vital if we are to create a new world around it.

Our desires and emotions can be transformed once we are freed from "the constraints of neoliberal growth logic", as philosopher Barbara Muraca (2019:5) suggests, envisaging "workshops of liberation where radical alternative can be thought through and tried out, wild and free from dominant narratives". Such workshops already exist as real-life experiments in collective living, such as the Tamera Peace, Research and Education community (2023), which explores free love based on trust. Imaginatively, we might even see one of the challenges of the Ecocene as transforming the individualistic, masculinist notions of techno-utopian sexual ecstasy described in Chapter 19 into authentically egalitarian, caring and mutually affirming modalities of sexual freedom.

Psychologist, activist and Rabbi Michael Lerner (2019:43 & 229) also endorses the idea that a democracy of love is needed and that it may be the only way to avert a Technocene future. He urges that "only a full-scale embrace of revolutionary love will save our world" from the current cult of fear and domination that could so easily slide into techno-dystopia:

> The only protection for the future of the human race is for us to become the kind of loving, caring, generous and awe-filled beings that our prophets and poets, our spiritual leaders, and our own inner voices have been calling us to become.

424 | THE AGE OF HUMACHINES

The Success of Failure

Unless a new psychology emerges from below in society and from within the heart of every person in it, learned from the first days of life and reflected in every facet of everyday experience, the Ecocene may remain beyond reach. Working within limits is one of humanity's greatest indigenous capacities and making do with little has got most humans through the last three hundred millennia. Only now has human society the resources to afford the basis for a truly beautiful way of living for all.

This is what the Ecocene offers – a recognition that the "failure" to produce endless economic growth can turn into the success of making the most of being human on a superabundant, life-loving planet which is several billion years in the making. If great art is based on limitations, so perhaps is great living. It starts with a pessimistic approach to resources and the limitations of technology but ends in optimism for the abundance of inventiveness and cooperative work which we have only just begun to explore as humans. It's what John Meyer (2010) calls "the democratic politics of sacrifice", which requires the maturity to consciously sacrifice your own consumption in the knowledge that others will be sacrificed if you don't. Or, as Gandhi is said to have observed, "live simply so that others may simply live".

Working with what we've got after so many years of human innovation would be plenitude enough, but in practice it will only be the start of an eruption of new human skills, talents and relationships which is beyond our current ability to imagine. Futures of sufficiency and celebration will open up, as will new forms of austere abundance, revolutionary solidarity and social and emotional interconnectedness. In embracing the tough, personality-building discipline of strict limits, our creative capacity could become almost limitless, whereas ignoring them in the lazy reverie of machine supremacism will surely end in the crumpled, sodden wings of the drowning Icarus. In our failure, lies our success.

EPILOGUE

Our Future, Our Choice
(or How to Stop Choosing the Technocene
and Start Opting for the Ecocene)

Whatever else may be uncertain in the age of humachines, one thing is not: we have a choice coming. The future will not just happen, it will be made, and almost certainly by humans not machines. Technology is always a political and social choice but not an easy one. As I've emphasized throughout this book, we've already used up our budget of easy decisions – now all that remain are the hard ones.

In one sense, we have to choose between political economies. Do we continue with the wealth-monopolized system that enables today's elite to choose the technology that not only suits their own financial interests but their peculiar dominator psychology and obsession with computers and science fiction? Or can democracy come to the fore and enable the majority to make the decisions that shape the future? Historically, this would mean the majority taking charge of our tools for the first time since the Agricultural Age, reviving the egalitarianism of the small societies of the Age of Origin, but on an incomparably larger, planetwide scale. Or do we stick with the plutotechnics that has prevailed since the pyramid society first emerged in the city states of Mesopotamia and Egypt six millennia ago?

If the economic thesis of this book is right, we also face an economic choice between the competing worldplans of the Anthropocene and the organizing principles they embody. Do we stick with the GUN principles of growth capitalism, never-ending economic expansion, the unequal distribution of its rewards and a war on nature that increasingly expresses itself in a determination to prove that machines are superior to living things? Or are we brave enough to shift to a worldplan based on the goals of sustainable, equitable wellbeing planetwide?

This, as I suggested in the Introduction, is essentially a decision between utopias, which resonates with the desire for a better world that is buried deep inside all of us. As we've explored, there are three versions of capitalist utopia on offer. The first is the carbon capitalism of the industrial revolution which despite its manifest destructiveness still holds attractions for many. The second is green growthism, a more alluring utopia which is unfortunately predicated on the fantasy that economic expansion can be dematerialized from grievous environmental harms. And third, we have the humachine model of utopia, which I've tried to fully describe and critique in this book for the first time. This phase of post-biological capitalism aims to preserve all previous forms of capitalism, but only at the cost of amalgamating humans and machines in the arrogant belief that evolution can literally be reengineered and a superior type of Homo sapiens created. It's an inherently anti-human, undemocratic mission, which will either end up in the dystopia of the Technocene, for which trials are already being run across the planet, or in the ultimate act of hubris, the creation of a superintelligent, digital-robotic species which has no place for humanity.

The alternative is another kind of utopia, characterized by a deadly serious realism but one which regards the Enlightenment goals of democracy and social equality as much more than political rhetoric. The Ecocene recognizes the extraordinary gifts that fossil fuel and human technology and science have conferred on us, but that we now need the self-discipline to say "enough is enough". Instead of smashing planetary limits in pursuit of profit, a new integrated, life-based science will seek harmony with nature. Rather than jeopardizing the essentials of humanity, the core skills and talents of being human will be built on and enhanced with the dignity of all respected. The Ecocene version of utopia aims to maximize the immense good fortune we have in possessing life, in the belief that this can enable us to bring out the very best of being human on planet Earth. It's a new culture of post-growth hedonism and conviviality which recognises there is much more to life than the production and consumption of commodities.

In reality, the twenty-first century may play out in many different political and conceptual models and in several temporalities and geographies, for as important as theory is as a guide to action, utopia is nothing if not a practice. As John Holloway writes (2002: 245):

> "The utopian star is unquenchable, but the light it casts does not create a highway that we can march upon. The only paths that are open to us we make ourselves by walking".

But that does not mean that the middle of the road route to the Ecocene is likely to be viable, however attractive this option may seem. Our addiction to capitalism is not negotiable. If we halt the collapse of the Earth's systems too slowly, we will lose the race altogether. To rely on the techno-utopianism of the humachinators, without balancing it against the all-too-plausible worst-case scenario of eco-techno dystopia, would be the height of strategic irresponsibility.

That's why we should think of the eco-democratic, post-growth world in terms of the French concept of "sobriety", suggesting a society that is not only purged of polluting technologies but also "clean" in the sense of sober, recovering from consumerist addictions and accepting that things that seemed like necessities must revert to the luxuries they always were. This future would also be cleansed of the mechanistic fantasy that machines can do all the hard work for humanity, enabling us to create a future in which living beautifully and sustainably becomes the right of every person, not the sole prerogative of an elite.

As I see it, these are some of the choices that face us in the near future, but the window of decision is shutting fast. Writing in what will almost certainly prove to be the hottest year on record, climate and biodiversity chaos is already ripping across the planet. The wrong choices promoted by climate delayism and technologism will endanger billions of lives and perhaps threaten the habitability of our planet forever. Simultaneously, the humanization of machines and the mechanization of humans, based on an outmoded concept of science, accelerate by the day, giving our trickster leaders the platform to claim that they represent our only viable future. Time has often moved imperceptibly slowly over the billions of years leading to human evolution but now in the blink of an eye that is the next decade or two, changes will be pressed upon us which may alter our species forever.

So whether we see our existential choice in terms of democracy, science, economics, ecology or moral values, now is not a time to look away. We have a history-making challenge to level the global pyramid and fully take control of our destiny for the first time. In a sense, those of us alive today are privileged to be standing at the point, to which the entire history of planet Earth has led, at the crossroads where the ages of human technology meet. Whatever we choose will be remembered, by our children, our grandchildren and by countless generations to come. We didn't ask for this choice but it falls to us to make it. What an opportunity we have to get it right.

REFERENCES

Abad-Santos, Alexander (2013) 'The Bill Gates handshake: Offensive, or just weird?' *The Atlantic*, 23rd April, 2013. https://www.theatlantic.com/international/archive/2013/04/bill-gates-handshake/315990/

Abbot, Derek (2013) 'The reasonable ineffectiveness of mathematics', Proceedings of the IEEE, 101(10): 2147-2153. DOI:*10.1109/JPROC.2013.2274907*

Abrahams, Yuval (2024) '"Lavender": The AI machine directing Israel's bombing spree in Gaza,' *+972 Magazine*, 3rd April 2024. https://www.972mag.com/lavender-ai-israeli-army-gaza/

Adler, Alfred (1956) *The Individual Psychology of Alfred Adler: A systematic presentation in selections from his writings*. Ansbacher, H.L. and Ansbacher R.R (eds.). New York: Basic Books.

Agar, Nicholas (2004) *Liberal Eugenics: In defence of human enhancement*. Chichester: Wiley-Blackwell.

Age UK (2020) 'Not like riding a bike: Why some older people stop using the internet', March 2020, London: Age UK. https://www.ageuk.org.uk/globalassets/age-uk/documents/reports-and-publications/lapsed_users_report_march-2020.pdf

Ahir, H. and Loungani, P. (2014) ' "**There will be growth in the spring**": How well do economists predict turning points',VoxEU, 26, 2014. *https://voxeu.org/article/predicting*-economic-turning-points (retrieved 20/11/2020).

Ahmed, Nabil et al (2022) 'Inequality Kills: The unparalleled action needed to combat unprecedented inequality in the wake of COVID-19', Oxfam, January 2022. https://oxfamilibrary.openrepository.com/bitstream/handle/10546/621341/bp-inequality-kills-170122-en.pdf

Ahmed, Nur et al (2023) 'The growing influence of industry in AI research', *Science*, 2nd March 2023,Vol 379, 6635: 884-886. *DOI: 10.1126/science.ade2420*

Aldin, Chris (2005) 'Looking back on the crash', *The Guardian*, 10th March, 2005.

Al Ghusain, Alia (2020) "The biggest problem with carbon offsetting is that it doesn't really work," Greenpeace.org. uk, 26th May, 2020, *https://www.greenpeace.org.uk/news/the-biggest-problem-with-carbon-offsetting-is-that-it-doesnt-really-work/*

Allard, La Donna Brave Bull et al (2019)'We stand in solidarity with Rojava, an example to the world', *The Guardian*, 1st November, 2019.

Allen, Mike (2017) 'Sean Parker unloads on Facebook: "God only knows what it's doing to our children's brains', *Axios*, 9th November, 2017. *https://www.axios. com/2017/12/15/sean-parker-unloads-on-facebook-god-only-knows-what-its-DOIng-to-our-childrens-brains-1513306792*

Alsever, Jennifer (2021)'Billionaire Marc Lore wants to build a utopian city based on "equitism"', *Fortune Magazine*,1st September 2021. https://fortune.com/2021/09/01/billionaire-marc-lore-utopian-city-equitism/

Alshami, Ali (2019)'Pain: Is It All in the Brain or the Heart?' *Current Pain and Headache Reports,* 14th November 2019, 23(12):88. DOI: 10.1007/s11916-019-0827-4. PMID: 31728781.

Amazon.com (2022) 'Delivering Progress every day: Amazon's 2021 Sustainability Report', About Amazon, August, 2022. *https://sustainability.aboutamazon.com/2021-sustainability-report.pdf*

American Psychiatric Association (2013) *Diagnostic and Statistical Manual of Mental Disorders, 5th edition.* Arlington, Va: American Psychiatric Publishing.

American Psychological Association (2017) 'Ethical Principles of Psychologists and Code of Conduct, Section 8: Research and Publication', Washington, DC: American Psychological Association, https://www.apa.org/ethics/code.

American Society of Plastic Surgeons (2020) '2020 Plastic Surgery Statistics Report', Plastic Surgery.org, 2020. https://www.plasticsurgery.org/documents/News/Statistics/2020/plastic-surgery-statistics-full-report-2020.pdf

Anderson, Benedict (1983) *Imagined Communities: Reflections on the origins and spread of nationalism.* London: Verso.

Anderson, Craig et al (2018) 'Our letter to the APA', Screen Time Action Network, 8th August, 2018. *https://screentimenetwork.org/apa?eType=EmailBlastContent&eId=5026ccf8-74e2-4f10-bc0e-d83dc030c894*

Anderson, Kevin (2015) 'Talks in the city of light generate more heat', *Nature,* 528 (437) (2015). DOI.org/10.1038/528437a

Anthes, Emily (2013 'Race to create "insect cyborgs"', *The Guardian*, 17th February, 2013.

Archbold, Phil (2016) 'The untold truth of Mark Zuckerberg's sisters', Nikkiswift.com, 7th May 2020, *https://www.nickiswift.com/207642/the-untold-truth-of-mark-zuckerbergs-sisters/*

Ardito, Rita and Rabellino, Daniela (2011) 'Therapeutic alliance and outcome of psychotherapy: Historic excursus, measurements, and prospect for further research', *Frontiers in Psychology*, 2011, 2:270. DOI: *10.3389/fpsyg.2011.00270*

Arfaee, Maziar, Vis, Annemijn and Kluin,Jolanda (2022) 'Future technologies in total artificial heart development: Can a robot become as good as a donor heart?', *European Heart Journal*, 21st December, 2021, 43 (48): 4970–972. *https://DOI.org/10.1093/eurheartj/ehac512*

Armour, J Andrew (2007) 'The little brain on the heart', *Cleveland Clinic Journal of Medicine*, 24th February 2007, 1: 548-51. DOI: *10.3949/ccjm.74.suppl_1.s48*

Armstrong Mckay, D.I. et al (2022) 'Exceeding 1.5C global warming could trigger multiple climate tipping points', *Science*, 9th September 2022, 377 (6611). *DOI: 10.1126/science.abn7950*

Asafu-Ajaye, John et al (2015) 'An Ecomodernist Manifesto', The Breakthrough Org, April 2015. https://thebreakthrough.org/articles/an-ecomodernist-manifesto

Asaro, Peter (2000) 'Transforming society by transforming technology; The science and politics of participatory design', *Accounting, Management and Information Technologies*, 2000, 10:257-290.

Ashton, John (2020) 'Shoe leather epidemiology in the age of COVID: Lessons from Cuba', *Journal of the Royal Society of Medicine*, 14th July 2020, 113 (7), *https://DOI.org/10.1177/0141076820938582*

Association for Advancing Automation (2019) 'How robots are taking on the dirty, dangerous, and dull jobs', Automate.org, 15th October, 2019, *https://www.automate.org/blogs/how-robots-are-taking-on-the-dirty-dangerous-and-dull-jobs* (retrieved 22/11/22).

Atanasoski, Neda and Vora, Kalinda (2019) *Surrogate Humanity: Race, robots, and the politics of technological futures.* Durham, NC and London: Duke University Press.

Athalye, Anish et al (2017) 'Synthesizing robust adversarial examples', Arxiv.org, 24th July, 2017. *https://arxiv.org/abs/1707.07397*

Babiak, P. and Hare, R. (2006) *Snakes in Suits: When psychopaths go to work.* New York: HarperBusiness.

Bailey, Matt (2021) 'What Mark Zuckerberg really means when he talks about the metaverse', *Slate Magazine*, 28th October, 2021. *https://slate.com/technology/2021/10/facebook-metaverse-privacy-meta-what-it-means.html*

Bajaj, Simar Singh et al (2022) 'Vaccine apartheid: Global cooperation and equity', *The Lancet*, April 2022,, 399 (10334): 1452–1453. DOI: *10.1016/S0140-6736(22)00328-2*

Bakan, Joel (2004) *The Corporation: The pathological pursuit of profit and power.* New York: HarperBusiness.

Bakan, Joel (2020) *The New Corporations: How "good" corporations are bad for democracy.* New York: Vintage Books

Baldwin, Alan (2020) 'How Garry Kasparov's defeat to IBM's Deep Blue supercomputer incited a new era in artificial intelligence', *The Independent*, 12th April 2020, https://www.independent.co.uk/sport/general/chess-garry-kasparov-deep-blue-ibm-supercomputer-artificial-intelligence-a9461401.html

Barej, Anthony (2017) 'Automation threatens public sector jobs, says PWC', *Public Finance*, 27th March 2017. *https://www.publicfinance.co.uk/news/2017/03/automation-threatens-public-sector-jobs-says-pwc*

Barnes, Peter (2001) *Who Owns the Sky? Our common assets and the future of capitalism*. Washington, DC: Island Press.

Barnes, Peter (2006) *Capitalism 3.0: A guide to reclaiming the commons*. San Franscio: Berrett-Koehler.

Baron-Cohen, Simon (2011) *Zero Degrees of Empathy: A new theory of human cruelty and kindness*. London: Penguin Books.

Barsamian, David and Chomsky, Noam (2001) *Propaganda and the Public Mind: Conversations with Noam Chomsky*. London: Pluto Press.

Bartlett, Jamie (2018) *The People vs. Tech: How the internet is killing democracy (and how to save it)*. London: Ebury Press.

Barton, LeRon (2021) 'What it's like to be a black man in tech', *Harvard Business Review*, 4th March, 2021. https://hbr.org/2021/03/what-its-like-to-be-a-black-man-in-tech

Bastani, Aaron (2020) *Communism: Fully Automated Luxury A manifesto*. London: Verso.

Bastin, J-F. et al (2019) 'The global tree restoration potential', *Science,* 365 (6448):76-79. DOI/10.1126/science.aax0848

Baum, Rudy (2003) 'Nanotechnology: Drexler and Smalley make the case for and aginst "molecular assemblers"', *Chemical and Engineering News*, 1st December 2003, 81 (48):37-42. *https://pubsapp.acs.org/cen/coverstory/8148/8148counterpoint.html*

BBC (2006) 'US plans "stealth shark spies"', BBC News, 2nd March, 2006. http://news.bbc.co.uk/1/hi/world/americas/4767428.stm

BBC (2013) 'Microsoft fined by European commission over web browse',BBC News, 6th March 2013. *https://www.bbc.com/news/technology-21684329*

BBC (2018) 'UN: Facebook has turned into a beast in Myanmar',BBC News, 13th March, 2013. *https://www.bbc.co.uk/news/technology-43385677*

BBC (2018a) 'How WhatsApp helped to turn an Indian village into a lynch mob', BBC News, 19th July, 2018. *https://www.bbc.co.uk/news/world-asia-india-44856910*

BBC (2020) 'Coronavirus: The conspiracy theories spreading fake news – BBC Newsnight', *https://www.youtube.com/watch?v=BkbztWS4-9I* 04.45-5.50 (retrieved 17/12/22).

Beaumont, Peter (2020) 'Tony Blair is wrong. Africa won't be the answer to Britain's post-Brexit problems', *The Guardian*, 21st January 2021.

Bender, Emily, Gebru,Timnit et al (2021) 'On the danger of stochastic parrots: Can language models be too big?' F*AccT '21: Proceedings of the 2021 ACM Conference on Fairness, Accountability, and Transparency*, March, 2021:610–23. *https://doi.org/10.1145/3442188.3445922*

Beck, Ulrich (1992) *Risk Society: Towards a new modernity*. New York: Sage.

Becker, Ernest (1973) *The Denial of Death*. New York: Free Press.

Bender, Emily, Gebru, Timnit et al (2021) 'On the danger of stochastic parrots: Can language models be too big?' F*AccT '21: Proceedings of the 2021 ACM Conference on Fairness, Accountability, and Transparency, March, 2021:610–23. https://doi.org/10.1145/3442188.3445922*

Benditt, John (1999) 'Humachines', *MIT Technology Review*, 1st May 1999. *https://www.technologyreview.com/1999/05/01/275799/humachines/*

Benjamin, Ruha (2019) *Race after Technology: Abolitionist tools for the New Jim Code*. Cambridge: Polity.

Bensinger, Rob(2021) '"Existential risk from AI" survey results', Alignmentforum. org, 21st June 2021. *https://web.archive.org/web/20221013014859/ https://www.alignmentforum.org/posts/QvwSr5LsxyDeaPK5s/ existential-risk-from-ai-survey-results*

Bergman, Marc G. et al (2019) 'Environmental neuroscience', *American Psychologist*, 74(9):1039-1052. DOI: 10.1037/amp0000583.

Bertalanffy, Ludwig von (1968) *General System Theory: Foundations, development, applications*. New York: Braziller.

Bianchi, Tiago (2024) 'Revenue of Google from 2002 to 2023', Statista, 31st January 2924. https://www.statista.com/statistics/266206/ googles-annual-global-revenue/

Biesecker, Michael and El Deeb, Sarah (2023) 'Hamas practiced in plain sight, posting video of mock attack weeks before border breach', *Associated Press*, 13th October 2023. *https://apnews.com/article/israel-palestinian-war-hamas-attack-border-wall-aa0b0f5f3613b6c6882cf37168e8e8ed*

BIJ (2022) 'Drone Strikes in Afghanistan', *The Bureau of Investigative Journalism, 2022. https://www.thebureauinvestigates.com/projects/drone-war/afghanistan*

Bilton, Nick (2016)'Silicon Valley's most disturbing obsession', *Vanity Fair*, 5th October, 2016.

Bittle, Jake (2020 'Lie detectors have always been suspect. AI has made the problem worse', *MIT Technology Review*, 13th March, 2020. https://www.technologyreview.com/2020/03/13/905323/ai-lie-detectors-polygraph-silent-talker-iborderctrl-converus-neuroid/

Blake, Wiiliam (1977) *The Complete Poems (*Alicia Ostriker, ed.). London: Penguin Books.

Blakely, Rhys (2023) 'Ai "could be like an alien invasion", says British professor', *The Sunday Times*, 13th May 2023.

Blanpain, Nathalie (2018) 'New data on life expectancy and standard of living in France', N-IuSSP, 4th June 2018. https://www.niussp.org/individual-and-population-ageing/new-data-on-life-expectancy-and-standard-of-living-in-france/

BIJ (2022) 'Drone Strikes in Afghanistan', *The Bureau of Investigative Journalism*, 2022. *https://www.thebureauinvestigates.com/projects/drone-war/afghanistan*

Bloom, Paul (2013) *Just Babies: The origins of good and evil.* New York: Crown Publishing.

Boardman, Felicity (2020) 'Human genome editing and the identity politics of genetic disability'. *Journal of Community Genetics,* 11: 125–127. https://DOI.org/10.1007/s12687-019-00437-4

Boddy, C.R. et al (2010) 'The influence of corporate psychopaths on corporate social responsibility and organizational commitment to employees', *Journal of Business Ethics*, November 2010, 97(1): 1-9. DOI:*10.1007/s10551-010-0492-3*

Boehm. Christopher (1999) *Hierarchy in the Forest: The evolution of egalitarian behaviour.* Cambridge: Harvard University Press.

Bohm, Nicholas et al (2022) 'The legal rule that computers are presumed to be operating correctly – unforeseen and unjust consequences', Bentham's Gaze, Information Security Research and Education, University College London, 30th June 2022.

Bolukbasi, Tolga et al (2016) 'Man is to computer programmer as woman is to homemaker? Debiasing word embeddings', Arxiv.org, 21st July 2016. https://arxiv.org/abs/1607.06520

Bookchin, Murray (1982) *The Ecology of Freedom: The emergence and dissolution of hierarchy,* revised edition. Palo Alto, California: Cheshire Books.

Booth, Robert (2023) 'Automated welfare system needs more human contact, ministers warned', *The Guardian*, 22nd May 2023.

Borowy, Iris (2017) 'Economic growth and health: Evidence, uncertainties and connections over time and place'. In *History of the Future of Economic Growth*, Iris Borowy and Matthias Schmelzer (eds.). London and New York: Routledge.

Bosetti, Rita and Jones, Stephen (2019) 'Cost-effectiveness of nano-medicine: Estimating the real size of nano-costs', *Nanomedicine*, 6th June 2019. 14(11). *https://DOI.org/10.2217/nnm-2019-0130*

Boston Dynamics (2017) 'Introducing Handle', Boston Dynamics, YouTube, 2017. https://www.youtube.com/watch?v=-7xvqQeoA8c

Boston Dynamics (2021) 'Atlas partners in parcour', Boston Dynamics, YouTube. https://www.youtube.com/watch?v=tF4DML7FIWk021

Breland, Ali (2017) 'How white engineers build racist code – and why it's dangerous for black people', *The Guardian*, 4th December, 2017.

Bridge, Mark (2018) ' Facebook investors try to oust "dictator" Mark Zuckerberg', *The Times*, 30th June, 2018.

Bostrom, Nick (2015) 'What happens when our computers get smarter than we are?', TED.com, 2015. https://www.ted.com/talks/nick_bostrom_what_happens_when_our_computers_get_smarter_than_we_are?language=en

Bostrom, Nick (2016) *Superintelligence: Paths, dangers, strategies*. New York: Oxford University Press.

Boulding, Kenneth (1973) 'Comment to the US Congress Hearing on the Energy Reorganization Act of 1973,' *Energy Reorganizations Act of 1973 Hearings, 93rd Congress, first session, HR* 11510:248.

Boyce, Daniel, Lewis, Marlon and Worm, Boris (2010) 'Global phytoplankton decline over the past century', *Nature,* 29th July 2010, 466(7306):591-6.DOI: 10.1038/nature09268. PMID: 20671703.

Breland, Ali (2017) 'How white engineers build racist code - and why it's dangerous for black people', *The Guardian*, 4th December, 2017.

Bridge, Mark (2018) ' Facebook investors try to oust "dictator" Mark Zuckerberg', *The Times,* 30th June, 2018.

Bridle, James (2018) *New Dark Age: Technology and the end of the future*. London: Verso.

Bridle, James (2018a) 'Known Unknowns', *Harper's Magazine*, July, 2018.*https://harpers.org/archive/2018/07/known-unknowns/*

Briggs, Joseph and Kodani, Devesh (2023) 'The potentially large effects of artificial intelligence on economic growth', *Goldman Sachs Economic Research*, 26th March 2023. https://www.ansa.it/documents/1680080409454_ert.pdf

British Board of Film Classification (2019) 'Children as young as seven see pornography, new report finds', Bbfc.co.uk, 26th September, 2019. *https://www.bbfc.co.uk/about-us/news/children-see-pornography-as-young-as-seven-new-report-finds*

British Psychological Society (2021) BPS Code of Human Research Ethics, Leicester: BPS. *https://cms.bps.org.uk/sites/default/files/2022-06/BPS%20 Code%20of%20Human%20Research%20Ethics%20%281%29.pdf*

Bromham, L. et al (2022) 'Global predictors of language endangerment and the future of linguistic diversity', *Nature, Ecology and Evolution,* 6: 163–173. https:// DOI.org/10.1038/s41559-021-01604-y

Brooke, John L. (2014) *Climate Change and the Course of History: A rough journey.* Cambridge: Cambridge University Press.

Brown, J et al (2017) 'Workforce of the Future: The competing forces shaping 2030', *PWC Report,* August 2017. *https://www.pwc.com/gx/en/services/ people-organisation/workforce-of-the-future/workforce-of-the-future-the- competing-forces-shaping-2030-pwc.pdf*

Brown, Mick (2014) 'Peter Thiel: The billionaire tech entrepreneur on a mission to cheat death', *The Daily Telegraph,* 19th September 2014.

Bruce, Andy (2023) ' UK's Labour vows to make Britain fastest-growing economy in G7', *Reuters,* 23rd February 2023. https://www.reuters.com/world/uk/eyeing- power-labour-pledges-five-missions-fix-uks-biggest-problems-2023-02-23/

Bryant, Ross (2013) 'People "will start becoming technology", says human cyborg', *Dezeen,* 20th November 2013. https://www.dezeen.com/2013/11/20/ interview-with-human-cyborg-neil-harbisson/

Brynjolfsson, Eric and McAfee, Andrew (2014) *The Second Machine Age: Work, Progress and prosperity in a time of brilliant technologies.* New York: Norton.

Buckman, Robert and Sabbagh, Karl (1993) *Magic or Medicine? An exploration of the world of healing.* London: Macmillan.

Bueno, Carlos (2014) 'Inside the Mirrortocracy', Carlos Bueno.org, June 2014. *https://carlos.bueno.org/2014/06/mirrortocracy.html*

Buettner, Dan (2008) *The Blue Zones: Lessons for living longer from the people who've lived the longest.* Washington, DC: National Geographic.

Burç, Rosa (2020) 'Non-territorial autonomy and gender Equality: The case of the autonomous administration of north and east Syria- Rojava', *Philosophy and Society* 31(3): 319-339.

Burgerrat (2023) 'Permanent climate assembly in Brussels', Burgerrat, 4th February, 2023. https://www.buergerrat.de/en/news/ permanent-climate-assembly-in-brussels/

Burke,K.D. et al (2018) 'Pliocene and Eocene provide best analogs for near-future climates', PNAS, 10th December 2018, 115(52) 13288-13293. *https://DOI. org/10.1073/pnas.1809600115*

Burn-Murdoch, John (2023) 'Smartphones and social media are destroying children's mental health', *The Financial Times,* 10th March 2023.

Burnett, Gary and Lee, Kate (2005) 'The effect of vehicle navigation systems on the formation of cognitive maps', *Traffic and Transport Psychology*, January, 2005: 407-418. DOI:*10.1016/B978-008044379-9/50188-6*

Busby, Eleanor (2018) 'Parents to receive advice on nursery rhymes in bid to close disadvantaged children's word gap', *The Independent*, 30th April, 2018. https://www.independent.co.uk/news/education/education-news/ parents-education-nursery-rhymes-preschool-social-mobility-word-gap- alphabet-a8329396.html

Busby, Eleanor (2018a) 'Children arriving at school unable to speak or read properly is a "scandal", says minister', *The Independent*, 31st July, 2018. *https://www.independent.co.uk/news/education/education-news/damian-hinds- preschool-children-social-mobility-parents-literacy-word-gap-a8470346.html*

Byler, Darren (2019) 'China's hi-tech war on its Muslim minority', *The Guardian*, 11th April 2019.

Byrnes, W. Malcolm (2003) 'Stock, Gregory. Redesigning our inevitable genetic future: Book review' , *The National Catholic Bioethics Quarterly*, 2003, 3(2):427- 429. https://philpapers.org/rec/BYRSGR

Cadwalladr, Carole (2020) 'Facebook is out of control. If it were a country it would be North Korea', *The Guardian*, 5th July 2020,

Campbell, Robert A.(2001) 'CYBORG SALVATION HISTORY: Donna Haraway and the Future of Religion', *Humboldt Journal of Social Relations*, 26 (1/2): 154– 73. *http://www.jstor.org/stable/23263409 (retrieved 29/12/ 2022.*

Capra, Fritjof (1996) *The Web of Life: A new synthesis of mind and matter.* London: HarperCollins,

Capra, Fritjof and Luisi, Pier Luigi (2014) *The Systems View of Life: A unifying vision.* Cambridge: Cambridge University Press.

Caradonna, Jeremy et all (2015) "A call to look past An Ecomodernist Manifesto: A degrowth critique', Resilience.org, 5th May, 2015. *https://www.resilience.org/ wp-content/uploads/articles/General/2015/05_May/A-Degrowth-Response-to- An-Ecomodernist-Manifesto.pdf*

Carlson, Nicholas (2012) 'How Mark Zuckerberg booted his co-founder out of the company', *Business Insider*, 15th May 2012. https://www.businessinsider.com/ how-mark-zuckerberg-booted-his-co-founder-out-of-the-company-2012-

Carmat (2019) ' Carmat presents positive interim results of the first part of its pivotal study', Carmatsa.com, 15th January 2019. *https://www.carmatsa.com/en/ news/carmat-presents-positive-interim-results-first-part-pivotal-study/*

Carpenter, Siri (2012) 'That gut feeling', *APA Monitor on Psychology*, September, 2012, 43(8). https://www.apa.org/monitor/2012/09/gut-feeling

Carreyrou, John (2018) *Bad Blood: Secrets and lies in a Silicon Valley startup.* New York: Alfred A Knopf.

Carrington, Damian (2024) 'Quest to declare the Anthropocene an epoch descends into epic row', *The Guardian*, 7th March, 2024.

Carrington, Damian (2024a) 'World's top climate scientists expect global heating to blast past 1.5C target', *The Guardian*, 8th May 2024.

CAT (2023) 'Costa Rica', Climate Action Tracker, 5th April 2023. https:// climateactiontracker.org/countries/costa-rica/

CAT (2023a) 'Temperatures: 2100 Warming Projections', Climate Action Tracker, 5th December 2023. *https://climateactiontracker.org/global/temperatures/*

Chakravorti, Bhaskar (2022) 'Why Ai failed to live up to its potential during the pandemic', *Harvard Business Review*, 17th December, 2022 *https://hbr. org/2022/03/why-ai-failed-to-live-up-to-its-potential-during-the-pandemic*

Chan, Henry (2022) 'More scientists in new China leadership: A model for 4th industrial revolution?', *The Manila Times*, 6th November, 2022.

Chan, Ray (2022) 'Rio Tinto's Gudai-Darri mine most technologically advanced in Pilbara', *Australian Mining*, 21st June, 2022. *https://www.australianmining.com. au/news/most-technologically-advanced-iron-ore-mine-in-pilbara/*

Chang, C.H. et al (2023) 'Environmental users abandoned Twitter after Musk takeover', *Trends in Ecology and Evolution*, 15th August 2023. https://www.cell. com/trends/ecology-evolution/fulltext/S0169-5347(23)00189-1

Chang, Kenneth (2021) 'SpaceX wins NASA $2.9 billion contract to build moon lander', *The New York Times*, 16th April 2021. *https://www.nytimes. com/2021/04/16/science/spacex-moon-nasa.html*

Chappell, Elliot (2022) 'Starmer is pledging "growth, growth, growth" but how will Labour deliver?' *Labour List*, 25th July 2022. https://labourlist.org/2022/07/ starmer-is-pledging-growth-growth-growth-but-how-will-labour-deliver/

Chin, Casey (2018) 'AI is the future – but where are all the women?', *Wired,* 17th August, 2018. https://www.wired.com/story/ artificial-intelligence-researchers-gender-imbalance/

Christoff, Peter (2013)'The climate state: Global warming and the future of the welfare state', *University of Queensland Political Science and International Studies Research Seminar Series*, 23rd September 2106. https://www.youtube. com/watch?v=w51QCIQAVCQ

Christophers, Brett (2020) *Rentier Capitalism: Who owns the economy and who pays for it?* London: Verso.

CIA (2023) 'The World Factbook: Costa Rica', CIA.gov, 25th September 2023. https:// www.cia.gov/the-world-factbook/countries/costa-rica/#people-and-society

Ciarrochi, J. et al (2016) 'The development of compulsive internet use and mental health: A four-year study of adolescence', *Journal of Development Psychology,*52(2):272-83. *https://pubmed.ncbi.nlm.nih.gov/28279545/*

CIEL (2023) '475 carbon capture lobbyists at COP28 exposes fossil fuels' grip', Center for International Environmental Law, 9th December 2023. *https://www.ciel.org/news/475-carbon-capture-lobbyists-at-cop28-exposes-fossil-fuels-grip/*

Clark, Andy (2004) *Natural-born Cyborgs: Minds, Technologies and the future of human intelligence.* Oxford and New York: Oxford University Press.

Clark, Andy (2013) 'Re-inventing ourselves. The plasticity of embodiment, sensing and mind'. In Max More and Natasha Vita-More (eds) *The Transhumanist Reader: Classical and contemporary essays on the science, technology , and philosophy of the human future.* Chichester: Wiley-Blackwell.

Clark, Stuart (2020) 'Are Elon Musk's "megaconstellations" a blight on the night sky?', *The Guardian*, 12th September, 2020.

Clarke, Laurie (2022) 'Why the sci-fi dream of cryonics never died', *MIT Technology Review*, 14th October 2022. *https://www.technologyreview.com/2022/10/14/1060951/cryonics-sci-fi-freezing-bodies/*

Clarke, Laurie (2022a) 'When AI can make art- what does it mean for creativity?' *The Guardian*, 12th November 2022.

Claxton, Guy (2015) *Intelligence in the Flesh: Why your mind needs your body much more than it thinks.* New Haven and London: Yale University Press.

CMS (2022) 'National Healthcare Expenditure Fact Sheet', Center for Medicare and Medicaid Services,14th December 2022. https://www.cms.gov/research-statistics-data-and-systems/ statistics-trends-and-reports/nationalhealthexpenddata/nhe-fact-sheet

Cobb, Matthew (2020) *The Idea of the Brain: A history.* London: Profile Books.

Cochrane, Maria Elizabeth et al (2019) 'The short-term effects of smartphone usage on the upper-back postures of university students', *Cogent Engineering*, 2019 6 (1). DOI: *10.1080/23311916.2019.1627752*

Cockbain, Ella and Tufail, Waqas (2020) ' A new Home Office report admits grooming gangs are not a 'Muslim problem'', *The Guardian*, 19th December 2020.

Coen, Susie (2023) 'Elon Musk can start implanting brain chips in humans as trial gets US approval', *The Daily Telegraph*, 26th May 2023.

Cohen, Ariel (20210 'A Bill Gates venture aims to spray dust into the atmosphere to block the sun. What could go wrong?', *Forbes Magazine*, 11th January 2021. *https://www.forbes.com/sites/arielcohen/2021/01/11/bill-gates-backed-climate-solution-gains-traction-but-concerns-linger/?sh=7dd1c667793b*

Cohen, Michael et al (2022) 'Advanced artificial agents intervene in the provision of reward', *AI Magazine*, 43 (3), 29th August 2022. https://onlinelibrary.wiley.com/ DOI/10.1002/aaai.12064

Cohn, David and Shrimp, William (2015) ' The cost implications of the use of pegylated liposomal doxorubicin when choosing an anthracycline for the treatment of platinum-resistant ovarian cancer: A low-value intervention?' *Gynecologic Oncology Reports*, 25th August 2015,13:47-48. https://www.ncbi.nlm.nih.gov/pmc/articles/PMC4563795/

Comfort, Nathaniel (2018) 'Can we cure genetic diseases without slipping into eugenics?' In Osagie K Obasogie and Marcy Darnovsky (eds.) *Beyond Bioethics: Towards a new biopolitics.* Oakland, Ca: University of California Press.

Commoner, Barry (1971) *The Closing Circle: Nature, Man and Technology.* New York: Random House.

Conger, Kate et al (2019) 'San Francisco bans facial recognition technology', *The New York Times*, 14th May 2019.

Conger, Kate et al (2022) 'Two weeks of chaos: Inside Elon Musk's takeover of Twitter', *The New York Times*, 11th November, 2022.

Congressional Research Service (2022) 'Defense primer: US policy on Lethal Autonomous Weapons Systems', Congressional Research Service, 14th November, 2022. https://crsreports.congress.gov/product/pdf/IF/IF11150

Conradi, Peter (2023) 'Was Slovakia election the first swung by deepfakes?' *The Times*, 7th October 2023.

Cook, Gary and Jardim, Elizabeth (2017) ' A Guide to Greener Electronics', Greenpeace.org, 17th October, 2017. https://www.greenpeace.org/usa/reports/greener-electronics-2017/

Cooper, Mick (2023) *Psychology at the Heart of Social Change: Developing a progressive vision for society.* Bristol: Policy Press.

Copernicus (2023) 'July 2023 sees multiple global temperature records broken', Copernicus Climate Change Service, 27th July 2023. https://climate.copernicus.eu/july-2023-sees-multiple-global-temperature-records-broken.

Cowan, Ruth Schwartz (1985) *More Work for Mother: The ironies of household technologies from the open heath to the microwave.* New York: Basic Books.

Cox, Josie (2019) 'From humble beginnings to master of the universe: How did Jeff Bezos make his millions?', *The Independent* , 28th February, 2019

Cox, Lisa (2019) 'CFMEU warns Adani coalmine risks selling out local jobs', *The Guardian*, 23rd May 2019.

Cowen, Tyler (2011 *The Great Stagnation: How America ate all the low-hanging fruit of modern history, got sick and will (eventually) feel better again.* New York: Dutton.

Cowen, Tyler (2013) *Average is Over: Powering America beyond the age of the great stagnation.* New York: Dutton.

CPPP (2022) 'CPP's latest report finds caring responsibilities are disproportionately impacting women in the UK', Centre for Progressive Policy, 11th April, 2022. *https://www.progressive-policy.net/publications/press-release-cpps-latest-report-finds-caring-responsibilities-are-disproportionately-impacting-women-in-the-uk*

Craig, Tom et al (2018) 'AVATAR therapy for auditory verbal hallucinations in people with psychosis: A single-blind, randomized controlled trial', *The Lancet*, 1st January 2018, (1): 31-40. https://www.thelancet.com/journals/lanpsy/article/PIIS2215-0366(17)30427-3/fulltext

Credit Suisse (2022) 'Global Wealth Report 2022', Credit Suisse, 20th September 2022. *https://www.credit-suisse.com/about-us-news/en/articles/media-releases/global-wealth-report-2022---record-wealth-growth-in-2021-tapered-202209.html*

Cremer, Carla Zoe and Kemp, Luke (2021) 'Democratizing Risk: In Search of a Methodology to Study Existential Risk', Arxiv.org, 27th December, 2021. https://arxiv.org/abs/2201.11214

Criddle, Cristina and Murgla, Madhumita (2023) 'Big Tech companies cut AI ethics staff, raising safety concerns', *The Financial Times*, 29th March 2023.

Crooks, Nathan (2018 'Elon Musk says you can change the world working 80 hours a week', *Industry Week*, 27th November 2018. https://www.industryweek.com/leadership/article/22026737/elon-musk-says-you-can-change-the-world-working-80-hours-a-week

Cuthbertson, Anthony (2022)'" Existential catastrophe" caused by AI is likely unavoidable, DeepMind researcher warns', *The Independent*, 15th September, 2022. https://www.independent.co.uk/independentpremium/uk-news/artificial-intelligence-deepmind-ai-catastrophe-b2168120.html

Csikszentmihalyi, Mihaly (1990) *Flow: The psychology of optimal experience.* New York: Harper.

Dahmani, Louisa and Bohbot, Veronique (2020) 'Habitual use of GPS negatively impacts spatial memory during self-guided navigation', *Scientific Reports*, 14th April 2020.DOI: 10.1038/s41598-020-62877-0.

Dale, Gareth (2017) 'Seventeenth-century origins of the growth paradigm'. In Iris Borowy and Matthias Schmelzer (eds) *History of the Future of Economic Growth. London* and New York: Routledge.

Daly, Herman (2007) *Ecological Economics and Sustainable Development: Selected essays of Herman Daly.* Cheltenham: Edward Elgar Publishing.

Daly, Herman (2019) 'Growthism: Its ecological, economic and ethical limits', Real-*World Economics Review*, 8th March, 2019, 87. *http://www.paecon.net/PAEReview/issue87/Daly87.pdf*

Daly, Herman and Farley, Joshua (2011) *Ecological Economics, Second Edition, Principles and Applications.* Washington, D.C.: Island Press.

D'Allesandro, Simone et al (2020) 'Feasible Alternatives to Green Growth', Nature Sustainability, 2020. DOI: https://doi.org/10.1038/s41893-020-0484-y

Damasio (1994) Descartes' Error: Emotion, reason and the human brain. New York: Putnam.

D'arcy Hughes, Abby (2011) 'Half of al German doctors prescribe placebos', The Guardian, 6th March 2011.

Davenport, Christian (2018) The Space Barons: Elon Musk, Jeff Bezos, and the quest to colonize the cosmos. New York: Public Affairs.

Davidson, Julia et al (2022) "European youth cybercrime, online harm and online risk-taking: 2022 research report," December, 2022. DOI:10.13140/ RG.2.2.20477.03049/1

Davies, Rob (2022) 'Up to 1 million women in the UK at risk of harm from gambling, study finds', The Guardian, 31st January, 2022.

Davis, David Brion (2006) Inhuman Bondage: The rise and fall of slavery in the New World. Oxford and New York: Oxford University Press.

Davis. Mike (2005) Planet of Slums. London: Verso.

Davis, Wes (2023) 'Lawyer used ChatGPT and now has to answer for its "bogus" citations"', The Verge, 27th May 2023. https://www.theverge. com/2023/5/27/23739913/chatgpt-ai-lawsuit-avianca-airlines-chatbot-research

Davison, Nicola (2019) 'The Anthropocene epoch: Have we entered a new phase of planetary history?', The Guardian, 30th May 2019.

Dawkins, Richard (1995) River out of Eden: A Darwinian view of life. London: Wedenfeld and Nicolson.

Dawson, Bethany (2021) 'Richard Dawkins's argument against women having babies with Down's Syndrome is nothing more than eugenics', The Independent, 18th May 2021. https://www.independent.co.uk/voices/richard-dawkins-downs-syndrome-disability-b1848956.html

Dawson, Ross (2022) '7 leading brain-computer interface companies and their current and prospective products', Rossdawson.com, 2022. https://rossdawson.com/futurist/companies-creating-future/ leading-brain-computer-interface-companies-bci/

Dearden, Lizzie (2020) 'Children filming themselves in graphic sexual videos for "likes" online is a growing trend', The Independent, 7th January, 2020. https://www.independent.co.uk/news/uk/home-news/paedophiles-online-child-sex-abuse-images-self-generated-streaming-iwf-a9272876.html

Decidim (2023) 'Free open-source Democracy', Decidim website, 2023. https://decidim.org/

Demaria, Federico, Kallis, Giorgos and Bakker, Karen (2019) 'Geographies of degrowth: Nowtopias, resurgences and the decolonization of imaginaries and places', *Environment and Planning E: Nature and Space*, 21ˢᵗ August 2019, 2(3):431-450. *https://DOI.org/10.1177/2514848619869689*

Dembicki, Geoff (2022) *The Petroleum Papers: Inside the far-right conspiracy to cover up climate change*. Vancouver: Greystone Books.

Dempsey, Michael (2020) 'Robot tanks: On patrol but not allowed to shoot', BBC News, 21ˢᵗ January 2020. *https://www.bbc.co.uk/news/business-50387954*

Descartes, Rene (1664/1972) *Treatise on Man*, trans. Thomas S. Hall. Cambridge, MA: Harvard University Press.

Descola, Phillipe (2013) *Beyond Nature and Culture*, trans. Janet Lloyd. Chicago and London: University of Chicago Press.

Devlin, Hannah (2016) 'The cryonics dilemma: Will deep-frozen bodies be fit for life?' *The Guardian*, 18ᵗʰ November 2016.

Devlin, Hannah (2020) 'Polygraph's revival may be about truth rather than lies', *The Guardian*, 21ˢᵗ January, 2021.

Diamandis, Peter and Kotler, Steven (2012) *Abundance: The future is better than you think*. New York: Free Press.

Diamond, Jared (1987)'The worst mistake in the history of the human race', *Discover Magazine*, May 1987. http://www.ditext.com/diamond/mistake.html

Diamond, Jared (1997) *Guns, Germs and Steel: The fates of human societies*. New York: Norton.

Dietz, Rob and O'Neil, Daniel W. (2013) *Enough is Enough: Building a sustainable economy in a world of finite resources*. London and New York: Routledge.

Diver, Tony (2019) 'Robot Carers to be funded by government scheme', *The Daily Telegraph*, 26ᵗʰ October 2019.

Doctorow, Cory (2023) *The Internet Con: How to seize the means of computation*. London: Verso Books.

Donnelly, Laura (2023) 'Tech giant started by US billionaire "clinches" £480m deal to handle NHS patient information', *The Daily Telegraph*, 20ᵗʰ November 2023.

Dorling, Danny (2017) The *Equality Effect: Improving life for everyone*. Oxford: New Internationalist Publications.

Dougherty, Conor (2016) 'How Larry Page's obsessions become Google's business', *The New York Times*, 24ᵗʰ January, 2016.

Drexler, Eric (1986) *Engines of Creation: The coming era of nanotechnology*. New York: Doubleday.

Dyble, Mark et al (2015) 'Sex equality can explain the unique social structure of hunter-gatherer bands', *Science,* 15th May 2025,348 (6236):796-798. https://www.science.org/DOI/10.1126/science.aaa5139

Dyson.co.uk (2022) 'Dyson confirms 2022 launch of purifying headphones delivering pure air and pure audio', Dyson.co.uk, March 2022. https://www.dyson.co.uk/newsroom/overview/news/march-2022/dyson-zone-announcement

Easterlin, Richard and O'Connor, Kelsey (2020) 'The Easterlin Paradox', Institute for the Study of Labor (IZA) Discussion Paper No. 13923. *https://ssrn.com/abstract=3743147*

EDF (2022) 'Methane: A crucial opportunity in the climate fight', Environmental Defense Fund, 2022. https://www.edf.org/climate/methane-crucial-opportunity-climate-fight.

EIU (2022) 'Democracy Index 2021: The China Challenge', Economist Intelligence Unit, February 2022. *https://www.eiu.com/n/campaigns/democracy-index-2021/*

Ekeli, Kristian Skagen (2005) 'Giving a vote to posterity – deliberative democracy and representation of future people', *Journal of Agricultural and Environmental Ethics* 18 (5):429-50.

Ember, Carol (2014) 'Hunter-gatherers (foragers)', Human Relations Area Files, Yale University, 1st June 2020. *https://hraf.yale.edu/ehc/summaries/hunter-gatherers*

Engels, Friedrich (1845/1984) *The Condition of the Working Class in England in 1844.* London: Lawrence and Wishart.

Engels, Friedrich (1878/1936) *Anti-Duhring: Herr Eugen Duhring's revolution in science,* trans. Emile Burns. London: Lawrence and Wishart.

Engels, Friedrich (1884/1946) *The Origin of the Family, Private Property and the State,* trans. A. West and D.Torr. London: Lawrence and Wishart.

Engler, M. and Engler, P. (2016) *This is an uprising: How nonviolent revolt is shaping the twenty-first century.* New York: Nation Press.

Epstein, Robert (2016) 'The empty brain', *Aeon,* 18th May 2016. https://aeon.co/essays/your-brain-does-not-process-information-and-it-is-not-a-computer

Espinoza, Javier and Johnston, Ian (2023) 'European parliament prepares tough measures over the use of AI', *The Financial Times,* 14th April 2023.

Evans, Bob (2011) 'Google's Eric Schmidt: Top 10 reasons bureaucrats drive me nuts', *Forbes Magazine,*28th October 2011. *https://www.forbes.com/sites/sap/2011/10/26/googles-eric-schmidt-top-10-reasons-bureaucrats-drive-me-nuts-2/*

Evans, Martin (2020) 'Children as young as six are suspects in "sexting" offences', *The Daily Telegraph,* 15th February, 2020.

Evans, Scarlett (2024) 'Elon Musk backs prediction of one billion humanoid robots by 2040'. IOT World Today, 23rd January 2024. *https://www.iotworldtoday.com/robotics/elon-musk-backs-prediction-of-1-billion-humanoid-robots-by-2040*

Evans, Simon (2021) 'Analysis: Which countries are historically responsible for climate change?' Carbon Brief, 5th October 2021. https://www.carbonbrief.org/analysis-which-countries-are-historically-responsible-for-climate-change/

Fabre, Adrien (2019) 'Evolution of EROIs of electricity until 2050: Estimation and implications on prices', *Ecological Economics*, 164, October 2019. *https://doi.org/10.1016/j.ecolecon.2019.06.006*

Fair Tax Mark (2021) 'The Silicon Six and their $100 billion tax shortfall', Fair Tax Mark, May 2021. https://fairtaxmark.net/silicon-six-end-the-decade-with-100-billion-tax-shortfall/

Ferguson, Niall (2008) *The Ascent of Money: A financial history of the world.* London: Allen Lane.

Festinger, L., Schachter, S., & Back, K. (1950). *Social pressures in informal groups; a study of human factors in housing.* New York: Harper.

Feynman, Richard (1961) 'There's plenty of room at the bottom'. In Gilbert, H.D. (ed.) *Miniaturization.* New York: Reinhold.

Field, Matthew (2023) 'Amazon launches humanoid robots to do "mundane and repetitive" tasks', *The Daily Telegraph*, 19th October 2023.

Fight Inequality Alliance (2022) 'Taxing extreme wealth: What it would raise and what it could pay for'. Fight Inequality, Oxfam, Institute for Policy Studies and Patriotic Millionaires, January 2022. https://inequality.org/wp-content/uploads/2022/01/Taxing-Extreme-Wealth-What-It-Would-Raise-What-It-Could-Pay-For.pdf

Filzwieser, Susanne (2022) 'Electronic skin: Physicist at TU Graz develops multisensory hybrid material', TU GRAZ (Graz University of Technology), 16th May 2022. *https://www.tugraz.at/en/tu-graz/services/news-stories/tu-graz-news/singleview/article/elektronische-haut-physikerin-der-tu-graz-entwickelt-multisensorisches-hybridmaterial0/*

Financial Times (2016) 'Pepper the "emotional" robot visits the FT', 29th April, 2016. https://www.ft.com/video/6b901f0c-6ce4-358a-ac25-4dc0a4739c17

Finlayson, Alan (2020) 'In Cummings' mind clever people break the rules. The rest of us follow them', *The Guardian*, 27th May 2020.

Fisher, Mark (2014) *Capitalist Realism: Is there no alternative?* Arlseford: Zero Books.

Fishkin, James (2009) *When the People Speak: Deliberative democracy and public consultation.* Oxford: Oxford University Press.

Fishkin, James et al (2017) 'Applying deliberative democracy in Africa', *Daedalus*, Summer, 2017, 146(3):140-154.

Fiske, Amelia, Henningsen, Peter and Buyx, Alena (2019) 'Your Robot Therapist Will See You Now: Ethical implications of embodied artificial intelligence in psychiatry, psychology, and psychotherapy', *Journal of Medical Internet Research*, 2019 May 9;21(5):e13216. DOI: 10.2196/13216.

Fizaine, Florian and Court, Victor (2016) 'Energy expenditure, economic growth and the minimum EROI of society', *Energy Policy*, 95:172-86. https://doi.org/10.1016/j.enpol.2016.04.039

Flood, Alison (2017) 'Jane Austen's Great House launches urgent appeal', *The Guardian*, 20th July 2017.

Foa, R.S. et al (2020) *The Global Satisfaction with Democracy Report 2020*. Cambridge, UK: Centre for the Future of Democracy.

Fontevecchia, Agostino (2012) 'Zuckerberg a dictator? ISS blasts Facebook's "autocratic" governance"', *Forbes Magazine*, 14th February 2012.

Fortson, Danny (2022) ' Elon Musk loses the race to sew implants in the brain', *The Sunday Times*, 4th September 2022.

Fowler, Brigid (2019) 'Finding support for a "strong leader" helps to provoke responses to the 2019 Audit of Political Engagement', The Hansard Society, 15th April, 2019. *https://www.hansardsociety.org.uk/blog/finding-of-support-for-a-'strong-leader'-helps-provoke-responses-to-2019*

Fowler, Susan (2017) 'Reflecting on one very, very strange year at Uber', Susanjfowler.com, 19th February, 2017. https://www.susanjfowler.com/blog/2017/2/19/reflecting-on-one-very-strange-year-at-uber

Frangoul. Aumar (2022) 'We're on "a highway to climate hell"', UN chief Guterres says, calling for a global phase-out of coal', CNBC, 7th November 2022. https://www.cnbc.com/2022/11/07/were-on-a-highway-to-climate-hell-un-chief-guterres-says.html

Fratiglioni, Laura et al (2000) 'Influence of social network on occurrence of dementia: A community-based longitudinal study', *The Lancet*, 35(9212):1315-9. DOI:*10.1016/S0140-6736(00)02113-9*

Frey, Carl Benedict (2019) *The Technology Trap: Capital, Labor, and power in the age of automation.* Princeton University Press: Princeton, NJ.

Frey, Carl Benedict and Osborne, Michael (2013) 'The future of employment: How susceptible are jobs to computerisation?'. Oxford Martin School, 17th September, 2013. *https://www.oxfordmartin.ox.ac.uk/downloads/academic/The_Future_of_Employment.pdf*

Friday, Enape (2023) 'Why NFTs are now almost worthless, DappGambi analysis finds', *Medium*, 23rd September, 2023. https://medium.com/@fridayenape10/why-nfts-is-now-almost-worthless-dappgambl-analysis-finds-89fe4abdfc02

Friedman, Milton (1962) *Capitalism and Freedom*. Chicago: University of Chicago Press.

Friend, Tad (2017) 'Silicon Valley's quest to live forever', *New Yorker Magazine*, 27th March 2017. https://www.newyorker.com/magazine/2017/04/03/silicon-valleys-quest-to-live-forever

Friends of the Earth, Scotland (2021) 'A review of the role of fossil-fuel-based carbon capture and storage in the energy system', Tyndall Centre for Climate Change Research report, January 2021. https://foe.scot/resource/report-carbon-capture-storage-energy-role/

Frischmann, Brett and Selinger, Evan (2018) *Re-engineering Humanity*. Cambridge: Cambridge University Press.

Frownfelter, John (2021) 'Why IBM Watson could never live up to its promises', Medcitynews.com, April, 2021. https://medcitynews.com/2021/04/why-ibm-watson-health-could-never-live-up-to-the-promises/

Future of Life Institute (2023) 'Pause giant AI experiments: An open letter', Future of Life Institute, 22nd March 2023. https://futureoflife.org/open-letter/pause-giant-ai-experiments/

Fukuyama, Francis (1992) *The End of History and the Last Man*. New York: Free Press.

Gagliardi, Mike (2023) 'Pedestrians, dying at record levels, now face Elon Musk's Cybertruck', NBC News, 13th December,2023. https://www.nbcnews.com/tech/tech-news/pedestrians-already-dying-record-levels-now-face-elon-musks-cybertruck-rcna128603

Gais, Hannah and Squire, Megan (2021) 'How an encrypted messaging platform is changing extremist movements,"' Southern Poverty Law Centre, 16th February 2021. https://www.splcenter.org/news/2021/02/16/how-encrypted-messaging-platform-changing-extremist-movements

Galeon, Dom (2017) 'Softbank CEO: The singularity will happen by 2047', *Futurism*, 1st March 2017. *https://futurism.com/softbank-ceo-the-singularity-will-happen-by-2047* t

Galor, Oded (2022) *The Journey of Humanity: The origins of wealth and inequality*. London: Bodley Head.

Gardner, Howard (1983) *The Theory of Multiple Intelligences*. New York: Basic Books.

Gates, Bill (2021) *How to avoid a climate disaster: The solutions we have and the breakthroughs we need*. New York: Allen Lane.

Gault, Matthew and Pearson, Jordan (2023) 'Prominent AI philosopher and "father" of Longtermism sent a very racist email to a 90s philosophy listserv', *Vice*,12th January 2023. *https://www.vice.com/en/article/z34dm3/ prominent-ai-philosopher-and-father-of-longtermism-sent-very-racist-email-to-a-90s-philosophy-listserv*

Gearey, Mary and Ravenscroft, Neil (2019) 'The Nowtopia of the riverbank: Elder environmental activism', *Environment and Planning E: Nature and Space*, 2(3):451-464.

Gene People UK (2023) 'About us', Gene People UK,2023. https://genepeople.org. uk/about-us/#

Geng, Qingge and Lo, Kevin (2023) 'Global ecological civilization: An analysis of macro-level policies of the Belt and Road Initiative', *Research in Globalization*, 7, December 2023. DOI: org/10.1016/j.resglo.2023.100141

Georgescu-Roegen, Nicholas (1986) 'The entropy law and the economics process in retrospect', *Eastern Economic Journal,12 (1):3-25. https://EconPapers.repec.org/ RePEc:eej:eeconj:v:12:y:1986:i:1:p:3-25*

Gigova, Radina (2017) 'Who Vladimir Putin thinks will rule the world', CNN, 2nd September 2017. https://edition.cnn.com/2017/09/01/world/putin-artificial-intelligence-will-rule-world/index.html

Gilbert, F. et al (2019) 'Embodiment and estrangement: Results from a first-in-human "intelligent" BCI trial', *Science and Engineering Ethics*, 2019, (1):83-96. DOI: 10.1007/s11948-017-0001-5

Global Witness (2022)'TikTok and Facebook fail to detect election disinformation in the US, while YouTube succeeds', Global Witness, 21st October 2022. https:// www.globalwitness.org/en/campaigns/digital-threats/tiktok-and-facebook-fail-detect-election-disinformation-us-while-youtube-succeeds/

Goddard, Emily (2021) 'The history of UK's housing crisis', *Vice*, 7th October 2021.https://www.vice.com/en/article/k78mm3/ the-history-of-the-uks-housing-crisis

Godfrey-Smith, Peter (2016) *Other Minds: The octopus, the sea and the deep origins of consciousness.* New York: Farrar, Strauss and Giroux.

Good, I.J. (1965) 'The logic of man and machine', *The New Scientist*, 15th April 1965, pp 182-3.

Good, I.J. (1966) 'Speculations concerning the first ultraintelligent machine', *Advances in Computers*, 1966, 6:31-88. https://DOI.org/10.1016/ S0065-2458(08)60418-0

Goodell, Jeff (2019) 'The world's most insane energy project moves ahead', *Rolling Stone*, 14th June, 2019. https://www.rollingstone.com/politics/politics-news/ adani-mine-australia-climate-change-848315/

Gordon, Robert (2016) *The Rise and Fall of American Growth: The US standard of living since the Civil War.* Princeton, NJ: Princeton University Press.

Gore, Tim et al (2020) 'Confronting carbon inequality', Oxfam, 21st September 2020. htttps://oxfamilibrary.openrepository.com/bitstream/handle/10546/621052/mb-confronting-carbon-inequality-210920-en.pdf

Gorz, Andre (1994) *Capitalism, Socialism and Ecology*, trans. Martin Chalmers. London: Verso.

Gough, Ian (2017) *Heat, Greed and Human Need: Climate change, capitalism and sustainable wellbeing.* Cheltenham: Edward Elgar Publishing.

Gov.uk (2019) 'Regulation for the Fourth Industrial Revolution', Department for Business, Energy and Industrial Strategy policy paper, 11th June, 2019. *https://www.gov.uk/government/publications/regulation-for-the-fourth-industrial-revolution/regulation-for-the-fourth-industrial-revolution#foreword* (retrieved 12/09/23).

Gov.uk (2019a) 'Boris Johnson's first speech as prime minster: 24 July 2019', Gov.uk, 24th July, 2019. https://www.gov.uk/government/speeches/boris-johnsons-first-speech-as-prime-minister-24-july-2019

Gov.uk (2021) 'New strategy to unleash the transformational power of artificial intelligence', Department for Digital, Culture, Media and Sport et al, 12th March, 2021. *https://www.gov.uk/government/news/new-strategy-to-unleash-the-transformational-power-of-artificial-intelligence*

Gov.uk (2021a) '"Strengthening the UK's position as a global science and technology superpower', Council for Science and Technology, 22nd July, 2021. *https://www.gov.uk/government/publications/the-uk-as-a-science-and-technology-superpower/*

Gowdy, John (2011) 'Hunter-gatherers and the mythology of the market', Libcom.org, 2nd November, 2011.https://libcom.org/article/hunter-gatherers-and-mythology-market-john-gowdy

Graeber, David (2018) *Bullshit Jobs: A theory.* London: Allen Lane.

Graeber, David and Wengrow, David (2021) *The Dawn of Everything: A new history of humanity.* London: Allen Lane.

Gramsci, Antonio (1971) *Selections from the Prison Notebooks*, trans. Quintin Hoare and Geoffrey Nowell Smith. London: Lawrence and Wishart.

Greenstone, Michael et al (2022) 'Air Quality Life Index: Annual update', AQLI, University of Chicago, June 2022. *https://aqli.epic.uchicago.edu/wp-content/uploads/2022/06/AQLI_2022_Report-Global.pdf*

Gregory, Andrew (2021)' Eco-anxiety: Fear of environmental doom weighs on young people', *The Guardian*, 6th October 2021.

Gregory, Andrew (2022) 'Women in England's poorest countries die younger than in most OECD countries', *The Guardian*, 17th April 2022.

Griffith, Erin (2017) 'Will Facebook kill all future Facebooks?' *Wired,* 25th October, 2017

Griggs, Mary Beth (2020) 'Elon Musk claims Neuralink is "about six months" away from first human trial', *The Verge*,30th November, 2019. https://www.theverge.com/2022/11/30/23487307/neuralink-elon-musk-show-and-tell-2022

Grove, Andrew S. (1997) *Only the Paranoid Survive: How to exploit the crisis points that challenge every company and career.* London: Profile Books.

Gurven, Michael and Kaplan, Hillard (2007) 'Longevity among hunter- gatherers: A cross-cultural examination, *Population and Development Review, 23 (2): 321-365. https://DOI.org/10.1111/j.1728-4457.2007.00171.x*

Haas, Randall et al (2020) 'Female hunters of the early Americas', *Science Advances*, 4th November 2020, 6 (450). DOI:*10. sciadv.abd0310*

Hall, Charles E.S. et al (2014) 'EROI for different fuels and implications for society', *Energy Policy*, 64: 141-152. https://DOI.org/10.1016/j.enpol.2013.05.049

Hamilton, Clive (2003) *Growth Fetish*. Crows Nest, N.S.W.: Allen and Unwin.

Hamming, R.W. (1980) ' The unreasonable effectiveness of mathematics', *The American Mathematical Monthly*, 87 (2):81-90. *https://doi.org/10.2307/2321982*

Hanfling, Oswald (1986)' Ayer, Language, Truth and Logic', Royal Institute of Philosophy Supplements, March 1986 , pp. 261 – 283. DOI: *https://doi.org/10.1017/S0957042X00004181*

Hanus, Martin et al (2022) 'Worldmindedness of young people during the rise in migration in Europe: a case study of Czechia, Finland, Germany and The Netherlands', *International Research in Geographical and Environmental Education*, 31 (3):222-241. DOI: 10.1080/10382046.2021.1969791

Hao, Karen (2019) 'This is how AI bias really happens – and why it's so hard to fix', *MIT Technology Review*, 4th February, 2019. *https://www.technologyreview.com/2019/02/04/137602/this-is-how-ai-bias-really-happensand-why-its-so-hard-to-fix/*

Happy Planet Index (2021) 'How happy is the planet?', The Happy Planet Index, 2021. https://happyplanetindex.org/wp-content/themes/hpi/public/downloads/happy-planet-index-briefing-paper.pdf

Harari, Yuval Noah (2014) *Sapiens: A brief history of humankind.* London: Harvill Secker.

Harari, Yuval Noah (2016) *Homo Deus: A brief history of tomorrow.* London: Harvill Secker.

Haraway, Donna (1985) 'A manifesto for cyborgs: Science, technology and socialist feminism in the 1980s', *Socialist Review*, 80:65-108. *https://monoskop.org/ images/4/4c/Haraway_Donna_1985_A_Manifesto_for_Cyborgs_Science_ Technology_and_Socialist_Feminism_in_the_1980s.pdf*

Hardt, Lukas & O'Neill, Daniel W. (2017) '*Ecological Macroeconomic Models: Assessing Current Developments*', *Ecological Economics*, vol. 134(C): 198-211. DOI: 10.1016/j.ecolecon.2016.12.027

Hardy, Jack (2023) 'Sharp surge in rapes and assaults linked to dating apps', *The Daily Telegraph*, 4th January 2023.

Harmon, Amy (2015) 'A dying young woman's hope in cryonics and a future', *The New York Times*, 13th September 2015.

Harris, John (2010) *Enhancing evolution: The ethical case for making better people*. Princeton, NJ: Princeton University Press.

Harrison, Ellie (2022) 'Elon Musk thinks Grimes is a "simulation" he has created in his mind', *The Independent*, 18th October 2022. https://www.independent. co.uk/arts-entertainment/music/news/elon-musk-grimes-relationship- simulation-b2204948.html

Harvey, David (2007) 'Neoliberalism as creative destruction', *The Annals of the American Academy of Political and Social Science*, 2007, 610 (1): 22–44. *https:// DOI.org/10.1177/0002716206296780*

Harvey, Michael D.B. (2019) *Utopia in the Anthropocene: A change plan for a sustainable and equitable world*. London and New York: Routledge.

Harvey, Michael D.B. (2015) *Interactional Leadership: The art of the choice-focused leader*. London and New York: Routledge.

Haskins, Caroline (2019) 'Gaggle knows everything about teens and kids in school', *BuzzFeed News*, 1st November 2019. Buzzhttps://www.buzzfeednews.com/ article/carolinehaskins1/gaggle-school-surveillance-technology-education

Hawksworth, John et al (2018) 'Will robots really steal our jobs?', PWC report, 2018. https://www.pwc.co.uk/economic-services/assets/international-impact-of- automation-feb-2018.pdf

Head, Simon (2014) *Mindless: Why smarter machines are making dumber people*. New York: Basic Books.

HeartMath Institute (2022) 'Science of the heart: Exploring the role of the heart in performance', HeartMath Institute, 2022. https://www.heartmath.org/research/ science-of-the-heart/heart-brain-communication/

Heaven, Will Douglas (2023) 'Geoffrey Hinton tells us why he's now scared of the tech he helped build', *MIT Technology Review*, 2nd May 2023.

Hegel, G.W.F (1807/1931) *The Phenomenology of Mind*, trans. J.B. Baillie, New York, Harper and Row.

Heidegger, Martin (1962) *Being and Time*, trans. J. Macquarrie and Edward Robinson, Oxford: Blackwell.

Heidegger, Martin (1977) *The Question concerning Technology and other Essays*, trans. William Lovitt. New York: Harper and Row.

Heikkila, Melissa (2020) 'Dutch scandal serves a warning for Europe over risks of using algorithms', *Politico*, 29th March 2022. https://www.politico.eu/article/dutch-scandal-serves-as-a-warning-for-europe-over-risks-of-using-algorithms/

Heikkurinen, Pasi (2018) 'Degrowth by means of technology? A treatise for an ethos of releasement, *Journal of Cleaner Production*, 197, Part 2:1654-1665. *https://DOI.org/10.1016/j.jclepro.2016.07.070.*

Hendrick, Michael (2015) 'The false science of cryonics,' *MIT Technology Review*, 15th September, 2015. *https://www.technologyreview.com/2015/09/15/109906/the-false-science-of-cryonics/*

Henshall, Will (2023) 'Elon Musk tells Rishi Sunak AI will eliminate the need for jobs', *Time Magazine*, 2nd November 2023.

Hern, Alex (2021) 'Tim Berners-Lee says too many young people are excluded from web', *The Guardian*, 12th March 2021.

Hern, Alex (2023) 'We've discovered the secret of immortality. The bad news is it's not for us': why the godfather of AI fears for humanity', *The Guardian*, 5th May 2023.

Hersh, Mollie (2020) 'Apple, Google, Amazon and Microsoft under the greenwash spotlight', *The Fifth Estate*, 1st September, 2020. https://thefifthestate.com.au/business/investment-deals/apple-google-amazon-and-microsoft-under-the-greenwash-spotlight/

Hickel, Jason (2017) *The Divide: A brief guide to global inequality and its solutions.* London: William Heinemann.

Hickel, Jason (2020) *Less is More: How degrowth will save the world.* London: Windmill Books.

Hickel, Jason et al (2022) 'Degrowth can work: Here's how science can help', *Nature*, 12th December 2022, 612:400-403. *https://www.nature.com/articles/d41586-022-04412-x*

Hickman, C. et al (2021) 'Climate anxiety in children and young people and their beliefs about government responses to climate change', *The Lancet Planetary Health*, 5:12, December 2021 *https://DOI.org/10.1016/S2542-5196(21)00278-3*

Hill, Emily (2020) 'How dating apps killed love in London', *ES Magazine* , 6th February, 2020. *https://www.standard.co.uk/esmagazine/how-the-dating-app-killed-love-in-london-a4354251.html*

Hilton, Benjamin (2022) 'Preventing an AI-related catastrophe' 80000hours.org, August, 2022. https://80000hours.org/problem-profiles/artificial-intelligence/

Hoadley, Daniel and Lucas, Nathan (2018) 'Artificial Intelligence and National Security', *Congressional Research Service*, 26th April, 2018. *https:// digital.library.unt.edu/ark:/67531/metadc1157028/m2/1/high_res_d/ R45178_2018Apr26.pdf*

Hobbes, Thomas (1651/1968) *Leviathan*, ed. C.B. Macpherson. London: Pelican Books.

Hofman, Mike (2015) 'Young Bill Gates was an angry office bully', *GQ Magazine*, 28th October 2015.

Ho-him, Chan (2023) 'AI-enabled teddy bears could tell children bedtime stories, says toymaker', *The Financial Times*, 16th June, 2023.

Holloway, John (2019) *Change the World without taking Power: The meaning of revolution today*, Fourth edition. London: Pluto Press.

Horkheimer, Max and Adorno, Theodor (1947/2002) *Dialectic of Enlightenment*, trans. Edmund Jephcott. Stanford, CA: Stanford University Press.

Horn, Jeff (2005) 'Machine-breaking in England and France during the age of revolution', *Labour/ Le Travail*, 1st January 2005, 55:143-166. https://www. lltjournal.ca/index.php/llt/article/view/5369

Hornberg, Alf (2011) *Global Ecology and Unequal Exchange: Fetishism in a zero-sum world.* Abingdon: Routledge.

House, Arthur (2014) 'The real cyborgs', *The Daily Telegraph*, 20th October 2014.

Houser, Kristen (2021) 'Total artificial heart approved for sale in Europe', *Freethink*, 24th January, 2021. *https://www.freethink.com/health/artificial-heart*

Howden, Daniel et al (2021) 'Seeing stones: pandemic reveals Palantir's troubling reach in Europe', *The Guardian*, 2nd April 2021.

Huesemann, Michael and Huesemann, Joyce (2011) *Techno-Fix: Why technology won't save the environment.* Gabriola Island, BC: New Society Publishers.

Human Rights Watch (2020) 'Stopping killer robots: Country positions on banning autonomous weapons and retaining human control', Human Rights Watch, 10th August, 2020. https://www.hrw.org/report/2020/08/10/stopping-killer-robots/ country-positions-banning-fully-autonomous-weapons-and

Humphries, Jane (2013) 'Childhood and child labour in the British industrial revolution', *The Economic History Review*, 66 (2): 395-418. *https://DOI.org/10.1 111/j.1468-0289.2012.00651.*

Ibbetsen, Ross (2020) 'Jeff Bezos' $10 billion pledge to fight climate change is slammed as "greenwash" by critics', *The Daily Mail*, 18th February, 2020. *https://www.dailymail.co.uk/news/article-8015509/Jeff-Bezos-10bn-pledge-fight-climate-change-slammed-greenwash-critics.html*

Ibrahim, Hazem et al (2023) 'Perception, performance, and detectability of conversational artificial intelligence across 32 courses', *Scientific Reports*,13 12187 (2023). https://DOI.org/10.1038/s41598-023-38964-3

IEP (2020) 'Over one billion people at threat of being displaced by 2050 due to environmental change, conflict and civil unrest', Institute for Economics and Peace, 9th September 2020. https://www.economicsandpeace.org/wp-content/ uploads/2020/09/Ecological-Threat-Register-Press-Release-27.08-FINAL.pdf

IFR (2021) 'IFR presents World Robotics 2021 reports', International Federation of Robotics, 28th October 2021. https://ifr.org/ifr-press-releases/news/ robot-sales-rise-again

Illich, Ivan (1973) *Tools for Conviviality*. New York: Harper and Row.

IMARC (2022) 'Artificial organs market: Global industry trends, size, growth, opportunities and forecast 2023-2028', IMARC Group, 2022. *https://www. imarcgroup.com/artificial-organs-market*

Isaacs, Amelia (2023) 'Chancellor Jeremy Hunt wants to turn the UK into the world's next Silicon Valley', AltFi, 30thJanuary 2023. https://www.altfi.com/ article/10344_chancellor-jeremy-hunt-wants-to-turn-the-uk-into-the-worlds- next-silicon-valley

Isaacson, Walter (2011) *Steve Jobs*. New York: Simon and Schuster.

Isaacson, Walter (2023) *Elon Musk*. New York: Simon and Schuster.

Ishiguro, Kazuo (2021) *Klara and the Sun*. London: Faber.

Istvan, Zoltan (2014) 'The transhumanist future of sex'. *Vice*, 20th October 2014. https://www.vice.com/en/article/ypwn4k/the-transhumanist-future-of-sex

Jackman, Jonathan (2022) 'Amazon produced more carbon emissions last year than Switzerland', The Eco Experts, 11th January, 2022. *https://www.theecoexperts. co.uk/blog/amazon-carbon-emissions*

Jackson, Tim (2018) 'The post-growth challenge – secular stagnation, inequality, and the limits to growth', *Centre for the Understanding of Sustainable Prosperity*, Working Paper 12, 13th May 2018. https://cusp.ac.uk/themes/aetw/wp12/

Jackson, Tim (2021) *Post Growth: Life after capitalism*. Cambridge: Polity.

Jackson, Tim (2022) 'Sunak's growth fetish is a problem: He's heading for the same budget trap as Truss', *The Guardian*, 16th November 2022.

Jackson, Tim and Victor, Peter A. (2020) '*The Transition to a Sustainable Prosperity-A Stock-Flow-Consistent Ecological Macroeconomic Model for Canada*', Ecological Economics, vol. 177, 2020. DOI: 10.1016/j. ecolecon.2020.106787

Jacques, Martin (2012): *When China Rules the World*, Second edition. London: Penguin Books.

James, Geoffrey (2020) 'Bill Gates promised to give away his wealth. Well, that was BS', *Inc.*, 20th October 2020. *https://www.inc.com/geoffrey-james/bill-gates-promised-to-give-away-his-wealth-well-that-was-bs.html* (retrieved 20/10/21).

James, Rory (2021) 'Anger after Indonesia offers Elon Musk Papuan island as launchpad for SpaceX', *The Guardian*, 9th March 2021.

Jasanoff, Alan *(2018)* The *Biological Brain: How brain, body and environment collaborate to make us who we are. New York: Basic Books.*

Jenkins, Holman (2010) 'Google and the search for the future', *The Wall Street Journal*, 14th August, 2010. *https://www.wsj.com/articles/SB10001424052748704 901104575423294099527212*

Jensen, K. et al (2014) 'The emergence of human prosociality: Aligning with others through feelings, concerns and norms', *Frontiers in Psychology*, 5 (2014). *https:// DOI.org/10.3389/fpsyg.2014.00822*

Jones, Ernest (1951) *Essays in Applied Psychoanalysis.* London: Hogarth Press.

Jones, Phil, (2021) *Work without the Worker: Labour in the age of platform capitalism.* London: Verso.

Jones, Phil, (2021a) 'Big Tech's push for automation hides the grim reality of microwork', *The Guardian*, 27th October 2021.

Joy, Bill (2000) 'Why the future doesn't need us', *Wired*, 1st April, 2000. https://www.wired.com/2000/04/joy-2/

Jung, Carl (1966) *Two Essays on Analytical Psychology*, trans. R.F.C. Hull, Second edition. London: Routledge.

Kallis, Giorgis (2018) *Degrowth*. Newcastle: Agenda Publishing.

Kallis, Giorgis, Paulson, Susan, D'Alisa, Giacomo and Demaria, Frederico (2020) *The Case for Degrowth*. Cambridge: Polity.

Katwala, Amit (2019) 'The race to create a perfect lie detector – and the dangers of succeeding', *The Guardian*, 5th September, 2019.

Katz, D.M., Bommanto, M,J. and Blackman, J. ((2017) 'A general approach for predicting the behavior of the Supreme Court of the United States', *Plos One*, 12th April 2017. *https://DOI.org/10.1371/journal.pone.0174698*

Kelion, Leon (2020) 'Why Amazon knows so much about you', BBC News, 2022. https://www.bbc.co.uk/news/extra/CLQYZENMBI/amazon-data

Keller, John (2022) 'US military spending heading up in 2023, with $773 billion proposed for programs, research, and procurement', *Military Aerospace Electronics*, 29th March, 2022. https://www.militaryaerospace.com/defense-executive/article/14270139/military-spending-research-procurement

Kets de Vries, Manfred (2012) 'The psychopath in the C-Suite: The SOB redefined', INSEAD working paper no 2012/119/EFE, 24th November 2012. https://papers.ssrn.com/sol3/papers.cfm?abstract_id=2179794

Keynes, John Maynard (1931) 'Economic possibilities for our grandchildren'. In J.M. Keynes, *Essays in Persuasion*, London: Macmillan.

Khalfan, Ashfaq et al (2023) *Climate Inequality: A planet for the 99%*. Oxford: Oxfam international. DOI:10.21201/2023.000001

Khazan, Olga (2017) 'Where not to use your phone', *The Atlantic*, 28th June 2017., *https://www.theatlantic.com/technology/archive/2017/06/where-not-to-use-your-phone/532053/*

Khasnabish, Alex (2010) Zapatistas: Rebellion from the grassroots to the global. London: Zed Books.

Khurana, Joe ((2021) 'When it comes to variety of patents, these companies are killing the competition', *IP Vision*, 2021. https://info.ipvisioninc.com/blog/when-it-comes-to-variety-of-patents-these-companies-are-killing-the-competition

King, Gary et al (2017) 'How the Chinese government fabricates social media posts for strategic distraction, not engaged argument', American Political Science Review, 111 (3):484-501. https://tinyurl.com/ycvo9zog

Klare, Michael (2019)'Autonomous weapon systems and the laws of war', Arms Control Association, March, 2019. https://www.armscontrol.org/act/2019-03/features/autonomous-weapons-systems-laws-war

Klein, Eran et al (2016) 'Brain-computer interface-based control of closed-loop brain simulation: Attitudes and ethical considerations', *Brain-computer Interfaces*, 3 (3): 140-148. DOI: *10.1080/2326263X.2016.1207497*

Korosec, Kirsten (2021) 'Emotion-detection software startup Affectiva acquired for $73.5 million', *TechCrunch*, 26th May,2021. https://techcrunch.com/2021/05/25/emotion-detection-software-startup-affectiva-acquired-for-73-5m/

Knapton, Sarah (2023) 'Advanced AI "could kill everyone", warn Oxford researchers', *The Daily Telegraph*, 25th January 2023.

Knapton, Sarah (2023a) 'Stargazing could soon be a thing of the past as satellites clog up space', *The Daily Telegraph*, 28th January 2023.

Knight, Will (2017) 'The dark secret at the heart of AI', *MIT Technology Review*, 11th April 2017. *https://www.technologyreview.com/2017/04/11/5113/the-dark-secret-at-the-heart-of-ai/*

Kohr, Leopold (1957) *The Breakdown of Nations*. London: Routledge and Kegan Paul.

Konrad, Alex (2019) 'From communism to coding: How Daniel Dines of $7 billion UiPath became the first bot billionaire', *Forbes Magazine*, 11th September, 2019.

Konyn, Carole (2021) 'How Costa Rica reversed deforestation and became an environmental model', Earth. Org, 19th October 2021. https://earth.org/how-costa-rica-reversed-deforestation/

Kotkin, Joel (2020) *The Coming of Neo-Feudalism: A warning to the global middle class.* New York: Encounter Books.

Krznaric, Roman (2020) *The Good Ancestor: How to think long term in a short-term world.* London: WH Allen.

Kuchler, Hannah (2023) 'The start-ups seeking a cure for old age', *The Financial Times,* 2nd February 2023.

Kuepper, Justin (2022)'CBOE volatility index (VIX): What does it measure in investing?', Investopedia, 3rd November 2022. *https://www.investopedia.com/terms/v/vix.asp*

Kuhn, Thomas (1970) *The Structure of Scientific Revolutions*, 2nd edition, Chicago: University of Chicago Press.

Kumar, Claire et al (2022) 'As the world rapidly ages, we need more migrant care workers', Overseas Development Institute, 30th April, 2022. https://odi.org/en/insights/as-the-world-rapidly-ages-we-need-more-migrant-care-workers/

Kurzweil, Ray (1999) *The Age of Spiritual Machines: When computers exceed human intelligence.* New York: Viking.

Kurzweil, Ray (2005) *The Singularity is Near: When humans transcend biology.* New York: Viking.

Kurzweil, Ray (2014) 'Don't fear artificial intelligence', *Time Magazine*, 19th December, 2014. https://time.com/3641921/dont-fear-artificial-intelligence/

Kurzweil, Ray and Grossman, Terry (2004) *Fantastic Journey: How to live long enough to live forever.* Emmaus, PA: Rodale Books.

Kynge, James and Yu, Sun (2021) 'China and Big Tech: Xi's blueprint for a digital dictatorship', *The Financial Times*, 6th September 2021.

Labour.org.uk (2019) 'John McDonnell speech on the economy and Labour's plans for sustainable investment' , Labour.org (The Labour Party), 24th June 2019. *https://labour.org.uk/press/john-mcdonnell-speech-economy-labours-plans-sustainable-investment/* (retrieved 1/9/2019).

Labour.org.uk (2022) "Keir Starmer's speech on Labour's mission for economic growth," Labour.org, 25th July 2022 *https://labour.org.uk/press/keir-starmer-speech-on-labours-mission-for-economic-growth/*

Lago, Cristina (2020) 'Black representation in tech: What the figures don't tell us', *Tech Monitor*, 18th November, 2020. *https://techmonitor.ai/leadership/workforce/black-representation-tech-what-figures-dont-tell*

Lai, Olivia (2022) 'Tyre pollution nearly 2,000 times worse than car exhaust admissions: Study', Earth.org, 7th June 2022. https://earth.org/tyre-pollution/

Lancefield, Neil (2023) 'Blindly following sat nav blamed for rise in wrong-way driving on UK's motorways', *The Independent*, 14th August 2023 https://www.independent.co.uk/news/uk/crime/motorway-wrong-way-driving-crash-b2392588.html

Lanchester, John (2017) 'You are the product', *London Review of Books*, 39(16), 17[th]August 2017. *https://www.lrb.co.uk/the-paper/v39/n16/john-lanchester/you-are-the-product*

Landesmore, Helene (2020) *Open Democracy: Reinventing popular rule for the twenty-first century.* Princeton: Princeton University Press.

Lanier, Jaron and Weyl, E. Glen (2020) 'AI is an ideology not a technology', *Wired*, 15th March, 2020.https://www.wired.com/story/opinion-ai-is-an-ideology-not-a-technology/

Latouche, Serge (2009) *Farewell to Growth*, trans. David Macey. Cambridge: Polity.

Laville, Sandra (2023) 'Twelve billionaires' climate emission outpollute 2.1m homes, analysis finds', *The Guardian*, 20th November 2023.

Lawson, Dominic (2021) 'Jeff Bezos and the triumph of "weirdness"', *The Sunday Times*, 7th February 2021.

Lawson, Michele Fabiola (2021) 'The DRC mining industry: Child labor and formalization of small-scale mining', The Wilson Center, 1st September, 2021. htps://www.wilsoncenter.org/blog-post/drc-mining-industry-child-labor-and-formalization-small-scale-mining

Lawrence, Matthew, Roberts, Carys and King, Loren (2017) 'Managing automation: Employment, inequality and ethics in the digital age', IPPR Commission on Economic Justice Report, The Institute for Public Policy Research, December 2017. https://www.ippr.org/files/2017-12/cej-managing-automation-december2017-1-.pdf

Leake, Jonathan (2013) 'Freeze a jolly good fellow: Three Oxford dons are paying to be cryonically frozen', *The Sunday Times*, 9th June 2013.

Lee, Dave and Rogers, Taylor Nicole (2021 '"The ultimate David and Goliath story": The fight to open a union at Amazon', *The Financial Times*, 29th March 2021.

Lee, Kai-Fu (2017) 'The real threat of artificial intelligence', *The New York Times*, 24th June 2017.

Lee, Kai-Fu (2018) *AI Superpowers: China, Silicon Valley and the new world order.* Boston: Houghton Mifflin Harcourt.

Lee, Richard Borshay (1979) The *!Kung San: Men, women and work in a foraging society.* Cambridge: Cambridge University Press.

Lee, Richard Borshay (1992) 'Art, science or politics? The crisis in hunter-gatherer studies', *American Anthropologist*, 94 (1):31-54. https://tspace.library.utoronto.ca/handle/1807/17933

Lekach, Sasha (2017) 'Fewer than half of newspaper jobs from 15 years ago still exist', Mashable, 4th April 2017.https://mashable.com/article/newspaper-publishers-jobs-decline-bls

Lempriere, Molly (2019) 'Inside the first fully automated offshore platform', Offshore Technology Focus, NRI Digital, February, 2019. *https://offshore.nridigital.com/offshore_technology_focus_feb19/inside_the_first_fully_automated_offshore_platform*

Leon, Harmon (2020) 'Artificial intelligence outperforms doctors in breast cancer diagnosis', *The Observer*, 3rd January, 2020.

Leonard, Christopher (2019) *Kochland: The secret history of Koch Industries and corporate power in America.* New York: Simon & Schuster.

Lent, Jeremy (2017) *The Patterning Instinct: A cultural history of humanity's search for meaning.* Amherst, MA: Prometheus Books.

Lenton, T.M., Xu, C., Abrams, J.F. et al *(2023)* 'Quantifying the human cost of global warming', *Nature Sustain*ability, 22nd May, 2023, 6:1237–1247. https://DOI.org/10.1038/s41893-023-01132-6

Leonard, Mike (2021) 'Palantir founders made themselves 'Emperors for Life', Suit says', Bloomberg Law, 1st April 2021. https://news.bloomberglaw.com/securities-law/palantir-founders-made-themselves-emperor-for-life-suit-says

Leslie, Heather et al (2022) 'Discovery and quantification of plastic particle pollution in human blood', *Environment International*, 163, May 2022, 107199. https://DOI.org/10.1016/j.envint.2022.107199

Levin, Beth (2023) 'If you've got the ruler, Elon Musk has the dick: Billionaire challenges Mark Zuckerberg to "literal dick measuring contest"', *Vanity Fair*, 10th July 2023.

Levi-Strauss, Claude (1967)' The social and psychological aspects of chieftainship in a primitive tribe: The Nambikwara of northwestern Mato Grosso'. In R. Cohen and J. Middleton (eds.), *Comparative Political Systems.* Austin and London, University of Texas Press.

Levy, David (2007) *Love and Sex with Robots: The evolution of human-robot relationships.* New York: HarperCollins.

Levy, Steven (2011) *In the Plex: How Google thinks, works and shapes our lives.* New York: Simon and Schuster.

Liao, Shannon (2019) 'Tesla violated labor laws with Elon Musk tweet, judge rules', CNN, 28th September 2019. *https://edition.cnn.com/2019/09/28/tech/tesla-elon-musk-labor-judge/index.html*

Liberatore, Stacy (2019) 'UFO-themed Nevada brothel is offering online interactive sex robots for clients who want to spend time with a "cosmic kitten" in a virtual world', The Daily *Mail*, 1st November 2019. *https://www.dailymail.co.uk/ sciencetech/article-7640309/Nevada-brothel-Alien-Cathouse-offering-AI-sex- robots-global-clients.html*

Linares, Matthew and Bychawski, Adam (2021) 'Five reasons to worry about "spy tech" firm Palantir handling your NHS data', Open Democracy,4th March 2021. *https://www.opendemocracy.net/en/digitaliberties/ five-reasons-to-worry-about-spy-tech-firm-palantir-handling-your-nhs-data/*

Little, Alan (1998) 'How I stopped nuclear war', BBC News, 21st October 1998. http://news.bbc.co.uk/1/hi/world/europe/198173.stm

Liversidge, Anthony (1987)' Interview with Claude Shannon: Father of the electronic information age', *Omni Magazine* pp 61-68, August 1987.

Locke, H. (2020) 'The psychological impact of video calls. What Zoom is DOIng to people, meetings and research'. *Medium*, 20th May, 2020. *https://medium. com/@h_locke/the-psychological-impact-of-video-calls-dbed57aa792b*

Lorde, Audre (1984) *Sister Outsider: Essays and speeches.* Trumansburg, NY: Crossing Press.

Losse, Kate (2018) 'I was Mark Zuckerberg's speechwriter."Companies over countries" was his early motto', *Vox*, 16th April 2018. https://www.vox.com/ first-person/2018/4/11/17221344/mark-zuckerberg-facebook-cambridge-analytica

Low-Tech Magazine (2023)'Low-tech solutions', Low-Tech Magazine, 2023. https:// solar.lowtechmagazine.com/

Luterman, Sarah (2021) 'The one big problem with Elon Musk's autism announcement', *Slate Magazine*, 12th May 2021. https://slate.com/ culture/2021/05/elon-musk-aspergers-snl-autism-spectrum.html

Machery, Pierre (1978) *A Theory of Literary Production,* trans. Geoffrey Wall. London: Routledge and Kegan Paul.

Macrotrends (2023) 'Costa Rica GDP per capita 1960-2023', Macrotrends. https:// www.macrotrends.net/countries/CRI/costa-rica/gdp-per-capita

Maddison, Angus (2007) *Contours of the World Economy 1-2030 AD: Essays in micro-economic history.* Oxford: Oxford University Press.

Makyrgiannis, K. (2020) 'Capital strategies being rewritten as C-Suite grapples with immediate impact of new reality', EY, 30th March, 2020. *https://www.ey.com/ en_gl/news/2020/03/capital-strategies-being-rewritten-as-c-suite-grapples-with- immediate-impact-of-new-reality*

Malm, Andreas (2016) *Fossil Capital: The rise of steam power and the roots of global warming.* London: Verso.

Malm, Andreas (2020) *Corona, Climate, Chronic Emergency: War communism in the twenty-first century*. London: Verso.

Mamtani, Harkishan et al (2021) 'The impact of videoconferencing applications on mental health', Cambridge University Press, 13th August 2021. https://www.cambridge.org/core/journals/bjpsych-international/article/impact-of-videoconferencing-applications-on-mental-health/4B9828ED413AD07B93043BD39109ABD8

Management Events (2019) 'Neil Harbisson: The integration between humans and machines', *Management Events*, 26th November 2019. https://govirtual.managementevents.com/neil-harbisson-the-integration-between-humans-and-machines/25234/

Manyika, James et al (2017) 'A Future that Works: Automation, employment and productivity', McKinsey Global Institute, January 2017. https://www.mckinsey.com/featured-insights/digital-disruption/harnessing-automation-for-a-future-that-works/de-DE

Margolis, Jane et al (2000) 'The anatomy of interest: Women in undergraduate computer science,' *Women's Studies Quarterly*, 28:104-127.

Margulis, Lynn and Sagan, Dorion (1986) *Microcosmos: Four billion years of microbial evolution*. New York: Summit Books.

Marcus, Gary (2023) 'What if generative AI turned out to be a dud?'. *Substack*, 13th August, 2023. https://garymarcus.substack.com/p/what-if-generative-ai-turned-out

Marcus, Gary and Davis, Ernest (2019) *Rebooting AI: Building artificial intelligence we can trust*. New York: Pantheon books.

Marshall, Aarian (2017) 'Musk reveals his awkward dislike of mass transit', *Wired*, 14th December, 2017. *https://www.wired.com/story/elon-musk-awkward-dislike-mass-transit/*

Marshall, Sam (1947) *Men against Fire: The problem of battle command*. New York: William Morrow Co.

Martin, Katie and Megaw Nicholas (2023) 'The seven companies driving the US stock market rally', *The Financial Times,* 15th June 2023.

Martinez-Alier, Juan (1987) *Ecological Economics: Energy, environment and society*. Oxford: Basil Blackwell.

Martinez, Antonio Garcia (2016) 'How Mark Zuckerberg led Facebook's war to crush Google Plus', *Vanity Fair*, 3rd June, 2016.

Marx, Karl and Engels, Friedrich (1948/1983) *The Communist Manifesto*, trans. S. Moore. London: Lawrence and Wishart.

Marx, Paris (2020) 'Elon Musk is planning for climate apocalypse', *Jacobin*, 1ˢᵗ December, 2020. *https://jacobin.com/2020/01/ elon-musk-climate-apocalypse-tesla-spacex*

Mason, Rowena (2019) 'Automation means future jobs will be more creative – Amber Rudd', *The Guardian*, 8ᵗʰ May, 2019. https://www.theguardian.com/politics/2019/may/08/ automation-means-future-jobs-will-be-more-creative-amber-rudd

Mason, Rowena (2022) 'Liz Truss promises "growth, growth, growth" in protest-hit speech', *The Guardian*, 5ᵗʰ October 2022.

Maturana, Humberto (1980) *Autopoiesis and Cognition: The realization of the living.* Dordrecht: Springer.

Maturana, Humberto and Varela, Francisco (1987) *The Tree of Knowledge: The biological roots of human understanding.* Boston: New Science Library.

Max-Neef, Manfred, Elizalde, Antonio and Hopenhayn, Martin (1991) *Human Scale Development: Conception, Application and further reflection.* New York: Apex Press.

Mayer, Jane (2016) *Dark Money: The hidden history of the billionaires behind the rise of the radical right.* New York: Doubleday.

Medical Futurist (2017) 'The world's most famous real-life cyborgs', *Medical Futurist*, 22ⁿᵈ June 2017. https://medicalfuturist.com/ the-worlds-most-famous-real-life-cyborgs/

Medium.com (2019) 'Google workers are striking for climate on Sept 20', *Medium*, 17ᵗʰ Sept 2019. https://medium.com/@googworkersac/ google-workers-are-striking-for-climate-sept-20-7eba2100b621

Merchant, Carolyn (1980) *The Death of Nature: Women, ecology and the scientific revolution.* New York: Harper & Row.

Metz, Cade (2023)' The "Godfather of AI" leaves Goggle and warns of dangers ahead', *The New York Times*, 1ˢᵗ May 2023.

Metz, Rachel (2018) 'This company embeds microchips in its employees, and they love it', *MIT Technology Review*, 17ᵗʰ August 2018. *https://www.technologyreview.com/2018/08/17/140994/ this-company-embeds-microchips-in-its-employees-and-they-love-it/*

Meyer, John (2010) 'A democratic politics of sacrifice? In Michael Maniates and John Meyer (eds.) The *Environmental Politics of Sacrifice.* Cambridge, MA: MIT Technology Press.

Miles, Kathleen (2015) 'Ray Kurzweil: In the 2030s nanobots in our brains will make us "Godlike"', *Noema Magazine*, 1ˢᵗ October, 2015. https://www.noemamag. com/ray-kurzweil-in-the-2030s-nanobots-in-our-brains-will-make-us-godlike/

Milman, Oliver (2020) 'Revealed: Quarter of all tweets about climate crisis produced by bots', *The Guardian*, 21st February, 2020.

Milmo, Dan (2023) 'AI-focused tech firms locked in "race to the bottom", warns MIT professor', *The Guardian*, 21st September, 2023.

Minsky, Carly (2020)' "Surveillance creep" as cameras spread on campus', *The Financial Times*, 10th March 2020.

Mirsky, Jeannette (1937) 'The Dakota'. In Margaret Mead (ed.) *Competition and Cooperation among Primitive Peoples*. New York: McGraw-Hill.

Mitchell, David M. (2020) 'The robotics of parenting', *Medium*, 23rd April 2020. *https://medium.com/disegno-quarterly-journal-of-design/ the-robotics-of-modern-parenting-1327f68d5a9d*

Mitchell, Melanie (2019) *Artificial Intelligence: A guide for thinking humans*. London: Pelican Books.

Moley Robotics (2023) 'The future is served: The world's first fully robotic kitchen', Moley, 2023. https://www.moley.com/

Molteni, Megan (2022) 'After three years in prison "CRISPR babies" scientist is attempting a comeback', STAT, 29th November 2022. https://www.statnews. com/2022/11/29/after-prison-crispr-babies-scientist-is-attempting-comeback/

Monbiot, George (2022) 'Feel the burn', Monbiot.com, 1st July 2022, *https://www.monbiot.com/2022/07/01/feel-the-burn/*

Monbiot, George (2022a) 'Fermenting a revolution', Monbiot.com, 26th November 2022. https://www.monbiot.com/2022/11/26/fermenting-a-revolution/

Moore, Barrington (1966) *Social Origins of Dictatorship and Democracy: Lord and peasant in the making of the modern world*. Boston: Beacon Press.

Moravec, Hans (1988) *Mind Children*. Cambridge, MA.: Harvard University Press.

More, Max (2013) 'A letter to Mother Nature'. In Max More and Natasha Vita-More (eds.) *The Transhumanist Reader: Classical and contemporary essays on the science, technology, and philosophy of the human future*. Chichester: Wiley-Blackwell.

Morgan, Gareth (1986) *Images of Organization*. Thousand Oaks, Ca: Sage.

Morgan, Steve (2022) 'Cybercrime to cost the world 8 trillion annually in 2023', *Cybercrime Magazine*, 17th October, 2022. https://cybersecurityventures.com/ cybercrime-to-cost-the-world-8-trillion-annually-in-2023/

Morozow, Evgeny (2020) 'The danger of Alphabet's move into the risk business', *The Financial Times*, 1st September 2020.

Morris, Andrea (2018) 'Meet the activist fighting sex robots,' *Forbes Magazine,* 26th September, 2018. https://www.forbes.com/sites/andreamorris/2018/09/26/ meet-the-activist-fighting-sex-robots/?sh=14d4b62f6e79

Morris, Ian (2010) *Why the West Rules – For Now: The patterns of history and what they reveal about the future.* London: Profile Books.

Mumford, Lewis (1934) *Technics and civilization.* San Diego, Harcourt.

Munnangi, Swapna et al (2022) *Placebo Effect*, StatPearls Publishing, January 2022. *https://pubmed.ncbi.nlm.nih.gov/30020668/*

Muraca, Barbara (2019 'Foreword'. In C. Burkhardt, M. Schmelzer and N. Treu (eds.) *Degrowth in Movement(s)*. Winchester and Washington: Zero Books.

Murgla, Madhumita (2023) 'Google's DeepMind-Brain merger: Tech giant regroups for AI battle', *The Financial Times*, 28th April, 2023.

Murgla, Madhumita (2023a) 'OpenAI chief seeks new Microsoft funds to build "superintelligence"', *The Financial Times*, 13th November, 2023.

Murgla, Madhumita and Neville, Sarah (2022) 'Palantir gears up to expand its reach into UK's NHS', *The Financial Times*, 9th June, 2022.

Muro, Mark et al (2019) 'Automation and Artificial Intelligence: How machines ae affecting people and places', Metropolitan Policy Programme, Brookings Institute, January 2019. https://www.brookings.edu/wp-content/ uploads/2019/01/ES_2019.01_BrookingsMetro_Automation-AI_Report_ Muro-Maxim-Whiton-FINAL.pdf'

Murray, Henry. A. (1955) 'American Icarus'. In Arthur Burton and Robert Harris (eds.) *Clinical Studies in Personality.* New York: Harper.

Musk, Elon (2022) 'Population collapse due to low birth rates is a much bigger risk to civilization than global warming', @elonmusk, Twitter, 26th August, 2022, 05.27. *https://twitter.com/elonmusk/status/1563020169160851456*

Mutlay, Ibrahim (2018) 'Is Elon Musk's Boring Company a sustainable idea?' *Medium*, 20th December, 2018. https://medium.com/@mutlay/ is-elon-musks-boring-company-a-sustainable-idea-ba1ccc84af3a

McCarthy, John et al (1955/2006) 'A proposal for the Dartmouth Summer research project in Artificial Intelligence', originally submitted to the Rockefeller foundation in 1955, reprinted in *AI Magazine* 2006:27(4):12-14.

McCarthy, Niall (2017) 'The countries with the most STEM graduates'. *Forbes Magazine*, 2nd February 2017. https:// www.forbes.com/sites/niallmccarthy/2017/02/02/ the-countries-with-the-most-stem-graduates-infographic/?sh=5e744487268a

McCauley, Brea (2018) 'Life expectancy in hunter-gatherers'. In Shackelford, T., Weekes-Shackelford, V. (eds.) *Encyclopaedia of Evolutionary Psychological Science.* Springer: New York, pp.1-3. https://DOI. org/10.1007/978-3-319-16999-6_2352-1

McClellan, James and Dorn, Harold (2015) *Science and Technology in History: An Introduction*, Third Edition. Baltimore: John Hopkins Press

McCool, Bill (2020) 'The history of plastic: The invention of throwaway living', *Dieline,* 3rd October, 2020. https://thedieline.com/blog/2020/3/10/the-history-of-plastic-the-invention-of-throwaway-living?

McDonald, Henry (2019) 'AI expert calls for end to UK use of "racially biased" algorithms', *The Guardian,* 12th December 2019.

McFarland, Matt (2015) 'DARPA's Robotics Challenge has a gender problem', *The Washington Post,* 5th June 2015.

McGee, Patrick (2019)'Elon Musk-backed Neuralink unveils brain-implant technology', *The Financial Times,* 17th July, 2019.

McGee, Patrick (2022) 'Google agrees $118 mn settlement over claim it underpaid women,' *The Financial Times,* 12th June 2022.

McGee, Patrick (2023) 'How Apple tied its fortunes to China,' *The Financial Times,* 17th January 2023.

McGilchrist, Iain (2009) *The Master and His Emissary: The divided brain and the making of the Western world.* New Haven and London: Yale University Press.

McGilchrist, Iain (2012) *The Divided Brain and the Search for Meaning: Why are we so unhappy?* New Haven and London: Yale University Press.

McGilchrist, Iain (2018) *Ways of Attending: How our divided brain constructs the world.* London and New York: Routledge.

McKibben, Bill (2019) *Falter: Has the human game begun to play itself out?* New York: Henry Holt.

McKie, Robin (2023) '"There's been a fundamental change in our planet": hunt on for the spot to mark the beginning of the Anthropocene', *The Guardian,* 1st January 2023.

McNamee, M.J. and Edwards, S.D. (2006) 'Transhumanism, medical technology and slippery slopes', *Journal of Medical Ethics,* September 2006, 32(9):513-8. DOI: 10.1136/jme.2005.013789.

McStay, Andrew (2018) *Emotional AI: The rise of empathic media.* Thousand Oaks, California: Sage Publications.

Nahm, Jonas M. et al (2022) 'G20's $14 trillion economic stimulus reneges on emissions pledges', *Nature,* 2nd March 2022. *https://www.nature.com/articles/d41586-022-00540-6*

NASA (2023) 'Carbon Dioxide: Latest Measurement', NASA Global Climate Change: Vital Signs, August 2023. https://climate.nasa.gov/vital-signs/carbon-dioxide/

Neal, Sarah et al (2019) 'Community and Conviviality? Informal Social Life in Multicultural Places', *Sociology, 53*(1): 69-86. *https://DOI.org/10.1177/0038038518763518*

Needham, Joseph (1956) *Science and Civilization in China, Volume 1, Introductory Orientations.* Cambridge: Cambridge University Press.

Neely, Amber (2019) 'Apple Environment Report demystified – what it all means to the consumer', *Apple Insider*, 9th October 2019. https://appleinsider.com/articles/19/10/09/apple-environmental-report-demystified---what-it-all-means-to-the-consumer

New Atlas (2014) 'Panasonic's robotic bed/wheelchair first to earn global safety certification', New Atlas, 5th April 2014. *https://newatlas.com/panasonic-resyone-robot-bed-wheelchair-iso13482/31656/* (retrieved 22/3/22).

Nicolopoulou-Stamati, P. et al (2016) 'Chemical pesticides and human health: The urgent need for a new concept in agriculture', *Frontiers in Public Health*, July 2016, 4:148. DOI: *10.3389/fpubh.2016.00148*

Nguyen, Tuan (2013) 'The world's first true artificial heart now beats inside a 75-year-old patient', *Smithsonian Magazine*, 25th December 2013. *https://www.smithsonianmag.com/innovation/the-worlds-first-true-artificial-heart-now-beats-inside-a-75-year-old-patient-180948280/*

Niketeghad, S., Pouratian, N (2019) 'Brain Machine Interfaces for Vision Restoration: The Current State of Cortical Visual Prosthetics', *Neurotherapeutics* 16:34–143. https://DOI.org/10.1007/s13311-018-0660-1

Niiler, Eric (2019) 'Can AI be a fair judge in court? Estonia thinks so', *Wired,* 25th March, 2019. *https://www.wired.com/story/can-ai-be-fair-judge-court-estonia-thinks-so/*

Nisbett, Richard (2003) *The Geography of Thought: How Asians and Westerners think differently – and why.* New York: Free Press.

Noble, Dennis (2006) *The Music of Life: Biology beyond the genome.* Oxford: Oxford University Press.

Nourbakhsh, Illa Resa (2013) *Robot Futures.* Boston: MIT Press.

Nowak, M (2011) *Super Cooperators: Beyond the survival of the fittest: Why cooperation, not competition, is the key to life.* New York: Free Press.

Nunn, Ryan et al (2020) 'A dozen facts about the economics of the US health-care system', The Brookings Institution, 10th March 2020. https://www.brookings.edu/research/a-dozen-facts-about-the-economics-of-the-u-s-health-care-system/

Obasogie, Osagie K and Darnovsky, Marcy (2018) 'Introduction'. In Osagie K Obasogie and Marcy Darnovsky (eds.) *Beyond Bioethics: Towards a new biopolitics.* Oakland, Ca: University of California Press.

O'Brien, Matt (2023) 'Tech experts are starting to doubt that ChatGPT and AI "hallucinations" will ever go away: 'This isn't fixable'', *Fortune Magazine*, 1st August,2023.

O'Connell, Mark (2017) *To be a machine: Adventures among cyborgs, utopians, hackers and the futurists solving the modest problem of death*. London: Granta.

O'Connor, M.R. (2019) *Wayfinding: The science and mystery of how human humans navigate the world*. New York: St. Martin's Press.

OECD (2020) 'Innovative Citizen Participation and New Democratic Institutions: Catching the Deliberative Wave'. Paris: OECD Publishing. *https://DOI. org/10.1787/339306da-en*.

OECD (2023), OECD Environmental Performance Reviews: Costa Rica 2023. Paris: OECD Publishing. *https://doi.org/10.1787/ec94fd4e-en*

Ofcom (2019 'Mobile Matters: Researching people's experience of using Android mobile services', 19th October, 2019, London: Ofcom. *https://www.ofcom.org. uk/__data/assets/pdf_file/0038/169769/mobile-matters-report.pdf*

Office of the Director of National Intelligence (2021) 'Assessing the Saudi Government's role in the killing of Jamal Khashoggi', 11th February 2021. *https://www.dni.gov/files/ODNI/documents/assessments/Assessment-Saudi-Gov-Role-in-JK-Death-20210226v2.pdf* (retrieved 22/10/2022).

O'Leary, Lizzie (2022) 'How IBM Watson went from the future of healthcare to sold off for parts', *Slate*, 31st January, 2022. https://slate.com/technology/2022/01/ibm-watson-health-failure-artificial-intelligence.html

O'Neill, Daniel. W., Fanning, A.L., Lamb, W.F. *et al (2018)* 'A good life for all within planetary boundaries', *Nature Sustainability,* vol 1, 88–95 (2018). https://doi.org/10.1038/s41893-018-0021-4

ONS (2022) 'Outcomes for disabled people in the UK: 2021', Office for National Statistics', 10th February 2022. *https://www.ons.gov.uk/peoplepopulationandcommunity/healthandsocialcare/disability/articles/outcomesfordisabledpeopleintheuk/2021*

ONS (2023) 'Gross Domestic Product: Year on year growth', Office for National Statistics, 11th August, 2023. https://www.ons.gov.uk/economy/grossdomesticproductgdp/timeseries/ihyp/pn2

Oppenheim. Maya (2020) 'Young girls groomed "within seconds" of going on to livestreaming websites in "sinister" trend', *The Independent,* 25th January, 2020. https://www.independent.co.uk/news/uk/home-news/girl-grooming-child-sex-abuse-livestreaming-internet-watch-a9300946.html

Oreskes, Naomi and Conway, Erik (2010) *Merchants of Doubt: How a handful of scientists obscure the truth on issues from tobacco to global warming*. New York: Bloomsbury Press.

O'Shaughnessy, Matt (2023) 'What a Chinese regulation proposal reveals about AI and democratic values', Carnegie Endowment for International Peace, 16th May 2023. https://carnegieendowment.org/2023/05/16/what-chinese-regulation-proposal-reveals-about-ai-and-democratic-values-pub-89766

Ottenburghs, Jente et al(2015) *'The Avian Hybrids Project: gathering the scientific literature on avian hybridization'*, Ibis, 157 (4): 892–894. DOI:*10.1111/ibi.12285*

Overshootday.org (2022) 'How many Earths? How many countries?' *https://www. overshootday.org/how-many-earths-or-countries-do-we-need/*

Oxfam (2022) 'Pandemic creates new billionaire every 30 hours – now a million people could fall into extreme poverty at the same rate', Oxfam, 23rd May 2022. https://www.oxfam.org/en/press-releases/pandemic-creates-new-billionaire-every-30-hours-now-million-people-could-fall

Packer, George (2013) *The Unwinding: An Inner history of the New America.* New York: Farrar, Strauss and Giroux.

Parrique, Timotee et al (2019) 'Decoupling debunked. Evidence and arguments against green growth as a sole strategy for sustainability', The European Environment Bureau, Brussels, 8th July 2019. https://eeb.org/library/decoupling-debunked/

Patel, Raj (2009) The Value of Nothing: How to reshape market society and redefine democracy. London: Picador.

Peachman, Rachel Rabkin (2017) 'Mattel pulls Aristotle children's device after privacy concerns", *The New York Times*, 5th October 2017.

Pearce, Steve and Haigh, Rex (2017) *The Theory and Practice of Democratic Therapeutic Community Treatment.* London and Philadelphia: Jessica Kingsley Publishers.

Pearsall, Paul, Schwartz, Gary and Russek, Linda (2000) 'Changes in heart transplant recipients that parallel the personalities of their donors', *Integrative Medicine*, April 2000, 2(2):65-72. DOI:*10.1016/S1096-2190(00)00013-5*

Peng, M., Chen X., Zhao Q., Zhou Z. (2018) 'Attentional scope is reduced by Internet use: A behavior and ERP study', *PLOS ONE*, 8th July 2018. DOI: 10.1371/journal.pone.0198543.

Perrigo, Billy (2023) 'OpenAI lobbied the EU to water down AI regulation', *Time Magazine*, 29th June 2023. https://time.com/6288245/openai-eu-lobbying-ai-act/

Peters, Jay (2023) 'For Elon Musk X equals everything', *The Verge*, 26th July 2023. https://www.theverge.com/2023/7/26/23808796/elon-musks-x-everything-app-vision

Pfister, Hans (2010) 'The "1950s Syndrome" and the transition from a slow-going to a rapid loss of global sustainability'. In Frank Uekotter (ed.) *The Turning Points of Environmental History*. Pittsburgh, PA: University of Pittsburgh, 90-118.

Phillips, Helen (2006) 'Introduction: The human brain', *New Scientist*, 4th September, 2006. *https://www.newscientist.com/article/dn9969-introduction-the-human-brain/*

Pimentel, David et al (2003) 'Sustainability of meat-based and plant-based diets and the environment', *American Journal of Clinical Nutrition*, 2003 Sep;78(3):660S-663S. DOI: 10.1093/ajcn/78.3.660S. PMID: 12936963.

Pitcher, Jack (2020) 'Jeff Bezos adds record $13 billion in single day to fortune', Bloomberg, 20th July 2020. https://www.bloomberg.com/news/articles/2020-07-20/jeff-bezos-adds-record-13-billion-in-single-day-to-his-fortune

Plant, Sadie (1996) 'Binary sexes, binary codes' lecture' Future Nonstop, June 1996. http://future-nonstop.org/c/cee09dd059c37acc692ef6ba19465afb

Plumwood, Val (1993) *Feminism and the Mastery of Nature*. London and New York: Routledge.

Pogue, James (2022) 'Inside the New Right: Where Peter Thiel is placing his biggest bets', *Vanity Fair*, 20th April 2022. *https://www.vanityfair.com/news/2022/04/inside-the-new-right-where-peter-thiel-is-placing-his-biggest-bets*

Polis (2023) 'input crowd, output meaning', Polis website, 2023. https://pol.is/home.

Pomeroy, Robin (2020) 'At Davos Trump urges the world to ignore "the prophets of doom"', World Economic Forum, 21st January 2020. https://www.weforum.org/agenda/2020/01/trump-davos-apocalypse-greta-climate/

Ponting, Clive (2007) A New Green History of the World: The environment and the collapse of great civilizations. London: Vintage.

Popper, Ben (2014) 'Google's project to "cure death", Calico, announces $1.5 billion research center', *The Verge*, 3rd September 2014. https://www.theverge.com/2014/9/3/6102377/google-calico-cure-death-1-5-billion-research-abbvie

Posadas, Dennis (2014) 'Sachets help low-income communities but are a waste nightmare', *The Guardian*, 22nd May 2014.

Powell, Justin et al (2017) 'Introduction'. In J. Powell, D. Baker and F. Fernandez (eds.) *The Century of Science: The global triumph of the research university*. Bingley: Emerald Publishing.

Prakash, Prarthana (2023) 'Elon Musk says that A.I. "humanoid robots" will eventually outnumber people: "It's not even clear what an economy means at that point"'. *Fortune Magazine*, 2nd March, 2023.

Preston, Kayla et al (2021) 'The black pill: New technology and the male supremacy of involuntarily celibate men', *Men and Masculinities*, 18th May 2021, 24(5). *https://journals.sagepub.com/DOI/full/10.1177/1097184X211017954*

Priess, Heather and Hyde, Janet Shibley (2010) 'Gender and academic abilities and preferences', in J. Chrisler, D. McCeary (eds.) *Handbook of Gender Research in Psychology. Volume 1*. New York: Springer.

Primack, Brian et al (2017) 'Social media use and perceived social isolation among young adults in the U.S., *American Journal of Preventative Medicine*, July 2017, 53 (1):1-8. *https://pubmed.ncbi.nlm.nih.gov/28279545/*

Prisco, Guilio (2013) 'Transcendent engineering'. In Max More and Natasha Vita-More (eds.) *The Transhumanist Reader: Classical and contemporary essays on the science, technology, and philosophy of the human future.* Chichester: Wiley-Blackwell.

Privacy International (2021) 'On the hypocrisy of using privacy to justify unfair competition', Privacy International, 15th January 2021. https://privacyinternational.org/news-analysis/4369/hypocrisy-using-privacy-justify-unfair-competition

Protalinski, Emil (2019) 'ctrl-labs CEO: We'll have neural interfaces in less than 5 years,' Venture Beat, 20th November, 2019. https://venturebeat.com/ai/ctrl-labs-ceo-well-have-neural-interfaces-in-less-than-5-years/

Przbyslski, Andrew and Weinstein, Netta (2012) 'Can you connect with me now? How the presence of communication technology influences face to face conversation quality', *Journal of Social and Personal Relationships*, 19th July 2012, 30(3). *https://journals.sagepub.com/DOI/10.1177/0265407512453827*

RAADfest (2020) 'Watch RAAD Festival 2020: Age Reversal Now'. *https://raadfest.com/about /* and https://vimeo.com/ondemand/raadfest2020

Ramey, Valerie (2008) 'Time spent in home production in the 20th century: New estimates from old data', *National Bureau of Economic Research,* working paper 13985, May 2008. https://www.nber.org/papers/w13985

Rand, Ayn (1967) *Capitalism: The Unknown Ideal.* New York: Signet.

Rand, Ayn (1982) *Philosophy, Who Needs It?* Indianapolis: Bobbs-Merril.

Rand, Ayn and Branden, Nathaniel (1964) *The Virtues of Selfishness: A new concept of egoism.* New York: New American Library.

Rapier, Graham (2019) '"If you can't beat them join them": Elon Musk says our best hope for competing with AI is to become better cyborgs', *Business Insider*, 29th August 2019. https://www.businessinsider.com/elon-musk-humans-must-become-cyborgs-to-compete-with-ai-2019-8?r=US&IR=T

Raskin, Paul et al (2002) *The Grand Transition: The promise and lure of the time ahead: A report of the global Scenario Group.* Boston: Stockholm Environment Institute.

Ravanshi, Astha (2023) 'Rishi Sunak wants the UK to be a key player in global AI regulation', *Time Magazine*, 14th June 2023.

Raworth, Kate (2017) *Doughnut Economics: Seven ways to think like a 21st-century economist.* London and New York, Random House.

Ronald, Reagan (1986) 'August 12 1986 news conference', The Reagan Foundation. https://www.reaganfoundation.org/ronald-reagan/reagan-quotes-speeches/news-conference-1/

Reboot Food (2022) 'The Reboot Food Manifesto', Reboot Food, 2022. *https://www.rebootfood.org/_files/ugd/dccfdc_ccdcd3668c264d6bb5dfaf7d3c3f5a44.pdf*

Reed, Caroline (2020) 'Can trees solve the climate crisis? Unfortunately, no. A note on Bastin et al's erratum (2020)', Climate Interactive, 14th August, 2020. https://www.climateinteractive.org/blog/can-trees-solve-the-climate-crisis-unfortunately-no-note-on-bastin-et-als-erratum-2020/

Regalado, Antonio (2019) 'China's CRISPR twins might have had their brains inadvertently altered', *MIT Technology Review*, 21st February 2019. https://www.technologyreview.com/2019/02/21/137309/the-crispr-twins-had-their-brains-altered/

Regalado, Antonio (2020) 'Elon Musk's Neuralink is neuroscience theatre', *MIT Technology Review*, 30th August, 2020. *https://www.technologyreview.com/2020/08/30/1007786/elon-musks-neuralink-demo-update-neuroscience-theater/*

Regalado, Antonio (2021) 'Meet Altos Labs, Silicon Valley's latest bet on living forever', *MIT Technology Review*, 4th September 2021. https://www.technologyreview.com/2021/09/04/1034364/altos-labs-silicon-valleys-jeff-bezos-milner-bet-living-forever/

Research and Markets (2022) 'Global Nanomedicine Market (2022-2027)', researchandmarkets.com, May 2022. https://www.marketresearch.com/Infogence-Marketing-Advisory-Services-v4010/Global-Nanomedicine-Indication-Drug-Delivery-31644875/

Restakis, John (2017) 'Rojava, Syria: A revolution of hope and healing', *The Vancouver Observer*, 19th April 2017.

Richardson, Kathleen (2020) 'The materialization of infant abuse in dolls and robots', The Campaign against Sex Robots. https://campaignagainstsexrobots.org/the-materialisation-of-infant-abuse/,

Ridley, Matt (2010) *The Rational Optimist: How prosperity evolves*. London: Fourth Estate.

Ridley, Matt (2016) 'Why eugenics won't come back', Rational Optimist website, 18th May 2016. https://www.rationaloptimist.com/blog/gene-editing-and-eugenics/

Ritchie, Hannah (2019) 'Global land use for agriculture', Our World in Data, 11th November 2019. *https://ourworldindata.org/global-land-for-agriculture*

Robot Companion AI (2022) 'Customized for you with Science and Technology', Robot Companion website. https://www. robotcompanion.ai/our technology/ (retrieved 18/12/2022).

Rockstrom, Johan et al (2023) 'Safe and just Earth system boundaries', *Nature,* 31st May 2023, 619: 102–111. https://DOI.org/10.1038/s41586-023-06083-8

Rodriguez, Salvador (2020) 'Facebook is a social network monopoly that buys, copies or kills competitors, antitrust committee finds', CNBC, 6th October, 2020. https://www.cnbc.com/2020/10/06/house-antitrust-committee-facebook-monopoly-buys-kills-competitors.html

Rogers, Deborah (2012) 'Inequality: Why egalitarian societies died out', *New Scientist,* 25th July 2012. *https://www.newscientist.com/article/ dn22071-inequality-why-egalitarian-societies-died-out/*

Rogers, Taylor Nicole (2023) 'Tesla workers claim they were fired in retaliation for union drive', *The Financial Times*, 16th February 2023.

Romm, Tony (2020) 'Apple to pay $113 million to settle state investigation into iPhone "batterygate"', *The Washington Post*, 18th November, 2020.

Rose, Steve (2023) 'Five ways AI could improve the world', *The Guardian* 23rd July 2023.

Rosenberg, Harriet G. (2020) 'Complaint Discourse, Aging, and Caregiving among the Ju/'Hoansi of Botswana'. In Jay Sokolovsky (ed.) *The Cultural Context of Aging,* Fourth edition. Santa Barbara, CA: Praeger.

Ross, Casey and Swetlitz, Ike (2018) 'IBM Watson recommended "unsafe and incorrect" cancer treatments, internal documents show', STAT, 25th July, 2018. https://www.statnews.com/2018/07/25/ ibm-watson-recommended-unsafe-incorrect-treatments/

Rossano, M.J.(2007) 'Did meditating make us human?' *Cambridge Archaeological Journal*, 17(1), 47-58. DOI:10.1017/S0959774307000054

Roth, Andrew et al (2020) 'Growth in surveillance may be hard to scale back after pandemic, experts say', *The Guardian*, 14th April 2020.

Rothwell, James (2020) 'Dominic Raab urged to boycott G20 over Saudi Arabia's bid to evict Bedouin tribe from homeland', *The Daily Telegraph*, 10th November 2020.

Rothwell, James (2022) 'Israel pilots robotic machine gun at West Bank checkpoint', *The Daily Telegraph*, 26th September, 2022.

Roubini, Nuriel (2022) *Megathreats: The ten trends that imperil our future, and how to survive them.* London: John Murray.

RSA (2019) 'Democratising decisions about technology: A toolkit', Royal Society for the Encouragement of Arts, Manufactures and Commerce, 2019. https://www. thersa.org/globalassets/reports/2019/democratising-decisions-tech-report.pdf

Sacks, David and Thiel, Peter (1995) *The Diversity Myth: "Multiculturalism" and the politics of intolerance at Stanford.* Oakland: Independent Institute.

Sadowski, Jathan (2017) 'Google wants to run cities without being elected. Don't let it', *The Guardian*, 24th October 2017.

Saha, Semanto et al (2021) 'Progress in Brain Computer Interface: Challenges and Opportunities', *Frontiers in Systems Neuroscience*, 25th February 2021. https://www.frontiersin.org/articles/10.3389/fnsys.2021.578875/full

Sahlins, Marshall (1972) *Stone Age Economics*. Chicago: Aldine-Atherton.

Sahlins, Marshall (2008) *The Western Illusion of Human Nature*. Chicago: Prickly Paradigm Press.

Sahm, Claudia (2012) 'How much does risk tolerance change?' *The Quarterly Journal of Finance*, 2 (4): 1250020. DOI: *10.1142/S2010139212500206*

Saini, Angela (2023) *The Patriarchs: How men came to rule*. London: 4th Estate.

Sample, Ian (2020) 'What are deepfakes – and how can you spot them?' *The Guardian*, 20th January, 2020.

Sample, Ian and Devlin, Hannah (2023) 'Forthcoming genetic therapies raise serious ethical questions, experts warn', *The Guardian*, 6th March 2023.

Sanders, Bernie (2021) 'The rich-poor gap in America is obscene. So let's fix it – here's how', *The Guardian*, 29th March, 2021

Sanders, Nada and Wood, John (2019) *The Humachine: Humankind, Machines and the future of enterprise*. New York and London: Routledge.

Sands, Leo (2022) 'Pakistan floods: One third of country is under water – minister', BBC News, 30th August, 2022. https://www.bbc.co.uk/news/world-europe-62712301

Saner, Emine (2021) 'The smart toilet era is here! Are you ready to share your analprint with big tech?' *The Guardian*, 23rd September 2021.

Sartre, Jean-Paul (1958) *Being and Nothingness; An essay on phenomenological ontology*, trans. H. Barnes. London: Routledge.

Sartre, Jean-Paul (1976) *Critique of Dialectical Reason: Volume One, Theory of practical ensembles*, trans. Alan Sheridan-Smith and John Ree (ed.). London: Verso.

Saunders, Tom (2023) 'September annihilates all-time global temperature record by "extraordinary amount"', Australian Broadcasting Corporation, 5th October 2023. https://www.abc.net.au/news/2023-10-05/nsw-new-record-warm-summer-september/102938932

Savulescu, Julian (2013) 'Unfit for life: Genetically enhance humanity or face extinction', *The Monthly*, 3rd May, 2013. https://www.youtube.com/watch?v=6pAMuFZRzyo

Savulescu, Julian, ter Meulen, Ruud and Kahane, Guy (eds.) (2011) *Enhancing Human Capacities*. Chichester: Wiley-Blackwell.

Savulescu, Julian and Singer, Peter (2019) 'An ethical pathway for gene editing', *Bioethics*, February 2019, 33(2):221-222. DOI: 10.1111/bioe.12570. PMID: 30695116.

Scammell, Robert (2024) 'Labour to publish AI strategy and revamp tech regulation, says Peter Kyle', UKTN, 12th March 2024. *https://www.uktech.news/ news/government-and-policy/labour-ai-strategy-regulation-peter-kyle-20240312*

Scharre, Paul (2018) *Army of None: Autonomous weapons and the future of war.* New York: Norton

Scheidel, Walter (2017) *The Great Leveler: Violence and the history of inequality from the stone age to the twenty-first century.* Princeton: Princeton University Press.

Schliefer, Theodore (2020) 'Working for Mark Zuckerberg's philanthropy isn't always easy since it means working for Mark Zuckerberg', *Vox*, 26th June 2020. *https://www.vox.com/recode/2020/6/26/21303664/ mark-zuckerberg-facebook-chan-zuckerberg-initiative-philanthropy-tension*

Schlogl, Lukas and Sumner, Andy (2018) 'The rise of the robot reserve army: Automation and the future of economic development, work, and wages in developing countries', Center for Global Development, Washington, DC, Working paper No 487, 2nd July 2018. https://papers.ssrn.com/sol3/papers. cfm?abstract_id=3208816#

Schmelzer, Mathias, Vetter, Andrea and Vansintjan, Aaron (2022) *The Future is Degrowth: A guide to a world beyond capitalism.* London: Verso.

Schmidinger, Thomas (2018) *Rojava: Revolution, war and the future of Syria's Kurds,* trans. Michael Schiffman. London: Pluto Press.

Scholten, Mark et al (2017) 'Self-guided web-based interventions: Scoping review on user needs and the potential of embodied conversational agents to address them', *Journal of Internet Medical Research*, November, 2017 19(11). DOI: *10.2196/jmir.7351*

Schor, Juliet (1991) *The Overworked American: The Unexpected decline of leisure.* New York: Basic Books.

Schneider, Eric C. et al (2021) 'Mirror, Mirror 2021: Reflecting Poorly: Healthcare in the US compared to other high-income countries', The Commonwealth Fund, 4th August 2021. https://www.commonwealthfund.org/publications/ fund-reports/2021/aug/mirror-mirror-2021-reflecting-poorly

Schwab, Klaus (2015) 'The Fourth Industrial Revolution: What it means and how to respond', *Foreign Affairs*, 12th December 2015. https://www.foreignaffairs.com/ world/fourth-industrial-revolution

Schwab, Klaus (2016) *The Fourth Industrial Revolution.* Geneva: World Economic Forum.

Scott, James, C. (2017) *Against the Grain: A deep history of the earliest states.* New Haven: Yale University Press.

Seddon, Max (2021) 'Doppelgangers and "dirty tricks" muddy run-up to Russian Elections', *The Financial Times*, 13th September, 2021.

Seligman, Martin (2002) *Authentic Happiness: Using the new Positive Psychology to realise your potential for lasting fulfilment.* New York: Simon and Schuster.

Sellman, Mark (2023) 'CES 2023: The latest tech including a $3,300 self-driving pram', *The Times*, 3rd January 2023.

Sellman, Mark (2023a) 'AI may have feelings, says tech pioneer', *The Times*, 26th July 2023.

Sellman, Mark (2023b) 'Mata's "stupid" Llama 2 is no threat to humanity, says Nick Clegg', *The Sunday Times*, 19th July 2023.

Serpell, Robert and Simatende, Barnabas (2016) 'Contextual Responsiveness: An enduring challenge for educational assessment in Africa', *Journal of Intelligence*, 2016, 4(1). *https://DOI.org/10.3390/jintelligence4010003*

Sharif, Marissa et al (2021) 'Having too little or too much time is linked to lower subjective well-being', *Journal of Personality and Social Psychology*, September 2021, *121*(4): 933–947. *https://DOI.org/10.1037/pspp0000391*

Sharkey, Amanda and Sharkey, Noel (2012) 'Granny and the robots: Ethical issues in robot care for the elderly', *Ethics and Information Technology,* 14 (1):27-40 (2012).

Shellenberger, Michael (2022) 'San Francisco is decaying. And Democrats have allowed it to happen', *The Spectator*, 13th February 2022.

Shelley, Mary (1818/1969) *Frankenstein or The Modern Prometheus*, Oxford: Oxford University Press.

Shelter England (2021 '17.5 million people now impacted by the housing emergency', Shelter England, 26th May 2021. *https://england.shelter.org.uk/media/ press_release/17_5million_people_now_impacted_by_the_housing_emergency*

Shelter England (2021a) '274,000 people in England are homeless, with thousands more likely to lose their homes', Shelter England, 9th December 2021. https:// england.shelter.org.uk/media/press_release/274000_people_in_england_are_ homeless_with_thousands_more_likely_to_lose_their_homes

Sheng, Emily et al (2019) 'The woman worked as a babysitter: On biases in language generation', Arxiv, 23rd October 2019. *https://arxiv.org/abs/1909.01326*

Shih, J.J. et al (2012) 'Brain-computer interfaces in medicine', *Mayo Clinic Proceedings*, March 2012, 87 (3): 268-279. DOI: *10.1016/j.mayocp.2011.12.008*

Shmerling, Robert (2022) 'Why life expectancy in the US is falling', *Harvard Health Publishing*, 20th October 2022. *https://www.health.harvard.edu/blog/ why-life-expectancy-in-the-us-is-falling-202210202835*

Shrubsole, Guy (2019) *Who owns England? How we lost our green and pleasant land, and how to take it back.* London: William Collins.

Siddiqui, Faiz and Merrill, Jeremy (2022) 'Musk issues ultimatum to staff: Commit to "hardcore" Twitter or take severance', *The Washington Post*, 16th November 2022.

Siegler, M.G. (2010) 'When Google wanted to sell to Excite for under $1 million – and they passed', Tech Crunch, 29th September 2010. https://techcrunch.com/2010/09/29/google-excite/

Silver, Lee (1997) *Remaking Eden: Cloning and beyond in a brave new world,* New York: Avon Books.

Singer, Peter (2019) 'Will robots have rights in the future?' Big Think video talk, 14th December 2019, 03.50-55. *https://www.youtube.com/watch?v=y_aK_njciZc*

Singer, Peter and Sagan, Agata (2009) 'When robots have feelings', *The Guardian,* 14th December, 2009.

Singh, Anita (2023) 'Quarter of five-year-olds watch TikTok videos that "blur fact and fiction"', *The Daily Telegraph*, 29th March 2023.

Skinner, B.F.(1948) *Walden Two.* New York: Macmillan.

Smil, Vaclav (2019) *Growth: From microorganism to Megacities.* Cambridge, MA: MIT Press.

Smith, Beckie (2020) 'Cummings seeks "weirdos and misfits" to work in No 10', *Civil Service World*, 3rd January, 2020. *https://www.civilserviceworld.com/professions/article/cummings-seeks-weirdos-and-misfits-to-work-in-no10*

Smith, E.A. and Codding B.F (2021) 'Ecological variation and institutionalized inequality in hunter-gatherer societies', *Proceedings of the National Academy of Sciences USA.* 30th March, 30, 18(13) e2016134118. DOI: 10.1073/pnas.2016134118

Smith, Matthew (2023) 'Britons lack confidence that AI can be developed and regulated responsibly', YouGov, 1st November, 2023. https://yougov.co.uk/technology/articles/47744-britons-lack-confidence-that-ai-can-be-developed-and-regulated-responsibly

Solon, Olivia (2017) "'It's digital Colonialism": How Facebook's free internet service has failed its users', *The Guardian*, 27th July 2017.

Soper, Kate (2020) *Post-Growth Living: For an alternative hedonism.* London: Verso.

Sorell, Tom (1991) *Scientism: Philosophy and the infatuation with science.* London and New York: Routledge.

Spangenberg, Joachim (2018) 'Looking into the future: Finding suitable models and scenarios'. In M. Duwell, G. Bos and N. van Steenbergen (eds.) *Towards the Ethics of a Green Future: The theory and practice of human rights for future people.* London and New York: Routledge.

Sparkes, Matthew (2023) 'UK's Online Safety bill to become law, but can it be enforced?' *New Scientist*, 20th September 2023.

Sparrow, Robert (2002) 'The march of the robot dogs', *Ethics and Information Technology*, 2002, 4:305-318. https://DOI.org/10.1023/A:1021386708994

Spataro, Jared (2020) '2 years of digital transformation in 2 months', Microsoft. com, 20 April 2020. *https://www.microsoft.com/en-us/microsoft-365/ blog/2020/04/30/2-years-digital-transformation-2-months/*

Spicer, Andre (2018) 'Amazon's "worker cage" has been dropped but its staff aren't free', *The Guardian*, 14th September, 2018.

Spicer, Andre (2019) 'Will Dominic Cummings turn No 10 into a NASA-style control centre?', *The Guardian*, 25th July, 2019.

Speed, B.C. et al (2018) 'Assertiveness training: A forgotten, evidence-based treatment', *Clinical Psychology*, 25 (1). DOI:10.1111/cpsp.12216

Srnicek, Nick and Williams, Alex (2015) *Inventing the Future: Postcapitalism and a world without work*. London: Verso.

Stannard, David (1992) *American Holocaust: The conquest of the New World*. Oxford and New York: Oxford University Press.

Statista (2022) 'Degree of urbanization in China from 1980 to 2021'. Statista, 21st June 2022. https://www.statista.com/statistics/270162/urbanization-in-china/

Statista (2022) 'Mobile phone penetration in the UK from 1996 to 2018', Statista, 2022. https://www.statista.com/statistics/289167/ mobile-phone-penetration-in-the-uk/

Statista (2022a)'Advertising media owners' revenue worldwide from 2014 to 2017, Statista, December 2022. https://www.statista.com/statistics/236943/ global-advertising-spending/

Statista (2023) 'Global plastic production, 1950-2021'. Statista, 25th Jan 2023. *https:// www.statista.com/statistics/282732/global-production-of-plastics-since-1950/*

Sternberg, Robert and Grigorenko, Elena (2006) 'Cultural intelligence and successful intelligence', *Group and Organization Management*, 31(1) February, 2006. *https://journals.sagepub.com/DOI/10.1177/1059601105275255*

Stock, Gregory (1993) *Metaman: The Merging of humans and machines into a global superorganism*. New York: Simon and Schuster.

Stock, Gregory (2002) *Redesigning Humans: Our inevitable genetic future*. Boston: Houghton Mifflin Harcourt.

Strauss, Neil (2017) 'Elon Musk: The architect of tomorrow', *Rolling Stone*, 15th November 2017. https://www.rollingstone.com/culture/culture-features/ elon-musk-the-architect-of-tomorrow-120850/

Susskind, Richard and Susskind, Daniel (2015) *The Future of the Professions: How technology will transform the work of human experts*. Oxford: University Press.

Swan, Shanna (2021) *Count Down: How our modern world is threatening sperm counts, altering male and female reproductive development, and imperilling the future of the human race*. New York: Simon and Schuster.

Swift, Jonathan (1726/2003) *Gulliver's Travels*, ed. Robert DeMaria. London: Penguin Books.

Takeuchi H. et al (2018) 'Impact of frequency of internet use on development of brain structures and verbal intelligence: Longitudinal analyses', *Human Brain Mapping*, **39**:4471–4479. DOI: 10.1002/hbm.24286

Tax Justice Network (2021) 'The state of tax justice 2021', Tax Justice Network, 16th November 2021. https://taxjustice.net/reports/the-state-of-tax-justice-2021/

Tegmark, Max (2017) *Life 3.0: Being human in the age of Artificial Intelligence*. New York: Knopf.

Than, Ker (2010) 'Neanderthals, humans interbred- first solid DNA evidence', *National Geographic Magazine*, 8th May 2010. *https://www.nationalgeographic.com/culture/article/100506-science-neanderthals-humans-mated-interbred-dna-gene*

Thiel, Peter (2009) 'Education of a libertarian', *Cato Unbound*, 13th April, 2009. *https://www.cato-unbound.org/2009/04/13/peter-thiel/education-libertarian/*

Thiel, Peter (2015) 'Against Edenism', *First Things*, June 2015. *https://www.firstthings.com/article/2015/06/against-edenism*

Tibken, Shara (2019) 'CES 2019: Moore's Law is dead says Nvidia CEO', CNET, 9th January 2019. https://www.cnet.com/tech/computing/moores-law-is-dead-nvidias-ceo-jensen-huang-says-at-ces-2019/

Tideman, Nicolaus et al (2022) 'Post-Corona balanced budget fiscal stimulus: The case for shifting taxes onto land', The Centre for Economic Policy Research, VoxEU, 14th January 2022. https://cepr.org/voxeu/columns/post-corona-balanced-budget-fiscal-stimulus-case-shifting-taxes-land

Thomas, Sean (2023) 'AI is the end of writing', *The Spectator*, 10th January 2023. https://www.spectator.co.uk/article/ai-is-the-end-of-writing/

Thompson, E.P. (1963) *The Making of the English Working Class*. London: Victor Gollancz.

Titcomb, Matthew (2023) '"A relationship with another human is overrated" – inside the rise of AI girlfriends', *The Daily Telegraph*, 16th July 2023.

Titcomb, James and Field, Matthew (2023) 'How the Oppenheimer of AI' defeated the doomsayers', *The Daily Telegraph*, 23rd November 2023.

Tobe, Frank (2016) 'How is Pepper, Softbank's emotional robot, doing?

The Robot Report, 27th May 2016, *https://www.therobotreport.com/how-is-pepper-softbanks-emotional-robot-DOIng/* (retrieved 19/3/22).

Topol, Eric (2012) *The Creative Destruction of Medicine: How the digital revolution will create better health care.* New York: Basic Books.

Transformation. gouv.fr (2022) 'Formation a la transition ecologique des cadres de l'etat', French Government press release, 2022. https://www.transformation.gouv.fr/files/presse/Dossier/

Travers, Martin (2019) *The Writing of Aletheia: Martin Heidegger in language.* Oxford: Peter Lang.

Trejo, Maniel Lopez et al (2022) 'The Cuban health care system', *The British Medical Journal,* 2nd February, 2022; 376. DOI: *https://DOI.org/10.1136/bmj.o123*

Tubb, Catherine and Seba, Tony (2019) 'Rethinking food and agriculture 2020-2030', Rethink X, September 2019. https://www.rethinkx.com/food-and-agriculture

Turkle, Sherry (2011) *Alone Together: Why we expect more from technology and less from each other,* Third edition. New York: Basic Books.

UN (2022) 'Goal 1: End Poverty in all its forms everywhere', United Nations Sustainable Development Goals. https://www.un.org/sustainabledevelopment/poverty/

UNDP (2023) '10 things to know about indigenous people', United Nations Development Programme, 2023. https://stories.undp.org/10-things-we-all-should-know-about-indigenous-people

UNEP (2021) 'Convention on Biological Diversity', United Nations Environment Programme, 5th July 2021. https://www.cbd.int/doc/c/abb5/591f/2e46096d3f0330b08ce87a45/wg2020-03-03-en.pdf

UNESCO (2008) 'Ngwenya Mines' Unesco, 31st December 2008. *https://whc.unesco.org/en/tentativelists/5421/*

UNHCR (1996) 'Displacement in the CIS: Ecological disasters – the human cost', United Nations High Commission for Refugees, May, 1996. https://www.unhcr.org/uk/publications/refugeemag/3b5584c24/unhcr-publication-cis-conference-displacement-cis-ecological-disasters.html (1996)

UNICEF (2022) 'Secondary Education Data', UNICEF, June 2022. *https://data.unicef.org/topic/education/secondary-education/*

UN News (2021) '2021: Critical year to "reset our relationship with nature" – U:N chief', UN News, 22nd February 2021. https://news.un.org/en/story/2021/02/1085382

UNstats (2021) 'Sustainable cities and communities,' United Nations Department of Economic and Social Affairs Statistics Division. https://unstats.un.org/sdgs/report/2021/goal-11/

Uppal, Rajesh (2019) 'DARPA's HI-MEMS (Hybrid Insect Micro-Electrical-Mechanical Systems) created cyborg insects for military micro air missions', *International Defense, Security and Technology*, 1st May, 2019. *https://idstch. com/technology/electronics/darpas-hi-mems-hybrid-insect-micro-electro-mechanical-systems-created-cyborg-insects-military-micro-air-vehicles-missions/*

Urban, Tim (2015) 'Elon Musk: The world's raddest man', Waitbutwhy.com, 7th May 2015. https://waitbutwhy.com/2015/05/elon-musk-the-worlds-raddest-man.html

Vaidhyanathan, Siva (2019) 'Digital democracy will face its greatest test in 2020', *The Guardian*, 25th November 2019.

Van Deurzen-Smith, Emmy (1997) *Everyday Mysteries: Existential dimensions of psychotherapy.* London and New York: Routledge.

Van Reybrouck, David (2016) *Against Elections: The case for democracy,* trans. L. Waters. London: Bodley Head.

Varoufakis, Yanis (2020) *Another Now.* London: Bodley Head.

Varoufakis, Yanis (2023) *Technofeudalism: What killed capitalism.* London: Bodley Head.

Vance, Ashlee (2015) *Elon Musk: How the billionaire CEO of SpaceX and Tesla is shaping our future.* London: Virgin Books.

Varela, Francisco J., Thompson, Evan and Rosch, Eleanor (2016) *The Embodied Mind: Cognitive science and human experience,* revised edition. Cambridge, Ma: MIT Press.

Vasilyeva, Nataliya (2022) 'Tearful families of Russian soldiers seek answers from Ukrainian hotline', *The Daily Telegraph*, 8th March, 2022.

Verbeek, David and Fouquet, Helene (2020) 'Can we get to space without damaging the Earth through huge carbon emissions?' *The Los Angeles Times*, 30th January 2020.

Victor, Peter (2012) 'Growth, degrowth and climate change: A scenario analysis', *Ecological Economics*, 84(C):206-12.

Vince, Gaia (2022) *Nomad Century: How to survive the climate upheaval.* London: Allen Lane.

Vincent, James (2017) 'Pretending to give a robot citizenship helps no one', *The Verge*, 30th August, 2017. *https://www.theverge.com/2017/10/30/16552006/ robot-rights-citizenship-saudi-arabia-sophia*

Vincent, James (2017a) 'Mattel cancels AI babysitter after privacy complaints', *The Verge*, 6th October, 2017. *https://www.theverge.com/2017/10/5/16430822/ mattel-aristotle-ai-child-monitor-canceled*

Vincent, James (2017b) 'Former Facebook exec says social media is ripping society apart', *The Verge*, 11th December, 2017. https://www.theverge. com/2017/12/11/16761016/former-facebook-exec-ripping-apart-society

Vinge, Vernor (1993) 'Technological Singularity', VISION 21 Symposium, NASA Lewis Research Centre, 1st December, 1993. https://ntrs.nasa.gov/citations/19940022856

Virilio, Paul (2006) *Speed and politics: An essay on dromology*, trans. Mark Polizzotti. Los Angeles: Semiotext(e)

Vis, A. et al (2022) 'The ongoing quest for the first total artificial heart as destination therapy', *Nature Reviews Cardiology*, 19, 813–828. https://DOI.org/10.1038/s41569-022-00723-8

Xu, Zichun (2022) 'Human judges in the era of artificial intelligence: Challenges and opportunities', *Applied Artificial Intelligence*, 36(1). https://www.tandfonline.com/DOI/full/10.1080/08839514.2021.2013652

Wagner, Kurt (2017) 'Why Twitter's Jack Dorsey chose computer science over becoming mayor of New York', *Vox*, 21st June, 2017. *https://www.vox.com/2017/6/21/15845686/jack-dorsey-twitter-square-ceo-time-management-mayor-new-york*

Wakefield, Jane (2019) 'Elon Musk reveals brain-hacking plans', BBC News, 17th July 2019. https://www.bbc.co.uk/news/technology-49004004

Wall, Mike (2019) 'Looks like Elon Musk is serious about nuking Mars', Space.com, 21st August, 2019. *https://www.space.com/elon-musk-serious-nuke-mars-terraforming.html*

Wallis, Nick (2021) *The Great Post Office Scandal: The fight to expose a multimillion pound IT disaster which put innocent people in jail*. Bath: Bath Publishing.

Wang, L. et al (2011) 'Economics education and greed', *Academy of Management Learning and Education*,10 (4):643-60. *https://doi.org/10.5465/amle.2009.0185*

Wapner, Paul (2010) 'Sacrifice in an age of comfort'. In Michael Maniates and John Meyer (eds.) *The Environmental Politics of Sacrifice*. Cambridge, MA: MIT Technology Press.

Ward, A.F. (2013) 'Supernormal: How the Internet is changing our memories and our minds', *Psychological Inquiry*, 2013, 24:341–348. DOI: 10.1080/1047840X.2013.850148.

Warneken, F. and Tomasello, M. (2009) 'The roots of human altruism', *British Journal of Psychology*, 100 (3):455-71. DOI: 10.1348/000712608X379061

Warner, Sam (2017) 'This Morning meets dad who introduced sex robot to his kids AND had threesomes with his wife', *Digitalspy*, 12th September, 2017. https://www.digitalspy.com/tv/a837845/this-morning-sex-robot/

Warwick, Kevin (2016) 'Transhumanism: Some practical possibilities', *Forum Informatikerinnen fur Frieden Kommunication*, 2016 (2):24-27. *http://www.fiff.de/publikationen/fiff-kommunikation/fk-2016/fk-2016-2/fk-2016-2-content/fk-2-16-p24.pdf*

Warwick, Kevin et al (2004) 'Thought communication and control: A first step using radiotelegraphy', *IEE Proceedings – Communications*, July 2004 151(3):185 – 189. DOI:*10.1049/ip-com:20040409(410)*

Waters, Richard (2014) 'FT Interview with Google co-founder and CEO Larry Page', *The Financial Times*, 31st October 2014.

Waters, Richard (2020) '"Regulation can get it wrong", Google's Sundar Pichai on AI and antitrust', *The Financial Times*, 23rd December, 2020.

Waters, Richard and Agnew, Harriet (2022) 'Meta shareholders vent anger at Zuckerberg's spending binge', *The Financial Times,* 31st October 2022.

Waters, Richard and Kinder, Tabby (2023) 'Microsoft's $10 billion bet on ChatGPT developer marks new era of AI', *The Financial Times*, 16th January, 2023.

Watson, John D. (1992) 'Foreword'. In Sandra Ackerman, *Discovering the Brain: Symposium on the Decade of the Brain papers*, Washington DC: National Academies Press.

Weaver, Courtney (2015) 'Inside the weird world of cryonics', *The Financial Times Magazine,* 18th December 2015.

Weber, Andreas (2016) *The Biology of Wonder: Aliveness, feeling, and the metamorphosis of science.* Gabriola Island, BC: New Society Publishers.

Weber, Andreas (2018) 'Interview', *Beshara Magazine*, Issue 7, 2017-18 *https://besharamagazine.org/well-being-ecology/andreas-weber-a-biology-of-wonder/*

Weinberger, Sharon (2009) 'Pentagon's cyborg beetle takes flight', *Wired,* 24th September, 2009. https://www.wired.com/2009/09/video-cyborg-beetle-takes-flight/

Weizenbaum, Joseph (1972) 'On the impact of the computer on society; How does one insult a machine?', *Science* 176 (4035):609-614. *DOI: 10.1126/science.176.4035.609*

Welin, Matilda (2023) 'The rise of the "no wash movement"', BBC News, 30th May 2023. https://www.bbc.com/culture/article/20230529-the-people-who-dont-wash-their-clothes

Welsby, D. et al (2021) 'Unextractable fossil fuels in a 1.5 °C world', *Nature,* 597: 230–234. https://DOI.org/10.1038/s41586-021-03821-8

Weyer, E.M. (1967) 'The structure of social organization among the Eskimo'. In R. Cohen and J. Middleton (eds.) *Comparative Political Systems.* Austin and London, University of Texas Press.

Wheelwright, Trevor (2022) '2022 cell phone usage statistics: How obsessed are we?', Reviews.org, 24th January, 2022. https://www.reviews.org/mobile/cell-phone-addiction/

White, Curtis (2017) *We, Robots: Staying human in the age of big data.* Brooklyn: Melville House.

WhiteHouse. gov (2023) 'Executive Order on the safe, secure and trustworthy development and use of artificial intelligence', The White House, 30th October 2023. https://www.whitehouse.gov/briefing-room/presidential-actions/2023/10/30/executive-order-on-the-safe-secure-and-trustworthy-development-and-use-of-artificial-intelligence/

Wilkinson, Carl (2018) 'Bot the builder: The robot that will replace bricklayers', *The Financial Times*, 23rd February 2018, *https://www.ft.com/content/db2b5d64-10e7-11e8-a765-993b2440bd73*

Winstanley, Gerard (1973) *The Law of Freedom and Other Writings*, ed. Christopher Hill. London: Pelican Books.

WMO (2023) 'Global temperatures set to reach new records in next five years', World Meteorological Organization, Press release number 17052023, 17th May 2023.

Woebot Health (2022) 'Relational agent for mental health' Woebot Health website. *https://woebothealth.com/* (retrieved 1/9/22).

Wolf, E.T. and Toon, O.B. (2013) 'Hospitable Archean climates simulated by a general circulation model', *Astrobiology* 13(7), 656–673. DOI: 10.1089/ast.2012.0936.

Wood, Charlie (2020) 'Climate activists accuse Jeff Bezos of hypocrisy over his $10 billion environment pledge because Amazon works with oil and gas firms', *Business Insider*, 18th February, 2020. *https://www.businessinsider.com/greenpeace-amazon-activists-accuse-jeff-bezos-hypocrisy-climate-pledge-2020-2?r=US&IR=T*

Woodburn, James (1982) 'Egalitarian societies', *Man*, 17 (3): 431–51. DOI. org/10.2307/2801707

Woolcock, Nicola (2022) 'Some primary school pupils unable to say their names, teachers report', *The Times*, 13th June, 2022.

Wong, Dorcas and Zhang, Zoey (2021) 'China's medical devices industry: Key market entry considerations', *China Briefing*, 16th November 2021. https://www.china-briefing.com/news/chinas-medical-devices-industry-key-market-entry-considerations/

Wong, Julia Carrie (2020) 'Neuralink: Elon Musk unveils pig he claims has computer implant in brain', *The Guardian*, 29th August, 2020.

World Bank (2022) 'GDP: All countries and economies', World Bank, 2022. https://data.worldbank.org/indicator/NY.GDP.MKTP.CD?year_high_desc=true

World Bank (2022a) 'School enrolment, tertiary (%) gross', Data World Bank, June 2022. *https://data.worldbank.org/indicator/SE.TER.ENRR?locations=ZG*

World Bank (2022b) 'Fact sheet: An adjustment to global poverty lines', The World Bank, 14th September, 2022. https://www.worldbank.org/en/news/factsheet/2022/05/02/fact-sheet-an-adjustment-to-global-poverty-lines

World Inequality Database (2023) 'Top 10% personal carbon footprint', World Inequality Database 2023. https://wid.world/world#lpfghg_p90p100_z/US;FR;DE;CN;ZA;GB;WO/2019/eu/k/p/yearly/l/false/2.92/100/curve/false/country

WWF (2021)'Over 15% of food is lost before leaving the farm – WWF report', World Wildlife Fund, 21st July, 2021. https://www.wwf.eu/?4049841/fifteen-per-cent-of-food-is-lost-before-leaving-the-farm-WWF-report

Young, E., Wajcman, J. and Sprejer, L. (2021). *Where are the Women? Mapping the Gender Job Gap in AI*. London: *The Alan Turing Institute*.

Yuste, R. et al (2017) 'Four ethical priorities for neurotechnologies and AI', *Nature*, 2017, 551:159-163. https://DOI.org/10.1038/551159a.

Zimbardo, P. and Boyd, J. (2008) *The Time Paradox: Using the new psychology of time to your advantage*. New York: Simon and Schuster.

Zuboff, Shoshana (2019) *The Age of Surveillance Capitalism: The fight for the future at the new frontier of power*. New York: Profile Books.

Zwarthoed, Danielle (2018) 'Political representation of future generations'. In M. Duwell, G. Bos and N. van Steenbergen (eds,) *Towards the Ethics of a Green Future: The theory and practice of human rights for future people*. London and New York: Routledge.

ABOUT THE AUTHOR

Michael D.B. Harvey was born in London and grew up in the Surrey Hills.

For the past twenty-five years, he has helped to develop organizations across Europe, coaching corporate leaders and promoting creativity, teamwork and open communication among employees at every level.

In the 1990s he trained and practiced as an existential-phenomenological psychotherapist (working in the NHS and privately) and as an organizational psychologist. In the 1980s he worked as a corporate manager and media-technology entrepreneur, helping to pioneer online communication and interactive services in advance of the internet revolution. He began his professional life as a university teacher of literature and cultural theory.

He has degrees in English Literature, Sociology, Psychology, Psychotherapy and Organizational Psychology. His recent publications include *Interactional Coaching* (Routledge, 2012), *Interactional Leadership* (Routledge, 2015) and *Utopia in the Anthropocene: A change plan for a sustainable and equitable world* (Earthscan/Routledge, 2019).

He is also a songwriter, having recorded several albums under his own name and with Bridge of Sound, including *Around the Planet* (2015), *Utopia/Dystopia* (2017) and *What do we really want?* (2020), which are available on Spotify and other music streaming sites.

He lives in London and is married with three children. He can be contacted at *michaeldbharvey@gmail.com*.

ACKNOWLEDGMENTS

Writing this book has been a four-year voyage of discovery and I want to thank everybody who supported me on it. Thanks go to all who read the book and generously provided endorsements: Ernesto Spinelli, Mark Dunhill, Fabian Frenzel, Gareth Dale, Andy Stirling, Giorgos Kallis, Mick Cooper, Brian Czech, Gerardo Nicoletta, Clare Saunders and Martin Travers. Special thanks go to Ernesto, Mark and Fabian who helped me through some dark times, long before the book was finished, when the final destination was sometimes hard to see. Barry Devlin and Catherine Heaney also made kind interventions, which were greatly appreciated. Thanks too to Camilla Erskine and Jeremy Lewis who provided encouragement at an early stage (even it things didn't quite work out as planned!)

My gratitude is also due to Kelly, Doug and Abigail for their help with typesetting and distribution, Jeff Willis for the cover design, Ruth Martin for the indexing and all at Interactional Books. (Of course, any mistakes in the book are my own.)

Lastly, I want to thank my family: Frances Harvey whose proof reading and overall support was invaluable and Patrick, James and Camille who stuck with me during the long, and often frustrating, vicissitudes of the journey. Above all, I want to thank my wife Helen for standing by me during these years, until the book could finally be piloted into the warm waters of home.

A SELECT GLOSSARY

Accelerationism. The belief that accelerating technological development is the key to sustaining economic growth and the solution to many of humanity's problems in the **Anthropocene**. Politically, right-wing and left-wing thinkers differ in how this can be achieved, while degrowthers argue for deceleration. The acceleration versus degrowth debate explored in this book is likely to become the most important of the 21st century.

AGI (Artificial General Intelligence). The goal of the AI project from the 1950s has been to equal human intelligence and potentially to exceed it (i.e. **superintelligence**). I argue this goal is an undemocratic, anti-human and anti-nature project in so far as it aims to create a source of decision-making superior to humanity, which potentially relegates the majority of humans– or all of us – to the status of second-class citizens. It's likely to fail because human intelligence is embodied but it could succeed in empowering a dystopian **alien intelligence**. In this sense, AGI is inherently a manifestation of the **dominator complex** of the **machine mindset**. AGI can also be seen as a hubristic attempt to create a digital divinity, the ultimate interventionist God.

AImageddon. The possibility of a coup against humanity by superintelligent machine learning, able to learn and develop its own goals, admitted by the AI community as a real possibility, which only the deeply problematic project of programming humachines with "human values " can prevent (the human alignment problem). AImageddon facilitated by bad human actors may be a more probable scenario.

Alien Intelligence. The most probable result of the search for **AGI** is not embodied, socially-based human intelligence (i.e. wisdom) but a mechanistic, disempathetic, one-sided form of IQ, exhibiting extreme left brain hemisphere bias (McGilchrist, 2011) and obsessed with manipulation and control. Politically this could provide "a ready-made dictatorship kit" for the automated surveillance state (ASS).

Anthropocene. An ecological term signifying "that our planet left its natural functioning state, sharply and irrevocably, in the mid-20th century" (p1) Although the period has yet to be ratified officially as a new geological epoch, it represents a declaration by scientists of a climate and biodiversity emergency which threatens all Earth's life systems (**the Anthropocene Crisis**). The Human Epoch also represents a unique moment of choice in history, an opportunity to contain our overweening influence over our biosphere or suffer the consequences. Who will make that choice?

Augmentation *see* **Mecans; Reparation versus augmentation**

Brain-computer myth. The mistaken belief that the human brain is a piece of sophisticated computer software, running a human body which can be compared to hardware. This fundamentally mechanistic theory of the human body-brain can be traced back to Descartes and Hobbes.

CANDID. Progressive values system and ethos, based on Cooperativism, Altruism, Non-materialism, Democracy, Internationalism and Deference to nature (ecologism). See also **SEWP worldplan.**

Carbon Capitalism. Economic system based on the exploitation of fossil fuel energy and human labour, developed during the Industrial Revolution and still present today in the form of petro-states, corporations and financial and political institutions seeking to exhaust all possible profits from coal, oil and gas.

Cart-before-the-horse strategy. Our current intention seems to be to take unregulated technological development as far as it can possibly go and then try to adapt to whatever implications that has for being human. It would be far better to develop a sustainable and equitable human mission and then decide how science can help us deliver it. Put otherwise: is technology our master or our servant?

ChinAImerica/Dictdataship. An eminently plausible version of the Technocene, proposed by Lee (2018), in which Chinese and American **humachine** corporations use their de facto monopoly of data to economically subordinate all other nations.

CIMENT. Capitalist values system and ideology, based on Competiveness, Individualism, Materialism, Elitism, Nationalism and Technologism.

Climate breakdown. A survey of 380 of the world's leading climate scientists, published as this book was going to press, revealed that 80% of them predict global warming of 2.5C by 2100, almost half forecast 3C and a significant minority foresee a temperature rise of 4-5C or more (Carrington, 2024). Only 6% think that the current 1.5C target can be met. The threat of a burning planet could not be starkly laid out.

Cyborgoisie: An imagined transhumanist class of rich consumers, competing with each other for the latest physical and neurological **augmentations**, fuelling a for-profit human mechanization market.

Decoupling myth. The contention that through new, "efficient" technologies growth in GDP can be totally stripped of all its negative environmental impacts. Some relative decoupling of impacts is possible but there is no evidence for the absolute version of it which forms the basis of **green growthism.**

Dominator Complex or Syndrome. A proposed personality type with an extreme degree of ego-inflation, a sense of entitlement and anti-social traits lacking in empathy. Also known as the God complex (Ernest Jones), it combines gross narcissism, perfectionism and self-aggrandisement with an all-consuming desire for divine powers, which can characterize both the mythical **Prometheus** and the real **humachinators** aspiring to "god-like" superintelligence.

Dromology. Technological domination achieved by speed of development, based on the idea that a small, fast army can outmanoeuvre a large slow one (Virilio, 2006). The "nine-times gap" between Big Tech corporations and governments trying to regulate them is a case in point (see p40).

Deathism. The theory behind anti-aging research that death is not inevitable and that human immortality is a plausible goal.

Degrowth or post-growth. The managed contraction of the economy by carefully reducing production and consumption, in order to achieve greater sustainability and social and personal wellbeing. The aim is to degrow some economic activities (e.g. waste, advertising) in order to grow others (health education). It is necessary in the high-consumption Global North so that economies in the South can expand basic industries and services until something resembling a point of global sustainability can be reached.

Demotechnics. The principle of democratic choice over new technologies and scientific developments.

Duck theory of history. A humorous description of a possible sustainable degrowth scenario based on the shape of a duck's head and beak, involving a managed economic reduction in GDP, followed by a gradual levelling off as a global steady state is reached.

EcoEqual. A characteristic of the hunter-gatherer world system, based on the ecological connectedness and social and political egalitarianism still to be found in some indigenous societies today. A revival of this combination of sustainability and equitability is a key goal of the **SEWP worldplan** for the Anthropocene, a formidable but worthy challenge for humanity on an interconnected planet of 8 billion people.

Ecocene. The positive outcome of Anthropocene Crisis that achieves the goals of sustainability, equitability and wellbeing planetwide.

Green growthism. An extreme application of the **decoupling myth**. This aims to create what I've dubbed a "decarbon copy of capitalism" (see p.138).

Growthism and the GUN principle of capitalism. The theory that capital accumulation is predicated on the pursuit of infinite Growth, the profits of which are Unequally distributed, using methods that negate Nature, downgrading it to the status of a free, perpetually exploitable resource. Also known as "the growth irrationale".

Humachination/ The age of humachines. The project of reducing the gap between humans and machines until "there won't be a distinction between humans and technology" (Kurzweil, 2005). The humanizing of machines, on the one hand and the mechanization of humans, on the other, is a simple way of explaining this complex, ambitious intentionality, which results in a proliferation of different types of humachine. I argue that the first humachine age began in early 2000; I suspect it will come to an end imminently, to be replaced by a second, very different humachine age.

Humachines. On pp.18-28, I propose five types of attempted human-machine fusion: 1. cognitive humachines; 2. relational (emotional and communicative) humachines; 3. robotic humachines; 4. mechanized humans (**mecans**); and 5. the humachinated environment ("the humash"), which combines all these humachine types –and probably many more.

Humachinators. Supporters and practitioners of the strategy of merging humans and machines.

"Humacho-nation". A term for the masculinist, "Tech bro" attitudes of Big Tech leaders and the male gender bias apparent in computer science education and corporate software engineering departments. This can possibly be traced back to the Baconian concept of nature as a woman to be conquered and subdued, in the origins of Western science.

Humanness. A radical, pro-social, pro-nature definition-in-the-making of what it is to be human on planet Earth. It involves an inventory of universal human capacities and talents – or the **human skills commons.** I argue this is not a fixed or essentialist concept but a historically based response to the current ecological emergency and the threat of humachination and human skills replacement. "What do we really want?" is a proposed worldwide research project to define the parameters of humanness by democratic means.

Hypergrowth. My term for the techno-utopian solution to the problem of stalling economic growth, based on exponentiality principle and **ultrascience.** A fantasy.

Individual or personal eugenics. The controversial theory that humans can be genetically engineered to increase their resistance to disease and enhance their health, strength, intelligence and personality profile. This project has a profoundly disturbing potential for increasing existing human inequalities.

Law of Enough (Enoughism). The recognition of the crucial importance of limits - planetary, economic, social and personal - deriving from an awareness of the whole and a critical understanding of how systems work. It also involves a keen sense of personal and interpersonal balance to counteract the **growthist** drive for continual accumulation and expansion.

Law of More. Analogous to the now defunct Moore's law (the constant doubling of computer power), this is the pursuit of never-ending economic growth, scientific discovery and "progress" without limits. Psychologically, it manifests itself as an insatiable lust for more of everything, especially power, and a contempt for moderation.

Machine mindset. A possible new psychological stance associated with humachinators, which is characterized by mechanicalism, the **dominator complex**, corporate psychopathy and elements of anti-social personality disorder. It also exhibits a bias towards the left hemisphere of the brain and is possibly related to autism spectrum disorder.

Machine supremacism. The belief that the machine represents a potentially higher form of organization than anything to be found in nature. It can be traced back to the 17th century concept of the universe as the product of a divine watchmaker which replaced the organicist idea of God as an ineffable creative force existing beyond human understanding. If everything is a machine, ultimately it can be decoded and reassembled, the idea at the core of human-machine fusion and **ontocapitalism.**

Madsanity. The psychological effects of normalizing the **growth irrationale** and living on the twin tracks of planetary breakdown and human-machine fusion. If the latter is the cure to the former, traditional versions of sanity become impossible. The creative destruction of reality is another way of describing this phenomenon.

Mecanimals/Animachines. Animals subject to experimental mechanization.

Mecans. Type 4 **humachines**, mechanized humans or cyborgs, possibly featuring computerized brain implants, artificial organs, internal nanorobotics, augmented senses, increased strength and sexual prowess. Mecans are intended to defy "death from medical causes" and potentially live for hundreds of years. They will possibly be modified for space travel, as part of Eon Musk's "multi-planetary species" project.

Neo-mechanicalism. One-sided, mechanistic view of science originating in 17th century Europe based on the supremacy of physics and mathematics, which has been reanimated recently by computer science, digital engineering and nanotechnology, but still lacks the holistic vision of integrated, systems-based life science (see Chapter 6).

Ontocapitalism. The economic fusion of neoliberalism and ultrascience in what may be a last desperate attempt to replicate the economic growth of the fossil-fuel era. Similar to, but larger than, **humachination**, ontocapitalism encompasses the **singularity**, transhumanism, unrestrained human genetic engineering, nanotechnology, blockchain, materials science, space and ocean colonialism and geoengineering, plus other creations of the techno-utopian, science fiction imaginary. Its ultimate goal is a race of digital superhumans emerging from an "applied evolution" in which biology is surmounted by physics and every scientific law is smashed. In the process, all energy and matter become controllable data, as does human consciousness,

Ontopreneurs. Ontocapitalists or **humachine** entrepreneurs..

Planetary dysmorphia. A warped perception of the size of planet Earth, based on the hypothesis that if extrapolated globally, American-style consumption would require five planets of natural resources, European-style consumption four.

Plexitism or Space colonialism. Planetary exit ("Plexit") is a key plank of **ontocapitalism** and **humachination**. The goal is to create new markets in travelling to, and colonizing, the solar system; to replace depleted Earth resources (via space mining) and possibly provide an escape from a burning planet for those who can afford it.

Plutotechnics. The principle which has governed human society since the advent of the city state civilization six millennia ago, by which the ruling elite make the most important decisions about the adoption and development of new technologies. Under 21st century capitalism the same system operates, with Big Tech corporations and investors calling the shots, although politicians, **CIMENT** ideology and (manipulated) consumer demand also play a part.

Post-growth, *see* **Degrowth or Post-Growth.**

Prometheus. I interpret this mythical character as a hugely ambitious trickster and opportunist exploiting technology for his own ends and as such a consistently destructive force in history. However, he can also be liberator if he uses his talent for innovation equitably in the service of the majority.

Psychocene. A destination within the **Anthropocene**, in which psychologically-informed societies develop forms of stable but dynamically creative consciousness which can only be partially imagined today.

Pyramid Pattern. The principle of social hierarchy, first established by the city states of Mesopotamia and Ancient Egypt, patterned around an elite at the apex of the pyramid, an upper echelon of bureaucratic, religious, military classes and a majority, descending to the most powerless classes at the pyramid's base, to which intricate layers of patriarchal, racialized, caste-based discrimination have subsequently been added.

Reparation versus augmentation. The fine bio-ethical line separating medical interventions that restore normal human functioning from techno-utopian technologies aimed at fabricating entirely new human sensory or physical capacities or types of appearance (e.g. restoring impaired visual ability as opposed to creating a third eye).

Robotics job myth The false claim that robotics only aims to replace dull dirty dangerous jobs, when in fact it potentially targets every current (and even future) occupation and every human cognitive, relational and creative activity.

Rocket theory of history. An ultra-modernist, approach which equates human history with the development of machines and technology, focusing on the rocket-like development of economic growth from 18th century industrialization onwards. An essentially **growthist** approach to history, which dismisses much of the past – and the present of many Global South economies -as irrelevant to the future. It builds on the 19th century "ladder of history" of technological determinism (see Chapter 5).

SEWP worldplan. Possible global and local strategy or **worldplan** based on achieving the goals of Sustainable, Equitable, Wellbeing Planetwide. The objective is to place technology in service of these goals and the **CANDID** values.

Singularity. The transformation of everything and everyone which is supposedly possible when the sum of human intelligence is exceeded by the computing power of a cheap computer (Kurzweil, 2005).

Skill-stripping. Deskilling effects of human-machine fusion, depriving humans of core competences, by analogy with asset stripping practices of private equity.

Smartheid. Social apartheid via smart technology. This is Type 5 humachination, creating a digital-robotic smart environment, dominated by new forms of segregation, surveillance and consumer manipulation enforcing civil obedience. The Chinese state seems to be leading the way.

Steady-state psychology. An outline of a psychological equalizing process that allows movement between the polar opposites of experience without impairing the ability to return to equilibrium. A projected mindset based on dynamic self-limitation, superb balancing skills and convivial social integration.

STEMpede. The headlong rush into science and technology education, promoted by the humachine age, which risks marginalizing the humanities, social science and life-based science subjects. The danger is that students are less able to develop the rounded life skills and the critical judgment necessary for an independent life and become wholly reliant on whatever jobs the techno-elite provide them with.

Superintelligence. The goal of creating machine-based intelligence and decision-making capabilities superior to that of humans; *also see* **AGI.**

Technocene. The humachinated version of the **Anthropocene**, resulting in ecologically-ravaged, surveillance-dominated fortress states and possibly a partially-automated machine slave economy. This socially-segregated techno-dystopia offers utopian prospects to a techno-elite, which may even try to genetically re-engineer itself into a new species of humanity.

Technologism. The quasi-religious belief that the development of new technology represents the true destiny of humanity. It's become a moral and political imperative, which equates technology and science with social progress, and elevates human tool-making to humanity's most important competence. A key element in CIMENT ideology.

Tricknology. The business of marketing, advertising, selling and lobbying new technology. It includes "selling the future", exploiting the unknowability of the future to sell actual and possible technologies, and lobbying for deregulation and other legislation that accelerates technological development. Tricknology also encompasses performative, theatrical promotional events and the psychological "reality distortion" which is a key factor in **ontocapitalist** "trickster" leadership.

Ultrascience. The belief that scientific research has no limits and the frontiers of knowledge should be constantly expanded, regardless of the social or environmental consequences. This innovation fetishism is institutionalized in theoretical and practical science but, I argue, it's more aggressively present in physics-based disciplines than in the biological sciences. When it moves out of the academic realm into for-profit market development (the basis of **ontocapitalism**), ultrascience takes on its most potentially dangerous form.

Unconscious capitalism. Assumptions about our current world system can be so deeply embedded in our unconscious thoughts that we may act as though there is no alternative to a system which places profit before people and planet.

Bringing these ideological assumptions to a state of conscious, reflective choice is a potentially revolutionary task.

Utopianism. The belief that a better world is possible is an essential element in all political thinking. Inner utopias also play an important role in human psychology, drawing us on to the future (*see* p.8). For the humachinators' idea of utopia, *see* the **Technocene.**

Worldplan. Individually and collectively, an intentional network of goals, values, priorities and beliefs which represents an interpretation of the world in the present and a powerful design on the future.

INDEX

9 781068 642302